TEACHER'S EDITION 4

Joseph Abruscato   Joan Wade Fossaceca   Jack Hassard   Donald Peck

HOLT SCIENCE

Holt, Rinehart and Winston, Publishers
New York · Toronto · Mexico City · London · Sydney · Tokyo

THE AUTHORS

Joseph Abruscato
Associate Dean
College of Education and Social Services
University of Vermont
Burlington, Vermont

Joan Wade Fossaceca
Teacher
Pointview Elementary School
Westerville City Schools
Westerville, Ohio

Jack Hassard
Professor
College of Education
Georgia State University
Atlanta, Georgia

Donald Peck
Supervisor of Science
Woodbridge Township School District
Woodbridge, New Jersey

Cover photos, front: Harold/Sund/The Image Bank; back: Dennis Dilaura/After Image. The photos on the front and back covers are of Monument Valley in Arizona. This desert habitat clearly shows the effects of physical weathering and wind erosion.

In the sections of Holt Science *dealing with evolution, scientific data have been used to present this material as theory rather than fact. The information presented allows for the widest possible interpretation that can be applied to any set of values, either religious or scientific. Every effort has been made to present this material in a nondogmatic manner.*

Photo and Art credits on pages 342–343

Printed in the United States of America
ISBN: 0-03-063483-0

4567 032 5432

ACKNOWLEDGEMENTS

Teacher Consultants

Armand Alvarez
District Science Curriculum Specialist
San Antonio Independent School District
San Antonio, Texas

Sister de Montfort Babb, I.H.M.
Earth Science Teacher
Maria Regina High School
Uniondale, New York
Instructor
Hofstra University
Hempstead, New York

Ernest Bibby
Science Consultant
Granville County Board of Education
Oxford, North Carolina

Linda C. Cardwell
Teacher
Dickinson Elementary School
Grand Prairie, Texas

Betty Eagle
Teacher
Englewood Cliffs Upper School
Englewood Cliffs, New Jersey

James A. Harris
Principal
Rothschild Elementary School
Rothschild, Wisconsin

Rachel P. Keziah
Instructional Supervisor
New Hanover County Schools
Wilmington, North Carolina

J. Peter O'Neil
Science Teacher
Waunakee Junior High School
Waunakee, Wisconsin

Raymond E. Sanders, Jr.
Assistant Science Supervisor
Calcasieu Parish Schools
Lake Charles, Louisiana

Content Consultants

John B. Jenkins
Professor of Biology
Swarthmore College
Swarthmore, Pennsylvania

Mark M. Payne, O.S.B.
Physics Teacher
St. Benedict's Preparatory School
Newark, New Jersey

Robert W. Ridky, Ph.D.
Professor of Geology
University of Maryland
College Park, Maryland

Safety Consultant

Franklin D. Kizer
Executive Secretary
Council of State Science Supervisors, Inc.
Lancaster, Virginia

Readability Consultant

Jane Kita Cooke
Assistant Professor of Education
College of New Rochelle
New Rochelle, New York

Curriculum Consultant

Lowell J. Bethel
Associate Professor, Science Education
Director, Office of Student Field Experiences
The University of Texas at Austin
Austin, Texas

Special Education Consultant

Joan Baltman
Special Education Program Coordinator
P.S. 188 Elementary School
Bronx, New York

TABLE OF CONTENTS

Why the Holt Science Program? vi
Scope and Sequence viii
Easy to Follow Pupil's Edition x
Clearly Organized Teacher's Edition xiv
Learning Center xx
Basic Science Skills xxi

Introduction: SKILLS OF SCIENCE T-1

UNIT 1 THE CHANGING EARTH

Unit Planning Chart T-7 a
Bulletin Board/Field Trip Ideas T-7 c
Chapter Test Masters T-7 d
Worksheet Masters T-7 l

Chapter 1 THE WHOLE EARTH T-10
1–1. Inside the Earth T-10
1–2. Earthquakes T-15
1–3. Volcanoes T-20
People in Science: Alfred Wegener T-25
Chapter Review T-26

Chapter 2 THE CRUST MOVES T-27
2–1. Moving Continents T-27
2–2. Broken Crusts T-31
2–3. Making Mountains T-35
Chapter Review T-40

Chapter 3 THE CRUST WEARS AWAY T-41
3–1. Breaking Down Rocks T-41
3–2. Moving Water T-45
3–3. River of Ice T-49
3–4. Humans Cause Change T-53
Chapter Review T-57
Investigating T-58
Careers T-59

UNIT 2 LIGHT

Unit Planning Chart T-59 a
Bulletin Board/Field Trip Ideas T-59 c
Chapter Test Masters T-59 d
Worksheet Masters T-59 l

Chapter 4 LIGHT BEAMS AND SHADOWS T-62
4–1. Light Sources T-62
4–2. Straight Lines T-66
People in Science: Harold E. Edgerton T-69
4–3. Spreading Light T-70
4–4. When Light Strikes T-74
Chapter Review T-77

Chapter 5 BOUNCING LIGHT T-78
5–1. Reflecting Light T-78
5–2. Flat Reflectors T-82
5–3. Curved Reflectors T-86
Chapter Review T-91

Chapter 6 BENDING LIGHT AND COLORS T-92
6–1. Light Bends T-92
6–2. Lenses Bend Light T-96
6–3. Prisms and Rainbows T-101
6–4. Seeing Colors T-105
Chapter Review T-109
Investigating T-110
Careers T-111

UNIT 3 TOMORROW'S WEATHER

Unit Planning Chart T-111 a
Bulletin Board/Field Trip Ideas T-111 c
Chapter Test Masters T-111 d
Worksheet Masters T-111 o

Chapter 7 WEATHER T-114
7–1. The Ocean of Air T-114
7–2. Observing the Weather T-119
7–3. Weather Forecasting T-123
People in Science: Vilhelm Bjerknes T-126
Chapter Review T-127

Chapter 8 AIR ON THE MOVE T-128
8–1. Air Rises and Falls T-128
8–2. Wind T-133
8–3. Air Masses T-136
Chapter Review T-140

Chapter 9 WATER IN THE AIR T-141
9–1. Rain and Clouds T-141
9–2. Cold and Warm Fronts T-145
9–3. Weather on the Move T-149
Chapter Review T-154

Chapter 10 WEATHER AND PEOPLE T-155
10–1. Violent Storms T-155

10–2. Hot, Wet Air T-160
10–3. The Changing Atmosphere T-164
Chapter Review T-169
Investigating T-170
Careers T-171

UNIT 4 MACHINES

Unit Planning Chart T-171 a
Bulletin Board/Field Trip Ideas T-171 c
Chapter Test Masters T-171 d
Worksheet Masters T-171 k

Chapter 11 MACHINES AND WORK T-174
11–1. What Is Work? T-174
11–2. Machines T-178
11–3. Hidden Inclined Planes T-183
People in Science: Seol Man Taik T-187
11–4. The Lever T-188
Chapter Review T-192

Chapter 12 MACHINES WITH WHEELS T-193
12–1. Pulleys T-193
12–2. The Wheel and Axle T-198
12–3. Gear Wheels T-202
12–4. Compound Machines T-206
Chapter Review T-210

Chapter 13 FRICTION AND WORK T-211
13–1. What Is Friction? T-211
13–2. Friction and Wheels T-216
13–3. Reducing Friction T-219
Chapter Review T-223
Investigating T-224
Careers T-225

UNIT 5 ANIMAL AND PLANT POPULATIONS

Unit Planning Chart T-225 a
Bulletin Board/Field Trip Ideas T-225 c
Chapter Test Masters T-225 d
Worksheet Masters T-225 j

Chapter 14 LIVING THINGS T-228
14–1. The Biosphere T-228
14–2. Is It Alive? T-232
14–3. Counting Living Things T-236
People in Science: Kes Hillman T-240
Chapter Review T-241

Chapter 15 THE CYCLES OF POPULATIONS T-242
15–1. Animal Life Cycles T-242
15–2. Plant Life Cycles T-247
15–3. Organisms on the Move T-252
15–4. Population Explosions T-257
Chapter Review T-262

Chapter 16 SURVIVAL AND CHANGE T-263
16–1. Comparing Organisms T-263
16–2. Changing Populations T-268
16–3. Disappearing Populations T-272
Chapter Review T-277
Investigating T-278
Careers T-279

UNIT 6 ANIMAL AND PLANT COMMUNITIES

Unit Planning Chart T-279 a
Bulletin Board/Field Trip Ideas T-279 c
Chapter Test Masters T-279 d
Worksheet Masters T-279 j

Chapter 17 ENERGY FOR LIVING T-282
17–1. Communities T-282
17–2. Green Plants T-287
People in Science: Rachel Carson T-291
17–3. Using Oxygen T-292
Chapter Review T-297

Chapter 18 THE FOOD CYCLE T-298
18–1. Food Makers T-298
18–2. Food Takers T-303
18–3. The Decomposers T-309
Chapter Review T-313

Chapter 19 THE WEB OF LIFE T-314
19–1. Food Chains T-314
19–2. Connected Food Chains T-318
19–3. The Balance of Nature T-322
19–4. People Affect Communities T-326
Chapter Review T-331
Investigating T-332
Careers T-333

GLOSSARY/INDEX T-334
Safety in the Science Classroom T-344
Keeping Plants and Animals T-346
Materials List T-348
AV Equipment and Suppliers T-350
Helping the Exceptional Student T-351

Why the HOLT SCIENCE Program?

The name *Holt* has meant excellence in science education for over sixty years. *Holt Science* is the result of careful research and evaluation and continues the tradition of quality texts that meet the needs of students and teachers.

Flexibility—Organization of the text chapters into short sections makes it easy for teachers to use with students of varying abilities.

Reading Level/Readability—Every pupil edition has been carefully monitored to be at grade reading level. Writing style, illustrations, and overall design make the text enjoyable to read.

Content—The ideal balance of life, earth, and physical science exposes students to all the major disciplines of science. Concepts appropriate to each grade level are taught using examples from everyday life.

Science Words—Vocabulary is carefully developed. All new science words appear in bold type.

Activities—Students are given opportunities for hands-on experiences that enable them to master concepts and practice science skills.

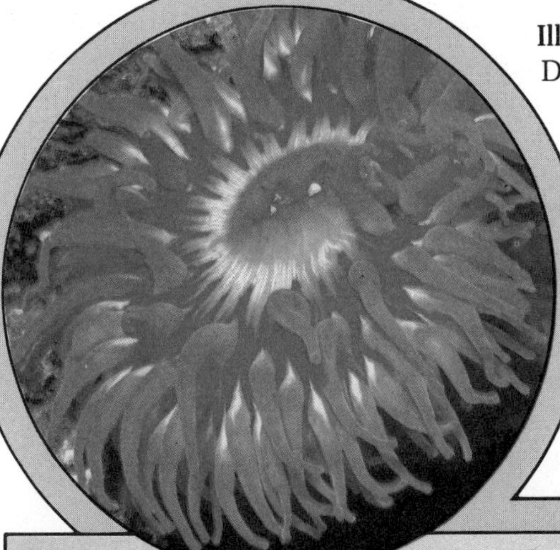

Illustrations—Diagrams and graphs were developed hand in hand with the text to explain concepts and give students a chance to practice interpreting skills.

Evaluation—Questions in the pupil's text, as well as extra worksheets and tests in the Teacher's Edition, help make the evaluation program for *Holt Science* one of the most comprehensive to be found.

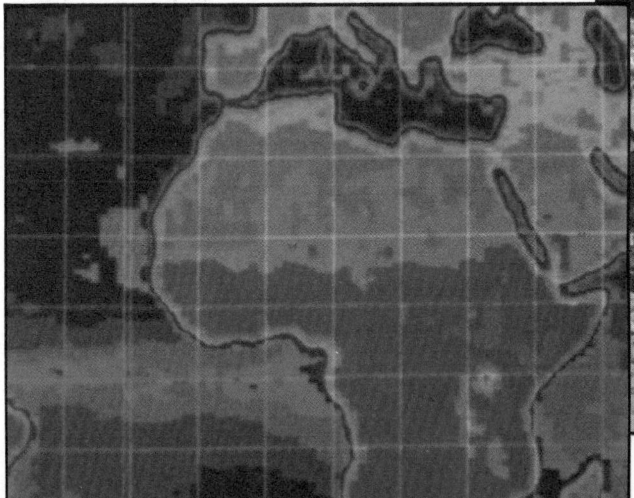

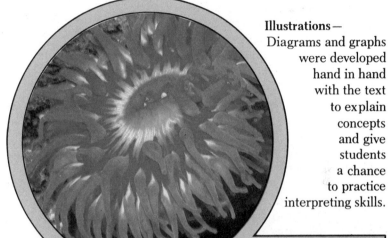

Affordable–The program for each grade level is complete with just the pupil text and Teacher's Edition. Worksheet masters and test masters are provided in the Teacher's Edition and can be easily reproduced. Activity materials are inexpensive and easy to find.

SCOPE AND SEQUENCE

Development of the scope and sequence for *Holt Science* called for careful attention to the selection of concepts and skills for each grade level. As children develop intellectually, it is important they be taught concepts and skills generally appropriate to their age group. At the same time, the curriculum must be flexible because of the variations in intellectual development among students within the same age group. The science program should continuously reinforce skills which are taught and provide opportunities for students to apply these newly acquired skills to many different areas of science. Toward this end, the scope and sequence for *Holt Science* has been carefully planned to include a balanced coverage of all the major science areas. The program spirals so that concepts taught in grades K–3 are reviewed and covered in greater detail in grades 4–6. Although this spiraling of topics increases the depth of study as students progress toward higher grades, understanding the content of one grade does not depend on having learned any previous grade's material. Thus, a student can enter the program at any grade level and anticipate success. The goal of the program is to expose students to all the major science disciplines and provide them with the fundamental science skills.

GRADE	LIFE SCIENCE
K	1. The Senses: Touch, Smell, Taste 2. The Senses: See and Hear 11. Plants 12. Animals
1	1. Use Your Senses 2. Living Things 4. Staying Alive 8. People Grow and Change
2	1. Animals are Different 2. More Animal Groups 11. Parts of Plants 12. Plants and Living Things
3	Unit 1 The Living World 1. What Is a Living Thing? 2. How Living Things Grow 3. Simple Living Things Unit 6 Where Plants and Animals Live 16. The Forest and the Grassland 17. The Desert and the Tundra 18. Water Habitats
4	Unit 5 Animal and Plant Populations 14. Living Things 15. The Cycles of Populations 16. Survival and Change Unit 6 Animal and Plant Communities 17. Energy for Living 18. The Food Cycle 19. The Web of Life
5	Unit 3 Sensing and Moving 6. Your Senses 7. Bones and Muscles Unit 5 Living Organisms 11. Cells and Simple Organisms 12. Plants 13. Animals without Backbones 14. Animals with Backbones
6	Unit 4 Human Body Systems 10. Food and Nutrition 11. Digestion and Circulation 12. Respiration and Excretion 13. Taking Care of Yourself Unit 6 Heredity 17. Reproduction 18. The Passing of Traits 19. Heredity, Environment, and Learning

EARTH SCIENCE	PHYSICAL SCIENCE
5. Weather 6. Up in the Sky 9. Properties of Water 10. Seasons	3. Describing Objects 4. Comparing Objects 7. Heat 8. Liquids
3. At Home on Earth 10. Air 11. Rocks 12. Soil	5. Place 6. Time 7. How Big Is It? 9. Magnets
3. Weather 4. Water in the Air 9. Oceans and Beaches 10. Living in the Ocean	5. Sound 6. Light 7. Force 8. Moving
Unit 2 Rocks and Fossils 4. Rocks 5. Changing Rocks 6. Fossils Unit 4 Our Solar System 10. The Earth and the Moon 11. The Sun and the Stars 12. Journey to the Planets	Unit 3 Changes in Matter 7. Matter 8. Heat 9. Matter in Water and Air Unit 5 Magnetism and Electricity 13. Magnets 14. Electricity 15. Using Electricity
Unit 1 The Changing Earth 1. The Whole Earth 2. The Crust Moves 3. The Crust Wears Away Unit 3 Tomorrow's Weather 7. Weather 8. Air on the Move 9. Water in the Air 10. Weather and People	Unit 2 Light 4. Light Beams and Shadows 5. Bouncing Light 6. Bending Light and Colors Unit 4 Machines 11. Machines and Work 12. Machines with Wheels 13. Friction and Work
Unit 1 Ocean Frontiers 1. The Ocean 2. Ocean Movements 3. Ocean Exploration Unit 6 Exploring the Universe 15. The Earth, Moon, and Sun 16. The Solar System 17. The Stars and Beyond	Unit 2 Sound 4. Hearing Sound 5. Sound Waves Unit 4 Electricity and Magnetism 8. Electricity 9. Magnetism 10. Using Electricity
Unit 2 The Changing Earth 4. How Rocks Are Formed 5. Studying the Earth's Crust 6. Earth History Unit 5 The Earth's Resources 14. Conserving Our Resources 15. Energy Resources 16. Future Resources	Unit 1 Motion and Energy 1. Motion 2. Forces 3. Energy Unit 3 Matter and Its Changes 7. Classifying Matter 8. Matter Changes Form 9. Reactions of Matter

EASY TO FOLLOW

All chapters are divided into short, titled sections to give the teacher maximum flexibility in planning lessons and assignments for students of varying abilities.

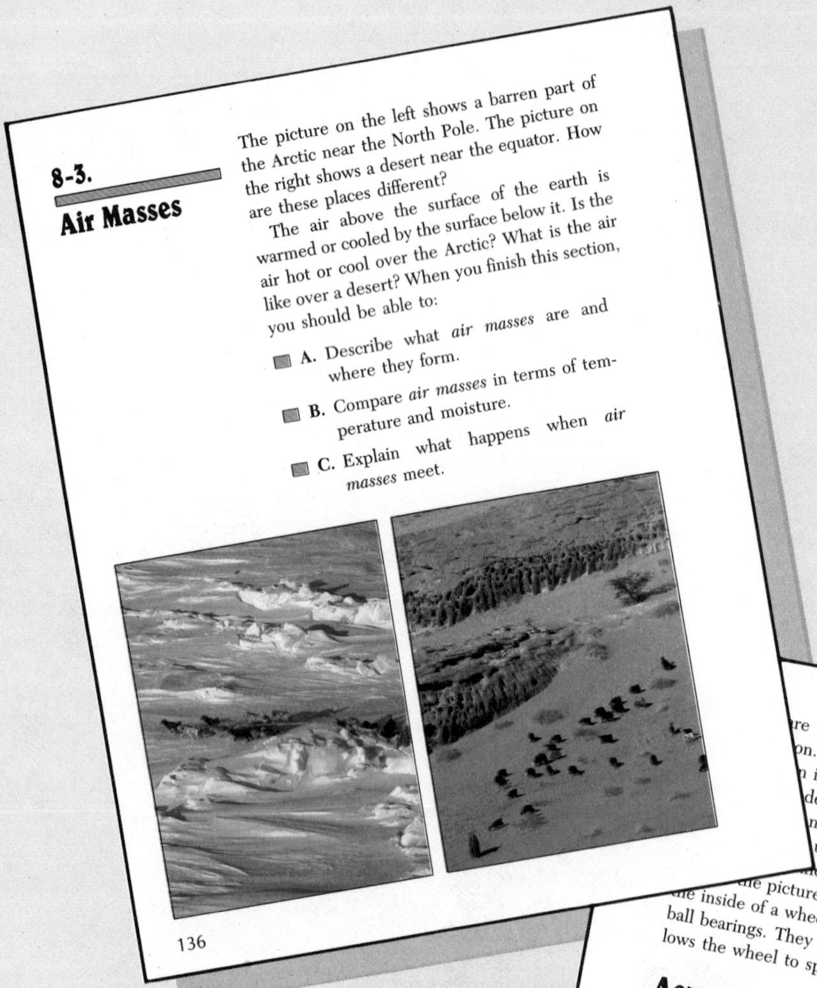

8-3.

Air Masses

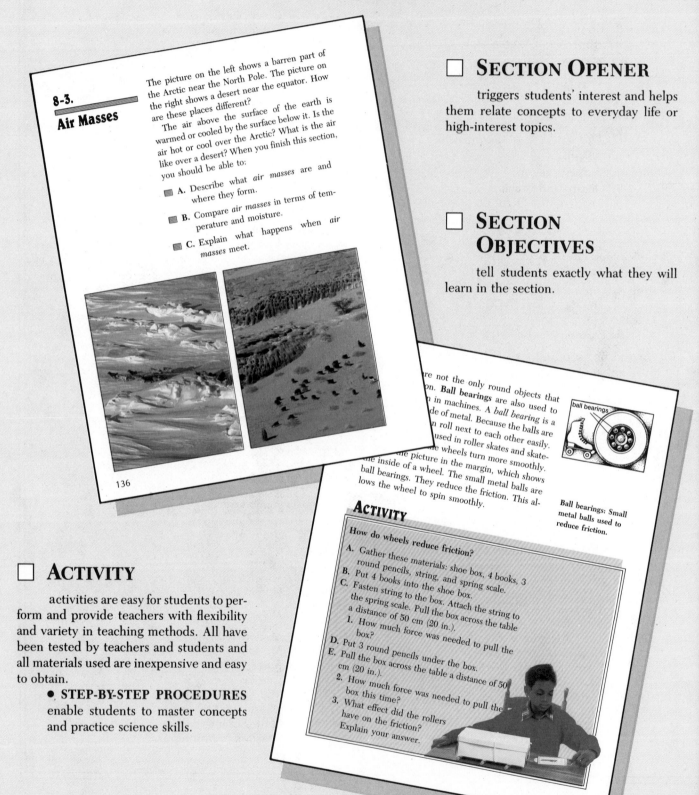

The picture on the left shows a barren part of the Arctic near the North Pole. The picture on the right shows a desert near the equator. How are these places different?

The air above the surface of the earth is warmed or cooled by the surface below it. Is the air hot or cool over the Arctic? What is the air like over a desert? When you finish this section, you should be able to:

- **A.** Describe what *air masses* are and where they form.
- **B.** Compare *air masses* in terms of temperature and moisture.
- **C.** Explain what happens when *air masses* meet.

136

☐ Section Opener

triggers students' interest and helps them relate concepts to everyday life or high-interest topics.

☐ Section Objectives

tell students exactly what they will learn in the section.

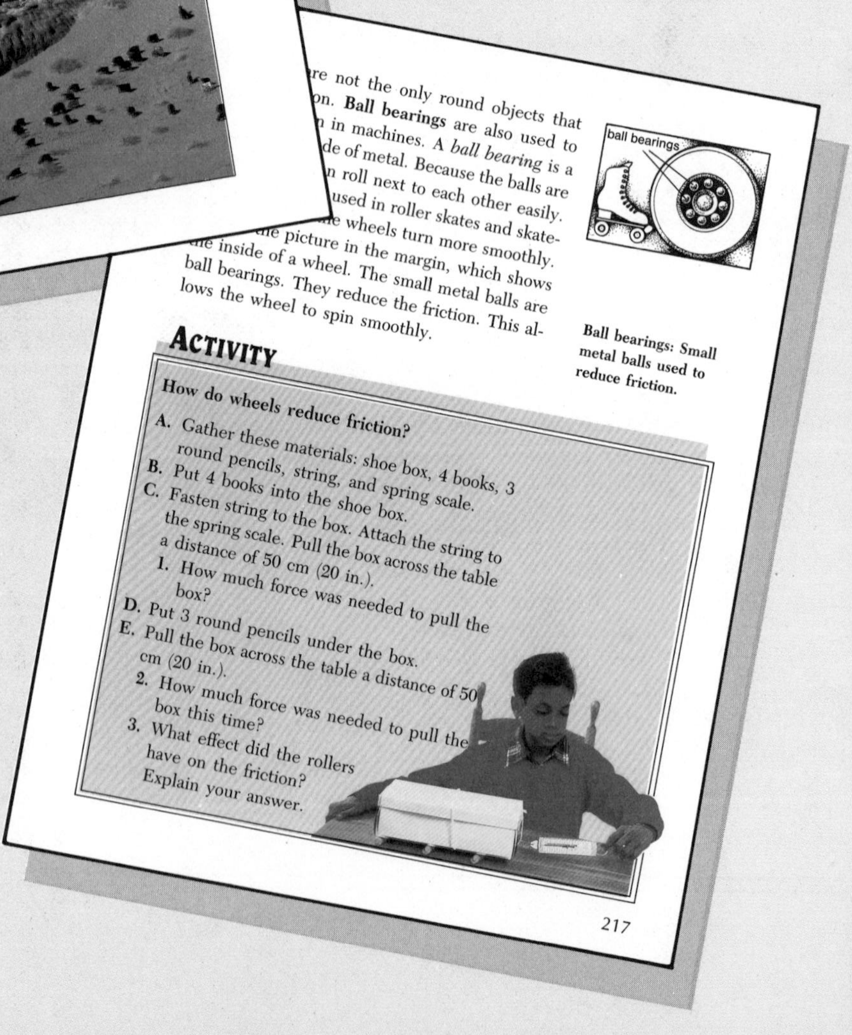

...re not the only round objects that ...on. **Ball bearings** are also used to ...n in machines. A *ball bearing* is a ...de of metal. Because the balls are ...n roll next to each other easily. ...used in roller skates and skate-... wheels turn more smoothly. ...e picture in the margin, which shows ...e inside of a wheel. The small metal balls are ball bearings. They reduce the friction. This allows the wheel to spin smoothly.

Ball bearings: Small metal balls used to reduce friction.

ACTIVITY

How do wheels reduce friction?

A. Gather these materials: shoe box, 4 books, 3 round pencils, string, and spring scale.
B. Put 4 books into the shoe box.
C. Fasten string to the box. Attach the string to the spring scale. Pull the box across the table a distance of 50 cm (20 in.).
1. How much force was needed to pull the box?
D. Put 3 round pencils under the box.
E. Pull the box across the table a distance of 50 cm (20 in.).
2. How much force was needed to pull the box this time?
3. What effect did the rollers have on the friction? Explain your answer.

217

☐ Activity

activities are easy for students to perform and provide teachers with flexibility and variety in teaching methods. All have been tested by teachers and students and all materials used are inexpensive and easy to obtain.

- **STEP-BY-STEP PROCEDURES** enable students to master concepts and practice science skills.

PUPIL'S EDITION

☐ DEVELOPMENT

of concepts is always logical and written at grade reading level.

- **ILLUSTRATIONS** work with text to explain concepts and reinforce science skills.
- **MARGIN VOCABULARY** points out new words in each section.

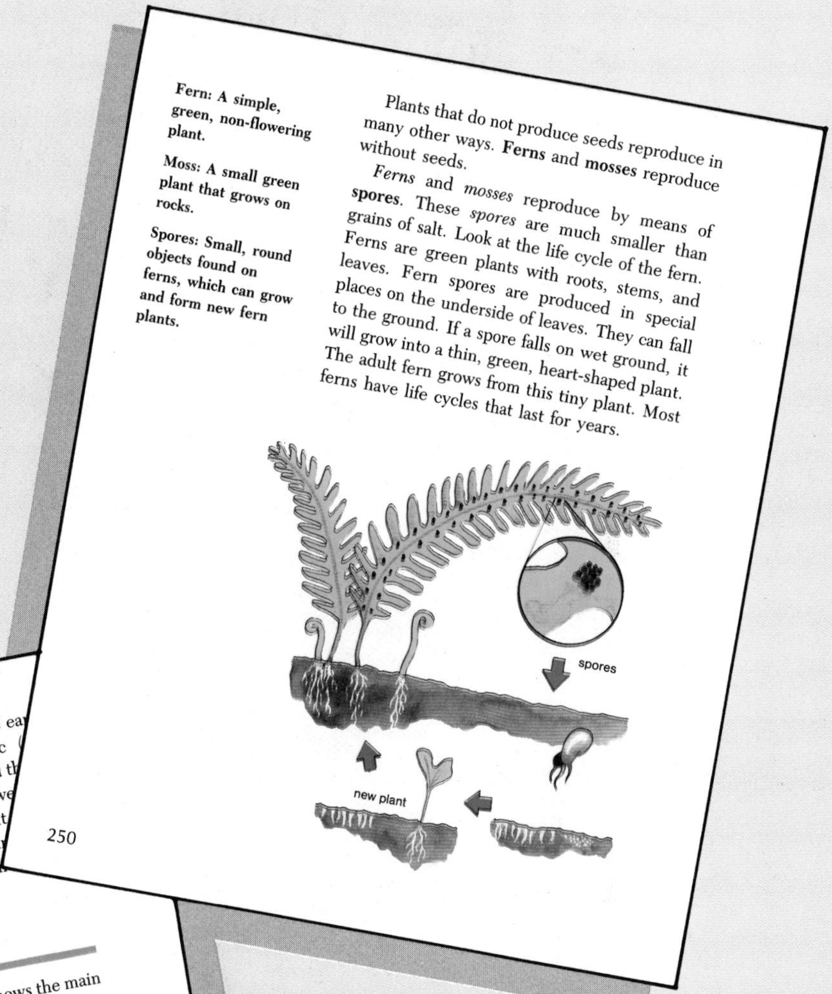

Fern: A simple, green, non-flowering plant.

Moss: A small green plant that grows on rocks.

Spores: Small, round objects found on ferns, which can grow and form new fern plants.

Plants that do not produce seeds reproduce in many other ways. **Ferns** and **mosses** reproduce without seeds.

Ferns and *mosses* reproduce by means of **spores**. These *spores* are much smaller than grains of salt. Look at the life cycle of the fern. Ferns are green plants with roots, stems, and leaves. Fern spores are produced in special places on the underside of leaves. They can fall to the ground. If a spore falls on wet ground, it will grow into a thin, green, heart-shaped plant. The adult fern grows from this tiny plant. Most ferns have life cycles that last for years.

250

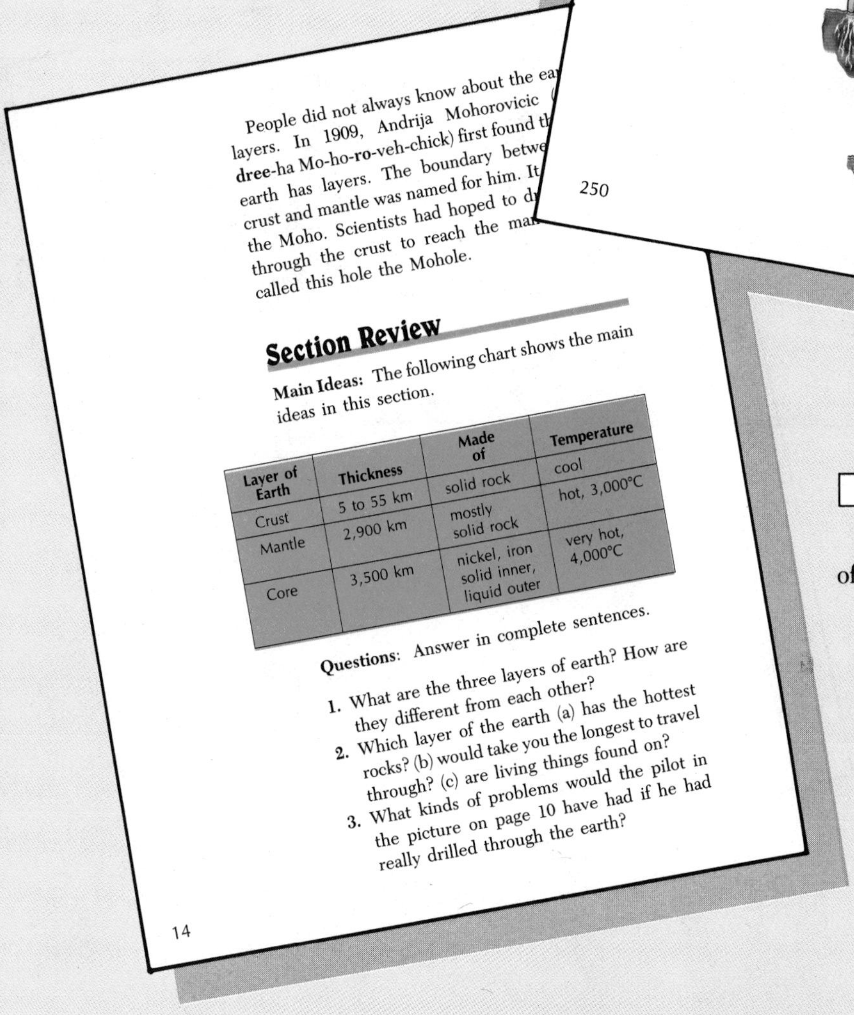

People did not always know about the ea[rth's] layers. In 1909, Andrija Mohorovicic (... dree-ha Mo-ho-ro-veh-chick) first found th[at the] earth has layers. The boundary betw[een the] crust and mantle was named for him. It[is called] the Moho. Scientists had hoped to d[rill] through the crust to reach the ma[ntle. They] called this hole the Mohole.

Section Review

Main Ideas: The following chart shows the main ideas in this section.

Layer of Earth	Thickness	Made of	Temperature
Crust	5 to 55 km	solid rock	cool
Mantle	2,900 km	mostly solid rock	hot, 3,000°C
Core	3,500 km	nickel, iron solid inner, liquid outer	very hot, 4,000°C

Questions: Answer in complete sentences.

1. What are the three layers of earth? How are they different from each other?
2. Which layer of the earth (a) has the hottest rocks? (b) would take you the longest to travel through? (c) are living things found on?
3. What kinds of problems would the pilot in the picture on page 10 have had if he had really drilled through the earth?

14

☐ SECTION REVIEW

provides reinforcement and evaluation of concepts developed in the section.

- **MAIN IDEAS** give students a summary of key concepts in the section.
- **QUESTIONS** of recall, interpretation, and application are keyed to student objectives at the beginning of each section and provide a self-test and immediate reinforcement.

SPECIAL FEATURES

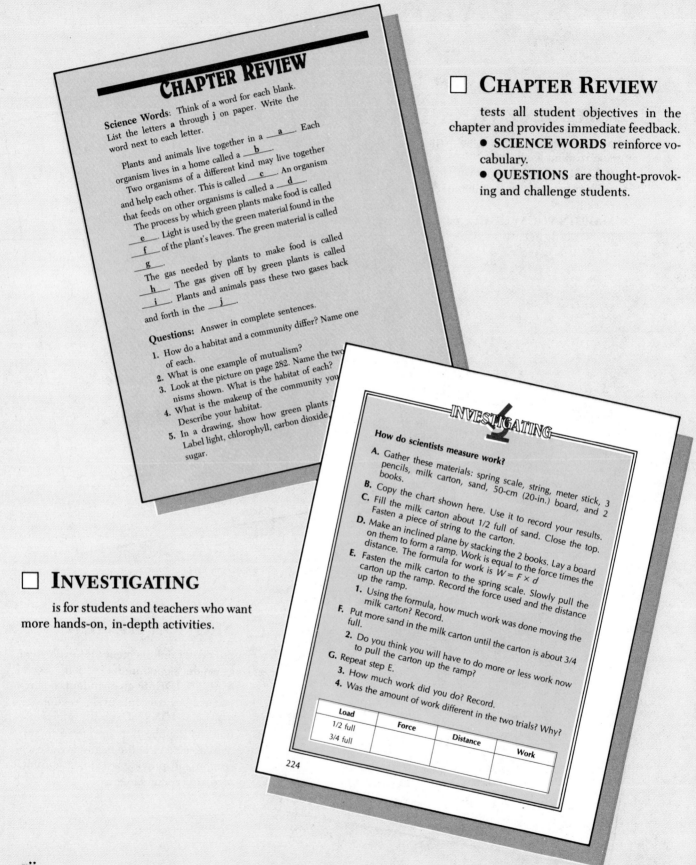

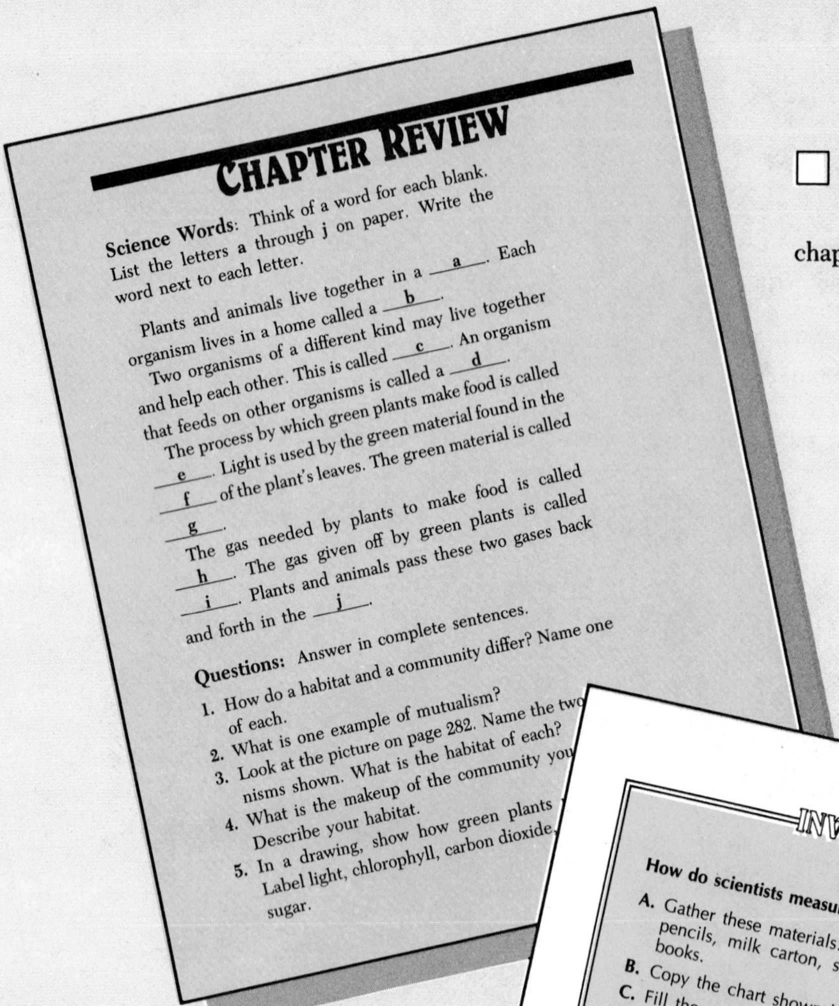

CHAPTER REVIEW

Science Words: Think of a word for each blank. List the letters **a** through **j** on paper. Write the word next to each letter.

Plants and animals live together in a __a__. Each organism lives in a home called a __b__.

Two organisms of a different kind may live together and help each other. This is called __c__. An organism that feeds on other organisms is called a __d__.

The process by which green plants make food is called __e__. Light is used by the green material found in the __f__ of the plant's leaves. The green material is called __g__.

The gas needed by plants to make food is called __h__. The gas given off by green plants is called __i__. Plants and animals pass these two gases back and forth in the __j__.

Questions: Answer in complete sentences.

1. How do a habitat and a community differ? Name one of each.
2. What is one example of mutualism?
3. Look at the picture on page 282. Name the two nisms shown. What is the habitat of each?
4. What is the makeup of the community you Describe your habitat.
5. In a drawing, show how green plants Label light, chlorophyll, carbon dioxide, sugar.

☐ CHAPTER REVIEW

tests all student objectives in the chapter and provides immediate feedback.

- **SCIENCE WORDS** reinforce vocabulary.
- **QUESTIONS** are thought-provoking and challenge students.

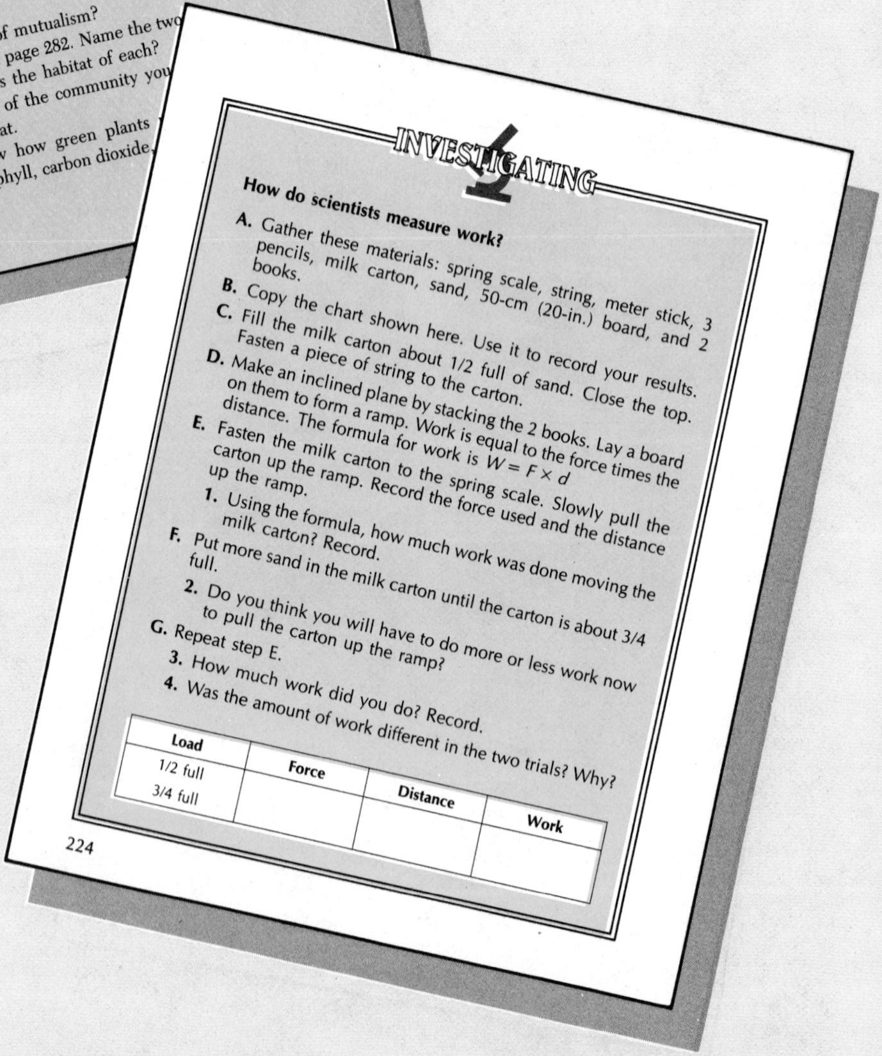

INVESTIGATING

How do scientists measure work?

A. Gather these materials: spring scale, string, meter stick, 3 pencils, milk carton, sand, 50-cm (20-in.) board, and 2 books.

B. Copy the chart shown here. Use it to record your results.

C. Fill the milk carton about 1/2 full of sand. Close the top. Fasten a piece of string to the carton.

D. Make an inclined plane by stacking the 2 books. Lay a board on them to form a ramp. Work is equal to the force times the distance. The formula for work is $W = F \times d$

E. Fasten the milk carton to the spring scale. Slowly pull the carton up the ramp. Record the force used and the distance up the ramp.

1. Using the formula, how much work was done moving the milk carton? Record.

F. Put more sand in the milk carton until the carton is about 3/4 full.

2. Do you think you will have to do more or less work now to pull the carton up the ramp?

G. Repeat step E.

3. How much work did you do? Record.

4. Was the amount of work different in the two trials? Why?

Load	Force	Distance	Work
1/2 full			
3/4 full			

224

☐ INVESTIGATING

is for students and teachers who want more hands-on, in-depth activities.

☐ Careers

features careers from major science areas, ranging from occupations requiring little advanced training to very specialized professions.

CAREERS

Horticulturist ▶

Horticulturists (hore-ti-**kull**-chur-ists) are people who work with plants. They work in greenhouses and gardens. They try to improve the plants they grow.

A visit to a greenhouse will help you understand what horticulturists do. They must know about soils and fertilizers.

A horticulturist needs to go to school after high school.

◀ Entomologist

Entomologists (en-toe-**moll**-eh-jists) study insect populations. They may study termites, cockroaches, bees, ants, or butterflies.

Some entomologists try to find ways to control harmful insects. Others do research. They work in universities. Entomologists need a college degree in biology. Many people study and collect insects as a hobby.

279

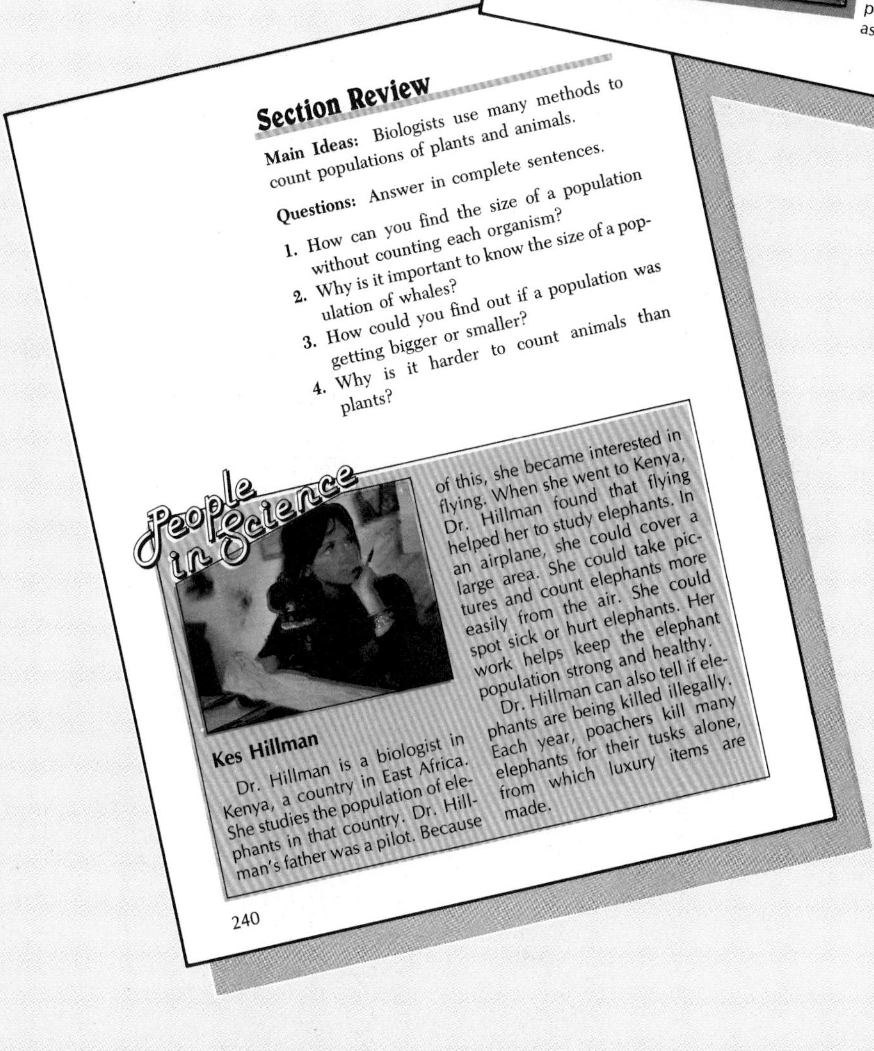

Section Review

Main Ideas: Biologists use many methods to count populations of plants and animals.

Questions: Answer in complete sentences.

1. How can you find the size of a population without counting each organism?
2. Why is it important to know the size of a population of whales?
3. How could you find out if a population was getting bigger or smaller?
4. Why is it harder to count animals than plants?

People in Science

Kes Hillman

Dr. Hillman is a biologist in Kenya, a country in East Africa. She studies the population of elephants in that country. Dr. Hillman's father was a pilot. Because of this, she became interested in flying. When she went to Kenya, Dr. Hillman found that flying helped her to study elephants. In an airplane, she could cover a large area. She could take pictures and count elephants more easily from the air. She could spot sick or hurt elephants. Her work helps keep the elephant population strong and healthy.

Dr. Hillman can also tell if elephants are being killed illegally. Each year, poachers kill many elephants for their tusks alone, from which luxury items are made.

240

☐ People In Science

presents biographical sketches of scientists—often contemporaries—encouraging career awareness in students by describing the scientists' work and accomplishments.

CLEARLY ORGANIZED

☐ CHAPTER OBJECTIVES

consolidate all student objectives for each section into broad chapter objectives for the teacher.

☐ SECTION BACKGROUND

supplies information about the science content of the section.

☐ MATERIALS

lists items needed to carry out the Activity.

☐ EXCEPTIONAL STUDENT IEP CHAPTER GOAL

states in measurable terms what the student should be able to do. It aids educators who are preparing individualized educational programs.

CHAPTER OBJECTIVES

1. Distinguish between objects that are light sources and those that are not.
2. Describe how a shadow is formed.
3. Describe the way light travels away from its source.
4. Describe how light can act like a particle or a wave.
5. Compare the way light behaves when it hits transparent, translucent, and opaque objects.

SECTION BACKGROUND

Light is a form of energy that is emitted by the sun and other stars in great amounts, and by other luminous objects, such as light bulbs and fireflies, in lesser amounts. Self-luminous objects are directly visible, but all other objects in the universe need light from a luminous source in order to be seen. When light falls on non-luminous objects, the light is reflected to our eyes. Light can also be transmitted through the object or absorbed by it.

MATERIALS

flashlight, 2 used chalkboard erasers, white index card

Exceptional Student IEP Chapter Goal

At the end of this chapter, the student will state the difference between opaque, transparent, and translucent materials.

T-62

CHAPTER 4

LIGHT BEAMS AND SHADOWS

4-1. Light Sources

Pretend that you are sitting around an open fire on a camping trip. The moving flames cast shadows that dance all around you. The shadows seem spooky. There is another kind of light shown in the picture. What is the source of this

62

BASIC TEACHING PLAN

MOTIVATION

You might start the unit by darkening the room. Try to shut out all light. Light a single candle in the center of the room. Let the students look at the light. After a few minutes, ask the students to make a list of things they observed about the candle and the light. You might write these on the chalkboard.

Text Questions—What is the source of this light? *The stars.*

☐ BASIC TEACHING PLAN

Provides everything needed to plan the teaching of each section—including ***Motivation***, ***Development***, ***Activity***, and ***Section Review***.

- ***Motivation*** gives information to develop student interest further. It contains suggestions for a teacher demonstration or discussion questions for the class.
- ***Development*** is a unique feature that uses a numbered square to key teaching suggestions to the pupil page.

TEACHER'S EDITION

light? When you finish this section, you should be able to:

- ☐ **A.** Identify objects that are light sources.
- ☐ **B.** Explain how we see objects that do not give off their own light.

What do fireflies, candles, the sun, light bulbs, and fireworks have in common? The answer is that they all give off light. Each of these objects, even the firefly, has the ability to make light. We call objects such as these **light sources**. Visible light is a kind of energy that we are able to see with our eyes. *Light sources* help us see things that do not give off their own light. Without them, we would live in a completely dark world.

Light sources include the sun, stars, light bulbs, headlights on cars, and matches. Light sources make their light in different ways. When a match gets hot enough, it starts to burn. The burning wood gives off light. Stars, like the sun, are balls of hot gases. Fireflies have chemicals in their bodies that make light without heat.

Light energy includes the light you see and also light you can't see. Have you heard of X rays, radio waves, and microwaves? These are forms of light that our eyes are not able to sense. When you have an X ray taken of a broken bone, the doctor shines a form of light at you. X rays are able to pass through your body and hit a piece of film. A picture of your bones appears on the film.

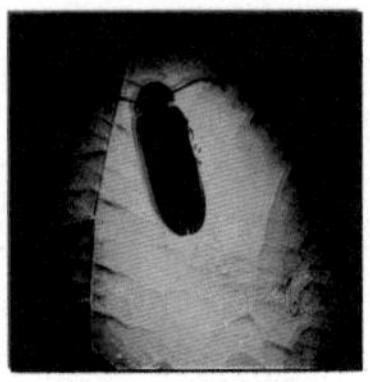

Light sources: Objects that produce light.

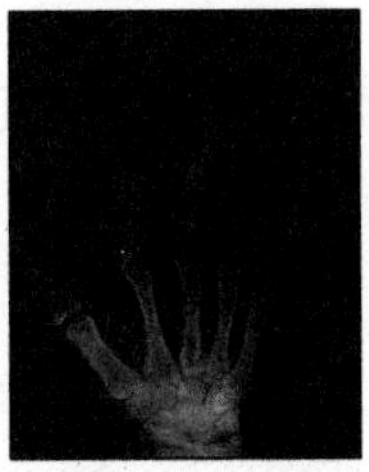

63

EXTENSIONS

Reinforcement
Science Skills—Classifying

The students can prepare a list of objects that they consider to be emitters of light. After they have created the list, review it and identify objects that do not give off their own light (the moon, roadside reflectors, and reflective paints). Students can then examine the list of luminous objects and group them according to whether their light is due to sunlight, batteries, electricity, heat, radioactivity, or chemicals.

DEVELOPMENT

1 Skill Development—Objects will be *classified* according to their luminous or nonluminous quality.
2 Teaching Tips—You might have a variety of objects on hand for your students to look at. Some should be luminous objects, such as a candle, light bulb, or a flashlight; and others should be nonluminous, such as reflector, paper, or glass.
3 Teaching Tips—Most of your students should be familiar with X rays and microwave ovens. An X ray is a form of energy of very short wavelength that can penetrate solid substances. X rays are principally used to study internal body structures. Ask your local hospital if you can borrow some X-ray photographs to show your students. Visible light is only one part of the electromagnetic spectrum. All the various forms of "light" energy are transmitted at the same speed but vary in wavelength.

Exceptional Student
Visually Impaired

The teacher should be aware that some visually impaired students are only able to see patterns of light and dark. Depending on the severity of the impairment, some Activities in this chapter may not be appropriate for the visually impaired student.

T-63

☐ EXTENSIONS

provide for three ways to extend the lesson:
Reinforcement– for all students to clarify a difficult topic. This can also be used with slower learners.
Enrichment– for students to learn more about the topic.
Application– for all students to show how science directly affects our lives.

Each type of Extension focuses on one of the three subcategories:

a. Science Skill
b. Activity
c. Research

This feature can be correlated with other disciplines for use in an interdisciplinary curriculum. Extensions give students the opportunity to practice and develop reading, math, writing, library, and research skills.

☐ EXCEPTIONAL STUDENT

provides specific suggestions to teachers who have a handicapped student mainstreamed into the regular classroom.

1 *Skill Development:* Each time a science skill appears it is identified, enabling the teacher to present concepts to students through the teaching of a science skill.
2 *Teaching Tips:* When students have difficulty understanding a topic, this offers the teacher suggestions to help get the concept across.
3 *Text Questions:* Pupil text questions are printed again for the teacher. Answers printed in *italics* follow immediately.

EXTENSIONS

Application
Activity

Challenge students to design a way to increase the mechanical advantage of a lever. You will need a lever-type can opener; a clean, empty tin can; two 30-cm rulers; and masking tape.

Give the can opener to the students and ask them to experiment to find a way to use the can opener so that it is easier to open the can. Give them the additional materials. Students who can solve the problem will realize that they must increase the length of the lever. Taping the rulers to the can opener will increase its length, thus increasing the mechanical advantage of the can opener.

ACTIVITY

How is the force of a lever related to the location of the fulcrum?

A. Gather these materials: box of paper clips, flat-sided pencil, 2 small paper cups, small box, tape, and wooden ruler (30 cm).

B. Label 1 cup L for load. Label the other cup F for force.

C. Tape a cup to each end of the ruler. Place a pencil on top of a small box.

D. Put 10 paper clips into cup L. Place cup L 8 cm from the fulcrum. Put enough paper clips into cup F to balance the load. Record your results in a chart like the one shown here.

1. How many paper clips did it take to balance the load?

E. Remove the paper clips from cup F. Repeat step D with the fulcrum at 12, at 15, and at 18 cm.

2. Did you use more or less paper clips as the fulcrum got farther from the load?
3. How does the location of the fulcrum affect the load a lever can lift?

Fulcrum at	Force*
8 cm	
12 cm	
15 cm	
18 cm	

*(Number of paper clips)

190

ACTIVITY

Skill Development—*Observing, Cause and Effect*

Teaching Tips—The students will have to work carefully on this Activity. It will take a steady hand and patience to balance the cups. Tape the cups to the rulers. If the rulers are wood, push a thumbtack through the cup into the ruler. In step D, make sure the students place the pencil 8 cm from the edge of the cup. For example, if the cup is 5 cm in diameter, then place the pencil at the 13-cm mark.

Answers to Questions—**1.** It should only take around one or two clips to balance ten clips. **2.** More. **3.** The closer the fulcrum is to the load, the less the force needed to lift it.

T-190

☐ ACTIVITY

1) *Teaching Tips:* Ways for the teacher to help students execute the Activity.
2) *Safety Tips:* Notes to teacher and students to insure proper procedure and care in using materials.
3) *Answers to Questions*

CHAPTER REVIEW

Science Words: Think of a word for each blank. List the letters **a** through **e** on paper. Write the word next to each letter.

The force caused when one object rubs against another is __a__. Small balls used to reduce friction are called __b__. To make a machine more __c__, we try to reduce the friction between its moving parts. Often, this is done by __d__. A liquid used to reduce friction is called a __e__.

Questions: Answer in complete sentences.

1. Why does a hockey puck slide across the ice easily?
2. Why can you use a nail file to change the shape of your nails?
3. Name one harmful example of friction.
4. Explain how friction acts in each of the following examples: (a) car brakes; and (b) an icy road.
5. When would it be helpful to increase friction?
6. Why does a flat tire increase friction with the road?
7. How do wheels help reduce friction in a machine?
8. Without pedaling faster, what is one way to make a bike go faster?
9. How does a lubricant reduce friction?
10. Why do you think highways and roads are slippery after it rains?

223

EXTENSIONS

Enrichment
Activity

Streamlining is a way of reducing friction. Students can observe this fact in the following Activity:

A. Gather these materials: string, a 2-in. × 4-in. board, clay, a water basin, and a force measurer.

B. Fill a sink or a rectangular basin with water.

C. Attach the force measurer to the board so that the board can be pulled through the water broadside. Add a mass of clay or some other mass to the board so that the board is just floating.

D. Using the force measurer, determine the amount of force needed to pull the board, broad side first, and then narrow side first, through the water.

1. Which side required less force, broad or narrow side? (Narrow)
2. Which shape required less force? (The more streamlined shape.)

E. Try sawing the end of the board to a point. Add the scraps of wood to the mass on top of the board. Measure the force needed to pull the board again.

3. Was there a difference in force needed? (Less force was needed.)

CHAPTER REVIEW

Science Words
a. Friction, **b.** ball bearings, **c.** efficient, **d.** lubricating, **e.** lubricant

Answers to Questions
1. The ice is smooth and slippery.
2. A nail file is rough. Rubbing it against your nails wears them down.
3. Friction wears down shoes.
4. **a.** The brakes rub against the car wheel, causing the wheel to slow down. **b.** An icy road has little friction, so objects slide over it.
5. On icy roads; on slippery floors
6. Because more of the wheel's surface is touching the road
7. Objects can roll rather than slide across a surface.
8. Reduce friction in the moving wheels
9. By making surfaces smoother
10. Rainwater acts as a lubricant, making the roads more slippery.

SUGGESTED WORKSHEET MASTERS
pp. T-171 q, r

SUGGESTED TEST MASTERS
pp. T-171 i, j

T-223

☐ CHAPTER REVIEW

provides answers to all questions.

UNIT PLANNING CHART

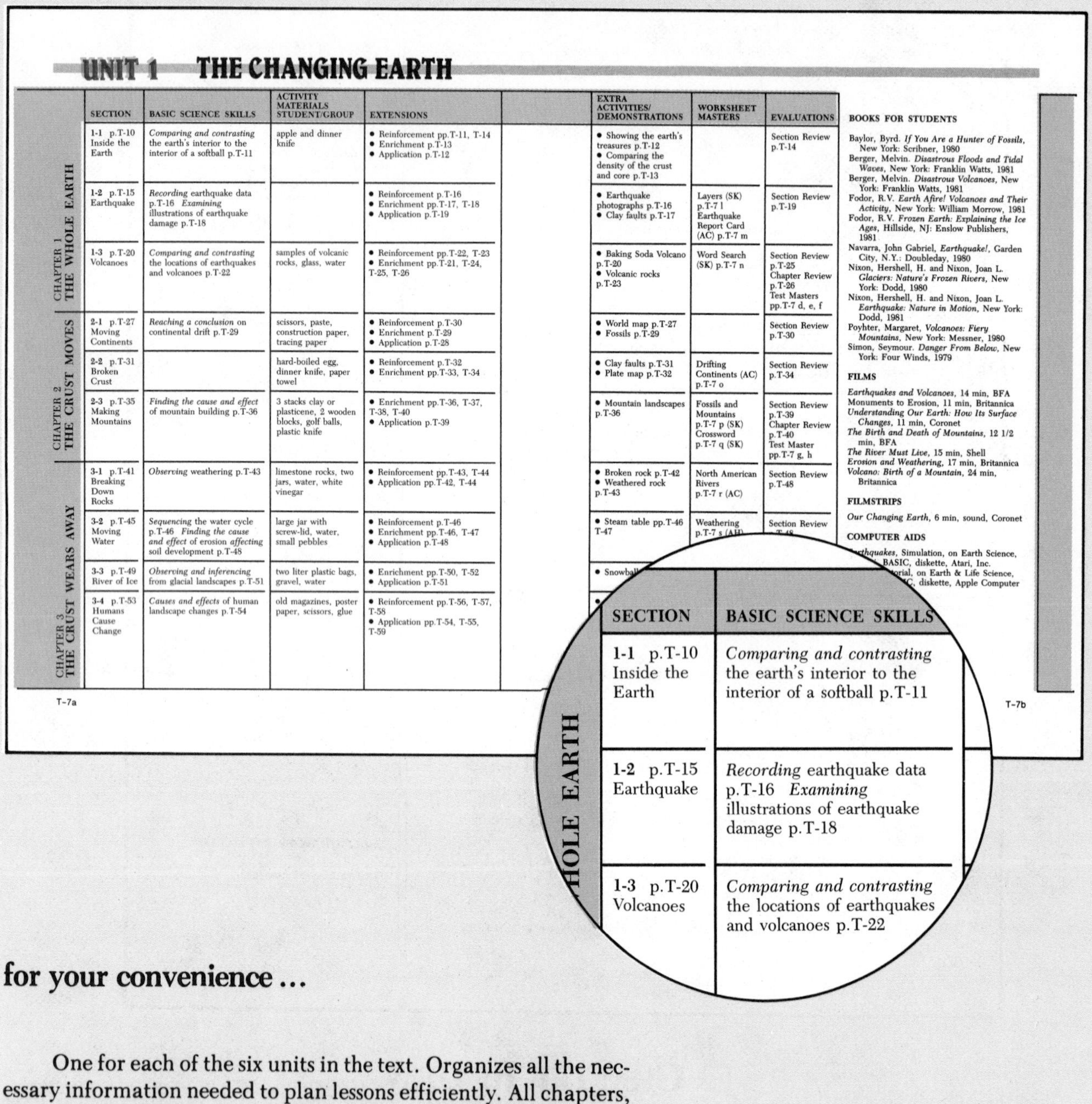

UNIT 1 THE CHANGING EARTH

	SECTION	BASIC SCIENCE SKILLS	ACTIVITY MATERIALS STUDENT/GROUP	EXTENSIONS	EXTRA ACTIVITIES/ DEMONSTRATIONS	WORKSHEET MASTERS	EVALUATIONS
CHAPTER 1 THE WHOLE EARTH	1-1 p.T-10 Inside the Earth	*Comparing and contrasting* the earth's interior to the interior of a softball p.T-11	apple and dinner knife	• Reinforcement pp.T-11, T-14 • Enrichment p.T-13 • Application p.T-12	• Showing the earth's treasures p.T-12 • Comparing the density of the crust and core p.T-13		Section Review p.T-14
	1-2 p.T-15 Earthquake	*Recording* earthquake data p.T-16 *Examining* illustrations of earthquake damage p.T-18		• Reinforcement p.T-16 • Enrichment pp.T-17, T-18 • Application p.T-19	• Earthquake photographs p.T-16 • Clay faults p.T-17	Layers (SK) p.T-7 l Earthquake Report Card (AC) p.T-7 m	Section Review p.T-19
	1-3 p.T-20 Volcanoes	*Comparing and contrasting* the locations of earthquakes and volcanoes p.T-22	samples of volcanic rocks, glass, water	• Reinforcement pp.T-22, T-23 • Enrichment pp.T-21, T-24, T-25, T-26	• Baking Soda Volcano p.T-20 • Volcanic rocks p.T-23	Word Search (SK) p.T-7 n	Section Review p.T-25 Chapter Review p.T-26 Test Masters pp.T-7 d, e, f
CHAPTER 2 THE CRUST MOVES	2-1 p.T-27 Moving Continents	*Reaching a conclusion* on continental drift p.T-29	scissors, paste, construction paper, tracing paper	• Reinforcement p.T-30 • Enrichment p.T-29 • Application p.T-28	• World map p.T-27 • Fossils p.T-29		Section Review p.T-30
	2-2 p.T-31 Broken Crust		hard-boiled egg, dinner knife, paper towel	• Reinforcement p.T-32 • Enrichment pp.T-33, T-34	• Clay faults p.T-31 • Plate map p.T-32	Drifting Continents (AC) p.T-7 o	Section Review p.T-34
	2-3 p.T-35 Making Mountains	*Finding the cause and effect* of mountain building p.T-36	3 stacks clay or plasticene, 2 wooden blocks, golf balls, plastic knife	• Enrichment pp.T-36, T-37, T-38, T-40 • Application p.T-39	• Mountain landscapes p.T-36	Fossils and Mountains p.T-7 p (SK) Crossword p.T-7 q (SK)	Section Review p.T-39 Chapter Review p.T-40 Test Master pp.T-7 g, h
CHAPTER 3 THE CRUST WEARS AWAY	3-1 p.T-41 Breaking Down Rocks	*Observing* weathering p.T-43	limestone rocks, two jars, water, white vinegar	• Reinforcement pp.T-43, T-44 • Application pp.T-42, T-44	• Broken rock p.T-42 • Weathered rock p.T-43	North American Rivers p.T-7 r (AC)	Section Review p.T-48
	3-2 p.T-45 Moving Water	*Sequencing* the water cycle p.T-46 *Finding the cause and effect* of erosion *affecting* soil development p.T-48	large jar with screw-lid, water, small pebbles	• Reinforcement p.T-46 • Enrichment pp.T-46, T-47 • Application p.T-48	• Steam table pp.T-46 T-47	Weathering p.T-7 s (AH)	Section Review
	3-3 p.T-49 River of Ice	*Observing and inferencing* from glacial landscapes p.T-51	two liter plastic bags, gravel, water	• Enrichment pp.T-50, T-52 • Application p.T-51	• Snowba		
	3-4 p.T-53 Humans Cause Change	*Causes and effects* of human landscape changes p.T-54	old magazines, poster paper, scissors, glue	• Reinforcement pp.T-56, T-57, T-58 • Application pp.T-54, T-55, T-59	•		

BOOKS FOR STUDENTS

Baylor, Byrd. *If You Are a Hunter of Fossils*, New York: Scribner, 1980
Berger, Melvin. *Disastrous Floods and Tidal Waves*, New York: Franklin Watts, 1981
Berger, Melvin. *Disastrous Volcanoes*, New York: Franklin Watts, 1981
Fodor, R.V. *Earth Afire! Volcanoes and Their Activity*, New York: William Morrow, 1981
Fodor, R.V. *Frozen Earth: Explaining the Ice Ages*, Hillside, NJ: Enslow Publishers, 1981
Navarra, John Gabriel, *Earthquake!*, Garden City, N.Y.: Doubleday, 1980
Nixon, Hershell, H. and Nixon, Joan L. *Glaciers: Nature's Frozen Rivers*, New York: Dodd, 1980
Nixon, Hershell, H. and Nixon, Joan L. *Earthquake: Nature in Motion*, New York: Dodd, 1981
Poyhter, Margaret, *Volcanoes: Fiery Mountains*, New York: Messner, 1980
Simon, Seymour. *Danger From Below*, New York: Four Winds, 1979

FILMS

Earthquakes and Volcanoes, 14 min, BFA
Monuments to Erosion, 11 min, Britannica
Understanding Our Earth: How Its Surface Changes, 11 min, Coronet
The Birth and Death of Mountains, 12 1/2 min, BFA
The River Must Live, 15 min, Shell
Erosion and Weathering, 17 min, Britannica
Volcano: Birth of a Mountain, 24 min, Britannica

FILMSTRIPS

Our Changing Earth, 6 min, sound, Coronet

COMPUTER AIDS

...rthquakes, Simulation, on Earth Science, ... BASIC, diskette, Atari, Inc.
...orial, on Earth & Life Science, ...C, diskette, Apple Computer

T-7a T-7b

for your convenience ...

One for each of the six units in the text. Organizes all the necessary information needed to plan lessons efficiently. All chapters, sections, and Activities are listed for the teacher. References to all evaluation material, including reproducible worksheet and test masters, are listed for each chapter.

BLACKLINE MASTERS

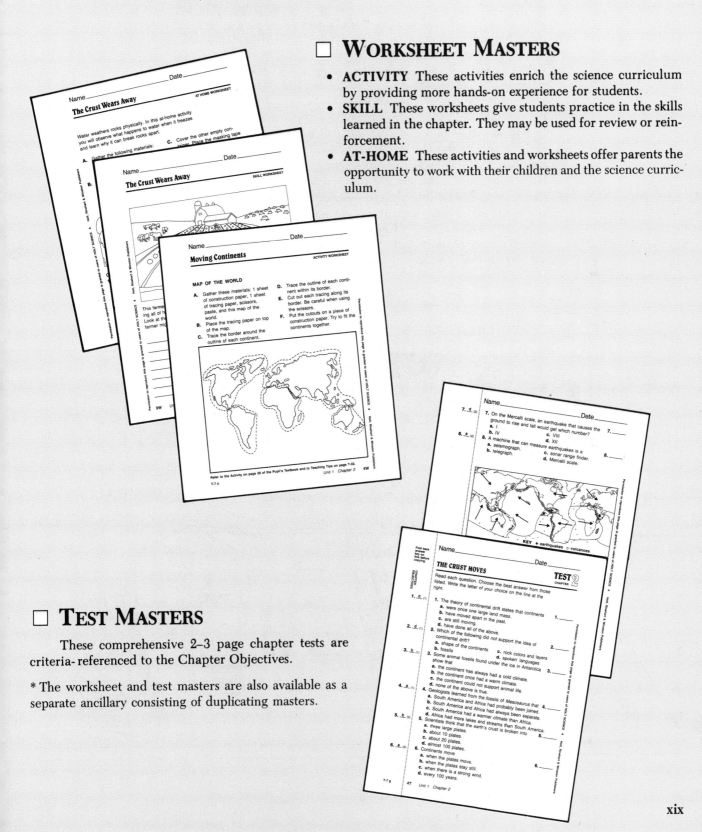

Every Teacher's Edition contains a complete set of worksheet and test masters.* They are located after each Unit Planning Chart and address a variety of needs.

□ WORKSHEET MASTERS

- **ACTIVITY** These activities enrich the science curriculum by providing more hands-on experience for students.
- **SKILL** These worksheets give students practice in the skills learned in the chapter. They may be used for review or reinforcement.
- **AT-HOME** These activities and worksheets offer parents the opportunity to work with their children and the science curriculum.

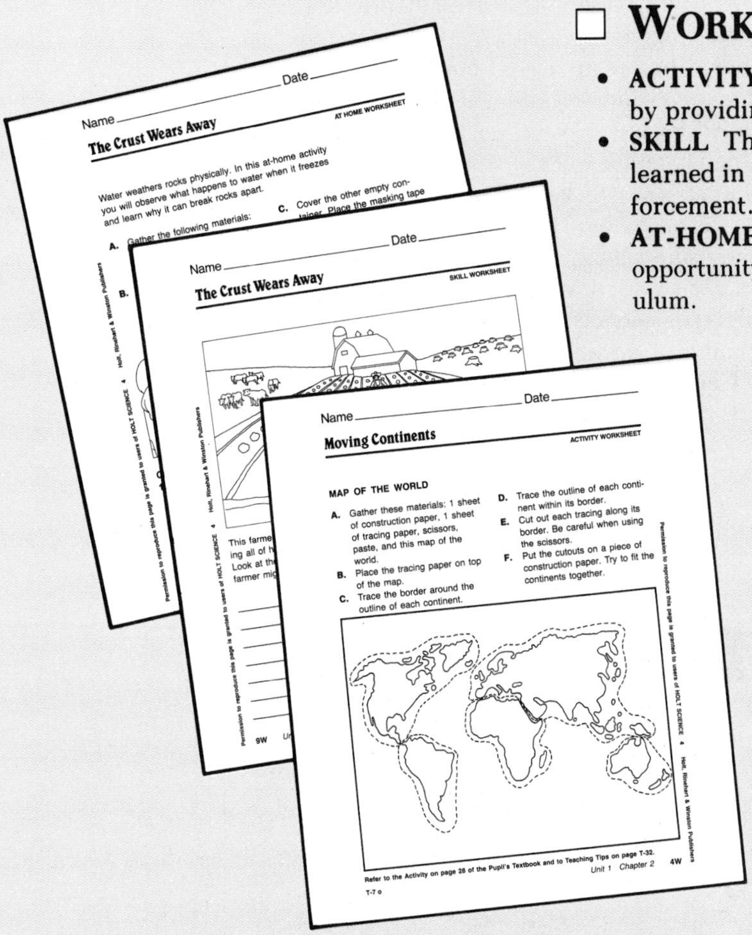

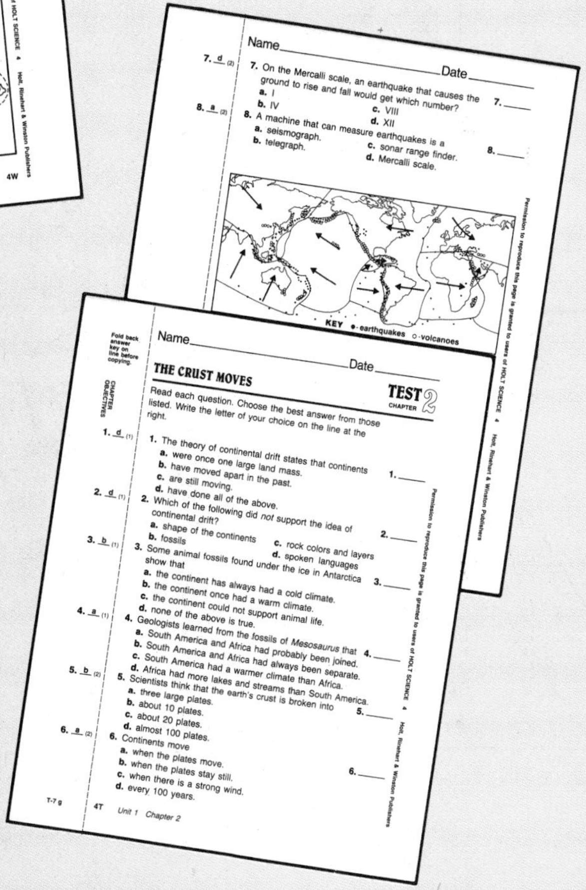

□ TEST MASTERS

These comprehensive 2–3 page chapter tests are criteria-referenced to the Chapter Objectives.

* The worksheet and test masters are also available as a separate ancillary consisting of duplicating masters.

LEARNING CENTERS

A Learning Center consisting of additional activities and research topics is a good way for teachers to expand the science curriculum. Students can work at the Learning Center by themselves or in small groups. The selection of work to be done at the Center should match the ability level of a particular class. Because students are encouraged to work independently, teachers will be able to meet their individual needs.

The Learning Center should be set up away from the rest of the class, preferably in a corner that receives indirect sunlight. If this is not possible, artificial lights may be needed for green plants. A large, low table is best, but several small tables pushed together will also work well. The table should be positioned next to a bulletin board which displays drawings, photographs, and the title of the Center. If no bulletin board is available, it is easy to construct a tri-fold backdrop using oaktag, cardboard, and duct tape. Shoe boxes and other containers can be used as files for activities and research topics, as well as for the materials needed to complete them. The Center is an ideal place for an aquarium or terrarium, if one is kept in the classroom.

Suggestions for Learning Center titles and displays appear at the beginning of each unit. Activities and worksheets that are found in the Teacher's Edition are also listed for the unit.

BASIC SCIENCE SKILLS

The term *basic science skills* is used in the *Holt Science* program to refer to a range of skills. These include reading and math skills, which are critical thinking skills. They are fundamental to all learning processes. Hence, the teaching of basic science skills involves the teaching of those same skills taught in reading and math. The only difference is the application of these skills in the science content area.

Science is the ideal setting for students to practice and reinforce the reading and math skills they have learned. Students are naturally curious about the world around them. The science skills they acquire become tools which they can use to find answers to their questions. They will in time discover, as often happens in science, that answers to questions often trigger new questions. This questioning approach, which requires a logical use of science skills, is the basis of the scientific method. Science is within the reach of all students once they understand that it includes the practice of the same skills that they have already been taught.

The rationale of the *Holt Science* program is to teach these basic science skills to students. This is done in a number of ways. First of all, specific skills are used to develop concepts. Through concrete experiences in which students can manipulate objects and materials, more skills are learned. The skills of observing, measuring, recording, and predicting take on meaning for students as they perform each Activity. And finally, thought-provoking questions encourage students to develop the ability to compare and contrast, classify, identify, form sequences, infer, hypothesize, and generalize.

For the teacher, the close parallel between science skills and reading and math skills is pointed out in the Basic Teaching Plan of each section. The applicable skills are identified for the teacher and additional teaching tips are suggested to help the teacher explain particularly difficult concepts. The teaching of reading and math skills and the teaching of science skills become one: the teaching of those critical thinking skills needed for all branches of learning.

The ability to communicate in written and oral form is one of the basic science skills strengthened by the *Holt Science* program. Students learn how to discuss and write about what they have learned. The Teacher's Edition contains suggestions for discussion questions. Research topics are often suggested in the Extensions. Activities are worded in a way that requires students to write their own conclusions and results.

Care has been taken to develop skills which are appropriate for each age group. In the lower grades, the concentration is on the more fundamental skills, such as *observing* and *comparing*. As students progress, more advanced skills are introduced at each grade level. Provision has been made for the fact that students within any age group progress at different rates. Extensions to each section have reinforcement of skills for slower learners and enrichment and application of skills for students of higher ability.

The chart on pages xxii and xxiii lists the basic science skills which have been stressed in the *Holt Science* program.

BASIC SCIENCE SKILLS

FOLLOWING DIRECTIONS

requires that students be able to follow both written and verbal instructions. The ability to follow directions in sequence will determine the successful outcome of an Activity or experiment.

READING ILLUSTRATIONS

requires that students be able to extract information from photographs, drawings, diagrams, charts, and graphs. Illustrations are especially important in the lower grades where children are just beginning to read.

BUILDING SCIENCE VOCABULARY

requires that students use word-attack skills as they are introduced to new science words. In science, the understanding of prefixes, suffixes, and root words is especially important.

FINDING THE MAIN IDEA

requires that students be able to pick out the main idea after reading a passage in the text. The ability to do this shows that students have comprehended what they have read. It is a skill that older students use when they prepare outlines and take notes in class.

OBSERVING

requires that students be able to use one or more senses to note and then describe the properties of objects or events.

COMPARING AND CONTRASTING

requires that students be able to identify common and distinguishing characteristics among items or events. In the lower grades, students are asked to tell how things are the same or different.

CLASSIFYING

requires that students be able to organize information into logical categories. The students should be able to arrange items, places, or events into groups by identifying a common characteristic. Hence the ability to compare and contrast is necessary before classifying can be done.

SEQUENCING

requires that students be able to arrange items or events according to a characteristic. This skill depends on the ability to observe, compare, and contrast. With younger children, the words "put things in order" can be used.

FINDING CAUSE AND EFFECT RELATIONSHIPS

requires that students be able to recognize the relationship of cause and effect. Younger children will learn to relate the two while older children may be asked to infer or predict the outcome of an event.

MEASURING

requires that students be able quantitatively to describe the length, area, volume, mass, and temperature of objects. The ability to use units of measure and read measuring equipment is part of this skill. This skill is important in increasing the accuracy of observations.

RECORDING DATA

requires that students be able to organize data in a logical way so that results can be interpreted and reviewed.

PREDICTING

requires that students be able to anticipate the consequences of a new or changed situation. Students must use their past experiences and the skill of recognizing cause and effect in making predictions.

HYPOTHESIZING

requires that students be able to suggest answers to questions or problems that can be tested.

INFERRING

requires that students be able to propose an explanation based on observations and data.

CONCLUDING AND GENERALIZING

requires that students be able to use and synthesize several skills so that results of an experiment and other observations can be explained.

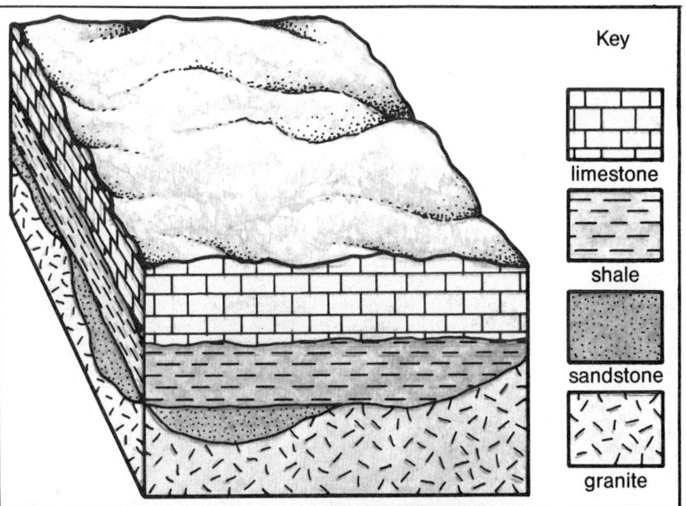

BACKGROUND

Science is the investigation and interpretation of the natural and physical world. Scientists conduct their investigations in a particular way, using a set of skills called the scientific method. This involves making observations, recognizing a problem, formulating hypotheses, and testing those hypotheses through observations and/or experimentation in order to arrive at certain conclusions. But scientists are not the only ones who use these skills. We are all observers of our world and universe and, therefore, are capable of acting as scientists.

This section acquaints students with some of the skills scientists use to study the world around them. The text, Activities, and Extensions are concerned with these skills. Within this section, emphasize these skills rather than the subject matter. The students should come to realize that they, too, can and often do use these skills to solve problems. For this reason, the text focuses on situations in which two students deal scientifically with a dilemma.

Try to dispel the idea that using the scientific method always ensures arriving at the right answer. Using these skills may not lead to any answer, but the information obtained during the course of research may still be useful. Very often it is the accidental discovery that leads to the development of many important ideas and products.

The intent of this section is to illustrate that scientists are not engaged in something that is mysterious or too difficult to understand.

MATERIALS

thread, piece of cardboard, 5 straight pins, tape, metric ruler, paper, pencil

SKILLS OF SCIENCE

Frank and Debbie had planned to go sailing on the lake. Then they saw dark clouds in the east. They checked to see from what direction the wind was blowing. The wind was also coming from the east. They called to get a weather report. As they thought, a storm was moving toward them. They did not take the boat out. They tied it up and went home.

BASIC TEACHING PLAN

MOTIVATION

It is important for students to realize that science is all around them and that everyone practices science to some extent. Ask: Have you ever seen a baby look at an object, listen to it while shaking it, taste it, smell it, or feel it? What is the baby doing? *The baby is finding out about, or exploring, the object.* Tell the students that the baby is involved in scientific research. Tell them that they, too, are involved in science and that science may be very helpful to them. For example, discuss weather forecasting. Ask: What kinds of things does the weather forecaster observe? *Temperature, pressure, wind, precipitation.* How are these things measured? *With instruments, such as thermometers, weather vanes, and barometers.* What do weather forecasters do for you? *They predict the weather so you know what to wear and how to plan your activities for the next day.* Tell the students that observing, predicting, and measuring are important scientific skills. In this section, they will learn about these skills and how they, too, can use them.

Why did Frank and Debbie think a storm was coming? Why did they call for a weather report? Frank and Debbie had **observed,** or noticed, two things. First, they observed dark clouds in the east. Next, they observed that the wind was also coming from the east. They compared these **observations** with what they knew. They knew that dark clouds often bring bad weather. But they also knew that this was not always the case. They needed more information. So they called for a weather report.

Frank and Debbie did some things weather scientists do. A scientist must observe things closely. A scientist can learn a lot about the world through observations. Sometimes a scientist has to check observations with other scientists. The observations of one person may not be enough to give a true picture of the world. The observations of many people may be needed. This is true of weather forecasting.

Observe: To notice something by seeing or using any of the five senses, such as hearing.

Observations: Anything that we can learn by using our senses, such as sight or hearing.

EXTENSIONS

Enrichment

Science Skills— Measuring, Recording Data, Concluding and Generalizing

Students could practice their temperature-recording skills and then use them to predict a weather pattern during the course of a day.

A. Have the students record the temperature outdoors in the same place three times daily (early morning, midday, late afternoon) for one week. They should also record the times of their readings.

B. Have them record the data in a table. They can then plot their data on a graph, where the *x*-axis is the time of day and the *y*-axis is the temperature. Using different colors for each day's data, each student can put all five days on a single graph.

C. Have the students compare their graphs and draw conclusions about fluctuations in temperature during the course of a day. For example, ask: Is it usually colder in the morning or at noon? Does it continually get hotter as the day progresses, or does the temperature peak at midday and then go down? Will it get cooler in the evening? Why?

DEVELOPMENT

1 Teaching Tips—Have the students discuss the way in which Frank and Debbie are thinking about and approaching their problem. The steps include observing, thinking, concluding, and acting.

2 Teaching Tips—To demonstrate how scientists must check and share information with other scientists, ask those students with pet dogs to describe their dogs' behavior when offered a treat. Most will answer that their dogs get excited. Tell the students that because they have shared information about a number of dogs, they can begin to make certain general conclusions. They may conclude that most dogs like treats. They may also hypothesize why some dogs beg for the treat while others are indifferent to it. For example, a dog that is sick or that has just been fed will not become excited.

EXTENSIONS

Application
Science Skills— Measuring

To achieve the greatest possible accuracy, scientists usually take many readings of a particular measurement. They use the average value of those readings as the final piece of data. They then confirm their measurements with other scientists. To demonstrate how difficult it is to measure something accurately and to show how deceiving our eyes can be, do the following demonstrations, with the entire class:

A. On the chalkboard draw these lines in this configuration:

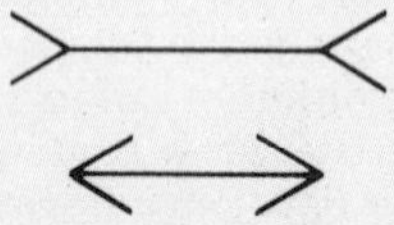
a
b

Fig. 1

Make sure the horizontal lines are as equal as possible. Ask: Which line, a or b, looks longer? (Most students will say a.) Have a student measure the lines. They should be equal. Tell the students they were deceived by an optical illusion. When doing science, they should be careful not to jump to conclusions before they have enough data. Being skeptical is part of being a scientist.

B. Have each of five students measure the width of the classroom and report the reading to you without telling it to the other students. Then write the five figures on the chalkboard. They will probably vary a bit. Unless one figure is extremely inaccurate, emphasize that all are approximately correct, though none is probably exactly right. Tell the students that all we can do to be accurate is to make measurements as carefully as we can and to share and check our data with each other. For an arithmetic exercise, have students determine the average value.

Record: To put down in writing.

Data: Facts, or pieces of information.

Predict: To forecast on the basis of observations or past experience.

There are over 9,000 weather stations around the world. Scientists at each station make observations. They also **record** information about the weather. They then share this information with each other. Pieces of information are called **data.** Scientists use data to forecast, or **predict,** the weather.

2

3 **Teaching Tips**—Scientists record and accumulate so much data that it is necessary to organize it into formats that make it understandable. Discuss ways to record data such as tables, charts, line graphs, bar graphs, and maps, and determine the usefulness of each method. You could take an applicable survey within your class and illustrate the data on several kinds of graphs.

4 Scientists often must make **measurements** to help them make predictions or forecasts. Suppose **5** a storm is moving across the country. Scientists need to know how fast it is moving. They must first measure how far it has moved. Then they measure how long it took to move that far.

Measurements: Observations that are made by counting something. Often an instrument, such as a ruler, is used to make measurements.

3

4 **Teaching Tips**—Have students list the tools they have in the classroom, such as rulers, thermometers, and clocks. Ask them to name more complex scientific tools, such as microscopes, barometers, telescopes, and weather satellites.

5 **Teaching Tips**—Discuss different kinds of storms with your students, particularly the kinds that are indigenous to your area. Have students research the characteristics of thunderstorms, tornadoes, cyclones, hurricanes, and blizzards in their dictionaries and encyclopedias. Ask: If the weather report said a blizzard was coming, what would you expect just by knowing the name of the storm? How would you prepare for it? How has an accurate weather forecast helped you or your family?

EXTENSIONS

Enrichment

Science Skills—Observing, Measuring, Recording Data, Inferring

As observers of natural phenomena, scientists must carefully isolate the conditions or variables within an experiment. Most environments are a combination of many interactive factors. As an example of an experiment in which different variables can be selected, students could study pendulum motion.

A. Obtain 1 long (30-cm or 12-in.) piece of string, 1 short (15-cm or 6-in.) piece, and 3 washers. Suspend the washers from the long piece of string first.

B. Hold the weight at a starting position that is approximately 90° higher than the vertical position. Allow the weight to swing freely and count the number of complete swings of the pendulum within a 15-sec time period. Discuss the variable (length of string) and the constants (weight, starting position, and time) in the experiment. Carry out at least three trials in the experiment.

C. Attach the weights to the shorter piece of string and carry out three trials for this variable.

D. Compute the averages. Discuss the reason for taking averages and how the computations bring you closer to an accurate value.

E. If desired, you could change the number of washers (weight) to investigate the effect of weight on pendulum motion.

EXTENSIONS

Enrichment

Science Skills—Classifying

Scientists classify different types of storms. They call them thunderstorms, hurricanes, tornadoes, blizzards, and so on. Each class of storm has certain properties such as the speed of its winds and the amount of precipitation it brings. Classification helps scientists describe different things and show the ways they are related to each other. Classification is based on observation and also involves comparing and contrasting.

A. Have students collect at least 20 different kinds of leaves with part of the stems still attached.

B. Ask them to develop a classification scheme that distinguishes the leaves from each other and at the same time indicates relationships. Suggestions for their classification systems include the following: needlelike or not needlelike, clustered or not clustered, paired or not paired, number of leaves in cluster, shape of leaves, texture of leaves.

SKILL BUILDING ACTIVITY

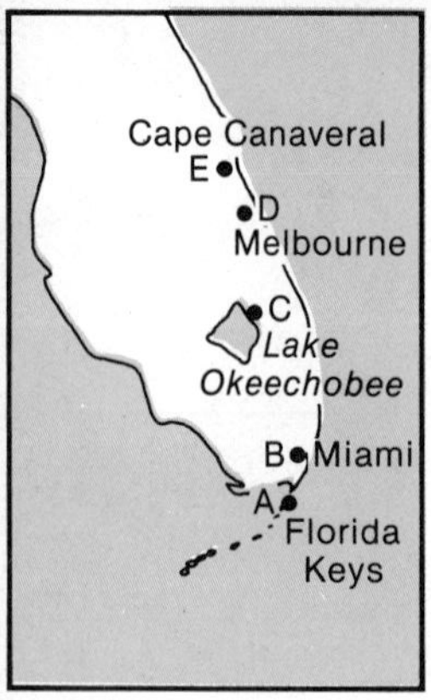

You can measure the movement of a storm.

A. Gather these materials: 10 cm (4 in.) thread, piece of cardboard, 5 straight pins, tape, metric ruler, paper, and pencil.

B. Trace the outline map of Florida. Tape your outline to a piece of cardboard.

C. Place a straight pin at each spot where the storm is shown on the map.

D. Tie 1 end of the thread around the first pin. Tie the thread to the second pin. Join all 5 pins with thread.

E. Use the ruler to measure the length of thread between each pin. Record your results in a table like the one shown.

F. Let 1 cm = 100 km (60 mi). Change your numbers to kilometers.

1. It took 5 hr for the storm to move from A to B. How fast was it moving?
2. At the same speed, how long would the storm take to move from C to D?

Positions	Distance (1 cm = 100 km)	
	cm	km
A–B		
B–C		
C–D		
D–E		

4

ACTIVITY

Skill Development—*Measuring, Recording Data, Inferring*

Teaching Tips—Tell students to tape their maps securely to the cardboard so they won't slip and to place the pins in deeply enough so they won't fall out. You may want to demonstrate how to tie the thread around each pin. Also explain that 1 cm = 100 km (in step F) is a distance scale, which simply relates the distance on the map with the real distance.

Safety Tips—Warn the students to be careful when handling the straight pins.

Answers to Questions—Table: A–B, 0.5 cm, 50 km; B–C, 1.5 cm, 150 km; C–D, 1 cm, 100 km; and D–E, 0.5 cm, 50 km.
1. 10 kph. 2. 10 hr.

The storm that upset Frank and Debbie's sailing plans was a hurricane. A hurricane is a storm with strong winds and heavy rain. About ten hurricanes a year form over the warm waters of the Caribbean Sea. Some of these storms may hit the United States. A hurricane that hits land can cause great damage. Luckily, most hurricanes never hit land.

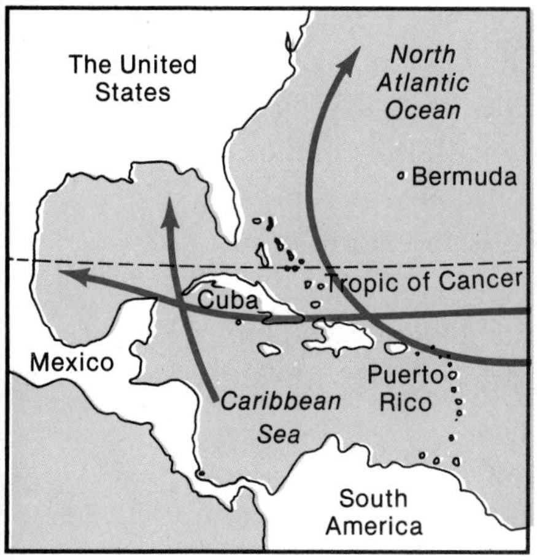

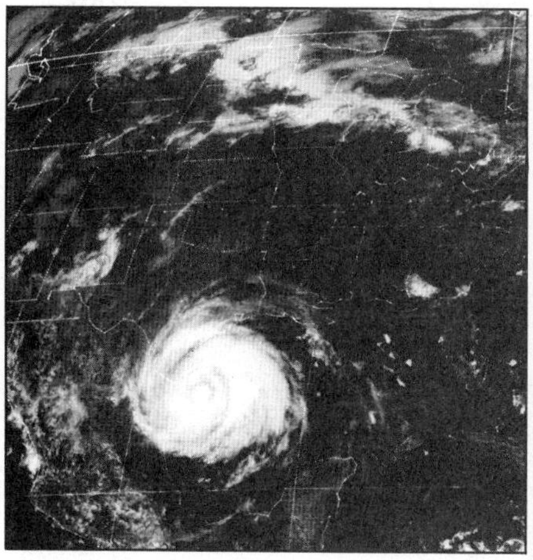

Weather scientists observe hurricanes closely. As a hurricane forms, scientists record information about it on maps. They keep track of its path. Then they can sometimes predict where it will go next. The map on this page shows three paths that a hurricane might follow.

Records are kept in all fields of science. In weather forecasts, good records can save lives.

EXTENSIONS

Enrichment

Research—Library

Since experimental data are presented in many forms, students could use atlases in the library to practice reading maps and determining distances. Students will need to take paper, pencil, and a ruler to the library. As a class you could select various destinations, and the students could compute the distances. Encourage them to use the kilometer scale.

6 Teaching Tips—Since scientific investigation includes researching accumulated knowledge, students could interview several adults who remember a severe hurricane, storm, or blizzard. They should ask the adults to describe the severity of the damage that occurred. Students could also research the topic in reference books.

7 Teaching Tips—Discuss how weather records are used to predict future patterns. Refer to the map of hurricane patterns.

EXTENSIONS

Applications

Science Skills—Predicting, Measuring, Recording Data, Concluding and Generalizing

To test whether girls in the fourth grade are, on the average, lighter, heavier, or the same weight as boys, bring a bathroom scale to the classroom. First ask for predictions. Then weigh each student and record the data in a table with two columns, one for girls and one for boys.

A. Have each student draw three bar graphs, one for the entire class taken together, one for the girls, and one for the boys. On all three, the *x*-axis is the number of students with a particular weight, and the *y*-axis is the weight.

B. Once the graphs are drawn, have students make conclusions. Were their predictions wrong or right? Are girls lighter, heavier, or the same as boys? What can be said about the shape of the graphs? How was the bar graph format helpful? From these data, can the students predict whether girls in another fourth-grade class will be lighter, heavier, or the same weight as boys? (A fair prediction could be made, but it would have to be tested.) What about the girls and boys in the first grade? (No prediction can be made.) in the tenth grade? (No prediction can be made.) Emphasize that the results of one experiment may only be generalized to another situation with the same conditions.

SKILL BUILDING ACTIVITY

Position	Day
F13	1
F12	2
F11	3
F10	4
F9	5
F8	6

You can track a hurricane and predict where it will go.

A. Gather these materials: paper, pencil, and metric ruler.

B. Trace the map shown on page 7 on a piece of paper. Use a ruler to help you draw straight lines.

C. Look at the hurricane table. Mark where the hurricane is each day on your map. Label each point with the number of the day. (Day 1 has been done for you.)

1. Where is the storm on day 2?
2. What city is it near on day 6?

D. Draw a line to join each point. Compare the storm's path to the 3 paths shown on the map on page 5.

3. Suppose the hurricane follows one of the 3 paths. Predict where it will be on day 7.
4. Pretend you are a weather forecaster. What cities and countries would you warn about the hurricane?

E. Use the metric ruler and the scale of kilometers to answer question 5.

5. How far is Miami from San Juan? Suppose the storm turns toward Miami. It is moving at 20 kilometers per hour (kph). How long will it take to hit the city?

6

ACTIVITY

Skill Development—*Comparing and Contrasting, Predicting*

Teaching Tips—Make sure students understand both the map detailing the typical hurricane paths and the map they must copy and fill in. Explain the grid system and how to plot the data points on it.

Answers to Questions—1. About 2,000 km northeast of San Juan. **2.** San Juan. **3.** About 500 km north of Haiti. **4.** San Juan (Puerto Rico), Haiti, Havana (Cuba). **5.** About 1,600 km; 3 days.

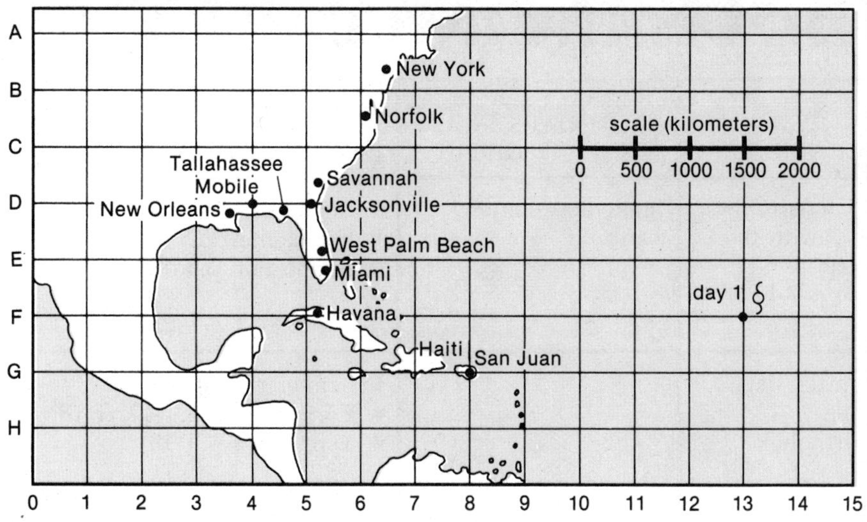

8 The chart shows some things that scientists do.
9 How did Frank and Debbie act like scientists?

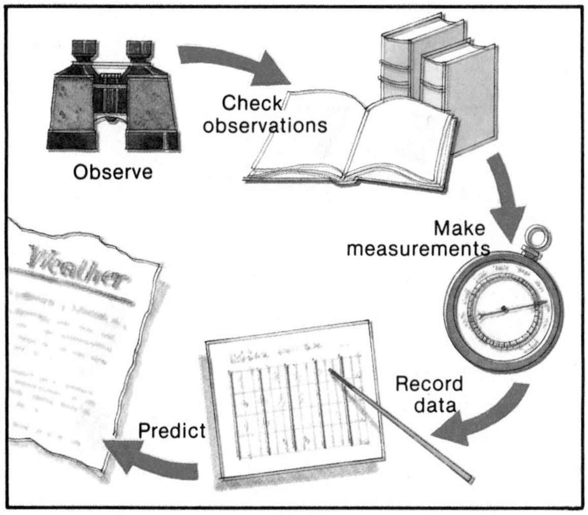

7

8 Teaching Tips—Review and discuss the chart showing the steps scientists take when they do research.

9 Text Questions—How did Frank and Debbie act like scientists? *They observed dark clouds and the wind direction. They checked their observations by calling for a weather report. They predicted that a storm was on the way, and concluded that it would be unsafe to go sailing.*

EXTENSIONS

Reinforcement

Science Skills—Hypothesizing, Recording Data

Have the students determine which of a variety of objects float when they are placed in water. Emphasize that it does not matter if they already know the answers. What is important here is to approach the problem scientifically.

A. Obtain such things as pebbles, shells, blocks of wood, toothpicks, bottle caps, empty tin cans, pencils, pens, paper clips, and scissors. Half fill a sink, plastic bucket, or glass aquarium with water.

B. Make a table with columns labeled OBJECT, PREDICTION, RESULT, CONCLUSION, WEIGHT. For each object listed, predict what it will do when placed in the water.

C. One by one, place each object in the water, observe what happens, and record the result in the table. In the CONCLUSION column, write down whether the students' predictions were right or wrong.

D. Finally, discuss why some things float and others sink. If students conclude that weight is a factor, have them weigh each object and include the data in their tables. They will note that some things that float are heavier than some things that sink. Tell them that they may not yet know enough to explain why things sink or float (factors to be considered are density and specific gravity), but that they do know now, in a scientific way, which things will sink and which will float. According to their data, weight alone cannot be the only determining factor.

UNIT 1 THE CHANGING EARTH

	SECTION	BASIC SCIENCE SKILLS	ACTIVITY MATERIALS STUDENT/GROUP	EXTENSIONS
CHAPTER 1 THE WHOLE EARTH	**1-1** p.T-10 Inside the Earth	*Comparing and contrasting* the earth's interior with the interior of a softball p.T-11 and with an apple p.T-12	apple and dinner knife	• Reinforcement pp.T-11, T-14 • Enrichment p.T-13 • Application p.T-12
	1-2 p.T-15 Earthquake	*Recording* earthquake data p.T-16 *Examining* illustrations of earthquake damage p.T-18		• Reinforcement p.T-16 • Enrichment pp.T-17, T-18 • Application p.T-19
	1-3 p.T-20 Volcanoes	*Sequencing* events in the formation of a volcano p.T-22 *Comparing and contrasting* the locations of earthquakes and volcanoes p.T-23	samples of volcanic rocks, glass, water	• Reinforcement pp.T-22, T-23 • Enrichment pp.T-21, T-24, T-25, T-26
CHAPTER 2 THE CRUST MOVES	**2-1** p.T-27 Moving Continents	*Reaching a conclusion* on continental drift p.T-29	scissors, paste, construction paper, tracing paper, world map	• Reinforcement p.T-30 • Enrichment p.T-29 • Application p.T-28
	2-2 p.T-31 Broken Crusts	*Observing* how plates move	hard-boiled egg, dinner knife, paper towel	• Reinforcement p.T-32 • Enrichment pp.T-33, T-34
	2-3 p.T-35 Making Mountains	*Finding the cause and effect* of mountain building p.T-36	3 stacks clay or plasticene, 2 wooden blocks, golf ball, plastic knife	• Enrichment pp.T-36, T-37, T-38, T-40 • Application p.T-39
CHAPTER 3 THE CRUST WEARS AWAY	**3-1** p.T-41 Breaking Down Rocks	*Observing* weathering p.T-43	limestone rocks, 2 jars, water, white vinegar	• Reinforcement pp.T-43, T-44 • Application pp.T-42, T-44
	3-2 p.T-45 Moving Water	*Sequencing* the water cycle p.T-45 *Finding the cause and effect* of erosion *affecting* soil development p.T-46	large jar with screw lid, water, small pebbles	• Reinforcement p.T-46 • Enrichment pp.T-46, T-48 • Application p.T-48
	3-3 p.T-49 River of Ice	*Observing* and *inferring* from glacial landscapes p.T-51	2-liter plastic bags, gravel, water	• Enrichment pp.T-50, T-52 • Application p.T-51
	3-4 p.T-53 Humans Cause Change	*Causes and effects* of human landscape changes p.T-54 and of beneficial changes to the environment p.T-55	old magazines, poster paper, scissors, glue	• Reinforcement pp.T-56, T-57, T-58 • Application pp.T-54, T-55, T-59

EXTRA ACTIVITIES/ DEMONSTRATIONS	BLACK LINE MASTERS	EVALUATIONS
• Showing the earth's treasures p.T-12 • Comparing the density of the crust and core p.T-13		Section Review p.T-14
• Earthquake photographs p.T-16 • Clay faults p.T-17	Layers (SK) p.T-7 l Earthquake Report Card (AC) p.T-7 m	Section Review p.T-19
• Baking Soda Volcano p.T-20 • Volcanic rocks p.T-23	Word Search (SK) p.T-7 n	Section Review p.T-25 Chapter Review p.T-26 Test Masters pp.T-7 d, e, f
• World map p.T-27 • Fossils p.T-29		Section Review p.T-30
• Clay faults p.T-31 • Plate map p.T-32	Drifting Continents (AC) p.T-7 o	Section Review p.T-34
• Mountain landscapes p.T-37	Fossils and Mountains p.T-7 p (SK) Crossword p.T-7 q (SK)	Section Review p.T-39 Chapter Review p.T-40 Test Masters pp.T-7 g, h
• Broken rock p.T-42 • Weathered rock p.T-43	Weathering p.T-7 r (AH)	Section Review p.T-44
• Stream table pp.T-46 T-47	North American Rivers p.T-7 s (AC)	Section Review p.T-48
• Snowball p.T-50		Section Review p.T-52
• Development field trip p.T-54 • Investigating p.T-58	Erosion p.T-7 t (SK) Missing Letters p.T-7 u (SK)	Section Review p.T-56 Chapter Review p.T-57 Test Master pp.T-7 i, j, k

KEY (AC)—Activity (AH)—At Home (SK)—Skill

BOOKS FOR STUDENTS

Baylor, Byrd. *If You Are a Hunter of Fossils*, New York: Scribner, 1980
Berger, Melvin. *Disastrous Floods and Tidal Waves*, New York: Franklin Watts, 1981
Berger, Melvin. *Disastrous Volcanoes*, New York: Franklin Watts, 1981
Fodor, R.V. *Earth Afire! Volcanoes and Their Activity*, New York: William Morrow, 1981
Fodor, R.V. *Frozen Earth: Explaining the Ice Ages*, Hillside, NJ: Enslow Publishers, 1981
Navarra, John Gabriel, *Earthquake!*, Garden City, N.Y.: Doubleday, 1980
Nixon, Hershell, H. and Nixon, Joan L. *Earthquake: Nature in Motion*, New York: Dodd, 1981
Nixon, Hershell, H. and Nixon, Joan L. *Glaciers: Nature's Frozen Rivers*, New York: Dodd, 1980
Poyhter, Margaret, *Volcanoes: Fiery Mountains*, New York: Messner, 1980
Simon, Seymour. *Danger From Below*, New York: Four Winds, 1979

FILMS

Earthquakes and Volcanoes, 14 min, BFA
Monuments to Erosion, 11 min, Britannica
Understanding Our Earth: How Its Surface Changes, 11 min, Coronet
The Birth and Death of Mountains, 12 1/2 min, BFA
The River Must Live, 15 min, Shell
Erosion and Weathering, 17 min, Britannica
Volcano: Birth of a Mountain, 24 min, Britannica

FILMSTRIPS

Our Changing Earth, 6 min, sound, Coronet

COMPUTER AIDS

Earthquakes, Simulation, on Earth Science, Atari, BASIC, diskette, Atari, Inc.
Quakes, Tutorial, on Earth & Life Science, Apple, BASIC, diskette, Apple Computer Co.

BULLETIN BOARD

This bulletin board display is designed to illustrate the changes caused in the earth by nature and by people. Have the students cut out pictures from magazines and newspapers. The bulletin board should be divided into two sections. One section should contain pictures showing changes caused by nature and the other should contain pictures showing changes caused by people. Have students label the pictures, indicating whether land is being built up, worn down, or preserved.

FIELD TRIP IDEAS

To find signs of changes in the land

Take the students on a walking tour of your area. Have them look for signs of changes in the land caused by nature and by people. Discuss the natural processes that shaped your area. Were they glaciers, volcanoes, mountain building, or flooding and wind erosion? Students should also look for human changes, such as building construction, excavations, and road work. When you return to the classroom, have the students make a list of the natural and human changes they observed and discuss whether these changes built up the land, wore it down, or preserved it.

To investigate future community plans

Inquire if your students are aware of any future plans for their community. Prepare a list of groups or individuals to contact to determine such plans (city planner, planning commission, and so on). Then make arrangements to have your class visit these people or their representatives. Prior to the visit, tell your students to make up a list of questions that they might want to ask. After the field trip, ask your students to pick one community plan that interests them. Suggest that they discuss the advantages and disadvantages of the plan with their families. Then have them write letters expressing their viewpoints to the appropriate people.

Name____________________________Date__________

Fold back answer key on line before copying.

THE WHOLE EARTH

TEST CHAPTER 1

CHAPTER OBJECTIVES

Read each question. Choose the best answer from those listed. Write the letter of your choice on the line at the right.

1. The layer of earth on which we live is **1.** ______ **1.** b (1)
- **a.** the core. **c.** the mantle.
- **b.** the crust. **d.** the stem.

2. The mantle of the earth is made of **2.** ______ **2.** a (1)
- **a.** mostly solid rock. **c.** melted rock.
- **b.** very cool rock. **d.** nickel and iron.

3. The layer of earth that is thick in some places and thin in others is **3.** ______ **3.** b (1)
- **a.** the mantle. **c.** the core.
- **b.** the crust. **d.** none of these.

4. Which of the following is *not* true about the earth's core? **4.** ______ **4.** c (1)
- **a.** There is probably an inner and outer core.
- **b.** It is the hottest layer.
- **c.** It is the thinnest layer.
- **d.** It is in the same position as an apple core.

5. An earthquake is **5.** ______ **5.** b (2)
- **a.** an opening in the earth's crust through which lava escapes.
- **b.** a sudden movement in the earth's crust.
- **c.** very easy to predict.
- **d.** always the cause of much damage.

6. Most earthquakes occur **6.** ______ **6.** b (2)
- **a.** very deep in the earth.
- **b.** within 60 km of the surface.
- **c.** mostly underwater.
- **d.** only when the weather is cold.

7. d (2)

8. a (2)

9. a (3)

10. a (3)

11. b (3)

Name_______________________ Date___________

7. On the Mercalli scale, an earthquake that causes the ground to rise and fall would get which number? **7.** ______

a. I
b. IV
c. VIII
d. XII

8. A machine that can measure earthquakes is a **8.** ______

a. seismograph.
b. telegraph.
c. sonar range finder.
d. Mercalli scale.

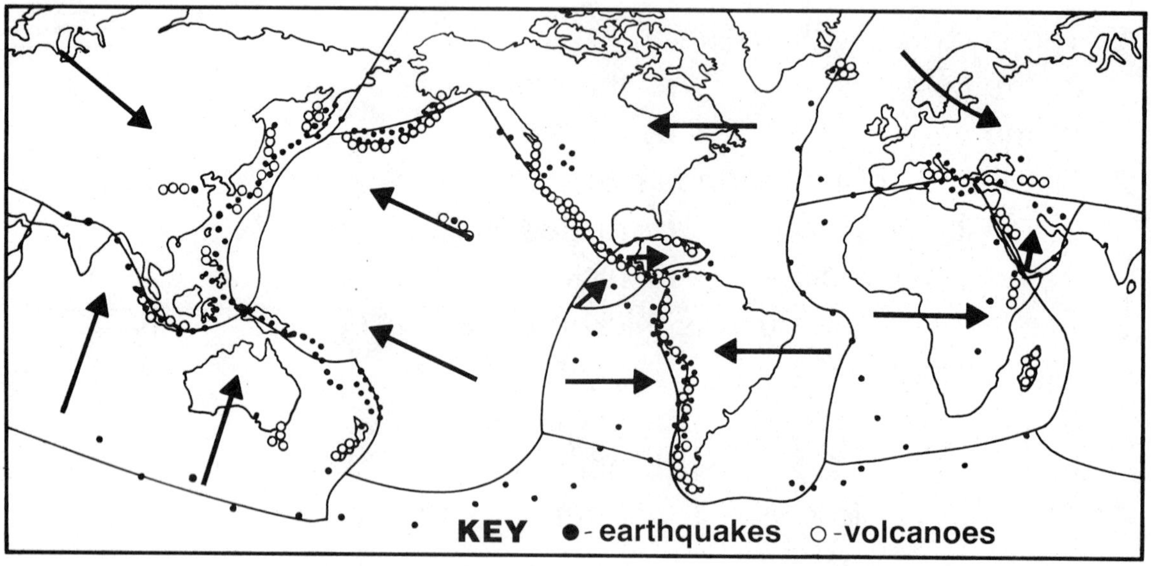

9. Each solid dot on the map shows where an earthquake **9.** ______

a. has taken place.
b. will take place.
c. never took place.
d. caused only a little damage.

10. Which part of the map makes up the "earthquake belt?" **10.** ______

a. the solid dots
b. the edge of the map
c. the entire map
d. the dot in the center

11. The name of the belt formed by volcanoes on the map is **11.** ______

a. the Hill of Heat.
b. the Ring of Fire.
c. the Earthquake Belt.
d. Mt. St. Helens.

Name________________________________Date____________

12. Look at the map. Which statement is true about earthquakes and volcanoes? **12.** _____ **12.** d (3)

a. They are not near each other.

b. They are located in exactly the same spots.

c. There are the same number of volcanoes as earthquakes.

d. They are located in the same general areas.

13. Magma forms **13.** _____ **13.** c (4)

a. in the crust. **c.** in the mantle.

b. in the core. **d.** in all of these.

14. Magma reaches the earth's surface **14.** _____ **14.** a (4)

a. through a crack in the crust.

b. after earthquakes.

c. as soon as it is formed.

d. after it cools off.

15. When an exploding volcano erupts, **15.** _____ **15.** b (4)

a. magma slowly oozes out.

b. hot material is thrown into the air.

c. material gently flows onto the ground.

d. nothing changes.

16. Magma rises to the earth's surface because **16.** _____ **16.** c (4)

a. earthquakes push it up.

b. it is a gas.

c. it is lighter than solid rocks.

d. it is heavy.

Fold back answer key on line before copying.

Name________________________________ Date __________

THE CRUST MOVES

TEST CHAPTER 2

CHAPTER OBJECTIVES

Read each question. Choose the best answer from those listed. Write the letter of your choice on the line at the right.

1. d (1)

1. The theory of continental drift states that continents **1.** ____
a. were once one large land mass.
b. have moved apart in the past.
c. are still moving.
d. have done all of the above.

2. d (1)

2. Which of the following did *not* support the idea of continental drift? **2.** ____
a. shape of the continents **c.** rock colors and layers
b. fossils **d.** spoken languages

3. b (1)

3. Some animal fossils found under the ice in Antarctica show that **3.** ____
a. the continent has always had a cold climate.
b. the continent once had a warm climate.
c. the continent could not support animal life.
d. none of the above is true.

4. a (1)

4. Geologists learned from the fossils of *Mesosaurus* that **4.** ____
a. South America and Africa had probably been joined.
b. South America and Africa had always been separate.
c. South America had a warmer climate than Africa.
d. Africa had more lakes and streams than South America.

5. b (2)

5. Scientists think that the earth's crust is broken into **5.** ____
a. three large plates.
b. about 10 plates.
c. about 20 plates.
d. almost 100 plates.

6. a (2)

6. Continents move **6.** ____
a. when the plates move.
b. when the plates stay still.
c. when there is a strong wind.
d. every 100 years.

Name________________________________Date____________

7. The plates of the earth are part of its 7. ______ 7. c (2)

a. mantle. c. crust.

b. core. d. mantle, core, and crust.

8. Which of the following is *not* a plate movement? 8. ______ 8. d (2)

a. colliding c. slipping

b. spreading d. rolling

9. What can result when two plates collide? 9. ______ 9. b (3)

a. volcanoes c. snowstorms

b. earthquakes d. hurricanes

10. Volcanoes are common where 10. ______ 10. b (3)

a. plates collide. c. plates are not in motion.

b. plates move apart. d. plates slip past each other.

11. Common occurrences along the San Andreas fault are 11. ______ 11. b (3)

a. volcanoes. c. floods.

b. earthquakes. d. all of these.

12. Magma squeezes up between plates when 12. ______ 12. c (3)

a. the plates collide. c. the plates move apart.

b. the plates stay still. d. the plates slide.

13. Which of the following causes folded mountains to form? 13. ______ 13. c (4)

a. magma pushing up c. bending and squeezing

b. cracking and tilting d. all of the above

14. Rock formations that are cracked and tilted are found in 14. ______ 14. b (4)

a. folded mountains. c. dome mountains.

b. fault block mountains. d. hills.

15. The Appalachian Mountains are 15. ______ 15. a (4)

a. folded mountains. c. dome-shaped mountains.

b. fault block mountains. d. a mixture of the above.

16. The Sierra Nevada Mountains were formed when two plates collided and the rocks 16. ______ 16. a (4)

a. cracked and tilted. c. were pushed up by magma.

b. were bent and squeezed. d. melted.

Fold back answer key on line before copying.

Name________________________Date__________

THE CRUST WEARS AWAY

TEST 3 CHAPTER

CHAPTER OBJECTIVES

Read each question. Choose the best answer from those listed. Write the letter of your choice on the line at the right.

1. b (1)

1. What changes in a rock during physical weathering? **1.**______
- **a.** minerals
- **b.** size and shape
- **c.** color
- **d.** nothing

2. d (1)

2. Which of these shows chemical weathering? **2.**______
- **a.** a water pipe that has burst
- **b.** a rock split by frozen water
- **c.** a sidewalk cracked by the roots of a tree
- **d.** a rock turned red from rust

3. c (1)

3. Which sentence is *not* true? **3.**______
- **a.** Frozen water in cracks in rocks causes physical weathering.
- **b.** Roots of plants can cause physical weathering.
- **c.** Rainwater mixed with carbon dioxide causes physical weathering.
- **d.** Rust in rocks is caused by chemical weathering.

4. a (2)

4. One cause of erosion is **4.**______
- **a.** runoff of rainwater.
- **b.** too many trees.
- **c.** cold weather.
- **d.** too much soil.

5. a (2)

5. Soil is first carried away by **5.**______
- **a.** small streams.
- **b.** large rivers.
- **c.** deltas.
- **d.** pieces of broken rock.

6. d (2)

6. Sediment carried by rivers **6.**______
- **a.** is dropped when the river reaches the ocean.
- **b.** piles up on the ocean bottom.
- **c.** forms a delta.
- **d.** All of the above are true.

Name________________________________Date______________

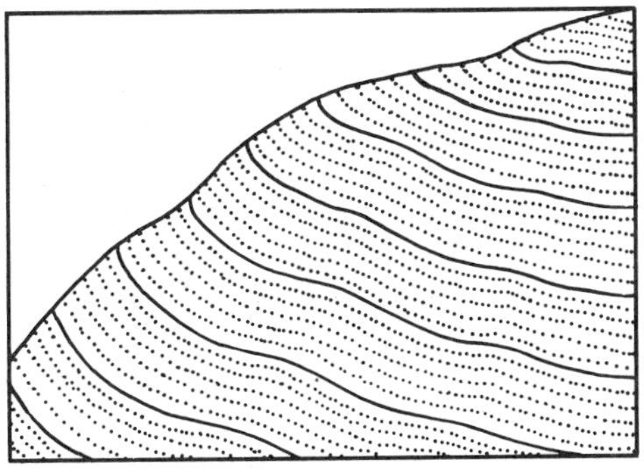

A

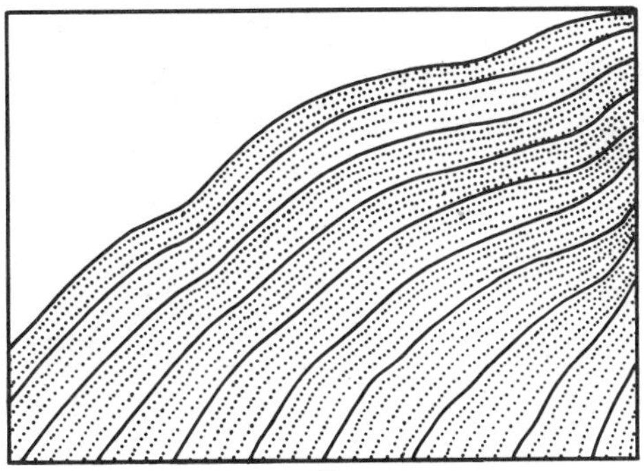

C

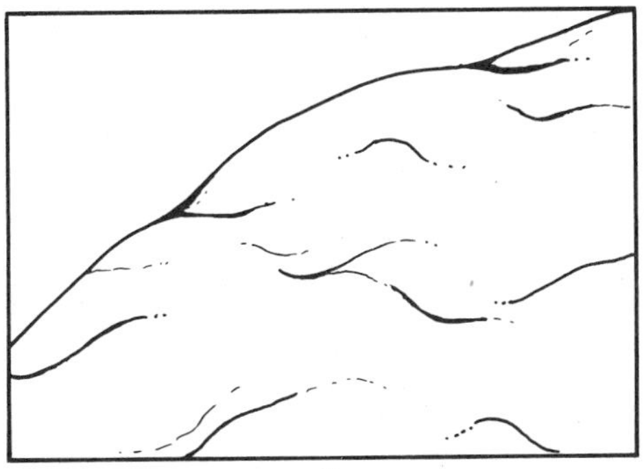

B

D

7. Look at the pictures above. Which picture shows a way to prevent soil erosion? **7.** ______ **7.** a (3)

8. Tell if the sentence below is true or false. If it is false, tell which words can be used in place of the underlined words to make the sentence true. **8.** ______ **8.** d (3)

<u>Heavy rain</u> helps prevent soil erosion.

a. The sentence is true. **c.** Cutting grass
b. Cutting down trees **d.** Planting grass and trees

9. Stopping soil erosion means stopping **9.** ______ **9.** b (3)

a. oceans. **c.** rain.
b. runoff. **d.** plowing.

10. A glacier begins to move because of **10.** ______ **10.** d (4)

a. the wind. **c.** large rocks.
b. the sun. **d.** the weight of the snow.

11. What do glaciers pull out of the ground as they move? **11.** ______ **11.** a (4)

a. rocks **c.** ice
b. grass **d.** nothing

Name________________________________ Date____________

12. d (4) **12.** Changes made by glacier are **12.** ______

a. scratches in rocks.
b. gouges or holes in rocks.
c. boulders in strange new places.
d. all of these things.

13. a (4) **13.** Rocks pushed in front of a glacier form **13.** ______

a. long, low hills.
b. high mountains.
c. deep holes.
d. flat ground.

14. c (5) **14.** Humans help to increase erosion by **14.** ______

a. planting grass.
b. planting trees.
c. removing rocks to get iron ore.
d. taking pictures of the ground.

15. d (5) **15.** Planting trees can help change the land by **15.** ______

a. slowing erosion.
b. replacing forests.
c. saving soil.
d. all of these activities.

16. a (5) **16.** A change in the earth's surface made by humans is a **16.** ______

a. dam
b. canyon.
c. mountain.
d. river.

17. b (5) **17.** In what way are humans and glaciers alike? **17.** ______

a. They are cold.
b. They remove rocks and soil from the land.
c. They do not change the land.
d. They only improve the land.

Name ______________________ Date ____________

The Whole Earth

SKILL WORKSHEET

A. Draw a diagram of the inside of the earth and label the layers.

B.

1. How would you rate this earthquake on the Mercalli scale? ____________
2. What device would you use to measure more accurately the strength of the earthquake? ____________
3. The scientist who would take these measurements is known as a ____________.
4. This earthquake was caused by ____________

____________.

Name ______________________________ Date ______________

Earthquakes

ACTIVITY WORKSHEET

FORM C&GS-680
(3-66)

U.S. DEPARTMENT OF COMMERCE
ENVIRONMENTAL SCIENCE SERVICES ADMINISTRATION
COAST AND GEODETIC SURVEY

Budget Bureau No. 41-RO 13.5;
Approval Expires June 30, 1970

EARTHQUAKE REPORT

1. An earthquake was felt ☐ ; not felt ☐

Date of shock ____________________

Time ____________ A.M.

____________ P.M.

If felt, please supply information below *(Underline appropriate words or fill spaces.)*
If not felt, please sign and return card, which requires no postage.

2. YOUR LOCATION DURING EARTHQUAKE

a. City, County, State (Exact location in city or rural area at time of shock is important.)

b. Ground:
Rocky, gravelly, loose, compact, marshy, filled in, or ____________
Level, sloping, steep, or ____________

c. If inside, type of construction
Wood, brick, stone, or ____________

d. Quality of construction
New, old, well built, poorly built, or ____________

e. No. of floors in building

f. Observer's floor

g. Activity when earthquake occurred: Walking, sitting, lying down, sleeping

h. If outside, you, others were: Quiet, active

3. EFFECTS ON POPULATION

a. Felt by:
Very few, several, many, all (in your home) (in community)

b. Awakened:
No one, few, many, all (in your home) (in community)

c. Frightened:
No one, few, many, all (in your home) (in community); general panic

4. RELATED SOUNDS

a. Rattling of windows, doors, dishes, etc. ____________

b. Creaking of building (Describe) ____________

c. Earth noises: Faint, moderate, loud ____________

5. PHYSICAL EFFECTS AND DAMAGE

a. Outside:

(1) Trees and bushes shaken, vehicles rocked, etc. ____________
(2) Ground cracked; landslides; water disturbed, etc. ____________
(3) Chimneys, tombstones, elevated water tanks, etc., cracked, twisted, overturned. ____________
(4) Other effects ____________

b. Building

(1) Hanging objects swung moderately, violently. Direction ____________
(2) Small objects shifted, overturned, fell ____________
(3) Furniture shifted, overturned, broken ____________
(4) Plaster cracked, broken, fell ____________
(5) Windows cracked ____________
(6) Structural elements of brick, wood, or ____________
Damage slight, moderate, great ____________

Signature and address of observer

Additional information will be appreciated. Use space on reverse side.

USCOMM-OC 36414-PER

Refer to the EXTENSIONS on page T-19

Name ______________________ Date ______________

The Whole Earth

SKILL WORKSHEET

Find these science words hidden in the box below. Look across, up, down, and diagonally. Match the words with their meanings.

Geologist	Mantle	Earthquake	Magma	Volcano
Crust	Core	Fault	Lava	Mercalli

M	A	N	T	L	E	O	D	C	E
A	E	Z	V	F	N	A	Y	R	Z
G	I	R	Y	A	X	R	O	F	Q
M	H	Q	C	O	F	C	B	A	C
A	C	L	U	A	U	A	H	V	R
Y	O	S	P	C	L	C	U	A	U
V	I	V	E	W	R	L	N	L	S
T	G	E	O	L	O	G	I	S	T
E	A	R	T	H	Q	U	A	K	E

1. A person who studies rocks ______________________
2. The thin, outer layer of the earth ______________
3. Melted rock under the earth ______________________
4. A sudden movement in the earth's crust ______________
5. A mountain formed by hot materials escaping from the earth's crust ______________
6. The center of the earth ____
7. A crack in the earth's crust ______________________
8. The middle layer of the earth ______________________
9. Melted rock on the earth's surface ______________
10. A scale to measure earth-quakes ______________

Name______________________________ Date______________

Moving Continents

ACTIVITY WORKSHEET

MAP OF THE WORLD

A. Gather these materials: 1 sheet of construction paper, 1 sheet of tracing paper, scissors, paste, and this map of the world.

B. Place the tracing paper on top of the map.

C. Trace the border around the outline of each continent.

D. Trace the outline of each continent within its border.

E. Cut out each tracing along its border. Be careful when using the scissors.

F. Put the cutouts on a piece of construction paper. Try to fit the continents together.

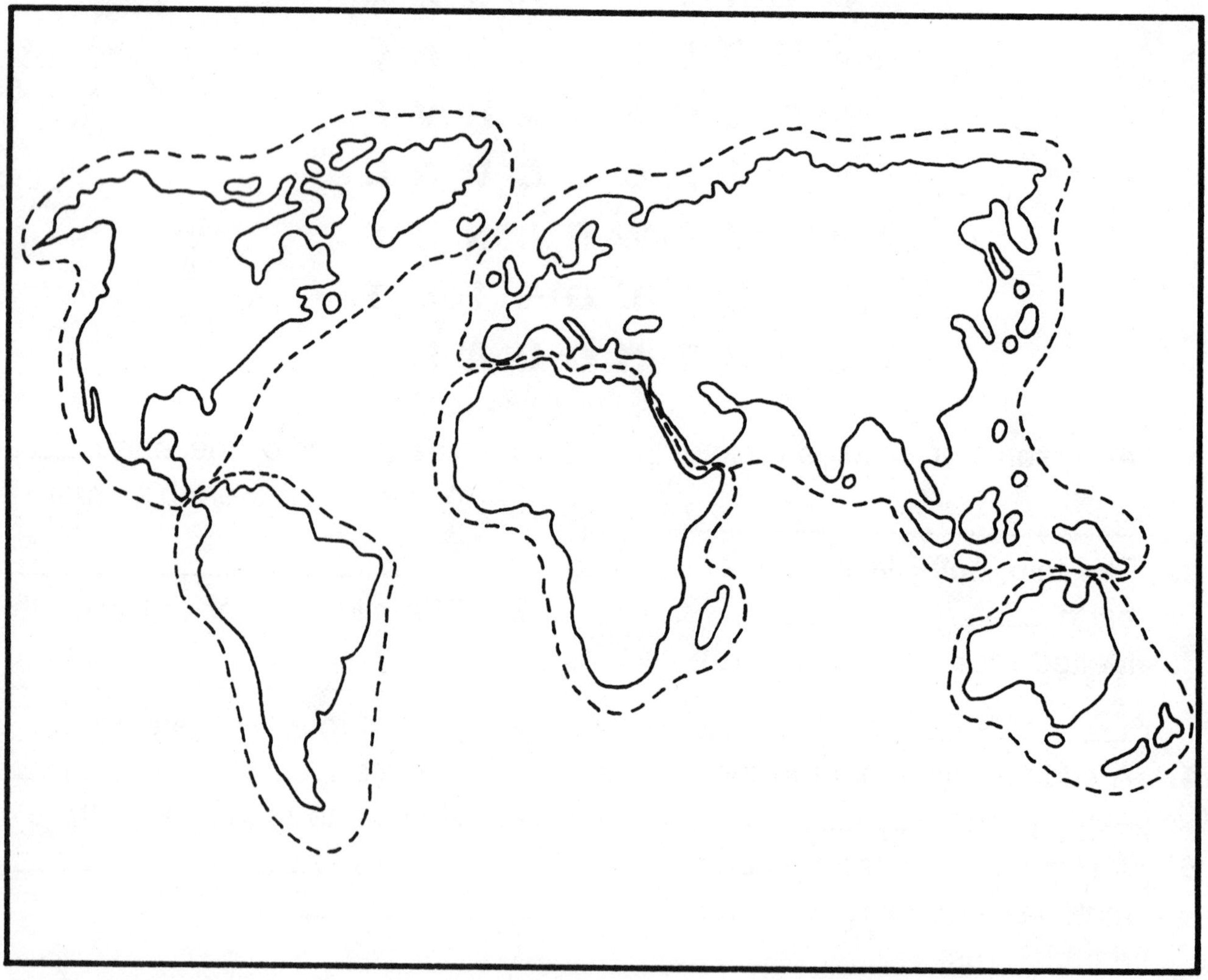

Refer to the Activity on page 28 of the Pupil's Textbook and to Teaching Tips on page T-32.

Name ______________________________ Date ________________

Moving Continents

SKILL WORKSHEET

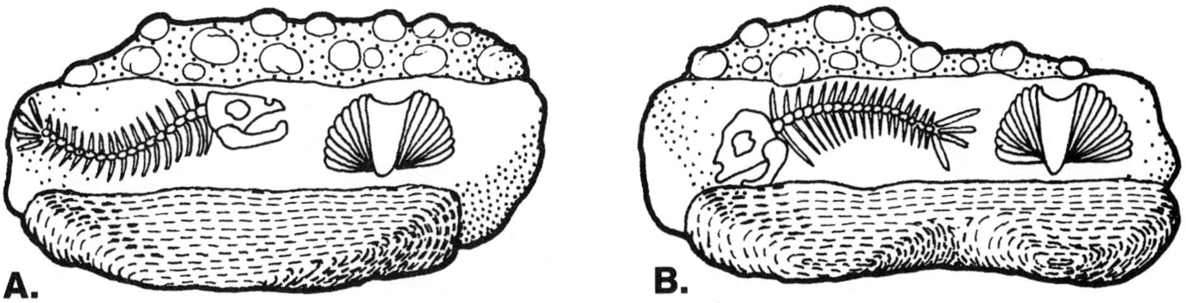

A. B.

A. These two rock samples are made of the same minerals. They contain similar fossils and are the same age. Sample A was found high in the mountains of one continent. Sample B was found near the coast of another continent. In the space below, explain why these two similar rock samples could have been discovered in two very different places.

____

____

____

____

B. Geologists group mountains according to how they were formed. Look at the drawings below. Write the name of each group under its picture.

__________ __________ __________ __________

Name________________________________ Date______________

Moving Continents

SKILL WORKSHEET

Use the clues below to solve the puzzle.

DOWN

1. A large section of the earth's crust
2. A trace of a plant or animal found in rock
3. Mountains formed by magma under the surface of the earth, pushing up part of the crust without breaking it
4. The movement of the continents

ACROSS

1. The single supercontinent of long ago
2. Mountains formed by the cracking and tilting of rock along cracks in the earth
3. A famous crack in the earth in California
4. Mountains formed by the folding and lifting of rock

Name ______________________________ Date ______________

The Crust Wears Away

AT HOME WORKSHEET

Water weathers rocks physically. In this at-home activity you will observe what happens to water when it freezes and learn why it can break rocks apart.

A. Gather the following materials: masking tape, 2 plastic margarine containers with lids, and water.

B. Fill one plastic container to the top with water. Cover this container with its lid. Place masking tape across the lid to hold it down tightly.

C. Cover the other empty container. Place the masking tape across its lid.

D. Place each container in the freezer for several hours.

E. Remove the plastic containers from the freezer.

Questions

1. What happened to the containers? ______________________

____

____

2. What do you think would happen if water seeped into a rock and froze? ______________________

____

Name ______________________________ Date ____________

Moving Water

ACTIVITY WORKSHEET

NORTH AMERICAN RIVERS

A. Choose a North American river.

B. Use an atlas to find the location of this river. Then draw it on this map. Show how the river flows. Draw in any tributaries it may have. Draw its delta, if it has one.

C. Below the map, write a brief description of the river; including its age, flooding problems, and the erosion it causes.

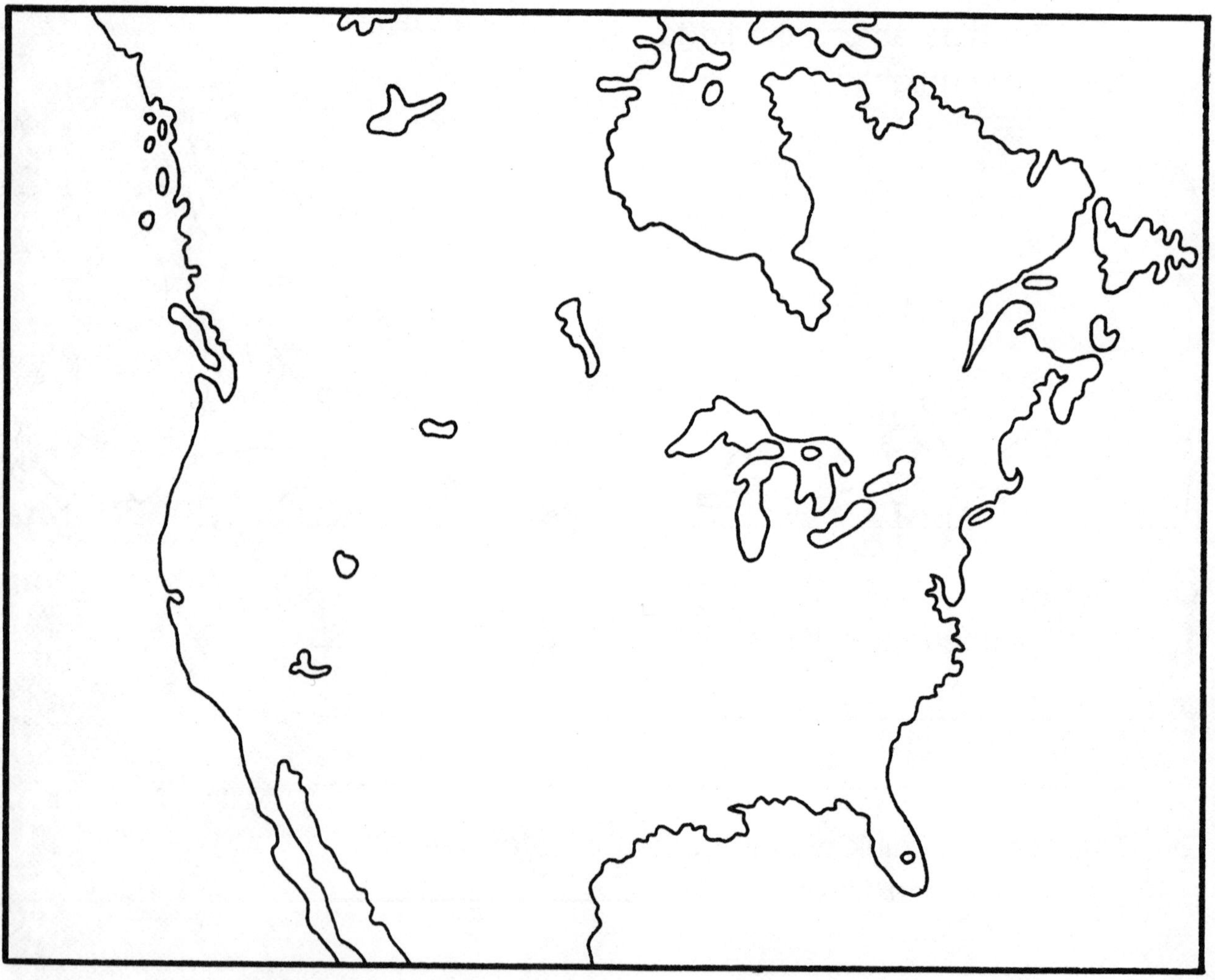

Refer to the EXTENSIONS on page T-48

Name ____________________ Date ____________

The Crust Wears Away

SKILL WORKSHEET

This farmer is having a problem with erosion. He is losing all of his topsoil and more and more of his land. Look at the picture above. List some things that the farmer might do to fight erosion and save the farm.

____

____

____

____

____

____

____

Name ______________________ Date ______________

The Crust Wears Away

SKILL WORKSHEET

The words below have been broken up as if they were weathered. Fill in the missing letters. Then match the word with its meaning.

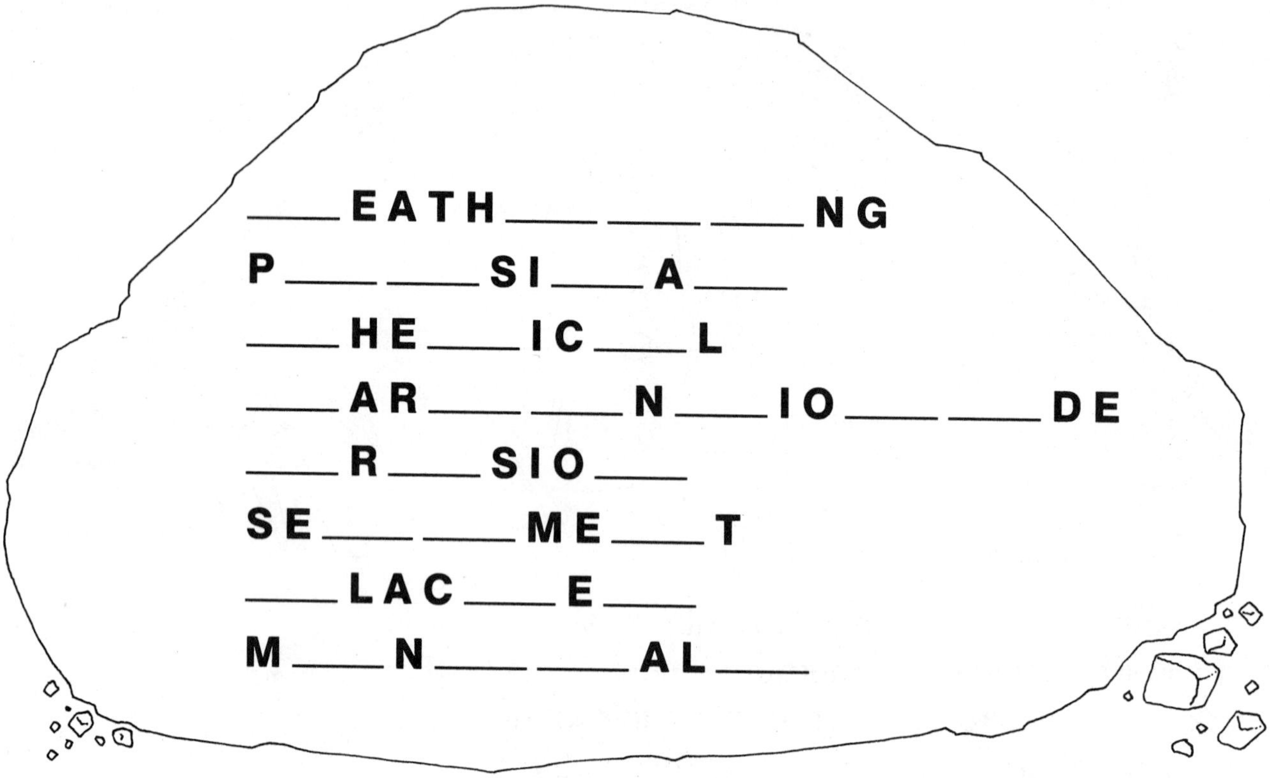

1. A large body of moving snow and ice ______________
2. The breaking of rock into small pieces ______________
3. The carrying away of rocks and soil from one place to another ______________
4. A gas in the air that will form a weak acid when mixed with water ______________
5. The materials rocks are made of ______________
6. A change in the minerals of a rock ______________
7. Material carried by rivers ______________
8. A change in the size or shape of a rock ______________

Name________________________ Date__________

The Whole Earth

CLASSIFYING, CONCLUDING AND GENERALIZING — SKILL WORKSHEET

A. Draw a diagram of the inside of the earth and label the layers.

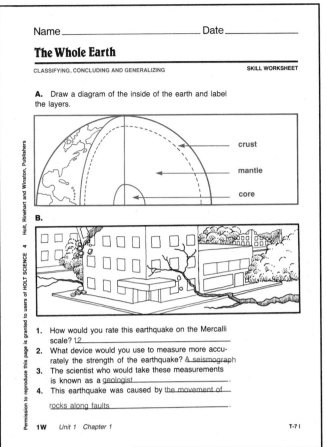

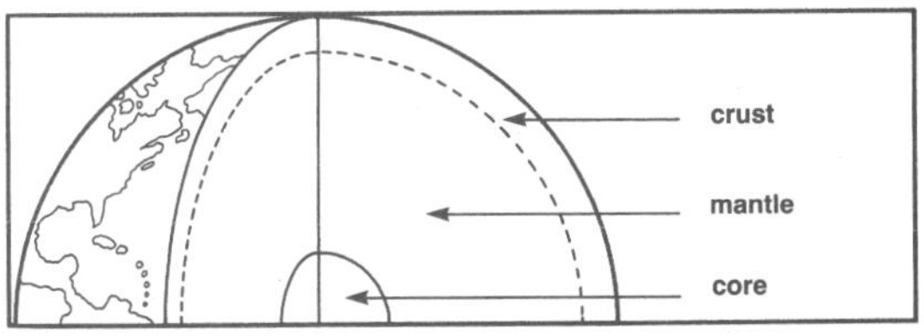

B.

1. How would you rate this earthquake on the Mercalli scale? 12
2. What device would you use to measure more accurately the strength of the earthquake? A seismograph
3. The scientist who would take these measurements is known as a geologist.
4. This earthquake was caused by the movement of rocks along faults.

Name________________________ Date__________

Earthquakes

ACTIVITY WORKSHEET

FORM C&GS-680 (3-66)

U.S. DEPARTMENT OF COMMERCE
ENVIRONMENTAL SCIENCE SERVICES ADMINISTRATION
COAST AND GEODETIC SURVEY

Budget Bureau No. 41-RO 13.5; Approval Expires June 30, 1970

EARTHQUAKE REPORT

1. An earthquake was felt ☐ ; not felt ☐ — Time __________ A.M. __________ P.M.

Date of shock ____________________

If felt, please supply information below *(Underline appropriate words or fill spaces.)*
If not felt, please sign and return card, which requires no postage.

2. YOUR LOCATION DURING EARTHQUAKE

a. City, County, State (Exact location in city or rural area at time of shock is important.)

b. Ground:
Rocky, gravelly, loose, compact, marshy, filled in, or ____________
Level, sloping, steep, or ____________

c. If inside, type of construction
Wood, brick, stone, or ____________

d. Quality of construction
New, old, well built, poorly built, or ____________

e. No. of floors in building

f. Observer's floor

g. Activity when earthquake occurred: Walking, sitting, lying down, sleeping

h. If outside, you, others were: Quiet, active

3. EFFECTS ON POPULATION

a. Felt by:
Very few, several, many, all (in your home) (in community)

b. Awakened:
No one, few, many, all (in your home) (in community)

c. Frightened:
No one, few, many, all (in your home) (in community); general panic

4. RELATED SOUNDS

a. Rattling of windows, doors, dishes, etc. ____________

b. Creaking of building (Describe) ____________

c. Earth noises: Faint, moderate, loud ____________

5. PHYSICAL EFFECTS AND DAMAGE

a. Outside:

(1) Trees and bushes shaken, vehicles rocked, etc. ____________
(2) Ground cracked; landslides; water disturbed, etc. ____________
(3) Chimneys, tombstones, elevated water tanks, etc., cracked, twisted, overturned. ____________
(4) Other effects ____________

b. Building

(1) Hanging objects swung moderately, violently. Direction ____________
(2) Small objects shifted, overturned, fell ____________
(3) Furniture shifted, overturned, broken ____________
(4) Plaster cracked, broken, fell ____________
(5) Windows cracked ____________
(6) Structural elements of brick, wood, or ____________
Damage slight, moderate, great ____________

Signature and address of observer

Additional information will be appreciated. Use space on reverse side.

USCOMM-OC 36414-PER

Refer to the EXTENSIONS on page T-19

Name________________________ Date__________

The Whole Earth

BUILDING SCIENCE VOCABULARY — SKILL WORKSHEET

Find these science words hidden in the box below. Look across, up, down, and diagonally. Match the words with their meanings.

Geologist Mantle Earthquake Magma Volcano
Crust Core Fault Lava Mercalli

M	A	N	T	L	E	O	D	C	E
A	E	Z	V	F	N	A	Y	R	Z
G	I	R	Y	A	X	R	O	F	Q
M	H	Q	C	O	F	C	B	A	C
A	C	L	U	A	U	A	H	V	R
Y	O	S	P	C	L	C	U	A	U
V	I	V	E	W	R	L	N	L	S
T	G	E	O	L	O	G	I	S	T
E	A	R	T	H	Q	U	A	K	E

1. A person who studies rocks Geologist
2. The thin, outer layer of the earth Crust
3. Melted rock under the earth Magma
4. A sudden movement in the earth's crust Earthquake
5. A mountain formed by hot materials escaping from the earth's crust Volcano
6. The center of the earth Core
7. A crack in the earth's crust Fault
8. The middle layer of the earth Mantle
9. Melted rock on the earth's surface Lava
10. A scale to measure earthquakes Mercalli

Name________________________ Date__________

Moving Continents

ACTIVITY WORKSHEET

MAP OF THE WORLD

A. Gather these materials: 1 sheet of construction paper, 1 sheet of tracing paper, scissors, paste, and this map of the world.

B. Place the tracing paper on top of the map.

C. Trace the border around the outline of each continent.

D. Trace the outline of each continent within its border.

E. Cut out each tracing along its border. Be careful when using the scissors.

F. Put the cutouts on a piece of construction paper. Try to fit the continents together.

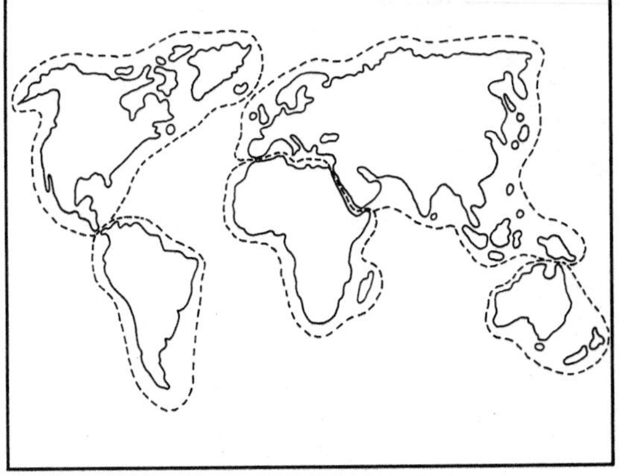

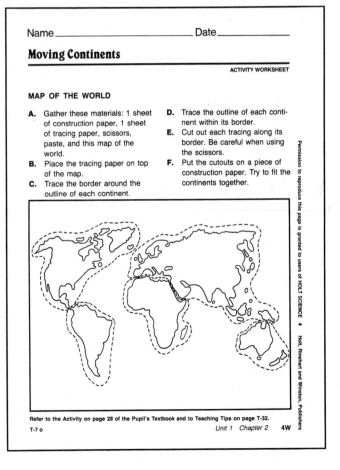

Refer to the Activity on page 28 of the Pupil's Textbook and to Teaching Tips on page T-32.

Name________________________ Date____________

Moving Continents

COMPARING AND CONTRASTING, INFERRING, CLASSIFYING — SKILL WORKSHEET

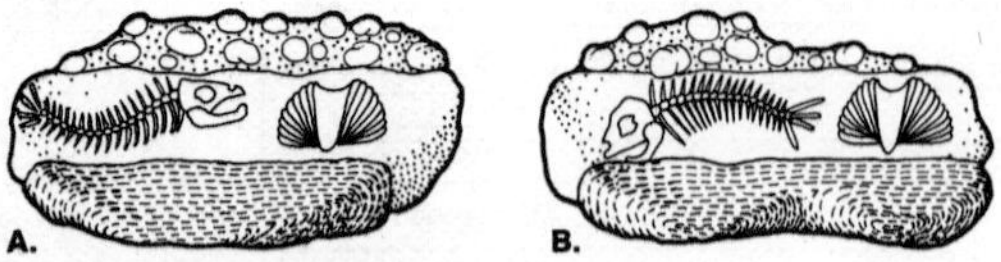

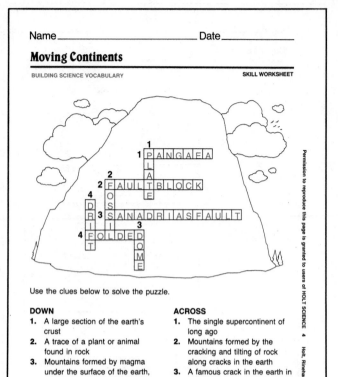

A. These two rock samples are made of the same minerals. They contain similar fossils and are the same age. Sample A was found high in the mountains of one continent. Sample B was found near the coast of another continent. In the space below, explain why these two similar rock samples could have been discovered in two very different places.

At one time the two rock samples were in the same place. Over millions of years, the continents drifted apart and mountains formed on the continent where sample A was found.

B. Geologists group mountains according to how they were formed. Look at the drawings below. Write the name of each group under its picture.

Folded — Fault block — Dome — Volcano

Name________________________ Date____________

Moving Continents

BUILDING SCIENCE VOCABULARY — SKILL WORKSHEET

Use the clues below to solve the puzzle.

DOWN

1. A large section of the earth's crust
2. A trace of a plant or animal found in rock
3. Mountains formed by magma under the surface of the earth, pushing up part of the crust without breaking it
4. The movement of the continents

ACROSS

1. The single supercontinent of long ago
2. Mountains formed by the cracking and tilting of rock along cracks in the earth
3. A famous crack in the earth in California
4. Mountains formed by the folding and lifting of rock

Name________________________ Date____________

The Crust Wears Away

AT HOME WORKSHEET

Water weathers rocks physically. In this at-home activity you will observe what happens to water when it freezes and learn why it can break rocks apart.

A. Gather the following materials: masking tape, 2 plastic margarine containers with lids, and water.

B. Fill one plastic container to the top with water. Cover this container with its lid. Place masking tape across the lid to hold it down tightly.

C. Cover the other empty container. Place the masking tape across its lid.

D. Place each container in the freezer for several hours.

E. Remove the plastic containers from the freezer.

Questions

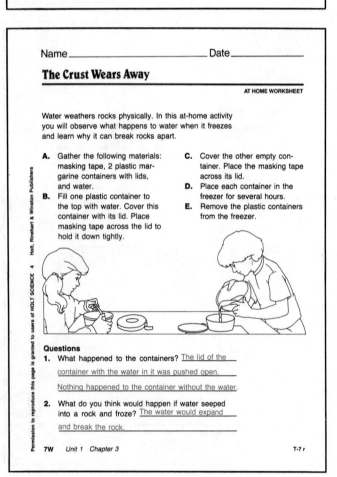

1. What happened to the containers? The lid of the container with the water in it was pushed open. Nothing happened to the container without the water.
2. What do you think would happen if water seeped into a rock and froze? The water would expand and break the rock.

Name________________________ Date____________

Moving Water

ACTIVITY WORKSHEET

NORTH AMERICAN RIVERS

A. Choose a North American river.

B. Use an atlas to find the location of this river. Then draw it on this map. Show how the river flows. Draw in any tributaries it may have. Draw its delta, if it has one.

C. Below the map, write a brief description of the river; including its age, flooding problems, and the erosion it causes.

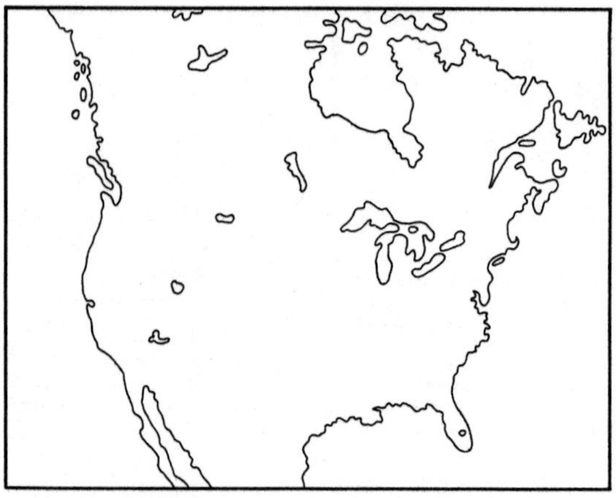

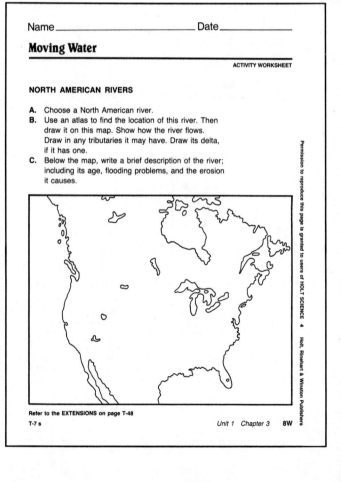

Refer to the EXTENSIONS on page T-48

Name ______________________ Date ____________

The Crust Wears Away

OBSERVING, FINDING CAUSE AND EFFECT, HYPOTHESIZING — SKILL WORKSHEET

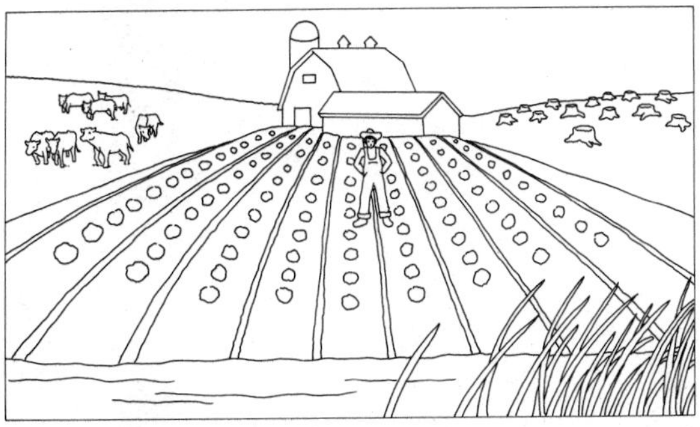

This farmer is having a problem with erosion. He is losing all of his topsoil and more and more of his land. Look at the picture above. List some things that the farmer might do to fight erosion and save the farm.

1. Plant new trees
2. Plant a variety of crops
3. Contour-plow the fields
4. Divert the stream away from the fields
5. Irrigate the soil so it does not dry out
6. Not let the farm animals overgraze the fields

Name ______________________ Date ____________

The Crust Wears Away

BUILDING SCIENCE VOCABULARY — SKILL WORKSHEET

The words below have been broken up as if they were weathered. Fill in the missing letters. Then match the word with its meaning.

W EATH E R I NG
P H Y SI C A L
C HE M IC A L
C AR B O N D IO X I DE
E R O SIO N
SE D I ME N T
G LAC I E R
M I N E R AL S

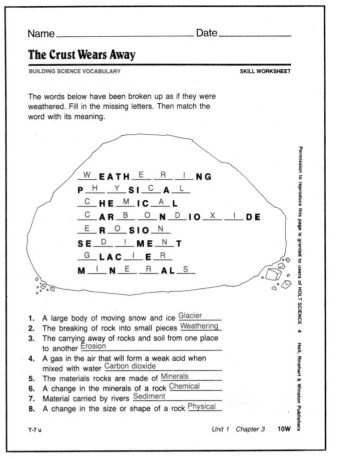

1. A large body of moving snow and ice Glacier
2. The breaking of rock into small pieces Weathering
3. The carrying away of rocks and soil from one place to another Erosion
4. A gas in the air that will form a weak acid when mixed with water Carbon dioxide
5. The materials rocks are made of Minerals
6. A change in the minerals of a rock Chemical
7. Material carried by rivers Sediment
8. A change in the size or shape of a rock Physical

UNIT OVERVIEW

This is an earth science unit on the structure of the earth and how it changes. The earth has three layers—a central core; a thick, hot mantle; and a thin crust. According to the theory of plate tectonics, the earth's crust is composed of about ten moving plates. These crustal plates can collide, move apart, and slip past one another. Mountain building, earthquakes, and volcanoes occur where the plates meet. Earthquakes are sudden movements of the earth's crust; volcanoes are openings in the earth's crust through which molten rock escapes. When two plates collide, rocks can be folded up to form folded mountains. Rocks can also be pushed up to form fault-block mountains along a fault.

The theory of continental drift is the belief that the continents float on crustal plates that were once joined together and have slowly drifted apart. The fact that the continents fit together like a puzzle supports this theory.

The earth's crust is also changed by eroding, or wearing away. Physical and chemical weathering breaks rock down into smaller pieces. Moving water erodes the land by carrying rocks and soil to the ocean.

During the ice ages, glaciers dramatically eroded the earth's surface. Humans change the land by removing rocks and minerals, and by building roads, factories, and houses.

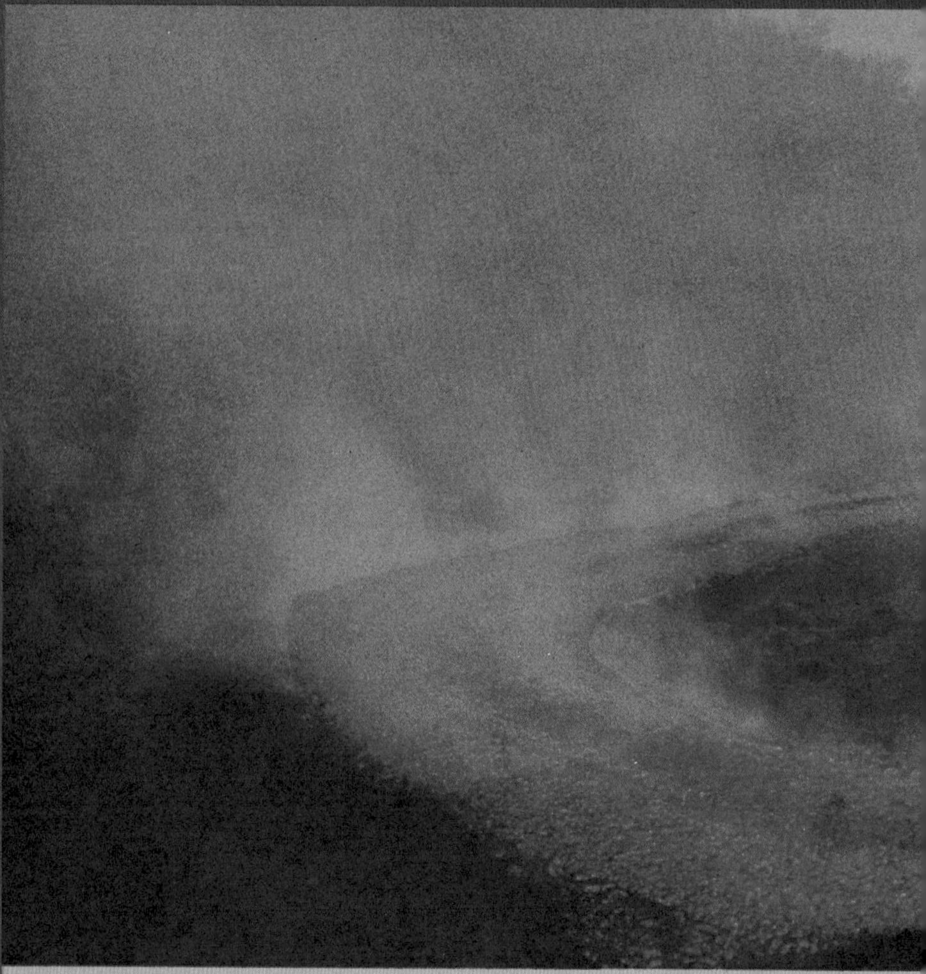

THE CHANGING EARTH

UNIT OPENER

This is a photo of the volcano Mt. Etna in Italy. On May 21, 1971, fissures opened up along the sides of the volcano at a height of 2,700 m (8,900 ft), and streams of hot lava poured out. Ask your students these questions: Where do you think the lava is coming from? *From a magma chamber far beneath the surface.* What does the lava tell you about the interior of the earth? *It is very hot.* Why are volcanoes located where they are? *Most volcanoes are located near colliding continental plates.* How do volcanoes change the earth? *They build mountains and deposit new material on the surface.*

UNIT 1

LEARNING CENTER

A suggested title for the Learning Center could be, "Our Active Earth." Photos showing the surface of the earth changing could be displayed, i.e., pictures of volcanoes, earthquakes, mountains, and strip mining. You may wish to create a file for copies of the worksheet masters and Extensions that students can work on independently.

The following Extensions are especially suitable for the Learning Center. The materials for these Extensions should be available in the Learning Center: a model of the earth's interior, p. T-14 (papier-mâché, plaster, clay, or Styrofoam); an earthquake watch, p. T-16 (map of the world, pins of three different colors, earthquake epicenter cards); locating important volcanoes on a wall map, p. T-24; clay models of three types of plate movements, p. T-32; models of North American mountain ranges, p. T-36 (map, potter's clay, index cards, string); models of glacial features, p. T-50 (plaster of paris, large milk cartons).

In addition, an index file of suggested research topics could be set up in the Learning Center, using the following Extensions: how tunnels are built, p. T-13; what to do during an earthquake, p. T-17; historic volcanoes, p. T-21; areas in the world that have a high incidence of volcanoes and earthquakes, p. T-34; young and old mountains, p. T-39; hot spots, p. T-40; chemical weathering of buildings and statues, p. T-44; the changing location of New Orleans, p. T-47.

Exceptional Student
IEP Unit Goal

At the end of this unit, the student will be able to name five forces that have changed the earth's surface.

Chapter Objectives

1. Describe the structure of the earth, and contrast its layers.
2. Describe causes of earthquakes and how the intensity of an earthquake can be measured.
3. Observe the pattern that locations of earthquakes and volcanoes make on a map.
4. Describe the relationship between magma, lava, and volcanoes.

SECTION BACKGROUND

Geologists believe the earth is composed of three layers: a thin outer layer called the crust (5–55 km thick); a thick mantle layer (2,900 km thick); and a heavy core (3,470 km thick). These three sections are not static, and there are interactions among them. The crust is divided into pieces called plates. Owing to high pressure and temperature (3,000°C), part of the mantle rock appears to be in the liquid state. Sometimes, this molten rock moves up from the mantle through cracks in the crust. With temperatures as high as 4,000°C, the core is composed of an outer and an inner core. The heat of the inner earth is thought to come from radioactive substances within the earth.

MATERIALS

apple, dinner knife

Exceptional Student
IEP Chapter Goal

At the end of this chapter, the student will define *geologist*, *earthquake*, *volcano*, *crust*, *mantle*, and *core*.

The Whole Earth

1-1. Inside the Earth

Pretend that you are in the machine that is shown in the picture above. The machine was made for use in a movie. In this movie, people took a trip to the center of the earth. The machine is able to drill straight through hard rock.

BASIC TEACHING PLAN

MOTIVATION

You might have the students pretend they are in the machine shown on the opening page of the section. Have them close their eyes and pretend to take a trip to the center of the earth. If you can obtain a copy of the book *At the Earth's Core* by Edgar Rice Burroughs, you can read a paragraph or two from it to motivate your students further.

Text Questions—What would you find? *Solid and liquid rocks under high temperature and pressure.* You might write the students' responses on the chalkboard, and then have the students compare their answers with what they learn in the section.

Imagine drilling to the center of the earth. What would you find? When you finish this section, you should be able to:

- **A.** Name the layers of the earth.
- **B.** Compare the layers of the earth to the inside of an apple.
- **C.** Describe how the three layers of the earth are different from each other.

1 How would you find out what the inside of a softball is like? It would be simple. Just rip the cover off the ball. Then unwind the string like the boy in the picture.

Finding out what the inside of the earth is like is not as easy. We cannot peel the earth open to look inside. We don't have machines that can travel deep into the earth. But clues from earthquakes and volcanoes help us make guesses about the inside of the earth. You will know more about these clues when you finish this unit.

Scientists who study the earth are called **geologists** (jee-**ahl**-oh-jists). *Geologists* think the
2 earth is made of three layers. You can compare the layers of the earth to the inside of an apple. Look at the pictures on page 12. Both the apple
3 and the earth have three layers. What are the three layers of the apple? What are the three layers of the earth?

4 Imagine we can go to the center of the earth. We begin with the top layer of the earth. It is mostly rock. It is called the **crust**.

Geologist: A scientist who studies rocks and other features of the earth's layers.

Crust: The thin, solid, outer layer of the earth.

11

EXTENSIONS

Reinforcement

Science Skills—Vocabulary

Three key words used in this section have more than one meaning. These words are *crust, mantle,* and *core.* Have the students make a chart in which they indicate the various meanings of these words. Encourage them to use the dictionary to find the meanings.

Word	Meaning #1	#2	#3
Crust			
Mantle			
Core			

When the chart is complete, challenge the students to write analogies using the following formula:

The *crust* of the earth is like a ______________ because ______________________________ .

DEVELOPMENT

1 Skill Development—Students will *compare and contrast* the earth's interior to the interior of a softball.

2 Teaching Tips—Ask the students to think of other objects whose structure could be compared to the earth's. *A hard-boiled egg, various fruits, a golf ball.*

3 Text Questions—What are the three layers of the apple? *Skin, pulp, and the core.* What are the three layers of the earth? *Crust, mantle, and core.*

4 Teaching Tips—To emphasize the imaginary nature of a trip to the center of the earth, you could make up a short story about it using the information given on pages 12 and 13.

EXTENSIONS

Application
Science Skills—Inferring

This Activity is analogous to geologists making inferences about the interior of the earth by using indirect evidence.

A. Prepare several shoe boxes containing mystery objects. Here are suggestions for objects to be placed in different boxes:

Box 1: balloon, half filled with water
Box 2: golf ball and small rock
Box 3: large washer and small ball

B. Seal the boxes so that the students cannot look inside.

C. Tell the students they are only permitted to turn and gently shake the boxes to find out what is inside.

D. Have the students list their observations for each box.

E. Have the students use their observations to make inferences about the contents of the boxes.

5

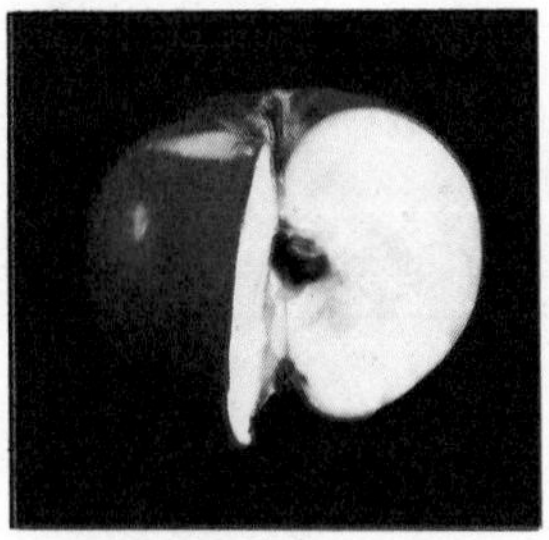

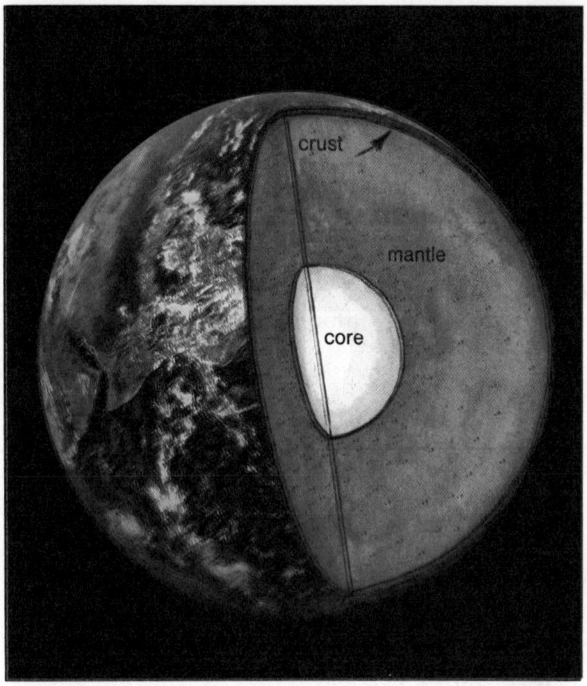

6 The *crust* is very important to us. It is where we live. It is like a giant treasure chest. Oil, coal, gas, metals, rocks, water, and plants are some of its treasures.

7 Pretend the earth is the size of an apple. The crust will be as thin as the apple's skin. The earth's crust is very thin in some places. It is thicker in others. It is from 5 to 55 kilometers (3–34 miles) thick.

Mantle: A thick, hot layer found under the crust of the earth.

Let's go deeper into the earth. Below the crust is a layer called the **mantle** (**man**-tuhl). It is about 2,900 kilometers (1,800 miles) thick. The *mantle* is made of mostly solid rock. If the earth

5 **Teaching Tips**—Refer the students to the photograph of the apple and the cutaway view of the interior of the earth.
6 **Teaching Tips**—Obtain samples of oil, coal, metals such as iron and copper, and a few rocks. Show these to the students so that they can see some of the earth's treasures.
7 **Skill Development**—Students are asked to *compare and contrast* the layers of the earth to an apple. Reinforce this skill in each of the next three paragraphs.

were the size of an apple, the mantle would be as thick as the white part under the skin. Geologists believe the mantle is as hot as 3,000° Celsius (5,400° Fahrenheit). The mantle is hot enough to melt rock.

8 As we continue our trip into the earth, we come to the third layer. This layer is called the **core**. The *core* of the earth is in the same position as the core of an apple. It is about 3,500 kilometers (2,200 miles) thick. The temperature at the center of the earth is very hot. It may be as high as 4,000° Celsius (7,200° Fahrenheit). This is hot enough to melt the metals. Scientists think that the core has two parts. The outer core is melted iron and nickel. The inner core is solid iron and nickel. If you could see the core, it probably would be glowing hot.

Core: The center of the earth; it is made of nickel and iron.

ACTIVITY

How is an apple like the earth?

A. Gather these materials: an apple and a dinner knife.

B. Look at the picture. Cut the apple in half. Draw a picture of the inside of the apple. Label the crust, mantle, and core.

C. Do not taste things used in a science activity. Your teacher will tell you what to do with the apple.

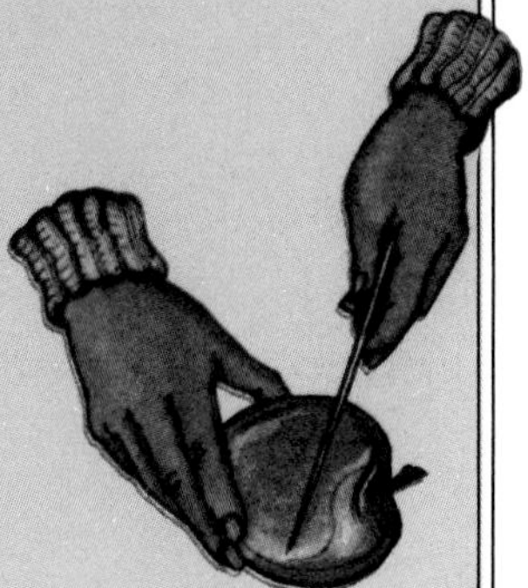

EXTENSIONS

Enrichment

Research—Library

Students might wish to explore how tunnels through mountains and under bays are built. They can investigate materials and methods of tunnel construction. Here is a list of several tunnels students might find interesting to study:

BART Trans-Bay Tube, San Francisco, 5.6 km (19,000 ft); Sumner Tunnel, Boston, 1.7 km (5,657 ft); Detroit-Windsor Tunnel, Detroit, 1.6 km (5,130 ft); Lincoln Tunnel, N.Y.C., 2.5 km (8,216 ft); Eisenhower Memorial Tunnel, Route I-70, Colorado, 2.7 km (8,941 ft).

8 Teaching Tips—To demonstrate the density of the core and contrast its density with that of the crust, obtain two cans of equal size. Fill one can with iron nails, and the other can with sand. The iron nails represent the composition of the core, while the sand represents the composition of the crust. Have students lift each can and compare their weights.

ACTIVITY

Skill Development—*Comparing and Contrasting*

Safety Tips—Caution students on the use of the knives.

Answers to Questions—Students' diagrams should include the information in the diagrams on page 12.

Exceptional Student

Visually Impaired

After the apple is cut in half, have the student feel its three layers.

EXTENSIONS

Reinforcement
Activity

A model of the inside of the earth can be made with the information about the thickness of the three layers of the earth.

A. Ask the students to construct their model as accurately as possible from a variety of materials (papier-mâché, plaster, clay, or Styrofoam).

B. The composition of their model should account for the relative thickness of each layer. You may have to help the students with the relative thickness. The chart below will help you.

Layer of Earth	Thickness	Relative Thickness
Crust	5–55 km	0.02
Mantle	2,900 km	1
Core	3,500 km	1.2

People did not always know about the earth's layers. In 1909, Andrija Mohorovicic (Ahn-**dree**-ha Mo-ho-**ro**-veh-chick) first found that the earth has layers. The boundary between the crust and mantle was named for him. It is called the Moho. Scientists had hoped to drill a hole through the crust to reach the mantle. They called this hole the Mohole.

Section Review

Main Ideas: The following chart shows the main ideas in this section.

Layer of Earth	Thickness	Made of	Temperature
Crust	5 to 55 km	solid rock	cool
Mantle	2,900 km	mostly solid rock	hot, 3,000°C
Core	3,500 km	nickel, iron solid inner, liquid outer	very hot, 4,000°C

Questions: Answer in complete sentences.

1. What are the three layers of earth? How are they different from each other?
2. Which layer of the earth (a) has the hottest rocks? (b) would take you the longest to travel through? (c) are living things found on?
3. What kinds of problems would the pilot in the picture on page 10 have had if he had really drilled through the earth?

SECTION REVIEW

Answers to Questions

1. Crust, mantle, and core. The crust is thin, whereas the mantle and core are thick. The crust is cool, the mantle is hot, and the core is very hot. Rocks within the crust are solid, whereas those within the mantle and core vary between solid and liquid.

2. a. Core, b. core, c. crust

3. Some problems would be the thickness of the layers, the high temperatures, and the high pressures.

1-2.

Earthquakes

Did you know that over 1 million earthquakes occur each year? Most of them cause little damage. But now and then a strong earthquake hits. If it happens in a city, the damage to buildings could be great. Many people could die.

Look at the picture. It was taken after an earthquake hit Anchorage, Alaska. What damage did this earthquake cause? When you finish this section, you should be able to:

- **A.** Describe the changes in the earth's crust during an *earthquake.*
- **B.** Describe two ways that geologists measure *earthquakes.*
- **C.** Describe the damage that *earthquakes* can cause.

SECTION BACKGROUND

An earthquake, a trembling of the earth's crust, occurs when rocks move along a fault or crack in the earth's crust. Earthquakes are also associated with the eruption of volcanoes. The location of earthquakes forms a pattern of an "earthquake belt" on a map of the world. Later in this chapter and in the next, the students will discover that this pattern is associated with the location of crustal plates. The existence of plates is supported by the theory of plate tectonics, which holds that the crust is composed of moving plates. Earthquakes occur along the separations or boundaries of the earth's plates.

Geologists measure and record the intensity of earthquakes by using a seismograph. The students are introduced to a simple observational system that they can use to classify earthquakes.

MATERIALS

none

BASIC TEACHING PLAN

MOTIVATION

In a dramatic voice say: What travels faster than a speeding bullet? . . . is able to topple tall buildings in a single second? . . . is more powerful than a locomotive? Have the students guess, and then have them look at the picture of the result of an earthquake, as seen on page 15 of their text. If you have a map of the world in the room, you might point out where Anchorage, Alaska, is and stick a pin in the map to mark the location. Ask the students if they are aware of any other major earthquakes. Use pins to locate these places. Some of your students might want to maintain a map of earthquakes (earthquake watch). The Extension on page T-16 gives further information for doing this.

Text Questions—What damage did this earthquake cause? *Houses collapsed, roads cracked and folded, buildings fell, cars turned over, and people were hurt.*

EXTENSIONS

Reinforcement

Science Skills— Recording Data

The students will record earthquake data by doing an "earthquake watch."

A. You will need a map of the world, pins of three different colors, and earthquake epicenter lists (report of locations of earthquakes occurring throughout the world). They can be obtained from the Government Printing Office. Single copies are also available from:
Eastern Distribution Branch
Text Products Section
U.S. Geological Survey
604 South Pickett St.
Alexandria, VA 22304

B. When the lists arrive, have students plot the locations of the reported earthquakes on a large wall map.

C. The epicenter lists also indicate the depth of the earthquakes as follows:
Normal: depth of 0 to 69 km
Intermediate: depth of 70 to 299 km.
Deep: depth of over 300 km.
Use colored pins to classify the earthquakes according to depth.

Earthquake: A sudden movement of part of the earth's crust.

Sudden movements in the earth's crust are called **earthquakes** (**erth**-kwakes). During an *earthquake*, the earth's crust shakes. An earthquake occurs when the crust moves, buckles, cracks, or bends. The earth's crust is very thin compared with the rest of the earth. It is thin like the skin of an apple. The crust of the earth can wrinkle like the skin of an apple.

Most earthquakes are not deep in the earth. They are within 60 km (36 miles) of the surface of the crust. A few earthquakes are deeper in the earth. Some are as deep as 650 km (400 miles).

1 Geologists keep records of where earthquakes happen. Look at the map on this page. Each red dot shows where a large earthquake has taken place in recent years. Earthquakes occur in some parts of the crust more than in others. These red dots make up what is called the "earthquake belt." Earthquakes happen here more often than in other places on earth.

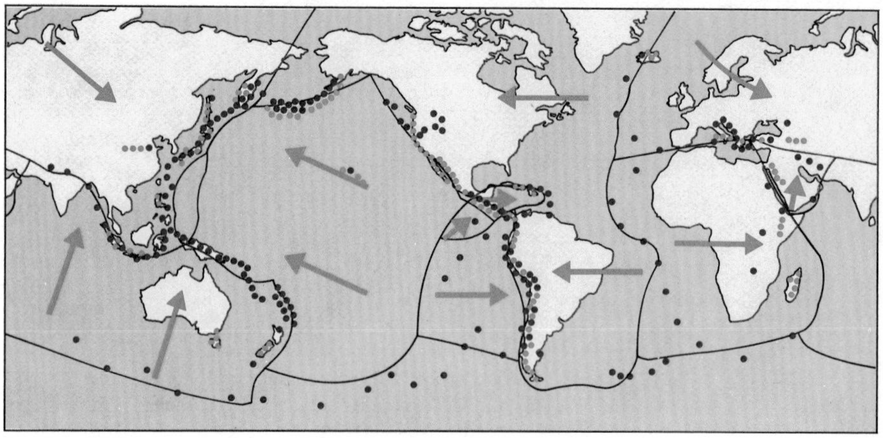

DEVELOPMENT

1 Skill Development—You can show the students how earthquake *data are recorded* on a map. Point out that each dot represents the location of an earthquake. By recording data in this way, patterns in nature are revealed that would otherwise go unnoticed. If you have started an earthquake watch map in your classroom, you can have the students *compare* the classroom map to the map in the text.

2

An earthquake causes objects on the surface of the crust to shake. Loose soil and rocks may slide down hillsides. Buildings made of stone or clay may crack. There is a chance of fire when buildings shake. Gas pipes can snap. The gases may catch fire when they leak out of the pipes. In 1906, the city of San Francisco had a big earthquake. After the quake, fires broke out. Almost all of the houses were made of wood. Most of the city burned to the ground.

3 Rocks in the crust can crack and move. One place where rocks move is called a **fault**. *Faults* are cracks in the earth's crust. Rocks along the sides of a fault may be stuck together. These

Fault: A crack in the earth's crust where rocks can move.

EXTENSIONS

Enrichment

Research—Library

Have your students do research to find out what people should do during an earthquake. They can research books in the library, or they can write for information about earthquakes to:

Chief, Seismological Field Survey, National Ocean Survey, N.O.A.A., 390 Main Street, Room 7067, San Francisco, California 94105.

2 **Skill Development**—Students will *examine illustrations* of earthquake damage.

3 **Teaching Tips**—You could use two stacks of clay to illustrate how rocks along a fault can slide past each other or can move in an upward or a downward direction.

EXTENSIONS

Enrichment

Science Skills—Classifying

Students can learn the classification system for earthquakes. Discuss with the class how the size or magnitude of an earthquake is reported on a scale of 1 to 9. This scale was invented by Dr. Charles F. Richter and is called the Richter Magnitude Scale. It is the scale that is referred to when an earthquake is reported on the news. As students hear of and read about earthquakes in the news, they will become more familiar with the Richter scale. The numbers on the scale are based on information from seismographs. The smallest earthquake that can be felt measures 1.5 on the scale. Earthquakes measuring less than 5 cause little damage on the earth's surface. Earthquakes of 7 or more cause a great deal of damage. A difference of 1 between two readings on the Richter scale actually equals a tenfold difference in the strength of the earthquakes. For example, an earthquake that measures 7 on the Richter scale is ten times as strong as an earthquake that measures 6.

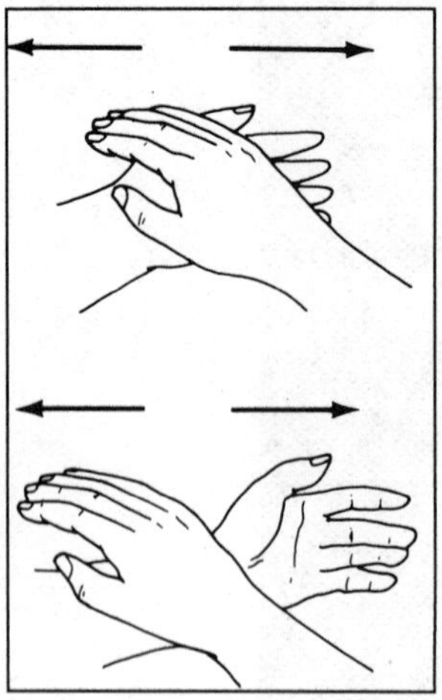

4 rocks can snap apart. Sometimes the rocks just slip past one another. Press the palms of your hands together. Look at the picture. Your hands will suddenly slide over one another. If this happened to rocks, an earthquake would occur.

Geologists have found ways to measure earthquakes. One way is by using a number scale. The number given to an earthquake tells how much damage was done. The scale below was made by an Italian scientist named Mercalli (mur-**kall**-ee).

5

THE MERCALLI EARTHQUAKE SCALE

Type of Earthquake	Observations
I.	Not noticed by our senses.
II.	Hanging objects will swing slightly.
III.	Slight vibration felt indoors.
IV.	Awakens light sleepers. Windows rattle.
V.	Doors open and close. Small objects fall.
VI.	Trees sway, small bells ring.
VII.	Frightens everyone. Walls crack and plaster falls.
VIII.	Walls fall.
IX.	Some houses collapse.
X.	Roads crack and fold.
XI.	Most buildings fall.
XII.	Objects thrown in air. Ground rises and falls.

4 **Teaching Tips**—This is an excellent demonstration of compressional forces like those that cause rocks to slip and slide past each other.
5 **Teaching Tips**—Students can study earthquake damage by looking at the picture on page 17 or at pictures in books or magazines. The damage done by an earthquake is measured by an observation of the earthquake's effects. The Mercalli Earthquake Scale is an observation system that is based on the physical effects of an earthquake on the environment. Have the students use the scale to classify pictures of earthquake damage.
6 **Text Questions**—What number from the Mercalli scale would you give that earthquake? *XII.*

6 Look back at the picture on page 15. What number from the Mercalli scale would you give that earthquake?

A machine can also be used to measure earthquakes. 7 Geologists use a seismograph (**size**-mo-graf) to measure earthquakes. A picture of one is shown here. The ink pen is attached to a long arm. The shaking of an earthquake causes the pen to move up and down. The moving pen marks the paper on the turning drum. These markings are the records of the crust's movement. A seismograph can measure earthquakes that are too small for us to feel.

Section Review

Main Ideas: Earthquakes are sudden movements in the crust. They are caused by the movement of rocks along cracks, or faults. Earthquakes can be mild or strong. Strong ones cause landslides and damage to buildings. Earthquakes are measured with a seismograph, or by the Mercalli earthquake scale.

Questions: Answer in complete sentences.

1. Several people reported to a local TV station that they thought an earthquake had occurred. They said that small objects fell off walls, and that some doors opened and closed. Using the Mercalli earthquake scale, what type of earthquake happened?
2. Look at the map shown here. Would an earthquake be most likely at point A, B, or C? How do you know?

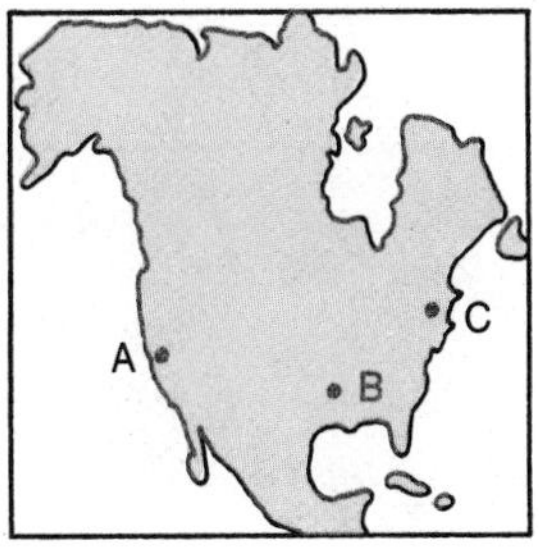

EXTENSIONS

Application

Science Skills—Recording Data

The earthquake report card, contained in the Interunit material, is the official data card used to report earthquakes.

A. Make copies of the card and distribute them to the students. Go over each item on the card.

B. If an earthquake were to occur, the students could use the report and send it to:
Chief, Seismological Field Survey, National Ocean Survey, N.O.A.A., 390 Main St., Room 7067, San Francisco, California 94105.

C. If earthquakes do not occur in your area, you could make up an account or read an actual account of an earthquake. The class could then record the information on the cards.

7 **Teaching Tips**—Seismographs record the movements within the earth's crust. Data from seismographs are used to infer the properties of rocks beneath the surface of the earth. Seismologists are able to identify different types of earthquake waves as they travel through the earth to seismic stations. The seismograph data also reveal the intensity of the earthquake.

SECTION REVIEW

Main Ideas—Write the words *earthquake*, *fault*, *seismograph*, and *Mercalli scale* on the chalkboard. Challenge the class to make up one informative sentence using these words.

Answers to Questions

1. The earthquake would be rated V.
2. A. See the map on page 16.

SUGGESTED WORKSHEET MASTERS
p. T-7 m; for Sections 1-1 and 1-2, p. T-71

SECTION BACKGROUND

Red-hot melted rock under the earth's surface is called *magma*. Magma rises toward the earth's surface because it is lighter than solid rock. It forces its way out through a crack or weak spot in the earth's crust, usually along the borders of crustal plates. When magma reaches the earth's surface, it is called *lava*. Steam, rocks, and hot gases may be mixed with lava. This hot material piles up, cools, and hardens, forming a mountain of solid rock. A mountain formed in this way is called a *volcano*. Volcanoes differ in the ways they erupt and in the composition of their magma.

MATERIALS

samples of volcanic rocks: obsidian, pumice, basalt, scoria, lava; glass, water

1-3. Volcanoes

For hundreds of years, Mt. St. Helens was a quiet snow-capped mountain. Then geologists began to see strange things near the mountain. Earthquakes began to increase in number. The ground around the mountain began to swell. Soon, geologists were saying that Mt. St. Helens was going to blow its top. And it did. The earth rumbled, and the ground split open.

Campers were trapped in the forests around Mt. St. Helens. A huge blast of hot gases and ash spread out over the mountain. Mt. St. Helens was now an active **volcano** (vohl-**kay**-no). What caused the *volcano* to erupt? When you finish this section, you should be able to:

Volcano: An opening in the earth's crust, through which lava escapes.

BASIC TEACHING PLAN

MOTIVATION

Using clay, make a small model of a volcano. Shape the model into a cone and mold a crater at the top of the model. Make the crater deep enough to hold a few tablespoons of a mixture of fine dirt and baking soda. Do this without the students present. For a demonstration of a volcano erupting, pour a few drops of vinegar into the crater containing the mixture of dirt and baking soda. The material will bubble up and start to run down the sides of the volcanic cone. Ask the students to describe what they saw, and how this was like a real volcanic eruption. Stress that a volcanic eruption can differ greatly in its intensity and thus, the shape of a volcano is not always so regularly formed.

Text Questions—What caused the volcano to erupt? *Hot material under the surface forced its way to the surface.*

A. Describe the stages in which a *volcano* forms.

B. Explain how *magma* and *lava* are alike and how they are different.

1 Some rocks deep under the earth's surface are so hot that they melt. This melted rock is called **magma** (**mag**-ma).

Magma forms in the earth's mantle. It rises toward the surface because it is lighter than solid rock. The magma may push its way out through a crack or weak spot in the earth's crust. If magma reaches the surface, it is called **lava** (**lah**-vah). Steam, rocks, and hot gases may be mixed with *lava*. This hot material piles up, cools, and hardens.

Magma: Red-hot melted rock under the earth's crust.

Lava: Red-hot melted rock coming out of the earth's crust.

EXTENSIONS

Enrichment

Research—Library

A. There are many interesting and historically important volcanic features the students might want to research. Students can investigate and make presentations on the following:

1. Eruption of Vesuvius in A.D. 79
2. Destruction of Saint Pierre
3. Eruption of Krakatoa
4. Origin of Crater Lake
5. Birth of Parícutin
6. The Hawaiian Island volcanoes
7. Surtsey
8. Mt. St. Helens

B. Students could write letters to a travel agency requesting brochures about the areas in which these volcanoes occurred.

C. The pictures can be used to create interesting volcanic collages on the bulletin board.

DEVELOPMENT

1 Teaching Tips—You can compare magma to fudge. When the fudge is cooking, it is a hot liquid, just as magma beneath the surface is hot and liquid. Removed from the heat, the fudge cools and becomes hard. When the magma forces its way to the surface, it cools and hardens to form rock.

EXTENSIONS

Reinforcement

Activity

You can demonstrate the behavior and movement of magma by using a partially used tube of toothpaste. Hold the tube so the students can see what happens when you squeeze the tube. The toothpaste is forced to move. With a pin, make a small hole in the tube. Squeeze the tube and let the students observe the toothpaste ooze out of the pinhole. The analogy here is that magma in the earth is usually contained in a chamber. The toothpaste is contained in the tube. The magma is under a lot of pressure. If a crack develops in the chamber, the magma can force its way out. When you put a hole in the tube and applied pressure, the toothpaste oozed out, just as magma would.

2 The diagrams below show how a volcano forms. (1) Magma forms in a pool deep in the earth. (2) Cracks form in the rocks above the magma pool. The magma slowly moves up the cracks. (3) As the magma nears the surface, pressure builds up. The rocks begin to push with great force. Sometimes the magma oozes out. At other times the volcano explodes. Material is thrown into the air. Magma also can reach the surface and flow out on the land. Geologists call this a lava flow. (4) A mountain formed in this way is called a volcanic mountain.

The materials that come out of volcanoes are clues. They tell us about the inside of the earth. The inside of the earth is very hot. The inside of the earth is always changing.

Mt. St. Helens is an exploding volcano. When it erupts, rocks and ash are tossed into the air.

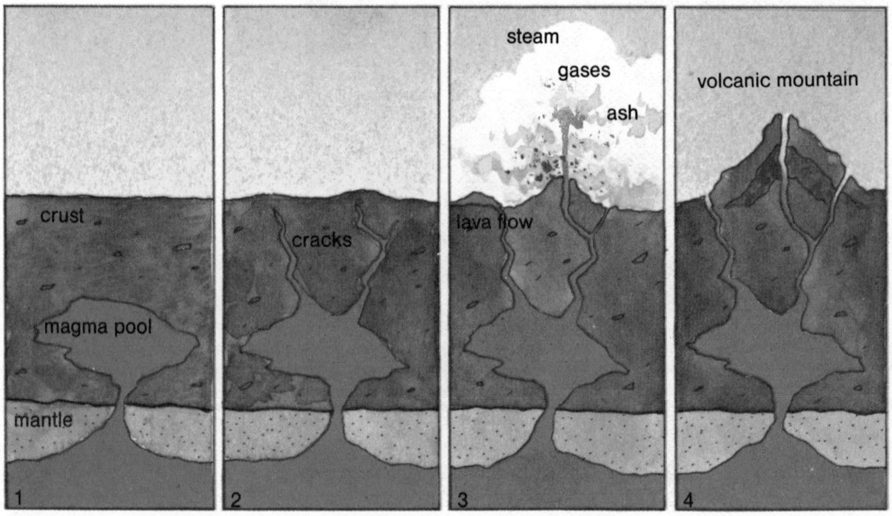

2 **Skill Development**—Students are asked to follow the *sequence* of events in the formation of a volcano.

3 The ash and rock cool as they fall. They pile up around the volcano opening. Finally, a cone-shaped mountain forms.

Not all volcanoes explode like Mt. St. Helens. All the Hawaiian islands are the tops of volcanoes. They reach up from the ocean floor. There are two active volcanoes on Hawaii Island. The one in the photo on this page is called Mauna Loa (Ma-oo-na **Lo**-a). Mauna Loa erupts quietly. The lava is very hot. It flows down the sides of the mountain like hot tar. The lava burns up the trees and plants in its path. As the lava cools, it slows down and stops.

4 Look back at the map on page 16. Each blue dot shows an active volcano on the earth's surface. Active volcanoes are erupting or have recently erupted. They form a belt called the "ring of fire." Look at the map. The ring of fire and the earthquake belt are almost in the same place. This makes geologists think that volcanoes and earthquakes may be caused by the same thing.

EXTENSIONS

Reinforcement

Science Skills—Vocabulary

Many people do not know the distinction between magma and lava, and they mistakenly use these terms synonymously. A *synonym* is a word that has the same meaning as another word.

Magma and *lava* have similar meanings, but not similar enough to be considered synonyms. Have your students find synonyms for the following words:

- core (center)
- erupt (explode)
- clue (hint)
- quake (tremble)
- Celsius (Centigrade)
- melted (molten)

3 Teaching Tips—Share with the students some of the types of rocks made by volcanoes. Have available samples of obsidian and pumice. You might demonstrate the unusual property of pumice by floating a piece in water.

4 Skill Development—Students are being asked to make some *conclusions* and general statements about the locations of volcanoes. They are also asked to *compare* the locations of volcanoes with the locations of earthquakes.

EXTENSIONS

Enrichment

Activity

A. Fasten a large map of the world to the wall. Use the map for students to locate the positions of some important volcanoes.

B. Assign two students to each volcano listed below. The students can look up the latitude, longitude, and pertinent information about the volcano they are assigned.

C. Here is a list of volcanoes you may wish to start with: Fujiyama, Kilauea, Mauna Loa, Tambora, Krakatoa, Lassen, Mt. St. Helens, Mount Pelée, Etna, Vesuvius, Stromboli, Chemborazo, Aconcagua.

ACTIVITY

What do rocks from a volcano look like?

A. Gather these materials: a set of volcanic rocks labeled A through E, a glass, and water.

B. Record your observations of each rock. Observe its color and its shape. Look carefully at the surface of each rock. Is it smooth? Does it have holes in it? Is it rough? What happens if you put each rock in a glass of water?

C. Go to a library to find books about geology and rocks. Find out the names of the rocks you observed.

ACTIVITY

Skill Development—*Classifying and Recording Data*

Teaching Tips—Rocks can be obtained through a supply house or a local junior or senior high school. Obsidian and pumice are sufficient to show the wide variation in volcanic rocks.

Exceptional Student

Visually Impaired

Have visually impaired students work with partners to record their observations. The partners can also describe to the special students what happens to the rocks in the water test.

Section Review

Main Ideas: Magma can move through cracks inside the earth. A volcano is a hole in the crust through which the magma escapes. Volcanoes and earthquakes are found in almost the same parts of the crust.

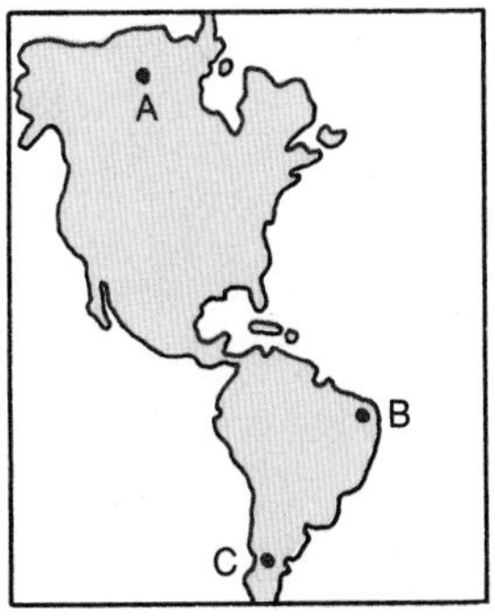

Questions: Answer in complete sentences.

1. What is the difference between magma and lava?
2. Where on the map shown here would you expect to find a volcano?
3. Why do geologists think that earthquakes and volcanoes may have the same cause?

People in Science

Alfred Wegener

Alfred Wegener was a German scientist. In 1912, he wrote a book about the continents. Wegener believed that the continents moved. He could see that the coasts of South America and Africa fit together like the pieces of a puzzle. At one time, Wegener believed, all the continents were part of one super-continent. They slowly drifted apart to form the continents as they are today. Wegener was not widely believed in his own time. But now scientists believe that the continents are still moving apart. This theory is known as Wegener's theory of continental drift.

Wegener went on four expeditions to the North Pole to test his theories. He died in Greenland on his last trip in 1930.

EXTENSIONS

Enrichment

Activity

Tell your students to look for small rocks that they think may be igneous rocks. They should look for the following identifying characteristics: interlocking crystals with flat reflecting faces, the inclusion of bubbles, and an appearance like glass. Have the class examine the rocks that were brought in, and discuss which ones are igneous and which ones are not.

SECTION REVIEW

Answers to Questions

1. Magma is molten rock located beneath the surface; lava is molten rock when it reaches the surface.
2. C
3. Earthquakes and volcanoes occur in almost the same areas.

EXTENSIONS

Enrichment
Activity

Start a rock collection for your classroom. Have your students go to the library to find out where to send for different rocks and minerals. They could also start an exchange with fourth graders from other areas. Collect specimens of rocks, and send them with a letter to schools in communities chosen from maps. The specimens you send should be clean, about 8 × 10 × 3 cm in size. Ask your correspondents to send you similar specimens in return.

CHAPTER REVIEW

Science Words: Think of a word for each blank. List the letters a through **i** on paper. Write the word next to each letter.

People who study rocks and other features of the earth are called __a__. Some of these people study the thin, solid, outer layer of the earth known as the __b__. Some scientists have become interested in the __c__, a thick layer of the earth below the surface layer. Scientists believe there is a hot layer made of metals deep in the earth. It is called the __d__.

Sudden movements of the earth are called __e__. They occur when rocks move along cracks called __f__.

Hot liquid in the crust is called __g__. When it comes to the surface, it is called __h__. The opening in the crust through which the material comes is called a __i__.

Questions: Answer in complete sentences.

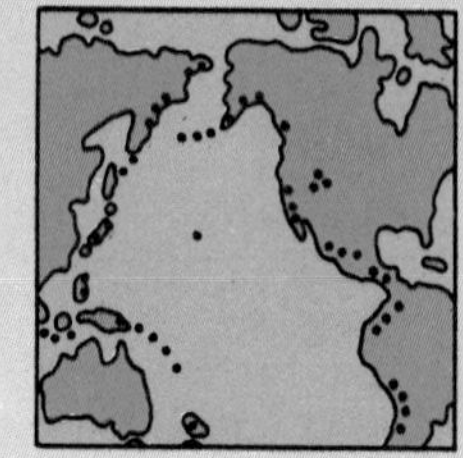

1. Make diagrams of an apple and the earth. Draw lines between the parts that are alike. Label the parts.
2. What kinds of damage can an earthquake cause?
3. List the correct order for the eruption of a volcano. (a) Cracks form in the crust. (b) Lava flows. (c) A magma pool forms. (d) Lava cools to form solid rock.
4. Can you predict where earthquakes may occur from this map of volcanoes?

CHAPTER REVIEW

Science Words
a. Geologists, **b.** crust, **c.** mantle, **d.** core,
e. earthquakes, **f.** faults, **g.** magma, **h.** lava, **i.** volcano

Answers to Questions
1. The students should identify the crust, mantle, and core of the earth as being similar to the skin, white part under the skin, and core of the apple.
2. An earthquake can cause objects to vibrate and crack, buildings to collapse, and roads to fold.
3. c, a, b, d
4. Yes, earthquakes and volcanoes usually occur in the same areas.

SUGGESTED WORKSHEET MASTER
p. T-7 n

SUGGESTED TEST MASTERS
p. T-7 d, e, f

CHAPTER 2

THE CRUST MOVES

Imagine going from the United States to France without crossing an ocean. You might only have to walk a few feet. Is it possible? What do you think? When you finish this section, you should be able to:

2-1. Moving Continents

BASIC TEACHING PLAN

MOTIVATION

If you have a large map of the world, show it to the class. Ask the students to consider whether they could travel to France from the east coast of the United States without crossing water. This is a puzzling situation. Some students may think of removing the water, that is, having the ocean drained. Other students may think of moving the continents together. Thus, the United States and France would be adjacent to each other.

Text Questions—Is it possible? *Yes.* What do you think? Students may view this as an impossible situation, or they may use their imaginations to arrive at a solution. Encourage the latter.

CHAPTER OBJECTIVES

1. Explain the theory of continental drift, and identify evidence to support this theory.
2. Explain the theory of plate tectonics.
3. Describe what happens when plates meet, separate, or slide past each other.
4. Explain how plate movements cause mountains to form; relate the shapes of mountains to the way they were formed.

SECTION BACKGROUND

Geologists believe that the continents have drifted apart at a rate of about 1–10 cm (1/2–4 in.) a year. Known as *continental drift*, this concept was formulated in 1912 by Alfred Wegener and is now part of a more inclusive concept known as *plate tectonics*.

The evidence to support this theory has come from the shape of the continents, similar rock formations existing on separated continents, and location of identical fossils of plants and animals on continents separated by over a thousand miles.

MATERIALS

1 sheet construction paper, 1 sheet tracing paper, scissors, paste, map of world

Exceptional Student
IEP Chapter Goal

At the end of this chapter, the student will state two clues that support the theory of continental drift.

EXTENSIONS

Application
Research

New ideas in science generally have had trouble finding acceptance. A well-known example is the initial rejection of the Copernican idea that the sun, rather than the earth, is the center of the solar system.

A. Students might conduct a survey to determine the opinions of people about the idea of continental drift.

B. The questionnaire might include questions such as the following:

1. Have you ever heard of the idea of continental drift?
2. Some scientists think the continents have drifted apart over a long period of time. Do you agree with this idea?
3. If you agree, what are your reasons?
4. If you disagree, what are your reasons?

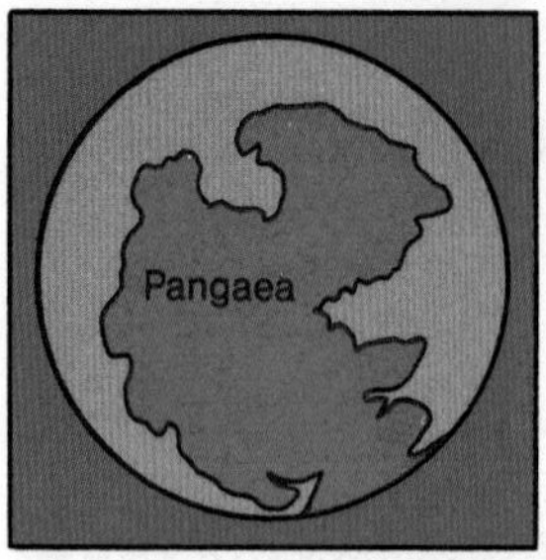

- **A.** Explain what is meant by *continental drift*.
- **B.** Describe two clues that show that the continents moved.
- **C.** Describe or show on a map how scientists think the continents moved.

Continental drift: The idea that the continents are moving.

1 In 1912, Alfred Wegener wrote that all of the continents were once one piece of land. The diagram shows what all the continents joined might look like. This super-continent was called Pangaea (Pan-**gee**-a). The name Pangaea comes from two Greek words meaning all (pan) lands (gea). Wegener said that Pangaea broke up. The continents moved apart. Geologists call this idea **continental drift**. They believe that the continents are still drifting.

ACTIVITY

Do the continents fit together?

A. Gather these materials: 1 sheet of construction paper, 1 sheet of tracing paper, scissors, paste, and map of the world.
B. Place the tracing paper on top of the map.
C. Trace the outline of North America.
D. Repeat step C for the other continents.
E. Cut out all the tracings.
F. Put the cutouts on the piece of construction paper. Paste the continents together.
1. Do you think that Pangaea might have existed in the past? Why?

DEVELOPMENT

1 Teaching Tips—Pangaea existed over 200 million years ago. It is believed to have split into a northern part named Laurasia and a southern part named Gondwanaland. Wegener proposed this idea in his book in 1912, but the idea was completely rejected by the scientific community until the 1960s.

ACTIVITY

Skill Development—*Following Directions, Inferring*

Teaching Tips—Using the worksheet master on page T-7o, prepare copies of the map in advance.

Answers to Questions—**1.** Yes. The fact that the present continents fit together so well is evidence to support the idea that Pangaea could have existed. It does not prove the idea, however.

Exceptional Student
Learning Disabled

A student with perceptual problems might have trouble tracing and cutting. Have the student work with a partner for this Activity.

Visually Impaired

Have the visually impaired student piece together precut continents made from oaktag.

2 Geologists have found clues that the continents moved. The first clue is the shape of the continents. Look at the maps below. The continents seem to fit like a puzzle. If you could cut them out and move them, they would fit nicely.

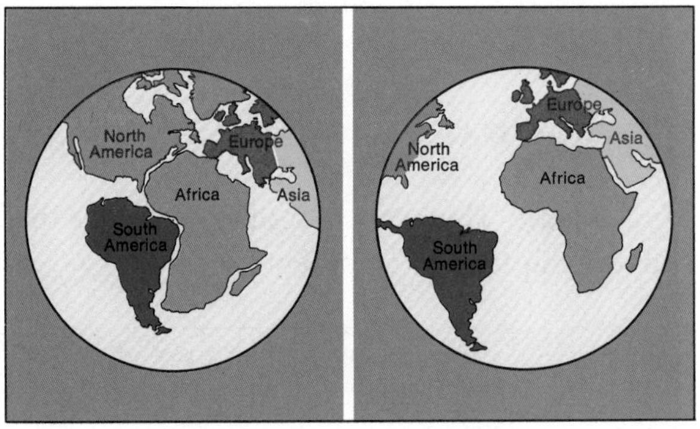

A second clue comes from rocks. The geologists compared the rocks on different continents. Some rocks have traces of plants and animals that lived long ago. These traces in the rock
3 are called **fossils** (**foss**-sills). The picture below shows a *fossil* of a reptile called Mesosaurus (me-zo-**sor**-us). This fossil has been found in only two places. One place is part of South America. The other place is the part of Africa that is right across from it. Mesosaurus lived in lakes and streams. But it was not a good swimmer. It could
4 not travel very far. How could it get across the ocean? Geologists think that when Mesosaurus was alive, South America and Africa were joined. Thus, Mesosaurus didn't have to swim very far.

Fossils: Traces of plants and animals in rocks.

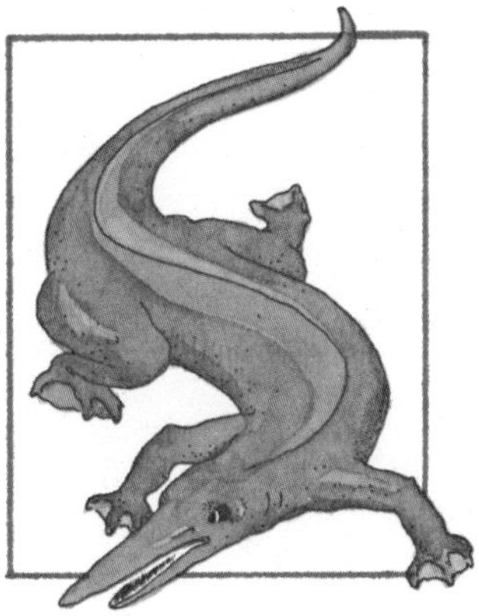

EXTENSIONS

Enrichment

Science Skills—Recording Data

A. From the results of the survey on continental drift on page T-28, have students record the results as the answers to the following questions:

1. What was the total number of people interviewed?
2. How many people agreed with the theory? How many disagreed?
3. How many people were previously aware of the theory? How many were not?
4. Of those people who agreed with the theory, how many were previously aware of it? How many were not?
5. Of those people who disagreed with the theory, how many were previously aware of it? How many were not?

B. A sample chart like the one shown below will help students tally their results.

	Aware	Not Aware	Total
Agree	20	15	35
Disagree	10	5	15
Total	30	20	50

2 Skill Development—Students will draw *conclusions* about the theory of continental drift by using the data presented in the remainder of the Development of this section. Point out the data to the students: shape of continents, location of identical fossils on distant continents, glacial scratches found in rocks in hot climates, and fossils of animals that live in warm climates found in the Antarctic.

3 Teaching Tips—Try to obtain samples of fossils. Let the students handle the fossils and, while they are doing so, ask them how they think fossils were formed.

4 Text Questions—How could it get across the ocean? *This animal could not swim the distance between the continents. The most reasonable conclusion is that South America and Africa were joined when this animal was alive.*

EXTENSIONS

Reinforcement
Activity

"Flip books" composed of small index cards can be made to show the drifting motion of the continents. South America and Africa are suggested. Have the students do the following:

A. Cut out the shapes of these two continents.

B. Trace the outlines of these shapes onto ten index cards. First, trace the continents in the position they were in when they were joined together.

C. On successive cards, the continents should be moved slightly apart.

D. The tenth and last card used should show the two continents as they are today.

E. The cards then should be stacked and stapled on the left edge. Flipping the cards shows the two continents drifting apart.

Other clues seem to fit the idea of *continental* **5** *drift*. Animal fossils have been found under the ice in Antarctica. These animals lived in warm **6** climates. Can the idea of continental drift explain this? Rock colors and layers look alike on continents thousands of miles apart. These clues add up to the idea that the continents were once attached.

Section Review

Main Ideas: The chart describes the clues that support the idea of continental drift.

Clue	How it supports the theory of continental drift
Shape of the continents	The outlines of the continents fit together just like a jig-saw puzzle.
Fossils	The animal could not cross the ocean. Perhaps the continents were joined together.

Questions: Answer in complete sentences.

1. What was Pangaea? What happened to it?
2. What are two clues that the continents may have drifted?
3. Was it ever possible to travel from the United States to France without going over water? Why?
4. Suppose the continents keep drifting. What may happen to the distance between Africa and South America?

5 Teaching Tips—Use a map to point out Antarctica. Fossils of animals that could only live in warm climates have been found under the ice.
6 Text Questions—Can the idea of continental drift explain this? *Antarctica probably drifted from a more northerly position where the climate was warmer.*

SECTION REVIEW

Answers to Questions
1. Pangaea is the name for the continents when they were all joined together. Pangaea broke in two, and the pieces gradually drifted apart.
2. The shape of the continents; location of fossils of the same kind of animal found on distant continents
3. Yes. The continents were once joined together.
4. It would increase.

2-2. Broken Crusts

This is a giant fault in the crust of the earth. It is along the coast of California. It is called the San Andreas (Sahn Ahn-**dray**-us) fault. The San Andreas fault divides two pieces of the earth's crust. Scientists think these two pieces are rubbing and bumping into each other. What could happen when pieces of the crust rub and bump into each other? When you finish this section, you should be able to:

- **A.** Explain that the earth's crust is broken into pieces.
- **B.** Describe the kinds of movement that occur where pieces of the crust meet.
- **C.** Explain that the movement of pieces of the crust may cause earthquakes and volcanoes.

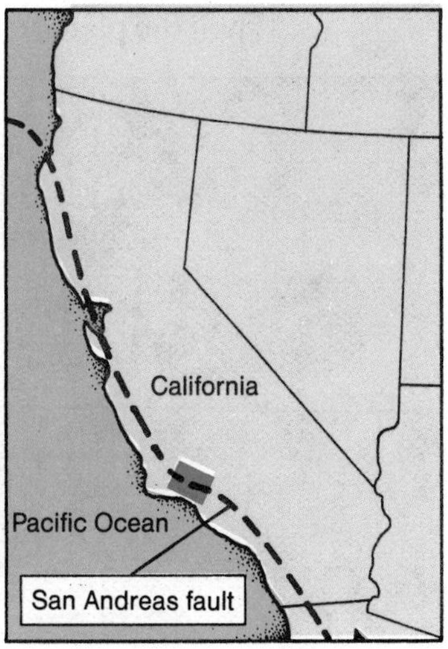

SECTION BACKGROUND

The plate tectonic theory proposes that the earth's crust is broken into about ten pieces, or plates. A plate is an area of the crust that can contain a continent and an ocean. The North American plate, for example, stretches from California in the west to include all of the continent and continues into the Atlantic Ocean basin to the midocean ridge (immense chain of mountains extending along the ocean's floor).

A central concept in the theory is that the plates can move. The movements of plates result in interactions, such as earthquakes and volcanoes. Plates can collide, they can separate, and they can slide past one another.

It is believed that the plates "float" on the upper part of the mantle, which has properties of a molten material. Some geologists think that convection forces in the mantle are responsible for causing the plates of the crust to move.

MATERIALS

hard-boiled egg, dinner knife, paper towel

BASIC TEACHING PLAN

MOTIVATION

You can demonstrate the movement of two plates along a fault. Make two stacks of clay, each composed of about four layers. Place the two stacks together (side by side) so that they are touching. The fault is the separation between the two. You can ask the students what they think might happen if these two blocks start slipping past each other. Grasp both stacks, and gently move one hand away from your body and the other toward your body. The stacks should begin to slip past each other. There will be a lot of drag, and the clay will appear to become deformed.

Text Questions—What could happen when pieces of the crust rub and bump into each other? *These actions can cause earthquakes, folding of rocks, faulting, and other events.*

EXTENSIONS

Reinforcement

Activity

Students can investigate the three types of plate movements developed in this section by using stacks of clay.

A. Have them make three stacks of clay, each stack four layers thick, and each layer 10 cm × 8 cm (4 in. × 3 in.).

B. Cut one of the stacks in half. Put the two halves back together. By gently pushing the two stacks together, the students can simulate the *collision* of two plates. There should be some folding and deformation of the clay.

C. Cut the second stack in half. Place the two halves back together. Gently pull the two stacks apart. A *separation* will occur between the two plates.

D. Cut the third stack in half. Put the two halves together. Grasp the two blocks and gently move the hands in opposite directions, causing the plates to *slide* past each other. There should be rubbing and some deformation of the clay.

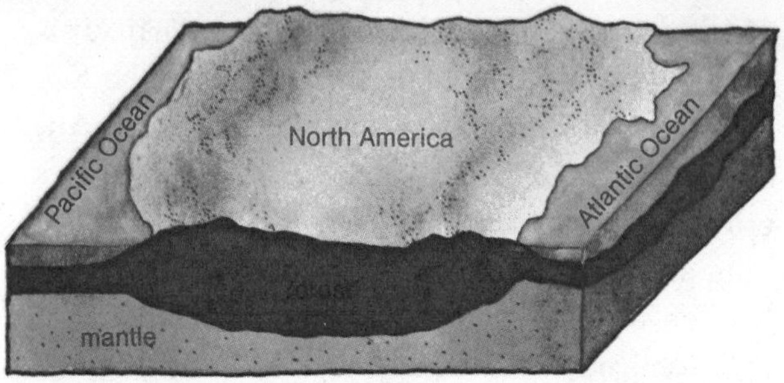

The crust may not cover the earth in a single piece. **1** How is this different from the skin of an apple? Scientists think that the crust is broken **2** into about ten pieces. These pieces are called **plates**. The map shows the major *plates* of the earth's crust. The diagram shows what scientists think each plate looks like.

Plates: Large sections of the earth's crust.

In the last section, you learned that the continents drifted apart. Scientists believe that the continents could drift apart because they were parts of plates. The plates of the crust move. When the plates move, the continents move, too.

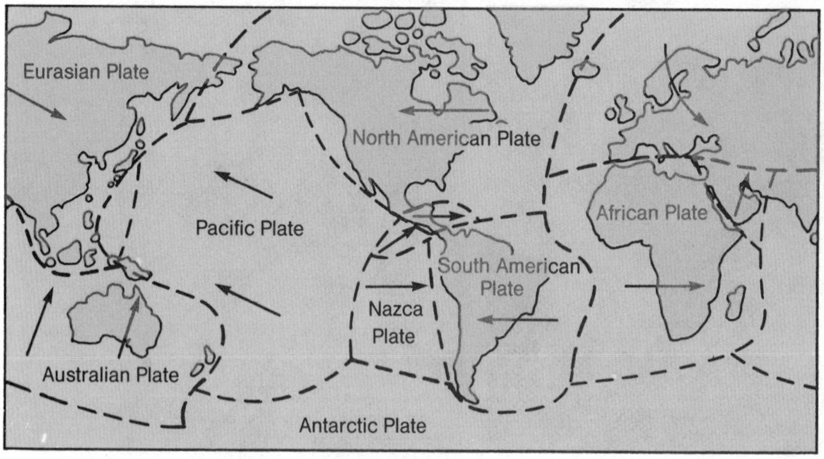

DEVELOPMENT

1 Text Questions—How is this different from the skin of an apple? *The skin of an apple is a single piece, whereas the crust of the earth is divided into pieces, or plates.*

2 Teaching Tips—The earth's crust is a jigsaw of plates. Using the worksheet master on page T-70, give each student a map of the world showing all the continents. Have them draw in the plates on this map by looking at the map on page 32. Have them label each plate, e.g., North American, African, etc. Then have them color each plate a different color.

3 Teaching Tips—A good example of plates colliding is found along the west coast of South America. Here the Pacific plate and the South American plate collide. The Pacific plate is plunging under the South American plate. On a map you can point out the Andes Mountains, which are caused by the collision of these two plates. A dramatic example is the collision of India with Asia. India is believed to have traveled (drifted) across the equator and collided with the continent of Asia. The collision created the Himalayas.

ACTIVITY

How is the earth like an egg?

A. Gather these materials: hard-boiled egg, dinner knife, and paper towel.

B. Keep the egg on the paper towel. Gently tap the egg to crack the shell in several places. Do not remove the pieces.

1. What layer of the earth is the shell of an egg like?
2. Why is a broken shell a better model than an unbroken one?

C. Gently push the pieces of shell against each other.

3. What happens to the shell pieces where they meet?
4. What is this like on the real earth?

D. Cut through the center of the egg.

5. What layer of the earth is the yolk like?
6. What layer is the white part like?

E. Students should not eat materials used in a science activity. Your teacher will tell you what to do with the egg.

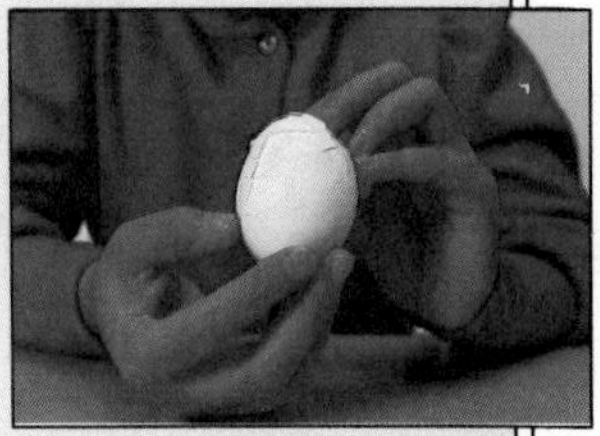

Scientists think that plates can move in three ways: (1) The plates can push against each other
3 (collide); (2) the plates can move apart (spread); and (3) they can also slide past each other (slip).
4 Let's look at the three movements. What happens to the earth's crust in each case?

Two plates can push against each other. When this happens, the plates collide. The thin part of

EXTENSIONS

Enrichment

Science Skills—Observing

As a demonstration of the way heat within the earth causes uneven heat currents in the mantle, set up the following experiment:

A. Make tissue tracings of North America, South America, Europe, and Africa. Tape them to aluminum foil and cut them out. Take the tissue off and keep the foil continents.

B. Place the foil continents together on the surface of water in a shallow pan. Place the pan on a hot plate. Apply the heat and ask the students to observe the movement of the foil continents.

C. Discuss how this model resembles the theory of continental drift and its cause.

ACTIVITY

Skill Development—*Comparing and Contrasting*

Answers to Questions—1. The crust. **2.** A broken shell illustrates that the earth's crust is divided into plates and is not one piece. **3.** The pieces collide and scrape against one another. **4.** The plates of the earth collide and slide past one another. **5.** The core. **6.** The mantle.

4 Text Questions—What happens to the earth's crust in each case? *(1) Collision—one part of the crust is pushed down under the other. (2) Spreading—liquid rock moves up to form new crust. (3) Slipping—earthquakes occur.*

EXTENSIONS

Enrichment

Research—Library

In addition to the San Andreas fault, students could investigate areas of the world that have a high incidence of earthquakes and volcanoes. Their research could be directed toward the plate interaction that is the cause of the disruption. The following areas are possible locations for your students' investigations: Kansu Province, China; Tokyo-Yokohama, Japan; Chile; Peru; Iran; Managua, Nicaragua; Aconcagua, Argentina; Mauna Loa, Hawaii; Mount Fuji, Japan; Popocatepetl, Mexico; and Mount Katmai, Alaska.

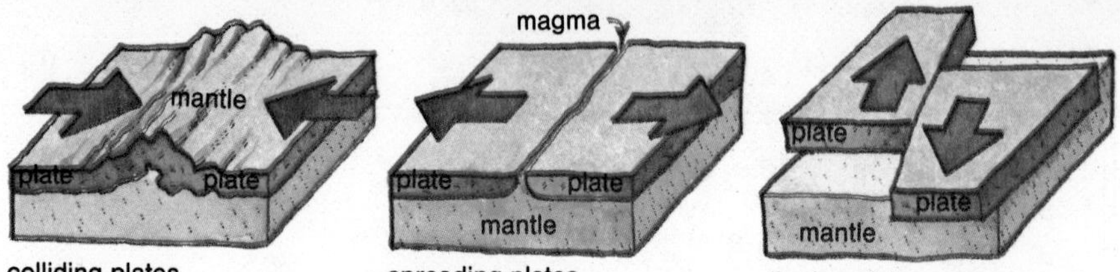

colliding plates   spreading plates   slipping plates

one plate slowly moves under the thick part of the other plate. Earthquakes are very common where plates collide.

Two plates can move apart. As this happens, magma squeezes up between the plates. The magma cools and forms new crust. Volcanoes and earthquakes are common where plates are moving apart.

Two plates can slide past each other. The San Andreas fault divides two plates. One is the North American Plate. The other is the Pacific Plate. These two plates are slipping past each other. Along this fault, earthquakes are very common.

Section Review

Main Ideas: Scientists think the earth's crust is broken into about ten plates. The plates can collide, move apart, and slip past one another.

Questions: Answer in complete sentences.

1. How is the crust of the earth different from the skin on a fresh apple?
2. What are three kinds of movement that occur when plates of the crust meet?
3. How are earthquakes and volcanoes related to plates of crust?

SECTION REVIEW

Answers to Questions

1. The crust of the earth is broken into about ten pieces, whereas the skin on an apple is not.
2. Collisions, spreading, and slipping past one another
3. When plates collide, spread apart, or slip past each other, earthquakes will occur. Volcanoes generally occur at plate boundaries, too.

SUGGESTED WORKSHEET MASTER
for Sections 2-1 and 2-2,
p. T-7 o

The picture shows a fossil of a sea animal. It lived a long time ago. When the animal was alive, it lived in the ocean. The fossil was found on top of a mountain. How did a sea animal get to the top of the mountain? When you finish this section, you should be able to:

2-3. Making Mountains

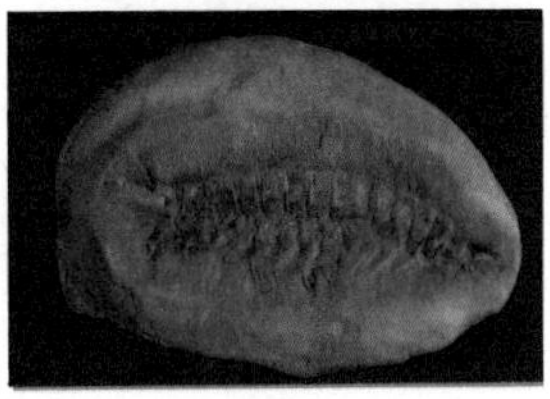

- **A.** Identify three changes in the earth's crust that make mountains.
- **B.** Describe how the shape of a mountain is the result of how it was formed.

The movement of crustal plates can cause mountains to form in three ways. One way is when two plates collide. When this happens, the crust is bent and squeezed. Squeezing causes the layers of rock to fold. These folded rocks form **folded mountains**. The Appalachian Mountains in the eastern United States are *folded mountains*. The Alps in Europe and the Himalayas in Asia are also folded mountains.

Folded mountains: Mountains formed by folding and squeezing the earth's crust.

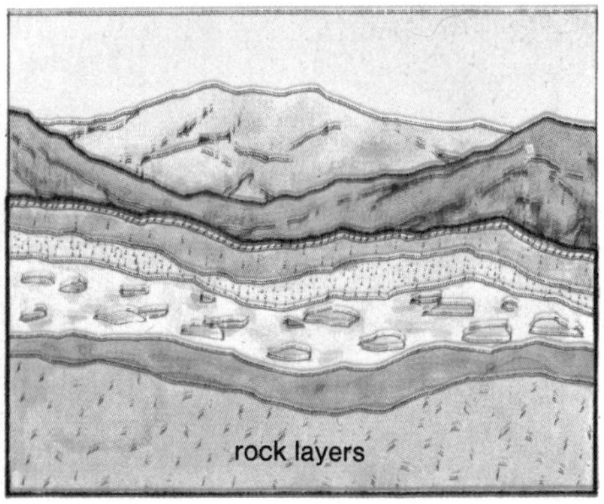

SECTION BACKGROUND

Earthquakes and volcanoes occur along crustal plates. There are also forces at work that result in mountain-building along these boundaries. Folded mountains are the result of the lateral movement and subsequent collision of crustal plates. They are formed by the squeezing together and lifting of rocks. Fault-block mountains are the result of earthquakes, or movements of large blocks of the crust along faults. They are formed by the cracking and tilting of rocks along faults. Sometimes magma may force its way up under the center of plates. When this happens, the magma lifts the crust to form dome-shaped or dome mountains.

MATERIALS

clay or plasticene (3 stacks, each 3 layers thick), 2 blocks of wood, golf ball, plastic knife

BASIC TEACHING PLAN

MOTIVATION

Show the class either fossils of seashells, or if you can't get any, present-day seashells. Discuss with the students where these animals live or lived. Fossils of animals that once lived in the ocean are sometimes found in rocks on the tops of mountains. The only logical explanation for this is that the mountain tops were once the bottom of the ocean and then rose up.

Text Questions—How did a sea animal get to the top of the mountain? *The rocks were lifted through the process of mountain formation.*

EXTENSIONS

Enrichment

Science Skills—Comparing and Contrasting

Have available a large map of North America so that students can label and identify the various mountain ranges. Students can identify where the mountains are located, what they look like, and how they were formed. For each mountain or range they study, they can make a model with potter's clay. Set the models on a table beneath the large map. The students can run string from their models to the location of the mountains on the map. They can put their information on small index cards and place them next to the mountains.

The following is a list of suggested mountains: Appalachian Mountains, Cascade Mountains, Sierra Nevadas, Rocky Mountains, Adirondacks, Green Mountains, Catskills, Smoky Mountains, Mt. St. Helens.

Fault-block mountains: Mountains formed by the pushing up of rocks along a fault.

1 When rocks are squeezed together, they do not always bend. They may crack and tilt. When this happens, mountains are formed. These mountains have large blocks of rock divided by faults. They are called **fault-block mountains**. The Sierra Nevadas, in the western part of the United States, are *fault-block mountains*.

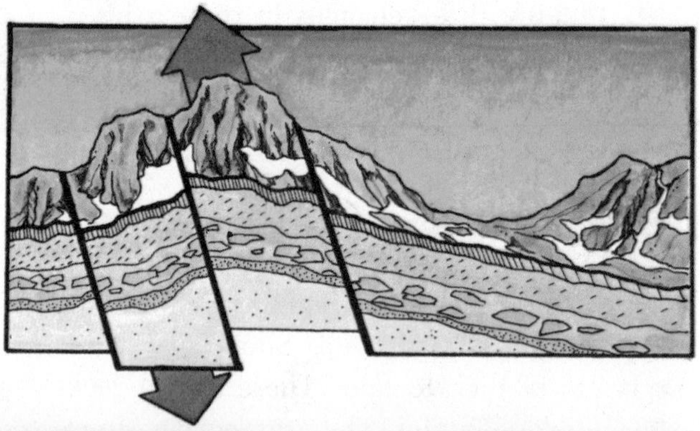

DEVELOPMENT

1 Skill Development—*Cause and effect* relationships are developed in this section. The cause of mountain building and the effect on the rocks and landscape are developed. To help with this skill, an illustration showing the landscape structure accompanies each of the three photographs of the mountains. Help the students with this by having them *compare and contrast* the photograph with the illustration.

2

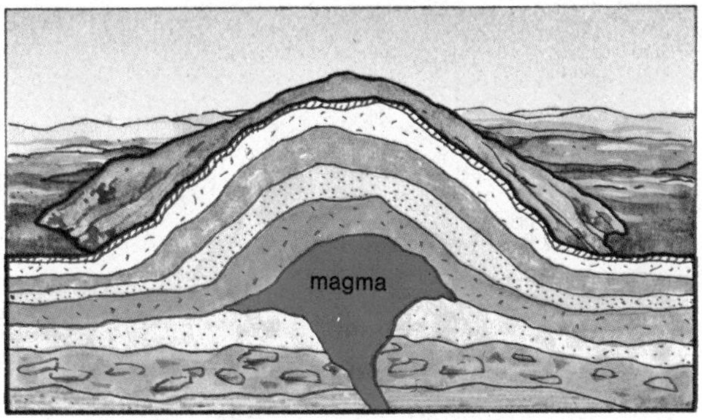

Magma may force its way under layers of rock. It pushes in between the layers, and bends the layers above. This action in the crust causes **dome-shaped mountains**. Stone Mountain, near Atlanta, Georgia, is a *dome-shaped mountain*.

Dome-shaped mountains: Mountains formed when magma pushes up part of the crust, without breaking the surface.

EXTENSIONS

Enrichment
Research

Rock layers that are folded are generally composed of sedimentary rocks. These include sandstone, shale, limestone, dolomite, and conglomerate.

Ask the students to bring in rock samples from home. There are many excellent books (e.g., *The World of Rocks and Minerals* by Anita Mason) to help your students identify and group the sedimentary rocks.

The students can create a rock display, indicating the type of rock and where it was found.

2 Teaching Tips—Make diagrams of folded, faulted, and dome-shaped landscapes as shown on pages 35–37. Show them to the class and ask if they can tell what forces in the earth's crust might have caused each landscape. This simple activity will be a check for you as to whether the students have understood the cause-and-effect relationships in mountain building.

EXTENSIONS

Enrichment
Activity

Have the students make more permanent models of the three types of mountains out of papier-mâché. Divide the class into three groups, and have each group make two models of one mountain type. One model could be a cross-sectional view of the rock layers in the mountain. The other model could be a surface view of the mountain. Have the students study photographs and diagrams so that they can make their models as realistic as possible. They can label important features on each of their models and write a report on how the mountains were formed. Set up a display for the models and reports. Photographs of the three types of mountains could also be a part of the display.

ACTIVITY

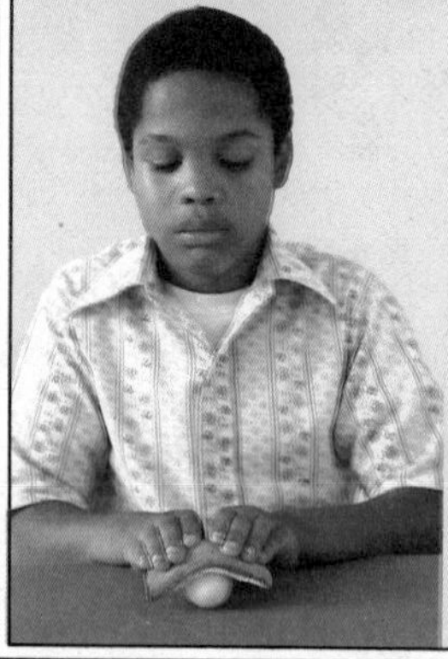

How are mountains formed?

A. Gather these materials: clay, 2 blocks of wood, a golf ball, and a plastic knife.

B. Make 3 stacks of clay, each with 3 thin layers. Pretend each layer of clay is a rock layer.

C. Hold 1 stack of clay between 2 blocks of wood. Hold 1 block of wood steady and press the clay layers together with your other hand as hard as you can.

1. What happened to the clay?
2. What kind of mountain did you make?

D. Make a cut in a second stack of clay with a knife, as shown in the picture. Hold one half of the stack steady. Push the other half along the cut in the stack.

3. What happened to the clay?
4. What kind of mountain did you make?

E. Hold the third stack of clay in your hand. Gently push a golf ball up under the clay. Remove the golf ball. Cut the stack of clay in half. Look at the layers of clay.

5. What happened to the clay?
6. What kind of mountain did you make?

F. Make a drawing of each stack of clay. Label the name of each type of mountain that you made.

ACTIVITY

Skill Development—*Following Directions, Finding Cause and Effect*

Teaching Tips—Prepare the clay before class. If you group the students in three's, you will only need one wood block for each student. Each student should receive two or three different colors of clay. The block of clay to be made need be no bigger than 10 cm × 6 cm, and each layer should be no more than 1 cm thick. Make a block consisting of three layers, each 10 cm × 6 cm × 1 cm (4 in. × 2 1/2 in. × 1/2 in.). Alternate the colors, and use this as the demonstration block for the class.

If you have the students work in groups of three, each student can make one of the three types of mountains. Each team of students can then make a display of their mountains. They can mount their models on oaktag and make their drawings on it, too.

Answers to Questions—**1.** The layers were bent. **2.** Folded. **3.** Parts of the layers were lifted. **4.** Fault-block. **5.** The layers were pushed up in the area of the golf ball. **6.** Dome.

Remember the fossil shown on page 35? The animal lived in the ocean. But the fossil was found on top of a mountain. Can you now explain why?

As you saw in this section, movements of the crust form mountains. The ocean floor was pushed up to become a mountain. The dead animal lay on the bottom of the ocean. When the crust moved, the animal was moved, too.

Section Review

Main Ideas: Movement in the earth's crust can make mountains. Folded mountains form when plates collide. This causes the rocks to fold and bend. Fault-block mountains form when blocks of crust are pushed up along a fault. Magma forces its way in between layers of rock to form a dome-shaped mountain.

Questions: For numbers 1–3, match the cause with its effect. Answer number 4 in a complete sentence.

Cause	Effect
1. Tilting of rocks along faults	a. Dome mountain
2. Magma forces its way under rocks	b. Folded mountain
3. Squeezing of layers of rock	c. Fault-block mountain

4. What could have caused the sea animal fossil on page 35 to end up on top of a mountain?

EXTENSIONS

Application
Research—Library

Students could investigate the difference between young (forces of folding, faulting, and doming are still at work) and old (weathering and erosion take over) mountains.

A. They could collect pictures of young mountains (Rocky Mountains or the Alps) and old ones (the Appalachians) and compare them visually on the bulletin board.

B. A chart could be made to compare their appearance, locality, and approximate age.

C. This idea will help prepare the students for the next section.

SECTION REVIEW

Answers to Questions

1. c
2. a
3. b
4. Years ago, plates may have collided and caused lower layers of the earth to move in an upward direction.

EXTENSIONS

Enrichment
Research—Library

Students would find it interesting to investigate the causes of "hot spots." These are areas of high volcanic activity that do not fall along crustal plates. Columns of hot material called "plumes" rise from within the mantle. An example of such an area in the United States is Old Faithful in Yellowstone Park.

CHAPTER REVIEW

Science Words: Match the words listed in column A with the definitions in column B.

Column A	Column B
1. Pangaea	a. Large sections of the earth's crust
2. Continental drift	b. Mountains formed when magma pushes up rock
3. Fossils	c. Mountains formed by squeezing of rock layers
4. Plates	d. The idea that the continents are moving
5. Folded mountains	e. Name of earth's super-continent
6. Fault-block mountains	f. Mountains formed when rocks move along a fault
7. Dome-shaped mountains	g. Traces of plants and animals in rocks

Questions: Answer in complete sentences.

1. How do the shapes of the continents help explain that the continents moved?
2. Why are earthquakes and volcanoes found in the same places?
3. What kinds of forces cause mountains to form?
4. What happens at the edges of two plates when they collide?
5. Imagine traveling in a time machine into the future. Would the earth look the same millions of years from now?

CHAPTER REVIEW

Science Words
1. e, **2.** d, **3.** g, **4.** a, **5.** c, **6.** f, **7.** b

Answers to Questions
1. When an attempt is made to fit the continents together on the basis of their shape, they fit together well. Thus, they probably were once joined.
2. Earthquakes and volcanoes are both caused by activity associated with crustal plate movements. The results of these movements usually occur along plate boundaries.
3. Folding, faulting, and doming
4. The rocks are folded, and one plate sinks while the other rides over.
5. No. New mountains would have formed as the result of the forces of folding, faulting, and doming within the earth. The distance between the continents would be different, and new islands possibly would have formed.

SUGGESTED WORKSHEET MASTERS
p. T-7 p, q

SUGGESTED TEST MASTERS
p. T-7 g, h

CHAPTER 3

THE CRUST WEARS AWAY

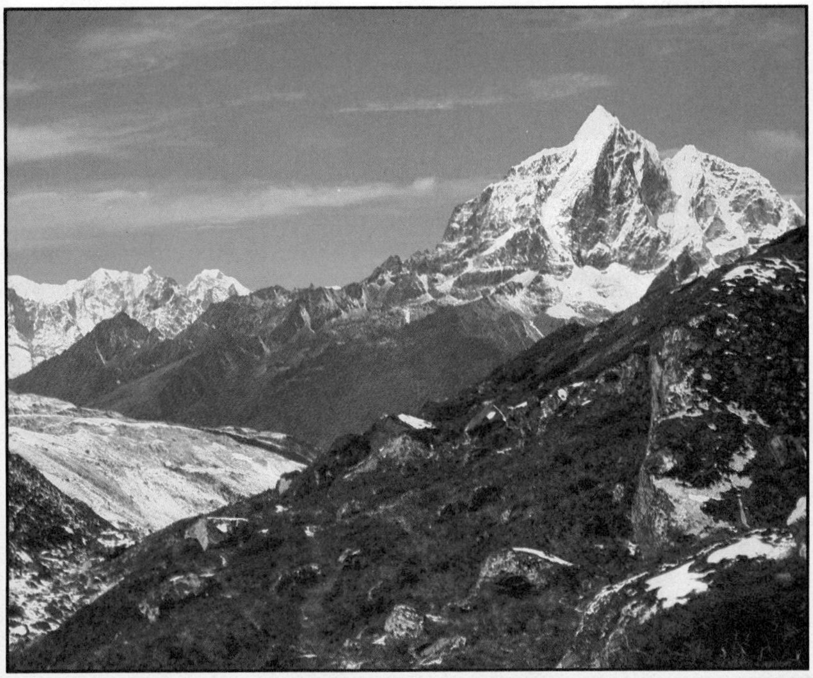

The picture above shows how the Appalachian Mountains might have looked when they were young. The picture on page 42 shows the Appalachians today. Have you ever thought of mountains getting old, like people? What happens to a

3-1. Breaking Down Rocks

CHAPTER OBJECTIVES

1. Describe the terms physical and chemical weathering, and classify weathering forces.
2. Explain erosion and how it affects sediment movement to the ocean.
3. Describe methods used to prevent erosion.
4. Explain how a glacier forms, and identify four ways that glaciers effect changes in the earth's crust.
5. Classify the ways in which humans change the land's surface, and describe the effects of these changes.

SECTION BACKGROUND

In addition to the forces of folding, faulting, and doming, the rocks in mountains are subjected to the forces of weathering. Weathering is the physical and chemical breakdown of rocks into small pieces. Physical weathering is the changing of a rock's size and shape. The minerals in a rock are not changed chemically. Chemical weathering changes the chemical composition of the minerals in a rock. Common reactions involve iron in rocks combining with oxygen (oxidation) and carbonic acid (formed by the addition of carbon dioxide to water) acting on rocks.

BASIC TEACHING PLAN

MOTIVATION

Ask the students to compare what happens when human beings get old with what happens when mountains get old. Students may not think of mountains getting old, so this idea may need some discussion.

Text Questions—Have you ever thought of mountains getting old, like people? *Answers will vary.* What happens to a mountain as it ages? *It loses elevation because of weathering; it becomes rounder; and because the elevation gets lower, there is a greater abundance of vegetation.* When the Appalachians were first formed and were very young, their elevations may have reached 14,000 feet (4,200 m), just as some of the peaks in the Rocky Mountains do today. The Rockies are much younger than the Appalachians, and thus they serve as a very good comparison. The Appalachians are over 200 million years old, while the Rockies are a young 60 million years old!

MATERIALS

limestone rocks (marble chips), 2 jars, water, white vinegar

Exceptional Student
IEP Chapter Goal
At the end of this chapter, the student will state four ways the earth's crust is weathered.

EXTENSIONS

Application
Science Skills—Observing

As a homework assignment or bulletin board project, ask the students to look around the inside and outside of their homes for objects that are undergoing weathering changes.

A. Ask each student to come in with a list and, if possible, to take pictures or make sketches to illustrate the example. The pictures or illustrations could be used to create a bulletin board display.

B. As a group, the class could classify each example according to the kind of weathering agent (mechanical or chemical) and describe how the given object has changed.

mountain as it ages? When you finish this section, you should be able to:

- **A.** Describe four things that cause rock to break down into smaller pieces.
- **B.** Group the ways in which rocks break down as either *chemical* or *physical weathering*.

Weathering: The breaking of rock into smaller pieces.

1 What would happen if you hit a large rock with a hammer? The rock would probably break into small pieces. Nature has its own way of breaking rocks and mountains. It is called **weathering** (**weather**-ing). Small pieces of broken rock can be found in most places. *Weathering* helps to change the surface of the earth.

Did you know that water can cause rocks to weather? Water drips into cracks in a rock.

DEVELOPMENT

1 Teaching Tips—Before class, put a rock about the size of a grapefruit in a canvas bag and then break the rock with a hammer. Wear safety goggles. Have available a rock about the size of the one you broke. Show the broken rock to the students to demonstrate the way in which nature breaks up rocks. But the process is slower. Weathering breaks rocks down into finer pieces, like sand. The sand at beaches is the result of the breakdown of rocks—often from mountains or higher ground—and the carrying of the pieces to the beach by rivers. Weathering is the breakdown of rocks in place. Erosion, which is explored in the next section, is the carrying away of these weathered bits of rock.

2 When the water freezes, it expands. The rock cracks and splits even more. This kind of weathering is called **physical weathering** (**fizz**-eh-kahl). As the rock breaks into small pieces, only its size and shape change. The **minerals** (**min**-err-als) that the rock is made of do not change.

Have you ever seen a sidewalk cracked by the roots of a tree? Plants also cause *physical weathering*. Plant roots work their way through small cracks in a rock. As the roots grow, they break the rock into smaller pieces. Sandblasting to clean stone buildings is like physical weathering.

Physical weathering: The changing of a rock's size and shape as it breaks down.

Minerals: Materials of which rocks are made.

3 Another kind of weathering breaks down rocks by changing the *minerals* in the rock. **Chemical weathering** (**kem**-eh-kahl) changes, adds to, or removes a rock's minerals. Rocks that contain iron can turn red. This is because the iron rusts.

Chemical weathering: A change in the minerals of a rock as it breaks down.

Rusting occurs when iron and water come in contact with each other. What examples of rusting have you seen around your home? A bicycle left out in the rain often will start to rust. The metal bike has iron in it. Rainwater, air, and iron mix to form rust.

Rocks can also be weathered by **carbon dioxide** (**kar**-bon die-**ox**-ide) and water. *Carbon dioxide* is a gas in the air. It mixes with rain and
4 falls on rocks. The mixture of carbon dioxide and water makes a weak acid. The rocks are slowly worn away by this acid. The acid changes the minerals that the rock is made of. This is a kind of *chemical weathering*.

Carbon dioxide: A gas in the air that mixes with rain to weather rocks.

EXTENSIONS

Reinforcement

Science Skills— Recording Data

A. Take your class on a field trip to observe weathering changes going on in your local environment. Observe such things as cracks in rocks or sidewalks; plants growing between these cracks; moss on rocks; the rate of water flow of a stream; areas where water accumulates to cause weathering; areas where wind would be a weathering force; and areas that are subjected to rusting (oxidation) or the action of acids.

B. Have the students list the changes they observe and classify them according to the kind of weathering.

C. Have the class discuss whether the observed changes are beneficial or harmful to their environment. If harmful, ask what could be done to prevent the given damage.

2 Skill Development—*Observing* the *effects* of physical and chemical weathering is developed on this page.
3 Teaching Tips—You should be able to locate rocks that are undergoing chemical change. Many rocks will show a discoloration and will easily crumble. Have students make observations of weathered rocks and rocks not yet visibly weathered.
4 Teaching Tips—The mixture of carbon dioxide and water makes a weak acid called carbonic acid.

EXTENSIONS

Reinforcement

Science Skills—Vocabulary

Just like rocks, words also can be broken down into smaller pieces or parts. Have the students break down each of the following words into its syllables and identify the root word where possible: weathering, temperature, chemical, dissolve, physical, mantle, mineral, carbon dioxide

Application

Research—Library

Urban structures are especially subjected to chemical weathering. Buildings and statues are worn down by pollutants from factories and automobiles. Your class could make a study of these effects in your locality or in other areas of the world, such as Italy, where classical monuments are subject to serious problems of weathering.

ACTIVITY

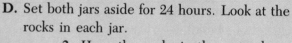

How can rocks be changed by weathering?

A. Gather these materials: marble chips, 2 jars, water, and white vinegar.
B. Fill each jar halfway with rocks.
C. Cover the rocks in one jar with water. Cover the rocks in the other jar with vinegar.
  1. What happens in each jar?

D. Set both jars aside for 24 hours. Look at the rocks in each jar.
  2. Have the rocks in the water been changed?
  3. How have the rocks in vinegar changed?
  4. Is this change an example of chemical weathering? Why?

Section Review

Main Ideas: Weathering breaks rocks into smaller pieces. Physical weathering only changes the rock's size and shape. Chemical weathering changes the minerals in the rock.

Questions: Answer in complete sentences.

1. What could happen if the seed of a tree started to grow in a small crack of a rock?
2. What is the difference between physical weathering and chemical weathering?
3. How do rocks change when water in them freezes?

ACTIVITY

Skill Development—*Observing, Finding Cause and Effect*

Safety Tips—Caution students not to rub their eyes. They should begin to realize that acids are often irritants.

Answers to Questions—1. Bubbles should appear in the vinegar jar. Not much will happen in the water jar. **2.** They have not been changed. **3.** They have begun to be broken down. **4.** Yes. The acid is changing the minerals in the rocks.

SECTION REVIEW

Answers to Questions

1. As the seed grows, the rock could be split apart.
2. Physical weathering is the change in size and shape of the rock; chemical weathering changes the kind of minerals in the rock.
3. When water freezes, it expands. The expanding water could push the rocks apart.

SUGGESTED WORKSHEET MASTER
p. T-7 r

Rain is not always good. Heavy rain causes rivers to flood. The rising water can cause much damage. What effect do you think a flood like the one shown has on soil, rocks, houses, and trees? When you finish this section, you should be able to:

3-2. Moving Water

- **A.** Explain *erosion* and how it can be stopped.
- **B.** Describe how water moves rocks and soil from one place to another.

What happens to rainwater when it falls to the ground? Some of it soaks into the soil. Some of it is used by plants. But much of the rainwater runs off along the ground. This runoff carries away soil and other loose material. The movement of rocks and soil by rainwater is a kind of **erosion** (ee-ro-zhun).

Erosion: The carrying away of rocks and soil by wind and water.

SECTION BACKGROUND

The rocks in the crust are also subjected to the forces of erosion. Erosion is the carrying of rocks and soil from one place to another. Running water, moving ice, wind, and waves are all agents of erosion. Running water (runoff) has the greatest effect on reshaping the land.

The continents of the earth have an interconnecting system of rivers and streams that carve and erode the landscape. Rivers transport millions of tons of sediment, eventually depositing most of this material in the oceans. The degree of erosion can be determined by such factors as the size of the rock particles, the compaction of the soil, the slope of the river channel, the intensity of the rainfall, and the plant cover of the land.

MATERIALS

large jar with screw lid, water, small pebbles

BASIC TEACHING PLAN

MOTIVATION

Newspaper clippings of flood damage would be an interesting way to start this section. Share with the students the effect of floods on the landscape, homes, and people.

Text Questions—What effect do you think a flood like the one shown has on soil, rocks, houses, and trees? *Soil and rocks are carried away, houses are severely damaged, and trees are uprooted.*

DEVELOPMENT

1 Skill Development—*Sequencing* is an important part of the total water cycle process. The water that hits the ground can go in a number of different directions as defined by the water cycle. Some of the water seeps into the ground. Some water is evaporated. If the water cannot seep into the ground or be evaporated, it runs downhill. This runoff is responsible for local erosion. Flash floods occur when runoff is severe.

EXTENSIONS

Reinforcement

Science Skills—Finding Cause and Effect

As a demonstration, you could make a model of a stream to illustrate how the velocity of a stream affects its eroding power.

A. Gather these materials: a foil pan or waterproof box, sand, and a gallon container for water.

B. Make a drainage hole on the wall of one short end of the pan. Fill the pan with 7.5 cm (3 in.) of sand. Leave about 10 cm (4 in.) of the bottom bare at the drainage end of the pan.

C. Punch a pencil-sized hole in the bottom of the water container. Set the container about 25 cm (10 in.) above the pan or box. Prop the pan up at a slight angle.

D. Fill the container with water to simulate runoff.

E. Observe the streams that form and where the velocity is the greatest. Change variables, such as the angle of the stream and the size of the hole in the water container, to see the effect on the velocity of the stream.

During heavy rains, a lot of soil can be removed by runoff. It takes a long time to replace the lost soil. Nature needs about 1,000 years to make 2 1/2 centimeters (1 inch) of soil. If the soil is washed away, farmers cannot grow the plants we eat. So people try to prevent soil *erosion*. Erosion can be stopped by planting grass and trees. Plowing across hillsides cuts down erosion. The plowed fields stop the water from flowing straight down the hill. 2

Soil is first carried away by small streams. The streams then carry the soil to rivers. One river may join other rivers. Let's see how rivers and
3 river systems change the surface of the earth. Rivers flow downhill. They carry along soil and

2 Skill Development—The *cause and effect* relationship between erosion and soil development is explained. Point out the importance of preventing soil erosion because of the enormous amount of time it takes nature to make soil.

3 Teaching Tips—You can demonstrate the way water flows in a river system by using a homemade stream table. Use a large flat pan. Put soil or sand in one end. Carve a small notch in the sand to simulate a river valley. Carefully pour water into the notch, and have the students observe the erosion of the sand or soil.

pieces of rock. These pieces of rock hit and loosen other rocks along the sides of the rivers. Rivers erode the land. After a long time, rivers can cut very deeply into rock. Look at the picture of the Colorado River flowing through the Grand Canyon. How do you think the Grand Canyon was formed?

What happens to the soil that rivers erode? The picture above shows the Russian River flowing into the ocean. The soil and rocks carried by the river are called **sediment** (**sed**-i-ment). When the river reaches the ocean, the *sediment* drops to the bottom. Over many years, the sediment piles up. This forms a piece of land called a delta.

Sediment: Broken-up rock carried in a river.

EXTENSIONS

Enrichment

Research—Library

Tell your students that in the early days of our country, New Orleans was located on the Gulf of Mexico. Ask several students to determine the distance of New Orleans from the Gulf of Mexico on a current map. Your students could then write a report in which they explain what changes occurred over the last several hundred years.

4 Text Questions—How do you think the Grand Canyon was formed? *The eroding force of the Colorado River formed the deep valley.*

5 Teaching Tips—Use the stream table to show how sediment is carried in a stream and deposited in a lake or the ocean. Students will be able to see grains of sand being tossed and carried along the bottom of the stream to be deposited in the ocean and to form a delta.

EXTENSIONS

Enrichment

Research

Flooding of rivers causes great damage to landscapes and harm to humans and wildlife. Have your students research the "flooding behavior" of streams or rivers in your locality. They should find out the answers to these questions:

Do any of the streams flood more than what is considered normal? What is being done to prevent flooding of these streams?

Many answers can be found by contacting the local natural resources department.

Application

Research—Library

A. Have your students investigate major North American rivers to determine effects of erosion and patterns of flooding.

B. They should include the following information: location on a map; photographs or sketches of the river's flow (show tributaries); age of the river; brief description of the origin of the river; problems caused by erosion along the river; delta formation; and flooding difficulties.

C. Here is a list of some major rivers in the United States from which to choose: Alabama, Allegheny, Arkansas, Apalachicola, Colorado, Cumberland, Delaware, Hudson, Mississippi, Missouri, Ohio, Platte, Sacramento, Saskatchewan, St. Lawrence, Susquehanna, Wabash, White

SUGGESTED WORKSHEET MASTER
p. T-7 s

ACTIVITY

How much rock can moving water carry?

A. Gather these materials: large jar with screw lid, water, and a handful of small pebbles.
B. Put the pebbles in the jar. Fill the jar with water. Screw the lid on tightly.
C. Imagine that the water in the jar is a river. Swirl the "river" in the jar quickly.
  1. What happens to the pebbles?
D. Swirl the "river" slower.
  2. What happens to the pebbles?
E. Swirl the jar until the water is barely moving.
  3. Where are the pebbles now?
  4. How does the speed of the water affect the number of pebbles that are held up?
  5. How does the speed of a flowing river affect the amount of sediment carried?

Section Review

Main Ideas: Moving water can carry away rocks and soil. Runoff erodes the land by carrying soil and broken rock away. The sediment in rivers is carried to the ocean.

Questions: Answer in complete sentences.

1. What happens to rain when it falls to the ground?
2. What happens to the soil and rock that rivers carry away?
3. What is erosion?

ACTIVITY

Skill Development—*Comparing and Contrasting, Finding Cause and Effect, Concluding and Generalizing*

Teaching Tips—Make sure the pebbles come in an assortment of sizes. One-qt mason-type jars will work very nicely.

Answers to Questions—1. They get all mixed up and start to move. **2.** The pebbles start to slow as well. The larger material will settle first. **3.** At the bottom of the jar. **4.** The faster the speed, the more pebbles that are held up. **5.** The faster the speed, the more rocks that are carried downstream.

SECTION REVIEW

Answers to Questions

1. It can seep into the ground, evaporate, or run off.
2. They eventually are deposited in the ocean.
3. Erosion is the carrying of weathered rocks and soil from one place to another.

The Houston Astrodome is hundreds of feet high. On the mountains of the world are chunks of snow and ice that are even larger than the Astrodome. Imagine how heavy these pieces of ice are! They press down on the mountain slopes below them. They can change the surface of the earth's crust. What are these giant pieces of ice called? When you finish this section, you should be able to:

- **A.** Explain how a *glacier* forms.
- **B.** Describe four ways that *glaciers* change the crust of the earth.

3-3. River of Ice

About 12,000 years ago, North America and Europe were much colder than they are today. Much of the snow that fell did not melt. Year after year, the snow piled up. Over 3 km (2 miles) of snow piled up. It pressed down the snow below it to make ice. How did this huge pile of ice change the surface of the land?

SECTION BACKGROUND

A large body of moving ice and snow is called a *glacier*. Glaciers can be found in a mountain valley (valley glacier) or in severely cold regions as huge sheets of ice (ice caps). They usually erode the land by flowing downhill to break up rocks and carry them away. Glaciers can act like bulldozers by pushing rocks in front of them. When the glacier starts to melt, a small ridge-like hill is left by the debris the glacier pushed. Rocks stuck in the bottom and sides of glaciers scrape, scratch, and dig into the rocks beneath the glacier. Glaciers can carry boulders a great distance and then drop them. These boulders are called *erratics*.

MATERIALS

2-l plastic container with tight lid, gravel, water

BASIC TEACHING PLAN

MOTIVATION

The comparison of the Astrodome to a glacier should give students a good idea of how huge glaciers can be. During the Ice Age, glaciers extended from the Arctic through Canada as far south and west as St. Louis and as far east as Long Island.

Text Questions—How did this huge pile of ice change the surface of the land? *The weight and, therefore, force of the ice resulted in its movement; this caused rocks and even boulders to be carried great distances.*

EXTENSIONS

Enrichment

Activity

A. Have your students make models of glacial features with plaster of paris. The models do not have to be large.

B. A convenient container is a large milk carton. Cut the container so that it is about 8 cm (3 in.) high.

C. The plaster must be mixed to a very thick consistency. Pour it into the carton, leaving a space of 1 or 2 cm at the top. As the plaster hardens, it can be molded to form any of the features that are formed by glaciers.

D. Here are some specific projects:

1. Replicate the development of the Matterhorn as shown in the textbook. The students will need three cartons to do this.
2. Show a mountain glacier moving downhill into a glacial valley.
3. Show a mountain with a glacier at the very top.
4. Show the effects of glacial movement in a valley by making till, boulders, and piles of debris pushed by the glacier.

1 Have you ever made a snowball? What happens when you squeeze the ball? The snow near the center turns to ice. The same thing happened during the Ice Age. The snow near the bottom was pressed together as more snow fell. Slowly, the snow at the bottom turned to ice. The body of ice and snow became heavy. It began to move. A large body of moving ice and snow is called a **glacier** (**glay**-shur). *Glaciers* flow downhill from mountains to lower ground. They erode the land by breaking rocks and carrying them away.

Glacier: A large body of moving snow and ice.

Look at the picture of the mountain. It has very steep sides and a pointed top. This mountain **2** was eroded by glaciers. Its rocks were pulled out by the moving ice. This mountain is called the Matterhorn. It is in the Alps. Glaciers were first studied in the Alps.

Glaciers often push rocks out in front of them. Large rocks, called boulders, are carried on the

DEVELOPMENT

1 Teaching Tips—You can demonstrate what happens to ice or snow when it is compacted. Crush up some ice or snow so that the pieces are very small. Pack the ice or snow together with your hands as hard as you can. Break the snowball, and notice the compactness of the ice.

Draw a diagram on the board showing snow piled up. Point out what the snow at the bottom would be like with all the snow piled on top. Actually, the ice in glaciers has been compressed so much, it is considered a metamorphic rock. It is very hard. Glacial ice is also able to "flow" under the extreme pressure caused by the ice and snow piled up. This "flow" enables the glacial ice to move.

2 Teaching Tips—Glaciers are able to remove rocks by a process known as *glacial plucking*. The ice and snow cling to the rocks in the winter. In the summer the snow melts, and during the winter the snow refreezes into the rocks. This alternate freezing and thawing of the ice loosens the material to prepare it for erosion.

top of glaciers. Rocks stuck in the bottom and sides of glaciers act like claws. They scrape, scratch, and dig into the crust of the earth as the glacier drags them along.

As the earth got warmer, most of the glaciers
3 melted. We can still see the changes caused by glaciers. Where a glacier pushed rocks in front of it, we now find long, low hills. Large boulders can be found in strange places. The ice carried them from far away. Look at picture 1. As the ice melted, the boulders dropped to the ground. In other places, we find scratches in rock. They
4 were caused by the glacier. Can you see the scratches in picture 2? Look at the map. It shows the glaciers of the last Ice Age in North America.
5 Was the place where you live once covered with ice? The glaciers moved down from Canada. They reached as far south as the present Ohio and Missouri rivers and central Long Island.

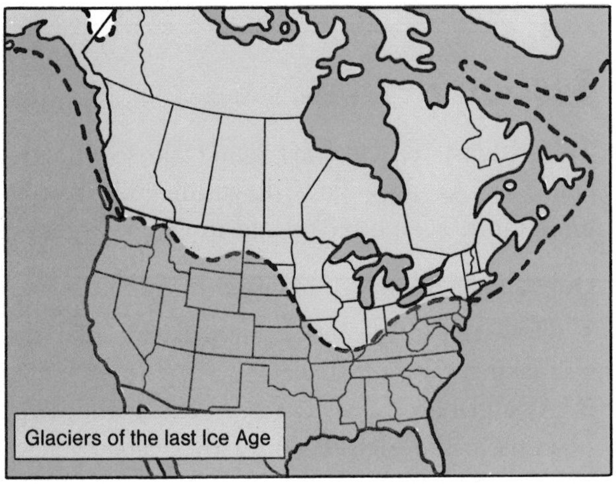

EXTENSIONS

Application

Research

A. Obtain maps of a glaciated area to study the effects of glaciers.

B. Have your students write to the United States Geological Survey, Washington, D.C., 20240 to request a listing of geological and topographical maps. For a small fee, the organization will send you the maps of your choice.

C. You can also write to the following national parks, requesting brochures and information: Mount Rainier National Park, Yosemite National Park, Crater Lake National Park, Rocky Mountain National Park, Glacier National Park, and Acadia National Park. The information will contain photographs and facts about the glaciers and their effects on each park.

3 Skill Development—The observation of landscape features allows geologists to make *inferences* about glacial activity.
4 Text Questions—Can you see the scratches in picture 2? *Yes, they are running from the upper right to the lower left of the picture.*
5 Text Questions—Was the place where you live once covered with ice? *Answers will depend on the exact area in which students live.*

EXTENSIONS

Enrichment

Research—Library

Glaciers have formed lakes as they moved over the earth's surface. The continental glacier (a continuous sheet of ice) that covered much of North America was responsible for the formation of many lakes in the northern part of the United States and Canada. Students could research the formation of the Finger Lakes in New York, the Great Lakes in the United States and Canada, and Lake Winnipeg in Canada.

ACTIVITY

How do glaciers change the landscape?

A. Gather these materials: 2-liter plastic container with a tight lid, gravel, and water.

B. Put a big handful of gravel in the container. Fill it with water. Close the lid tightly.

C. Put the container in a freezer overnight.

D. When the water is frozen solid, remove the ice from the container.

1. In what ways is the ice like a glacier?

E. Take the ice outdoors. Lean on the ice as you push it over the ground.

2. How does pressing down on the ice make it act like a glacier?
3. How did the ice and gravel mixture change the ground?
4. Would the same changes have happened without the gravel?

Section Review

Main Ideas: Glaciers are giant masses of snow and ice. As they flow downhill, they erode mountains, scrape rocks, and move loose rocks.

Questions: Answer in complete sentences.

1. How is the formation of a glacier like the making of a snowball?
2. As a glacier moves over the land, what happens to the ground under the glacier?
3. Why do you think the glaciers melted?

ACTIVITY

Skill Development—*Comparing and Contrasting, Finding Cause and Effect*

Answers to Questions—1. It is frozen and contains fragments of rocks and soil. **2.** Leaning on the ice adds pressure to the ice, and glaciers are under a good deal of pressure. **3.** The gravel stuck in the bottom should scratch the ground, and there may be some material pushed ahead and to the sides. This will depend upon the material the students push into it. **4.** Probably not.

SECTION REVIEW

Answers to Questions

1. Both require compaction and pressure.
2. The ground is scratched, and rocks and soil are pushed ahead by the moving glacier.
3. The climate got warmer.

3-4. Humans Cause Change

Did you know that some of the largest lakes in the United States were made by humans? The lake shown in the picture was once part of a river. Norris Dam was built on the Tennessee River. This trapped the river water. A lake was formed. Building dams is one way people change the earth's surface. When you finish this section, you should be able to:

☐ **A.** Identify ways people change the surface of the earth.

☐ **B.** Describe the effects of changes on the land.

The pictures on the next page show ways humans change the land. Let's look at these more closely to see how we change the land.

SECTION BACKGROUND

Humans have an effect on changing the land. They alter the landscape when they construct roads, buildings, and factories. They erode the land when they dig for rocks, minerals, and fuels. They help to save the land by setting aside portions of the landscape that can only be used as parks. Places such as national parks and forest preserves protect animals, rivers, mountains, and plant life.

MATERIALS

old magazines, poster paper, scissors, glue

BASIC TEACHING PLAN

MOTIVATION

Capture the students' awareness of how humans change the land by bringing in examples from newspapers. Have them make a list of ways in which they think humans change the landscape.

EXTENSIONS

Application

Activity

A. Make a collection of photographs showing various human landscapes in your community. Mount the photographs on construction paper.

B. Have your students classify the photographs, based on the types of landscapes defined in the section. If you have a map of the community, you can use a key to show where each picture was taken.

1 Picture 1 shows how humans speed up erosion. This giant shovel removes tons of rocks. The rocks contain iron ore. Steel is made from iron ore. It is used to make such things as cars, airplanes, and rockets. Humans remove rocks and soil from the land just as rivers and glaciers do.

Picture 2 is an example of how humans help to save the land. It is a picture of a national park. Signs in national parks often say, "Take only pictures, leave only footprints." These signs remind people that parks have a special purpose. Parks like these save the homes of many plants and animals. Rivers and mountains are saved. Humans can enjoy the park's beauty.

You learned how nature builds up the surface of the land. Mountains and volcanoes are formed by changes in the earth's crust. Picture 3 shows **2** how humans build on the land. We build cities,

DEVELOPMENT

1 Skill Development—The *causes* of human landscape changes and their *effect* on the land are introduced by the photographs. Many of the processes the students already have learned about will be applied to the ways humans change the landscape.

2 Teaching Tips—You might take the students on a brief field trip outside so that they can find examples of human changes in the environment: new construction, park development, pollution, and littering.

houses, factories, highways, and piles of garbage. All this building changes the land.

Building can cause erosion of land. Removing
3 plants can cause soil to be washed away. What would the land look like if plants were not returned to it? By planting trees and grass, humans prevent erosion.

4 Humans can work with nature to bring about helpful changes. For example, humans do not cut down all the trees in a forest. Only the older trees are cut. The smaller trees are left behind. They prevent erosion as they grow larger. Often, too many trees are cut down. Humans can replace these trees with young trees. This will help prevent erosion. It will also speed up the growth of the forest.

Humans have learned that planning is important. Before people change the land, they need to think about the effects the change will have.

EXTENSIONS

Application
Science Skills—Classifying

As environmental changes and our responsibility for them are emphasized within this section, it would be beneficial to make students aware of their immediate environment and how it is being changed by humans.

A. Ask the class as they go home today to find five ways in which their environment is being altered by humans. They could also listen to the news or read the newspaper for these changes, e.g., oil spills, toxic wastes, or sewage plants.

B. They should write a brief description of the changes and, if appropriate, include a drawing for each example.

C. Based on their findings, compile a selected class list of human landscape changes in your area. If desired, explore how several of these could be improved to create a better environment.

D. Ask a local town or environmental official to address the class on specific problems with which your community is confronted.

3 **Text Questions**—What would the land look like if plants were not returned to it? *If there are no plants on sloping ground, runoff water washes the soil away and leaves gullies behind.*
4 **Skill Development**—It is important that students understand the beneficial *effects* that human intervention can have upon the environment.

EXTENSIONS

Reinforcement
Science Skills—Vocabulary

This section provides practice in using details to derive the main idea of a reading passage.

A. Write the following titles on the chalkboard:
Changing the Land
Not Changing the Land

B. Explain to the class that each title represents the main idea of a different reading passage.

C. Instruct your students to list under these titles examples they find in the passages. For example, *factory* and *tunnel* could be listed under Changing the Land; and *national park* under Not Changing the Land.

ACTIVITY

How do humans change the land?

A. Gather these materials: old magazines, poster paper, scissors, and glue.

B. Look at the magazines. Find pictures of humans changing the land. Find at least 10 pictures.

C. On the poster paper, put the pictures into three groups:
Group 1: How humans erode the land.
Group 2: How humans build on the land.
Group 3: How humans help to save the land.

D. Paste the pictures on the poster paper.

E. Draw a star next to the pictures that show changes that will last for a long time.

Section Review

Main Ideas: Humans change the land in many ways. Removing rocks and minerals from the earth's crust wears down the land. Building roads, factories, and houses changes the appearance of the land. Humans can save the land.

Questions: Answer in complete sentences.

1. Look at picture 1 on page 54. What type of change have humans caused?
2. What are some ways humans change the land? Find pictures in this book for each change you list.
3. What would be the effect of building apartments in wooded areas?

Exceptional Student
Visually Impaired

The visually impaired student can do a variation of this Activity without using pictures. Have the student recite ten ways that humans change the landscape.

SUGGESTED WORKSHEET MASTER
p. T-7 t

ACTIVITY

Skill Development—*Observing, Classifying*

Teaching Tips—The students could do this Activity at home, using their own magazines. Make sure they have poster paper and glue. If you do the Activity in class, you might have students bring in magazines so that you will have a large number of them.

SECTION REVIEW

Answers to Questions

1. Eroding the land
2. Humans change the land by eroding the land, building up the land, and creating areas where the land is protected from change.
3. The land would be eroded, and then built up. Trees would be removed, which would have an effect on other plants and the wildlife in the area.

CHAPTER REVIEW

Science Words: Match the words in column A with the definitions in column B.

Column A	Column B
1. Physical weathering	a. Materials rocks are made of
2. Weathering	b. A large body of moving snow and ice
3. Erosion	c. Carrying away rocks and soil
4. Carbon dioxide	d. Changing the size and shapes of rocks
5. Chemical weathering	e. Changing the minerals in a rock
6. Glacier	f. Material carried by rivers
7. Minerals	g. Breaking rocks into smaller pieces
8. Sediment	h. Mixes with rain to weather rocks

Questions: Answer in complete sentences.

1. How can water and plants weather rocks?
2. How is physical weathering different from chemical weathering?
3. How does rain cause erosion of the earth's crust?
4. What clues on the land show that a glacier passed over it?
5. Listed below are changes humans have made to the land. Classify each as (a) building up the land, (b) wearing down the land, or (c) not changing the land.

   1. Building a tunnel
   2. Making a state park
   3. Building a skyscraper
   4. Farming the land

EXTENSIONS

Reinforcement

Science Skills—Vocabulary

A. To improve your students' ability to use the Index quickly and efficiently, have them look up the following words:
weathering, erratic, erosion, delta, glacier, sediment, minerals

B. In addition to indicating page numbers, ask your students to refer to the Table of Contents and list other chapters where they think they may be able to find additional information about each word.

CHAPTER REVIEW

Science Words

1. d, **2.** g, **3.** c, **4.** h, **5.** e, **6.** b, **7.** a, **8.** f

Answers to Questions

1. If water freezes while inside a rock, it may break the rock because water expands when it freezes. If a seed settles in a crack, the growing plant may force the rock apart, thereby increasing the size of the crack.
2. Physical weathering changes the size and shape of rocks, whereas chemical weathering changes the minerals in the rock.
3. If it does not seep into the land or if it evaporates, rain accumulates in streams and can then carry sediment to lakes and oceans.
4. Scratches or gouges in rock
5. 1. b, 2. c, 3. b, 4. b or c

SUGGESTED WORKSHEET MASTER
p. T-7 u

SUGGESTED TEST MASTERS
p. T-7 i, j, k

EXTENSIONS

Reinforcement

Science Skills—Measuring and Recording Data

A demonstration of the advantages of contour plowing in preventing runoff is as follows:

A. Line two wooden or heavy cardboard boxes of equal size (40 cm × 30 cm × 10 cm) with watertight material.

B. At one end of each box, cut a small (3-cm) hole.

C. Fill the boxes with soil. In one of the boxes, make small gullies by running your finger horizontally across the soil.

D. Place the boxes side by side, and elevate one end of the boxes. Place an empty can under each hole.

E. Sprinkle each sample with equal amounts of water.

F. Measure and compare the runoff that collects in each can.

INVESTIGATING

How do plants affect erosion?

A. Gather these materials: 2 large aluminum roasting pans, soil, sod, sprinkling can, hammer, nail, 2 jars, and water.

B. Use the hammer and nail to make a 1-cm-wide hole in the bottom of each pan. The hole should be near the pan's end.

C. Cut a piece of sod to fit in one pan. Fill the other pan with soil. Make the soil the same depth as the sod.

1. What is different about the 2 "hills"?
2. What do you think will happen to the surface of these "hills" when you pour water on them?

D. Fill the sprinkling can with water. Sprinkle water over the top of each "hill." Hold a jar under the hole at the bottom of each "hill."

3. How did the water affect the surface of each "hill"?
4. How does grass on a hillside affect erosion? Why?

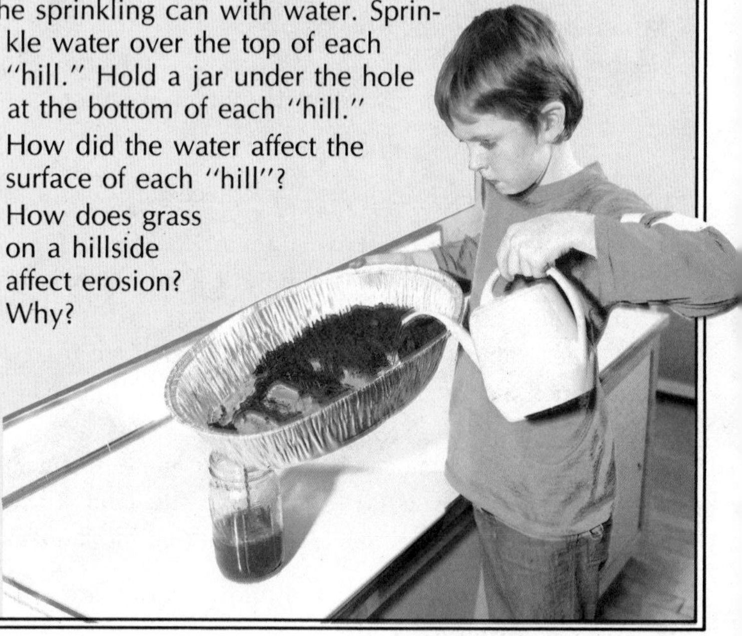

INVESTIGATING

Skill Development—*Observing, Comparing and Constrasting*

Teaching Tips—You may wish to do this experiment as a demonstration. As a follow-up, find photographs of eroded hillsides and hillsides that have been conserved by planting vegetation. Look for hillsides in your community that have either eroded or that have been conserved.

Answers to Questions—1. One has ground cover and the other does not. **2.** Water will flow easily through the soil without ground cover. **3.** In the sample without any cover, small gullies were formed. **4.** It slows it down. The roots of the grass absorb the water.

CAREERS

Seismologist ►

You have learned that earthquakes cause a lot of damage. It is important to know about earthquakes before, during, and after they happen. Seismologists are people who study earthquakes. They use a machine called a seismograph to measure earthquakes. People who are seismologists have studied geology and math in college.

◄ Surveyor

You may have seen surveyors working near your home. A surveyor uses machines to measure the high and low places of the land. Surveyors can also measure the size and shape of pieces of land. They usually work in teams. A surveyor needs some background in mapmaking and math. Some surveyors are trained on the job.

EXTENSIONS

Application

Research—Library

Have interested students go to the library to do research on careers as paleontologists and cartographers.

Paleontologists and cartographers contribute to the study of the earth. A paleontologist needs a sound knowledge of geology to be able to classify fossilized plants and animals. A cartographer assists in assembling geological maps.

CAREERS

Teaching Tips—Seismologists are involved in oil and mineral exploration and are consulted for information by engineers who are designing structures in earthquake areas. Additional information can be obtained by writing to the American Geological Institute, 2201 M St., N.W., Washington, D.C. 20037. Surveyors need to have a good ability to judge distances and to do mathematical calculations very quickly. Additional information can be obtained by writing to the American Congress on Surveying and Mapping, 733 15th St., N.W., Washington, D.C. 20005.

UNIT 2 LIGHT

CHAPTER	SECTION	BASIC SCIENCE SKILLS	ACTIVITY MATERIALS STUDENT/GROUP	EXTENSIONS
CHAPTER 4 LIGHT BEAMS AND SHADOWS	**4-1** p.T-62 Light Sources	*Classifying* qualities p.T-63 *Comparing and contrasting* objects p.T-64	1 flashlight, 2 used chalkboard erasers, 1 white index card	• Reinforcement p.T-63 • Enrichment pp.T-64, T-65
	4-2 p.T-66 Straight Lines	*Comparing* blinking p.T-67 *Comparing and contrasting* p.T-67	4 index cards, hole punch, clay, a light source	• Reinforcement pp.T-67, T-69 • Enrichment p.T-68
	4-3 p.T-70 Spreading Light	*Observing* how light spreads out	1 piece of cm graph paper, flashlight, meter stick	• Enrichment p.T-73 • Application pp.T-71, T-72
	4-4 p.T-74 When Light Strikes	*Classifying* objects by how light passes through them	flashlight, small samples of glass, clear plastic, tissue paper, waxed paper, fabrics, cellophane, wood, metal, rubber	• Reinforcement p.T-75 • Enrichment pp.T-76, T-77
CHAPTER 5 BOUNCING LIGHT	**5-1** p.T-78 Reflecting Light	*Finding the cause and effect* of reflection	flashlight, 2 squares of aluminum foil white paper, mirror	• Enrichment p.T-80 • Application pp.T-79, T-81
	5-2 p.T-82 Flat Reflectors	*Comparing and contrasting* mirrors	clay, light box, mirror, sheet of white paper	• Reinforcement p.T-84 • Enrichment p.T-83 • Application p.T-85
	5-3 p.T-86 Curved Reflectors	*Comparing and contrasting* concave and convex mirrors p.T-89	file card, lightbox or flashlight, 4 mirrors, white paper, clay	• Reinforcement pp.T-87, T-88 • Enrichment pp.T-90, T-91 • Application p.T-89
CHAPTER 6 BENDING LIGHT AND COLORS	**6-1** p.T-92 Light Bends	*Observing* the demonstrations in the text p.T-93	clear shoe box, flashlight, milk, black paper, water, eraser	• Reinforcement p.T-94 • Enrichment p.T-95 • Application p.T-93
	6-2 p.T-96 Lenses Bend Light	*Comparing* different magnifications p.T-97 *Classifying* objects using a microscope p.T-99	thin jar, thick jar, water, flashlight, aluminum foil, white paper, ruler	• Reinforcement p.T-99 • Enrichment p.T-98 • Application pp.T-97, T-100
	6-3 p.T-101 Prisms and Rainbows	*Comparing and contrasting* colors p.T-102 *Hypothesizing* p.T-104	flashlight, mirror, water, crayons, white paper	• Enrichment p.T-102 • Application pp.T-103, T-104
	6-4 p.T-105 Seeing Colors	*Observing* colors	flashlight, sheets of red, green, blue, and white paper	• Reinforcement p.T-108 • Enrichment pp.T-106, T-107, T-109, T-110 • Application p.T-111

EXTRA ACTIVITIES/ DEMONSTRATIONS	WORKSHEET MASTERS	EVALUATIONS
• Materials, p.T-63 • X ray p.T-63		Section Review p.T-65
• Three-dimensional objects p.T-67		Section Review p.T-69
• Spraying water p.T-71 • Dropping sand into water p.T-73	Light Sources (SK) p.T-59 l Spreading Light (AH) p.T-59 m	Section Review p.T-73
• Light strikes different materials p.T-75	When Light Strikes (AC) p.T-59 n Science Vocabulary (SK) p.T-59 o	Section Review p.T-76 Chapter Review p.T-77 Test Masters pp.T-59 d, e, f
• Tennis ball p.T-79 • Surfaces p.T-79 • Kaleidoscope p.T-81		Section Review p.T-81
• Ball p.T-82 • Flashlight p.T-84	Bouncing Light (SK) p.T-59 p	Section Review p.T-85
• Four mirrors p.T-87	Reflecting Light (AH) p.T-59 q Pinhole Camera (AC) p.T-59 r	Section Review p.T-90 Chapter Review p.T-91 Test Masters pp.T-59 g, h
		Section Review p.T-95
• Bend light p.T-97 • Microscope p.T-99		Section Review p.T-100
• Roy G. Biv p.T-101	Bending Light and Colors (SK) p.T-59 s	Section Review p.T-104
• Color p.T-106 • Passing light p.T-107 • Paint p.T-108 • Investigating p.T-110	Seeing Colors (AC) p.T-59 t Vocabulary (SK) p.T-59 u	Section Review p.T-108 Chapter Review p.T-109 Test Masters pp.T59 i, j, k

KEY (AC)—Activity (AH)—At Home (SK)—Skill

BOOKS FOR STUDENTS

Branley, Franklyn M. *Color: From Rainbows to Lasers*, ill. by Henry Roth, New York: Crowell, 1978

Branley, Franklyn M. *Light and Darkness*, New York: Crowell, 1975

Cooper, Miriam. *Snap! Photography*, New York: Messner, 1981

Goor, Ron & Nancy. *Shadows: Here, There & Everywhere*, New York: Crowell, 1981

Heuer, Kenneth, *Rainbows, Halos & Other Wonders: Light & Color in the Atmosphere*, New York: Dodd, 1978

Hoban, Tana. *Is It Red? Is It Yellow? Is It Blue? An Adventure in Color*, New York: Greenwillow, 1978

Horsburgh, Reg. *Living Light: Exploring Bioluminescence*, New York: Messner, 1978

Kohn, Bernice. *Light*, illus. by Janina Domanska, New York: Dandelion, 1979

Lewis, Bruce. *What Is a Laser?*, New York: Dodd, 1979

Schneider, Herman & Nina. *Science Fun With a Flashlight*, New York: McGraw-Hill, 1975

Simon, Hilda. *The Magic of Color*, New York: Lothrop, Lee & Shepard, 1981

Simon, Seymour. *Mirror Magic*, illus. by Lisa Campbell Ernst, New York: Lothrop, Lee & Shepard, 1980

FILMS

Color and Light: An Introduction, 11 min, Coronet

How To Bend Light, 11 min, Britannica

FILMSTRIPS

The Magic of Sight, 1 filmstrip, 1 cassette, 13 min, National Society to Prevent Blindness

What Is a Wave?, 1 filmstrip, 1 cassette, 16 min, Focus

COMPUTER AIDS

Light, Tutorial, Apple, Pet, Basic, 16K & tape/disk, Right On Programs

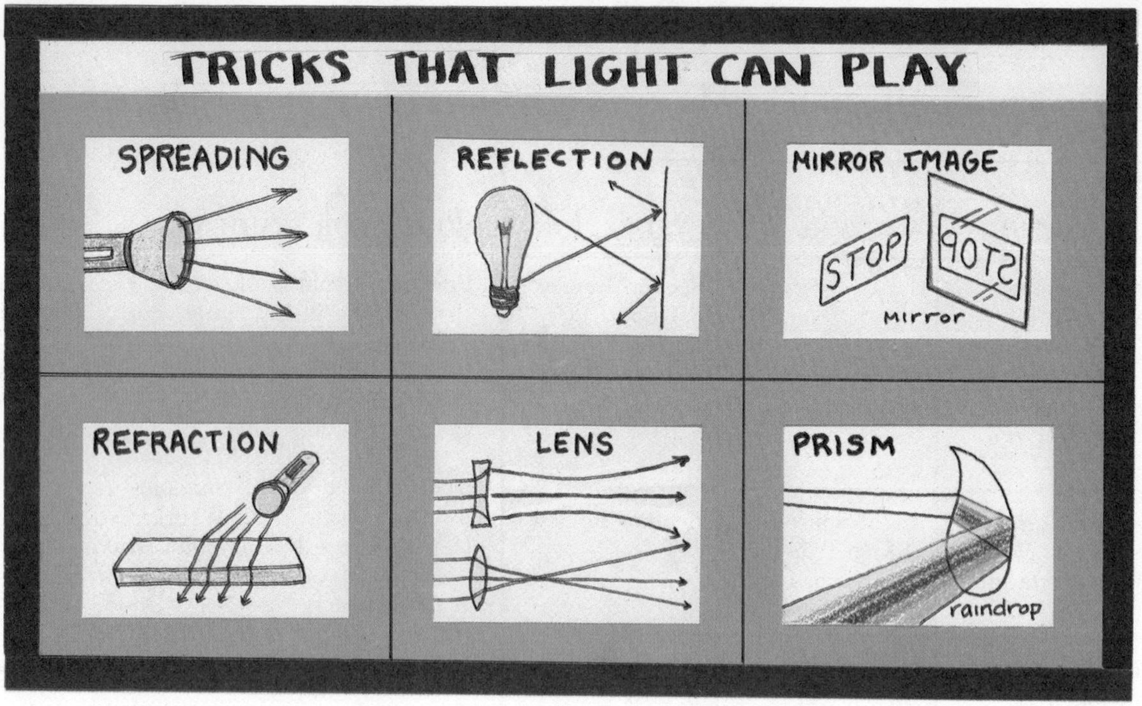

BULLETIN BOARD

The theme of this Bulletin Board could center around the tricks that light plays. Among the topics that should be shown are the spreading, reflection, and refraction of light; the uses of lenses and mirror images; and the effect of prisms on light. The class should be divided into five groups and each group should be asked to give illustrative examples of one phenomenon. Paging through magazines at home may help students think of ideas that will be appropriate to their topic.

FIELD TRIP IDEAS

To visit an optician's office or store

Arrange a visit to an optician for your class. Ask the optician to show the students various lenses and to discuss how they are used to correct eyesight. Prior to the visit, it would be helpful to discuss the anatomy of the eye.

To observe the A-V room or media center

Find an appropriate time for your class to visit these facilities in your school. Ask the specialist who coordinates the use of the equipment to show the students how light and lenses are used in projection devices. If possible, the students should be shown the location of the lenses and a diagram of the light beam.

Name________________________________Date______________

LIGHT BEAMS AND SHADOWS

TEST CHAPTER **4**

Fold back answer key on line before copying.

CHAPTER OBJECTIVES

Read each question. Choose the best answer from those listed. Write the letter of your choice on the line at the right.

1. Which of the following is *not* a light source? **1.** ______ **1.** d (1)
a. car headlights **c.** sun
b. matches **d.** earth

2. When light bounces off an object, **2.** ______ **2.** b (1)
a. the object becomes invisible.
b. the object becomes visible.
c. an X ray is taken.
d. the object becomes blurred.

3. X rays are able to pass through the body because **3.** ______ **3.** c (1)
a. they have no light energy.
b. they have less energy than the light we see.
c. they have more energy than the light we see.
d. they move very slowly.

4. What forms when an object gets in the way of a light beam? **4.** ______ **4.** d (2)
a. a curved light beam **c.** a sunny spot
b. a straight line **d.** a shadow

5. Which of the following proves that light travels in straight lines? **5.** ______ **5.** a (2)
a. a shadow that is the same shape as the object
b. a shadow that is a different shape than the object
c. a shadow that is darker than the object
d. a shadow that is bigger than the object

6. In the time it takes for a light beam to travel to the moon, you could **6.** ______ **6.** a (2)
a. blink your eyes. **c.** fly around the world.
b. eat a sandwich. **d.** run around the block.

Name________________________________Date____________

7. c (3) 7. Which does *not* happen to light as it travels away from its source? 7. ______

a. It spreads out. **c.** It gets brighter.
b. It gets thinner. **d.** It gets dimmer.

8. b (3) 8. Light looks dim when 8. ______

a. there are many light beams.
b. there are few light beams.
c. there are no light beams.
d. the sun is directly overhead.

9. c (3) 9. Light beams are like water from a spray bottle because they both 9. ______

a. are cold.
b. travel at the same speed.
c. are most concentrated at their sources.
d. are thinnest at their sources.

10. a (4) 10. Which sentence is true? 10. ______

a. Light particles spread apart as they move away from their source.
b. Light particles are closer together as they move away from their source.
c. Light waves get bigger as they travel.
d. Light gets dimmer as light waves get bigger.

11. c (4) 11. Light acts like a wave when 11. ______

a. it gets brighter as it travels.
b. it travels in one direction from its source.
c. it travels in all directions from its source.
d. it does not travel at all.

12. c (4) 12. Which sentence does *not* explain why light gets dimmer? 12. ______

a. Light waves become weaker.
b. Light spreads out as it travels from its source.
c. There are more light particles.
d. Light particles spread out.

13. a (5) 13. Objects that let light pass through are called 13. ______

a. transparent. **c.** opaque.
b. translucent. **d.** solid.

Name_____________________________Date____________

14. An opaque material **14.** ______ **14.** b (5)
a. lets light pass through.
b. blocks light.
c. scatters light.
d. has no effect on light.

15. An example of a translucent material is **15.** ______ **15.** c (5)
a. water. **c.** tissue paper.
b. cardboard. **d.** glass.

Fold back answer key on line before copying.

CHAPTER OBJECTIVES

Name________________________________Date__________

BOUNCING LIGHT

TEST CHAPTER 5

Read each question. Choose the best answer from those listed. Write the letter of your choice on the line at the right.

1. d (1)

1. A good reflector is one that is *not* **1.** ______

a. shiny. **c.** smooth.
b. bright. **d.** dull.

2. a (1)

2. When light hits an uneven surface, the light particles **2.** ______

a. are scattered. **c.** reflect off in a straight line.
b. are absorbed. **d.** pass through the surface.

3. c (1)

3. Which of the following is the best reflector? **3.** ______

a. a wooden floor **c.** a flat mirror
b. pond water **d.** wrinkled aluminum foil

4. a (1)

4. A light beam reflects back on itself when **4.** ______

a. a mirror is directly in front of it.
b. a mirror is at an angle to it.
c. the light reflects at an angle.
d. it shines on a rough mirror.

5. b (2)

5. To change the direction in which a light beam is reflected off a shiny surface, **5.** ______

a. the focus is changed.
b. the angle at which it hits the surface is changed.
c. the surface is changed.
d. all of the above happen.

6. c (2)

6. If light hits a shiny surface, it reflects off **6.** ______

a. in a curved line.
b. in the same direction.
c. in the opposite direction.
d. around corners.

7. a (2)

7. A periscope is used to **7.** ______

a. see around corners. **c.** see underwater.
b. focus light. **d.** make light brighter.

Name______________________ Date ____________

8. In a periscope, mirrors are placed so that one mirror reflects light beams **8.** ______ **8.** b (2)
   a. to 3 mirrors in a row. **c.** back to the source.
   b. to a second mirror. **d.** in a curved line.

9. Curved mirrors are used in car headlights because **9.** ______ **9.** b (3)
   a. they spread light in many directions.
   b. they focus light.
   c. they make things look smaller.
   d. they make things look bigger.

10. To focus light, mirrors are placed **10.** ______ **10.** a (3)
   a. at slight angles to each other.
   b. at right angles to each other.
   c. next to each other in a straight line.
   d. on top of each other.

11. Which of the following does *not* use curved mirrors? **11.** ______ **11.** b (3)
   a. a spotlight **c.** a flashlight
   b. a periscope **d.** a telescope

12. When light reflects from a curved mirror, it is **12.** ______ **12.** a (3)
   a. focused. **c.** not as bright.
   b. unfocused. **d.** a different color.

13. Concave mirrors make things look **13.** ______ **13.** d (4)
   a. darker. **c.** smaller.
   b. lighter. **d.** bigger.

14. Which of the following is a convex mirror? **14.** ______ **14.** d (4)
   a. a flat piece of glass **c.** the inside of a spoon
   b. a periscope **d.** the outside of a spoon

15. A mirror that curves in is **15.** ______ **15.** a (4)
   a. concave. **c.** flat.
   b. convex. **d.** round.

16. Convex mirrors are used in stores **16.** ______ **16.** a (4)
   a. to watch many people at the same time.
   b. to watch one person at a time.
   c. to get a close-up of people.
   d. to make people look curved.

Fold back answer key on line before copying.

Name______________________________ Date__________

BENDING LIGHT AND COLORS

TEST CHAPTER **6**

CHAPTER OBJECTIVES

Read each question. Choose the best answer from those listed. Write the letter of your choice on the line at the right.

1. b (1)

1. When light passes from one material to another, it **1.** ______
- **a.** is reflected.
- **b.** bends.
- **c.** changes color.
- **d.** changes the material.

2. a (1)

2. A mirage is caused by the difference between **2.** ______
- **a.** hot and cold layers of air.
- **b.** roads and air.
- **c.** air and water temperatures.
- **d.** hot and cold water.

A

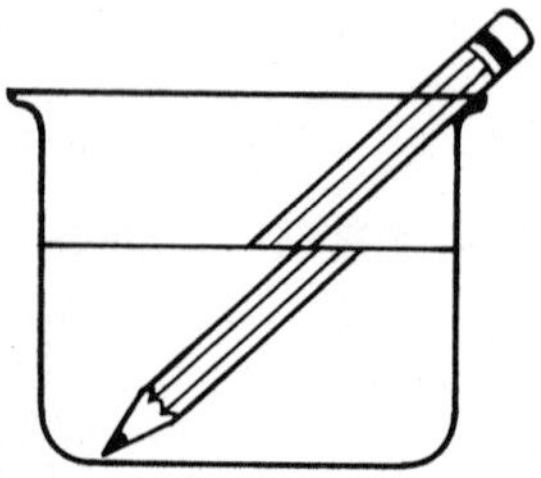

C

B

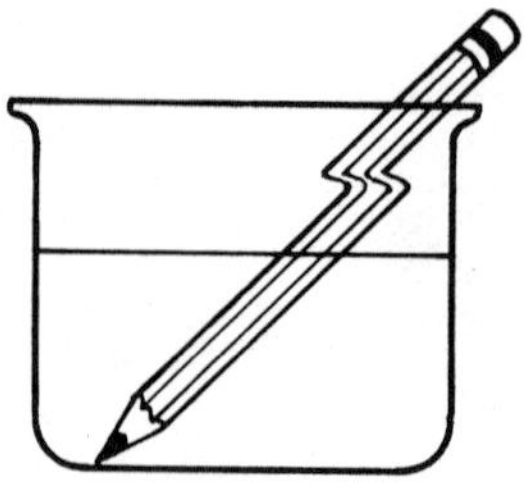

D

3. c (1)

3. Look at the pictures above. Which picture shows how a pencil looks when it is in water? **3.** ______

Name________________________________Date____________

4. Which sentence is *not* true? **4.** _____ **4.** b (2)

a. A lens can be curved on one side and flat on one side.

b. A lens can be flat on both sides.

c. A lens can be made of glass.

d. A lens can be made of plastic.

5. When light passes through a lens, it **5.** _____ **5.** c (2)

a. changes color. **c.** bends.

b. reflects back. **d.** becomes dim.

6. The point where light beams meet after they pass through a lens is called the **6.** _____ **6.** d (2)

a. mirror. **c.** reflection.

b. curve. **d.** focal point.

7. An instrument that uses lenses to magnify objects that are very faraway is the **7.** _____ **7.** b (3)

a. magnifying glass. **c.** microscope.

b. telescope. **d.** hand lens.

8. We can see an insect much larger than it really is if we look through **8.** _____ **8.** a (3)

a. a microscope. **c.** eyeglasses.

b. a telescope. **d.** a glass of water.

9. Lenses in eyeglasses help the eyes to **9.** _____ **9.** b (3)

a. reflect light. **c.** keep light beams apart.

b. focus light. **d.** all of the above.

10. Isaac Newton showed that white light **10.** _____ **10.** b (4)

a. can be split into three colors.

b. can be split into seven colors.

c. can be split into hundreds of colors.

d. cannot be split into any colors.

11. How does a prism separate colors? **11.** _____ **11.** a (4)

a. It bends each color a different amount.

b. It bends each color the same amount.

c. It only bends violet.

d. It only bends colors when they enter the prism.

Name______________________________Date__________

12. a (4) **12.** A rainbow can form when sunlight **12.** ______

a. strikes drops of water in the air.

b. reflects off a pond.

c. shines on a mirror.

d. strikes a rough surface.

13. a (5) **13.** Which of the following absorbs all colors except red? **13.** ______

a. an apple **c.** grass

b. an egg **d.** a raindrop

14. b (5) **14.** A blue-tinted glass **14.** ______

a. absorbs blue light. **c.** stops blue light.

b. lets blue light pass through. **d.** is a prism.

15. d (5) **15.** When all the colors of the spectrum are reflected, an object will look **15.** ______

a. blue. **c.** black.

b. red. **d.** white.

16. a (5) **16.** The primary colors of light are **16.** ______

a. red, green, blue. **c.** red, green, yellow.

b. red, yellow, blue. **d.** blue, green, yellow.

Name ______________________ Date ______________

Light Sources

SKILL WORKSHEET

A. Tell if each of the objects below (a) is a light source, or (b) reflects lights.

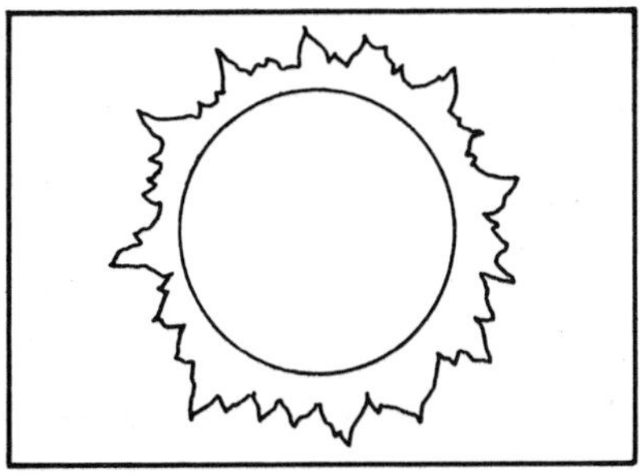
______

______

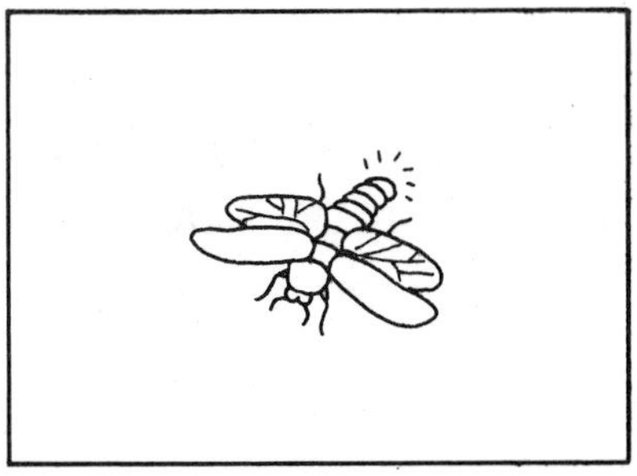
______

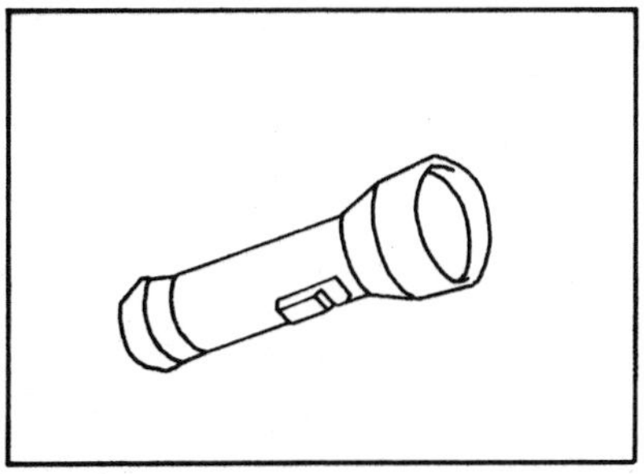
______

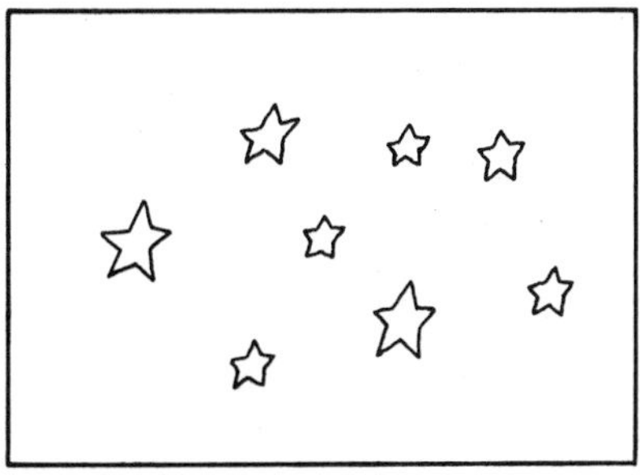
______

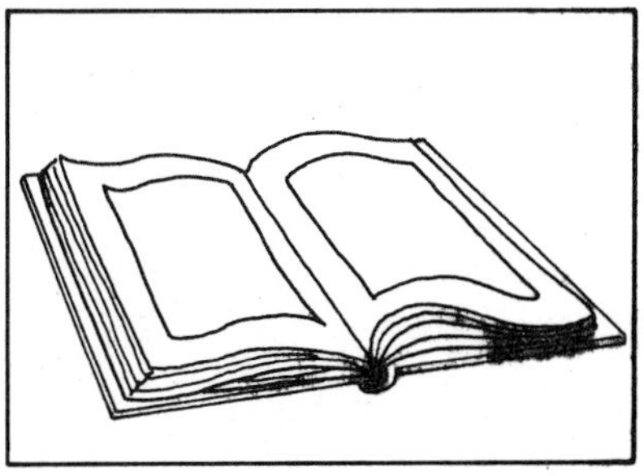
______

B. Which of the flashlights shown below would shine the brightest spot of light on the screen? ______
Which spot of light would be the largest? ______

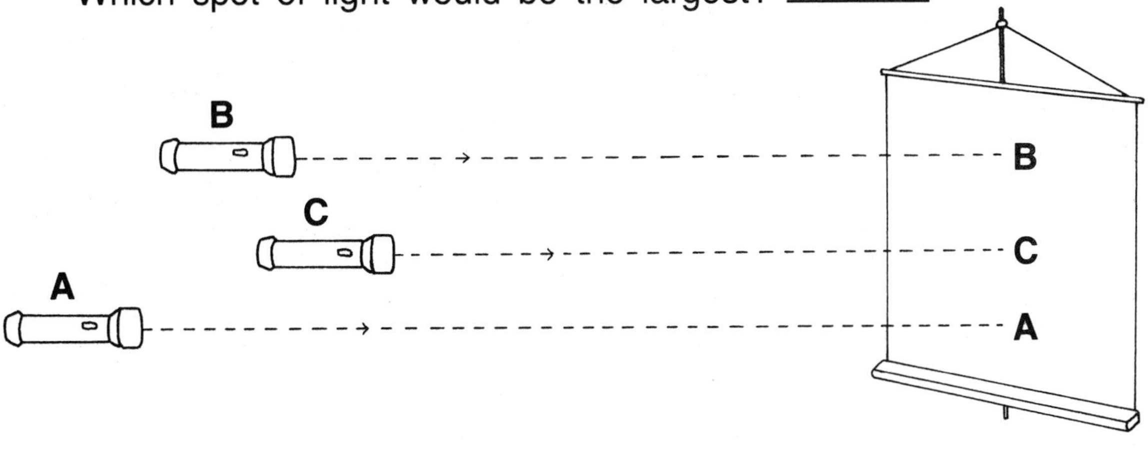

Name________________________________ Date______________

Spreading Light

AT HOME WORKSHEET

You have learned that stars are sources of light. In this at-home activity, you will observe how they differ in brightness due to their size or distance from earth.

A. Use the star map below to find the Big Dipper.
B. Mark the brightest and dimmest stars in the Big Dipper on the map.

Refer to EXTENSION on page T-72

Name ______________________________ Date ________________

When Light Strikes

ACTIVITY WORKSHEET

You can tell whether an object is transparent, translucent, or opaque by the type of shadow it casts. A transparent object casts no shadow. Light passes right through it. An opaque object casts a sharp shadow. All the light is blocked by the object. A translucent object casts a blurred shadow. Some of the light is blocked or scattered as it passes through.

A. Gather these materials: water, set of 4 clear glasses, brown wrapping paper, waxed paper, blue food coloring, flashlight.

B. Label the glasses 1–4. Leave glass 1 empty. Add water and blue coloring to glass 2. Wrap the brown paper around glass 3. Wrap the waxed paper around glass 4.

C. Shine the flashlight beam at each glass. Observe what kind of shadow forms. Record your observations in the chart below.

Glass	Shadow Formed	Object Is
1.		
2.		
3.		
4.		

D. Gather other materials from around your home. Repeat step C and observe the results.

Name ______________________ Date __________

Light Beams and Shadows

SKILL WORKSHEET

Only some of the letters that make up the science words below are in the spotlight. The others are in shadow. Fill in the letters in the shadows to complete each word. Then place the number of each word next to its definition.

1. L _ _ _ _   _ O _ _ C _
2. _ E _ L _ _ T _ _ N _
3. S _ _ _ O _
4. _ A _ T _ _ _ _ E
5. _ _ V _ _
6. T _ _ _ S _ _ R _ _ T
7. _ R _ _ _ L _ _ E _ _
8. O _ _ Q _ _

____ a. The bouncing back of light
____ b. A very small piece of matter
____ c. An object that produces light
____ d. A movement like a swell of water
____ e. A material that blocks light
____ f. The dark area caused when an object blocks light
____ g. A material that blurs light as it passes through
____ h. A material through which light can pass

Name ______________________________ Date ______________

Bouncing Light

SKILL WORKSHEET

A. Complete each drawing below to show the path of light after it is reflected.

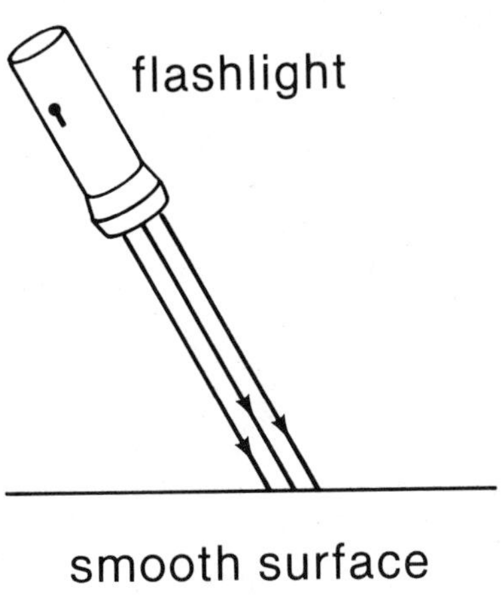

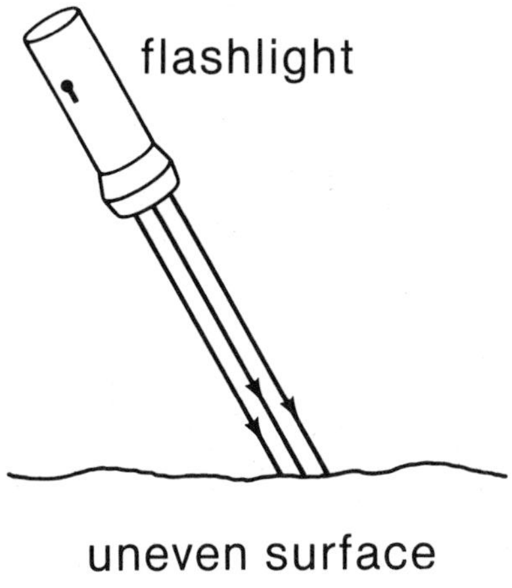

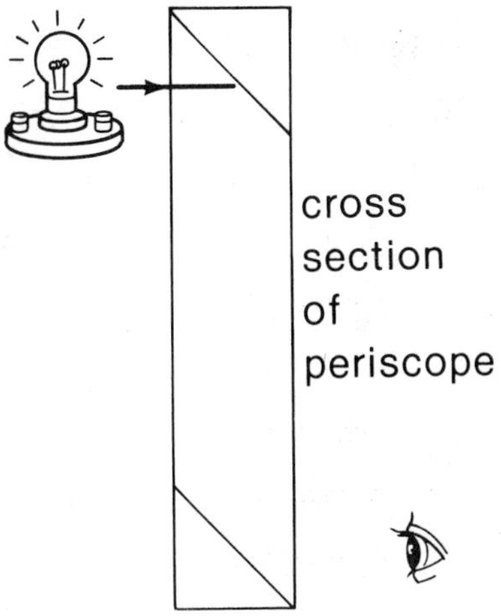

B. Tell whether the person's reflection in each mirror would be larger, smaller, or the same size. Label each mirror to tell whether it is flat, concave, or convex.

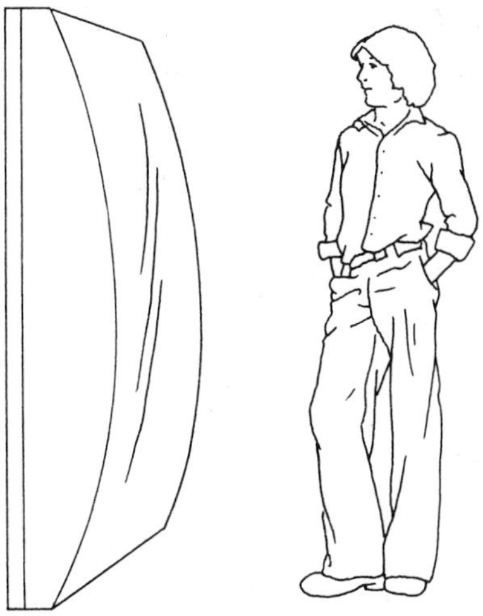

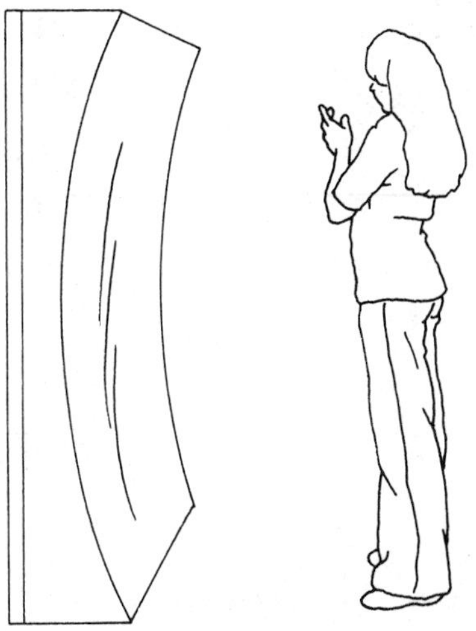

______________________ ______________________ ______________________

______________________ ______________________ ______________________

Name ______________________ Date ____________

Reflecting Light

AT HOME WORKSHEET

You are learning how light is reflected by mirrors. In this at-home activity, you will observe the images formed by two mirrors. SAFETY TIP: USE EXTRA CARE WHEN HANDLING MIRRORS. THIS ACTIVITY SHOULD BE SUPERVISED BY AN ADULT.

A. Gather these materials: 2 mirrors, a coin, and tape.

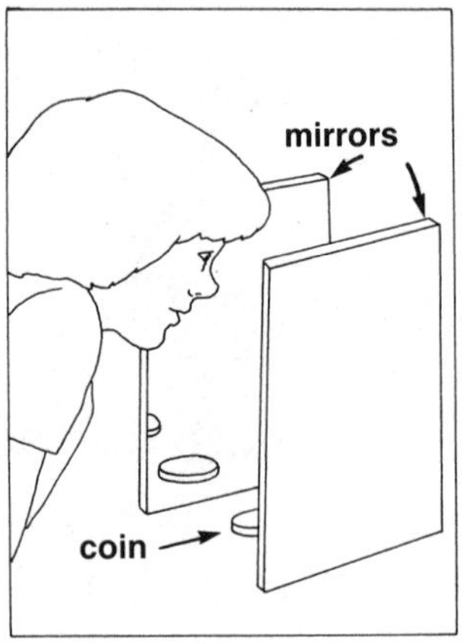

B. Stand the two mirrors on edge facing each other. Place the coin between the mirrors. Look in one mirror. Then look in the other mirror.

1. How many images did you see in the mirror?

____

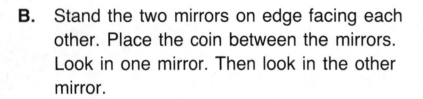

C. Hinge the two mirrors together with a piece of tape. Set them on edge at an angle to each other. Place a coin between the two mirrors. Observe the number of images formed as you increase and decrease the angle between the mirrors.

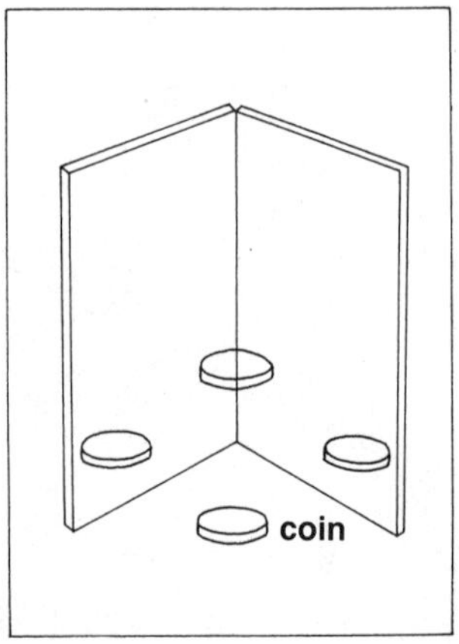

2. How many images did you see?

____

3. What happened as you increased the angle?

____

____

Name ______________________ Date ______________

Bouncing Light

ACTIVITY WORKSHEET

You can make a simple camera. It is called a pinhole camera. You can used the camera to learn more about light.

A. Gather these materials: round cereal box, tissue paper, rubber band, straight pin, light bulb.

B. Take the top off the box. Cover the end of the box with tissue paper. Stretch the tissue paper across the top. Fasten it with a rubber band.

C. Use the pin to make a small hole in the other end of the box. You now have a pinhole camera. When you look at something through the pinhole, an image will form on the tissue.

D. Darken the room. Light the bulb. Point the pinhole end of the camera toward the light bulb. Look through the tissue end of the camera.

1. What do you see when you look through the tissue?

____

2. What does the image on the tissue look like?

____

E. Point the pinhole camera out the window. Look through the tissue end of the camera.

3. How do the images you see appear on the tissue?

____

F. Go to the library. Find a book about cameras. Try to find out why the images formed are upside down.

Name______________________________ Date________________

Bending Light and Colors

SKILL WORKSHEET

A. Write the name of each of the instruments shown below. Tell whether it makes objects look larger or closer.

B. Complete the drawing below.

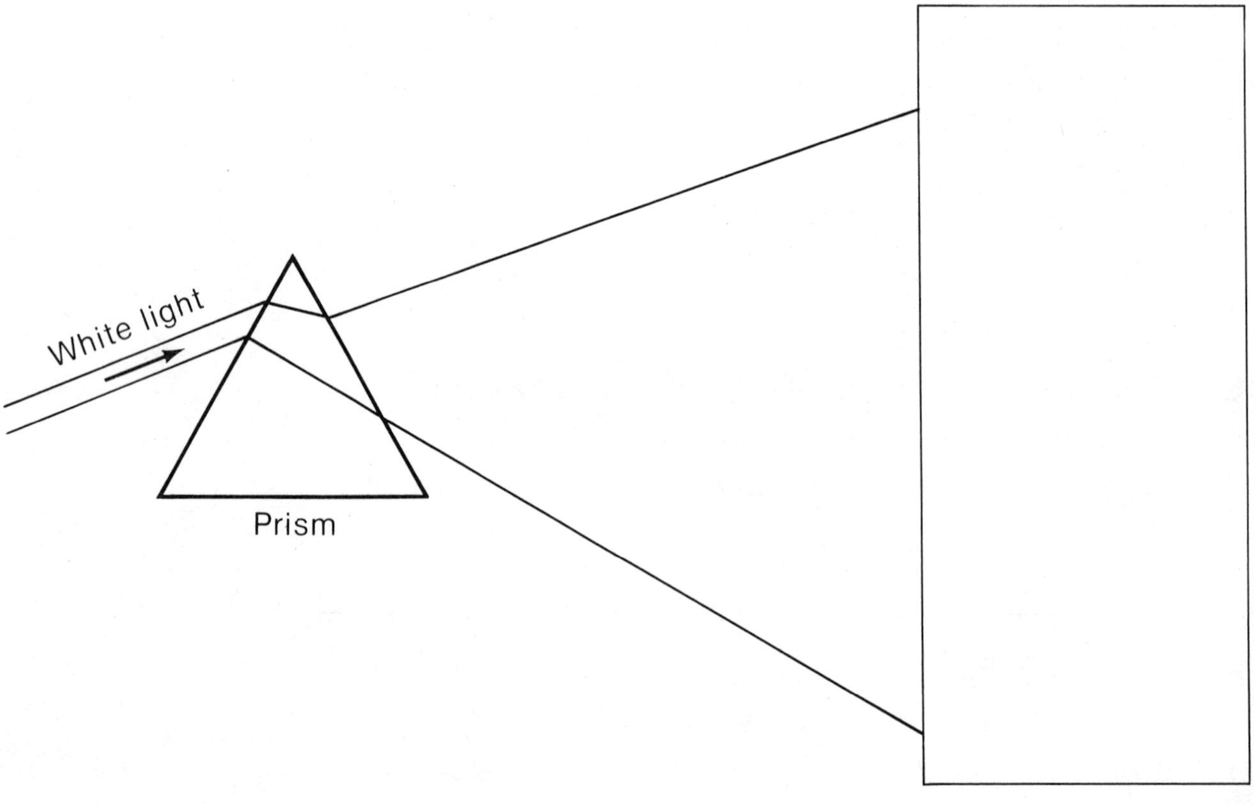

Name ______________________ Date ______________

Seeing Colors

ACTIVITY WORKSHEET

You can make a color wheel to learn more about how we see color.

A. Gather these materials: 9-cm cardboard circle; 1.5 m (5 ft.) of string; red, green, and blue crayons.

B. Divide the circle into three equal section as shown in the drawing.

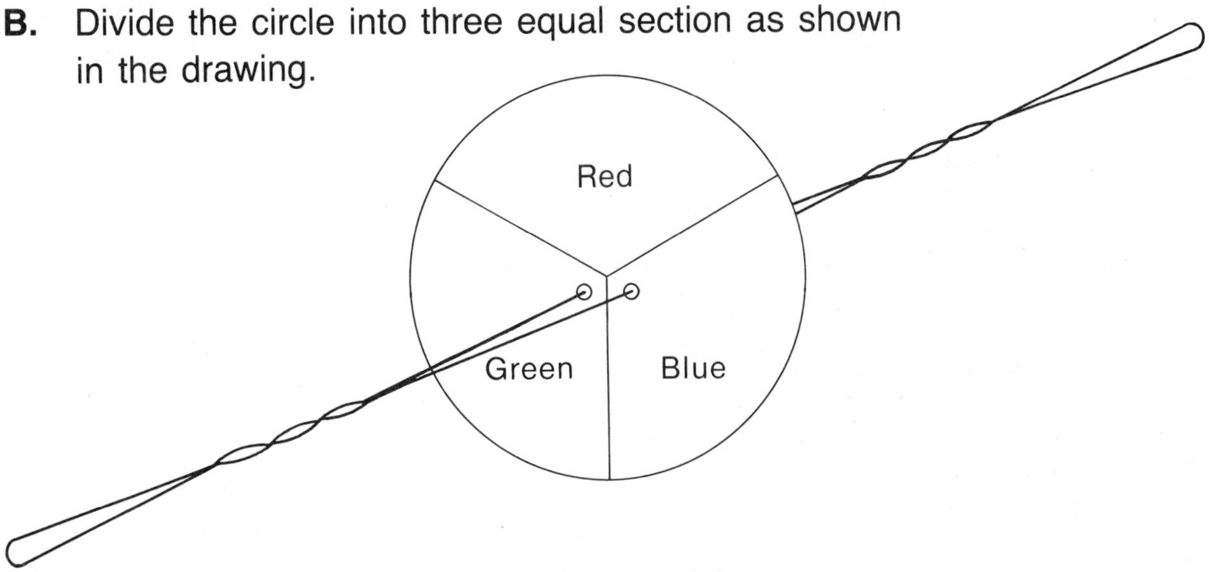

C. Using the crayons, color one section red, the second blue, and the third green.

D. Punch two small holes in the wheel about 3 mm (0.1 in.) on each side of the center. See the drawing.

E. Pass the string through two holes as shown. Tie the ends.

F. Turn the wheel to twist the string. You can now spin the wheel by pulling the string in and out. (This may take some practice.)

1. What happens to the colors as the wheel spins?

____

2. What color do you see?

____

Name ______________________ Date ____________

Bending Light and Colors

SKILL WORKSHEET

Rearrange the letters below to make science words.
Match the number of each word to its definition.

1. _ _ _ _ _ _
   G E M I A R
2. _ _ _ _
   S L N E
3. _ _ _ _ _ _ _ _ _ _   _ _ _ _ _
   F I M A N G Y N I G   L A S G S
4. _ _ _ _ _ _ _ _ _ _
   P O M I S R O C C E
5. _ _ _ _ _ _ _ _ _
   S L E T E P O C E
6. _ _ _ _ _
   M I R S P
7. _ _ _ _ _ _ _ _
   E C S T U R M P
8. _ _ _ _ _ _
   B O B R A S

___ **a.** A piece of curved glass that bends light

___ **b.** A piece of glass that bends light causing colors to form

___ **c.** The group of seven colors that make up white light

___ **d.** An instrument that makes faraway things look closer

___ **e.** A lens used to make things look larger

___ **f.** Something we see that is really not there

___ **g.** An instrument that makes small things look larger

___ **h.** To take in and hold light

Name______________________________ Date______________

Light Sources

CLASSIFYING, COMPARING AND CONTRASTING, FINDING CAUSE AND EFFECT **SKILL WORKSHEET**

A. Tell if each of the objects below (a) is a light source, or (b) reflects lights.

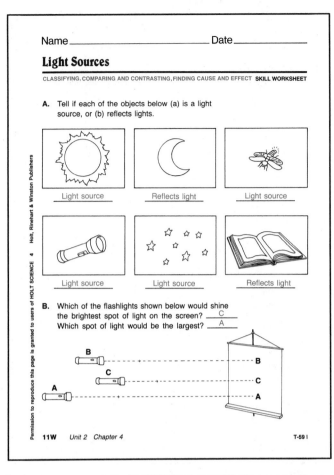

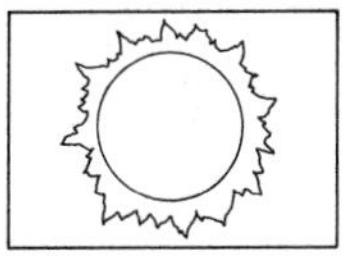

Light source

Reflects light

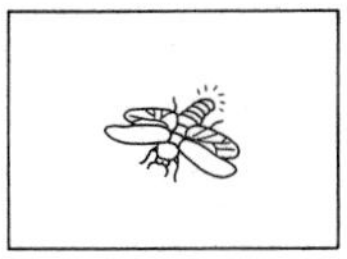

Light source

Light source

Light source

Reflects light

B. Which of the flashlights shown below would shine the brightest spot of light on the screen? C
Which spot of light would be the largest? A

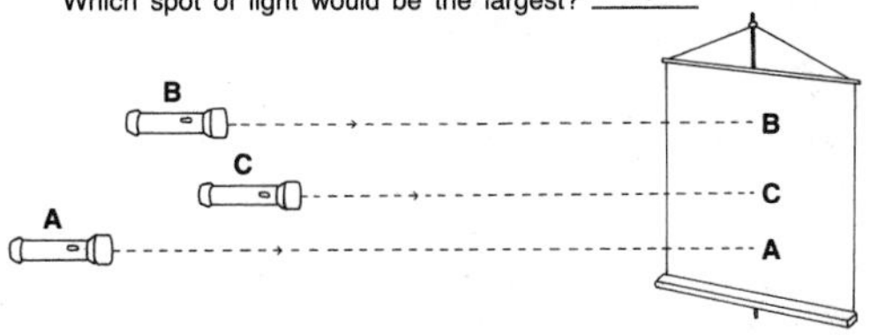

Name______________________________ Date______________

Spreading Light

AT HOME WORKSHEET

You have learned that stars are sources of light. In this at-home activity, you will observe how they differ in brightness due to their size or distance from earth.

A. Use the star map below to find the Big Dipper.
B. Mark the brightest and dimmest stars in the Big Dipper on the map.

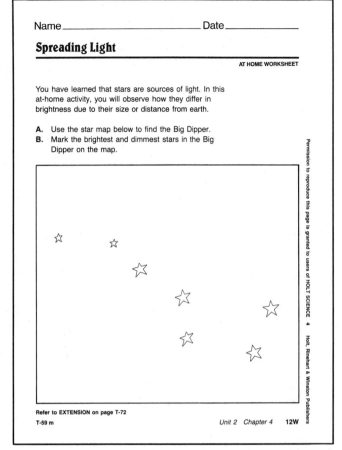

Refer to EXTENSION on page T-72

Name______________________________ Date______________

When Light Strikes

ACTIVITY WORKSHEET

You can tell whether an object is transparent, translucent, or opaque by the type of shadow it casts. A transparent object casts no shadow. Light passes right through it. An opaque object casts a sharp shadow. All the light is blocked by the object. A translucent object casts a blurred shadow. Some of the light is blocked or scattered as it passes through.

A. Gather these materials: water, set of 4 clear glasses, brown wrapping paper, waxed paper, blue food coloring, flashlight.
B. Label the glasses 1–4. Leave glass 1 empty. Add water and blue coloring to glass 2. Wrap the brown paper around glass 3. Wrap the waxed paper around glass 4.
C. Shine the flashlight beam at each glass. Observe what kind of shadow forms. Record your observations in the chart below.

Glass	Shadow Formed	Object Is
1.	no	transparent
2.	blurred	translucent
3.	sharp	opaque
4.	blurred	translucent

D. Gather other materials from around your home. Repeat step C and observe the results.

Name______________________________ Date______________

Light Beams and Shadows

BUILDING SCIENCE VOCABULARY **SKILL WORKSHEET**

Only some of the letters that make up the science words below are in the spotlight. The others are in shadow. Fill in the letters in the shadows to complete each word. Then place the number of each word next to its definition.

1. L I G H T S O U R C E
2. R E F L E C T I O N S
3. S H A D O W
4. P A R T I C L E
5. W A V E S
6. T R A N S P A R E N T
7. T R A N S L U C E N T
8. O P A Q U E

2 **a.** The bouncing back of light
4 **b.** A very small piece of matter
1 **c.** An object that produces light
5 **d.** A movement like a swell of water
8 **e.** A material that blocks light
3 **f.** The dark area causes when an object blocks light
7 **g.** A material that blurs light as it passes through
6 **h.** A material through which light can pass

Name________________________ Date____________

Bouncing Light

FINDING CAUSE AND EFFECT, CLASSIFYING — SKILL WORKSHEET

A. Complete each drawing below to show the path of light after it is reflected.

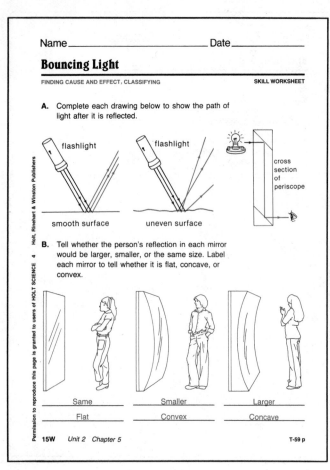

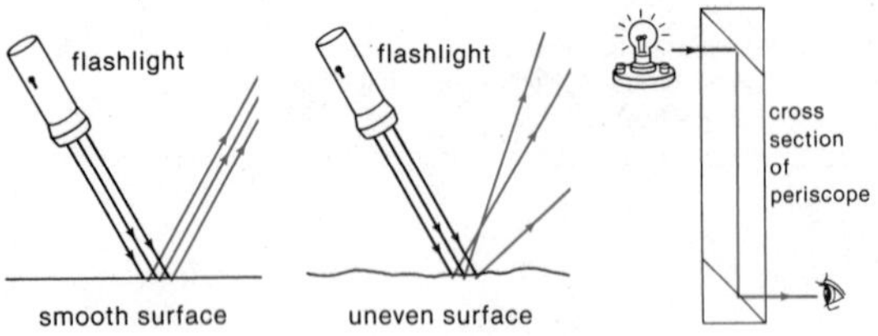

B. Tell whether the person's reflection in each mirror would be larger, smaller, or the same size. Label each mirror to tell whether it is flat, concave, or convex.

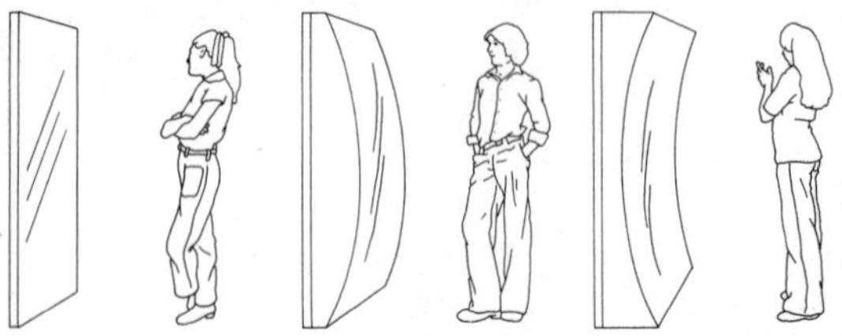

Same	Smaller	Larger
Flat	Convex	Concave

Name________________________ Date____________

Reflecting Light

AT HOME WORKSHEET

You are learning how light is reflected by mirrors. In this at home activity, you will observe the images formed by two mirrors. SAFETY TIP: USE EXTRA CARE WHEN HANDLING MIRRORS. THIS ACTIVITY SHOULD BE SUPERVISED BY AN ADULT.

A. Gather these materials: 2 mirrors, a coin, and tape.

B. Stand the two mirrors on edge facing each other. Place the coin between the mirrors. Look in one mirror. Then look in the other mirror.

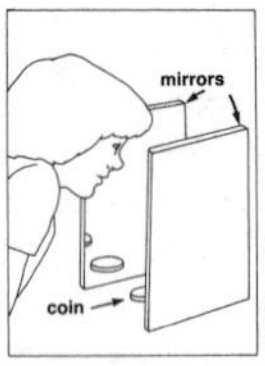

1. How many images did you see in the mirror?

   They will see a series of images.

C. Hinge the two mirrors together with a piece of tape. Set them on edge at an angle to each other. Place a coin between the two mirrors. Observe the number of images formed as you increase and decrease the angle between the mirrors.

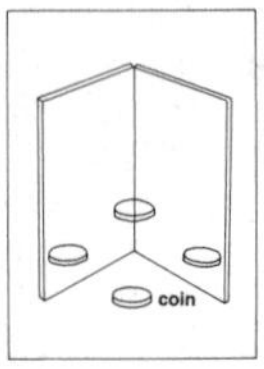

2. How many images did you see?

   Answers will vary depending on the angle.

3. What happened as you increased the angle?

   The number of images decreased as the angle got larger.

Name________________________ Date____________

Bouncing Light

ACTIVITY WORKSHEET

You can make a simple camera. It is called a pinhole camera. You can used the camera to learn more about light.

A. Gather these materials: round cereal box, tissue paper, rubber band, straight pin, light bulb.

B. Take the top off the box. Cover the end of the box with tissue paper. Stretch the tissue paper across the top. Fasten it with a rubber band.

C. Use the pin to make a small hole in the other end of the box. You now have a pinhole camera. When you look at something through the pinhole, an image will form on the tissue.

D. Darken the room. Light the bulb. Point the pinhole end of the camera toward the light bulb. Look through the tissue end of the camera.

1. What do you see when you look through the tissue?

   An image of the light bulb

2. What does the image on the tissue look like?

   It is upside down.

E. Point the pinhole camera out the window. Look through the tissue end of the camera.

3. How do the images you see appear on the tissue?

   They are upside down.

F. Go to the library. Find a book about cameras. Try to find out why the images formed are upside down.

Name________________________ Date____________

Bending Light and Colors

CLASSIFYING, FINDING CAUSE AND EFFECT — SKILL WORKSHEET

A. Write the name of each of the instruments shown below. Tell whether it makes objects look larger or closer.

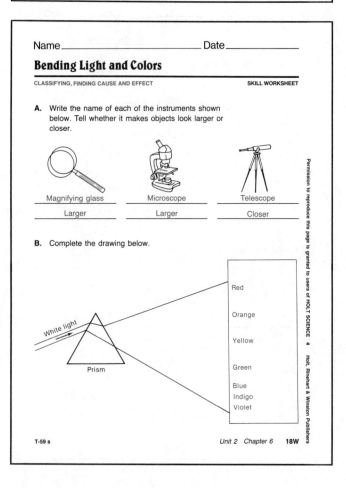

Magnifying glass	Microscope	Telescope
Larger	Larger	Closer

B. Complete the drawing below.

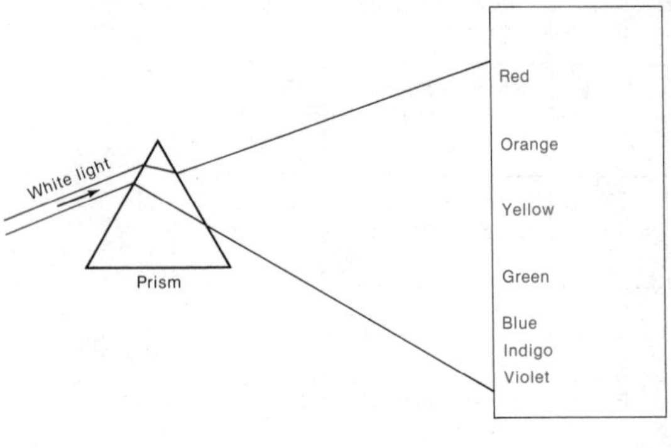

Name________________________ Date______________

Seeing Colors

ACTIVITY WORKSHEET

You can make a color wheel to learn more about how we see color.

A. Gather these materials: 9-cm cardboard circle; 1.5 m (5 ft.) of string; red, green, and blue crayons.

B. Divide the circle into three equal section as shown in the drawing.

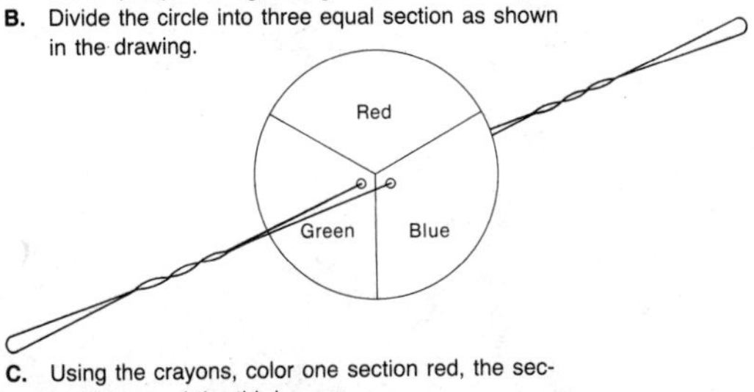

C. Using the crayons, color one section red, the second blue, and the third green.

D. Punch two small holes in the wheel about 3 mm (0.1 in.) on each side of the center. See the drawing.

E. Pass the string through two holes as shown. Tie the ends.

F. Turn the wheel to twist the string. You can now spin the wheel by pulling the string in and out. (This may take some practice.)

1. What happens to the colors as the wheel spins?

   They seem to blur and blend together.

2. What color do you see?

   White

Name________________________ Date______________

Bending Light and Colors

BUILDING SCIENCE VOCABULARY — SKILL WORKSHEET

Rearrange the letters below to make science words. Match the number of each word to its definition.

1. M I R A G E
   G E M I A R
2. L E N S
   S L N E
3. M A G N I F Y I N G G L A S S
   F I M A N G Y N I G L A S G S
4. M I C R O S C O P E
   P O M I S R O C C E
5. T E L E S C O P E
   S L E T E P O C E
6. P R I S M
   M I R S P
7. S P E C T R U M
   E C S T U R M P
8. A B S O R B
   B O B R A S

_2_ **a.** A piece of curved glass that bends light

_6_ **b.** A piece of glass that bends light causing colors to form

_7_ **c.** The group of seven colors that make up white light

_5_ **d.** An instrument that makes faraway things look closer

_3_ **e.** A lens used to make things look larger

_1_ **f.** Something we see that is really not there

_4_ **g.** An instrument that makes small things look larger

_8_ **h.** To take in and hold light

UNIT OVERVIEW

This is a physical science unit on light. Light is a form of energy. The sun is visible because it emits light energy. Most objects need reflected light to be visible. Light passes through some objects; it is blurred or blocked by others. When light is blocked, a shadow is formed. The farther light travels from its source, the more it spreads and dims.

When a beam of light falls upon a reflecting surface, the beam is reflected so that its incoming angle equals its returning angle. Light reflects better off a smooth surface than a rough one. Mirrors can be used to change the direction of light. A curved mirror can be thought of as a series of flat mirrors. It can be used to focus light to a point.

When light passes from one material to the next at an angle, it is bent or refracted because its velocity changes. A lens is a curved piece of transparent material that refracts light passing through it. Lenses can either be convex (curving out) or concave (curving in). Light passing through a prism is refracted and is broken up into a spectrum.

Exceptional Student IEP Unit Goal

At the end of this unit, the student will define *light source*, *reflection*, *transparent*, *mirage*, and *periscope*.

LIGHT

UNIT OPENER

This photo shows the fireworks display for the Thomas Jefferson exhibit at the National Gallery of Art in Washington, D.C., during June of 1976. The following questions can be asked as motivation: What is making these lights in the sky? *The fireworks blowing up.* Why are there different colors? *Fireworks are made of different chemicals. When they burn, they give off different colored lights.* Would the light and colors be so bright if the picture were taken from farther away? *No, the light would spread out and dim.*

UNIT 2

LEARNING CENTER

A possible title for a Learning Center Unit could be "Bouncing, Bending, and Blocking Light." Photos of various light sources, mirrors, lenses, and prisms can be used to create displays. You may wish to create a file for copies of the worksheet masters and Extensions, which students can work on independently.

The following Extensions are especially suitable for the Learning Center. The materials for these Extensions should be available in the Learning Center: casting shadows in a pin circle, p. T-69 (1 sq ft of corrugated cardboard, 10 common pins, flashlight, compass); observing light spread out, p. T-73 (flashlight, graph paper); making a kaleidoscope, p. T-79 (2 10 cm x 3 cm mirrors, piece of cardboard); observing reflected light, p. T-84 (comb, mirror, cardboard, light source); the reappearing nickel, p. T-93 (nickel, opaque bowl or cup, water); colored afterimage, p. T-107 (white paper, crayons).

In addition, an index file of suggested research topics could be set up in the Learning Center, using the following Extensions: lightning bugs, p. T-65; speed of light and other things, p. T-68; vocabulary words for light, p. T-77; Mt. Palomar telescope, p. T-89; optics vocabulary, p. T-91; space telescope, p. T-90; speed of light, p. T-95; van Leeuwenhoek and Galileo, p. T-109; careers, p. T-111.

Chapter Objectives

1. Distinguish between objects that are light sources and those that are not.
2. Describe how a shadow is formed.
3. Describe the way light travels away from its source.
4. Describe how light can act like a particle or a wave.
5. Compare the way light behaves when it hits transparent, translucent, and opaque objects.

SECTION BACKGROUND

Light is a form of energy that is emitted by the sun and other stars in great amounts, and by other luminous objects, such as light bulbs and fireflies, in lesser amounts. Self-luminous objects are directly visible, but all other objects in the universe need light from a luminous source in order to be seen. When light falls on nonluminous objects, the light is reflected to our eyes. Light can also be transmitted through the object or absorbed by it.

MATERIALS

flashlight, 2 used chalkboard erasers, white index card

CHAPTER 4

LIGHT BEAMS AND SHADOWS

4-1. Light Sources

Pretend that you are sitting around an open fire on a camping trip. The moving flames cast shadows that dance all around you. The shadows seem spooky. There is another kind of light shown in the picture. What is the source of this

BASIC TEACHING PLAN

MOTIVATION

You might start the unit by darkening the room. Try to shut out all light. Light a single candle in the center of the room. Let the students look at the light. After a few minutes, ask the students to make a list of things they observed about the candle and the light. You might write these on the chalkboard.

Text Questions—What is the source of this light? *The stars.*

Exceptional Student IEP Chapter Goal

At the end of this chapter, the student will state the difference between opaque, transparent, and translucent materials.

light? When you finish this section, you should be able to:

- ☐ **A.** Identify objects that are light sources.
- ☐ **B.** Explain how we see objects that do not give off their own light.

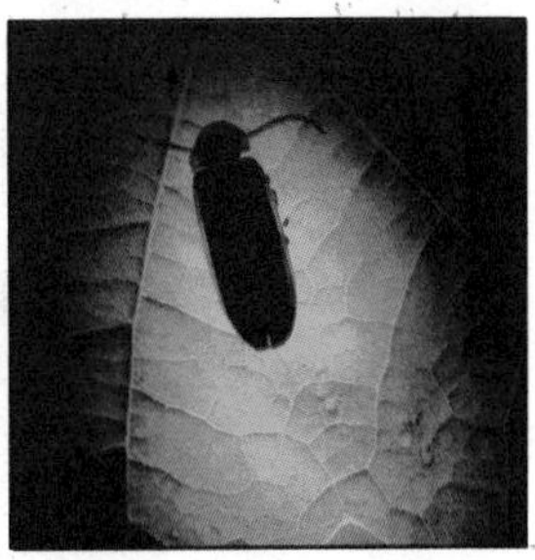

1 What do fireflies, candles, the sun, light bulbs, and fireworks have in common? The answer is that they all give off light. Each of these objects, even the firefly, has the ability to make light. We call objects such as these **light sources**. Visible light is a kind of energy that we are able to see with our eyes. *Light sources* help us see things that do not give off their own light. Without them, we would live in a completely dark world.

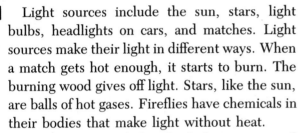

Light sources: Objects that produce light.

2 Light sources include the sun, stars, light bulbs, headlights on cars, and matches. Light sources make their light in different ways. When a match gets hot enough, it starts to burn. The burning wood gives off light. Stars, like the sun, are balls of hot gases. Fireflies have chemicals in their bodies that make light without heat.

Light energy includes the light you see and
3 also light you can't see. Have you heard of X rays, radio waves, and microwaves? These are forms of light that our eyes are not able to sense. When you have an X ray taken of a broken bone, the doctor shines a form of light at you. X rays are able to pass through your body and hit a piece of film. A picture of your bones appears on the film.

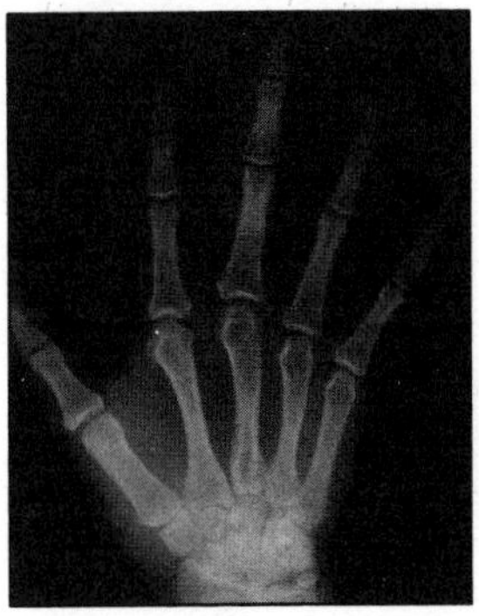

EXTENSIONS

Reinforcement

Science Skills—Classifying

The students can prepare a list of objects that they consider to be emitters of light. After they have created the list, review it and identify objects that do not give off their own light (the moon, roadside reflectors, and reflective paints). Students can then examine the list of luminous objects and group them according to whether their light is due to sunlight, batteries, electricity, heat, radioactivity, or chemicals.

DEVELOPMENT

1 Skill Development—Objects will be *classified* according to their luminous or nonluminous quality.

2 Teaching Tips—You might have a variety of objects on hand for your students to look at. Some should be luminous objects, such as a candle, light bulb, or a flashlight; and others should be nonluminous, such as reflector, paper, or glass.

3 Teaching Tips—Most of your students should be familiar with X rays and microwave ovens. An X ray is a form of energy of very short wavelength that can penetrate solid substances. X rays are principally used to study internal body structures. Ask your local hospital if you can borrow some X-ray photographs to show your students. Visible light is only one part of the electromagnetic spectrum. All the various forms of "light" energy are transmitted at the same speed but vary in wavelength.

Exceptional Student

Visually Impaired

The teacher should be aware that some visually impaired students are only able to see patterns of light and dark. Depending on the severity of the impairment, some Activities in this chapter may not be appropriate for the visually impaired student.

EXTENSIONS

Enrichment
Science Skills—Observing

To demonstrate both a light source and an object that reflects light, gather these materials: a flashlight, a mirror, and a shoe box.

A. Set the shoe box on edge so that the open side points away from the class.

B. Hide a lighted flashlight behind the shoe box so that its beam is also pointed away from the class.

C. Hold the mirror so that it reflects the beam to various points in the room.

D. Have the students observe the difference between a light source and an object that reflects light.

It's true that you can do many things. But no matter how hard you try, you cannot give off visible light. The book you are reading does not give off light. Then, how can other people see you? How can you see the pages of this book? Light sources, like the sun or a light bulb, make objects visible. Let's see how this happens.

When light hits an object like this book, some of it bounces off. The light is bounced off the book to your eyes. This is called **reflection**. In this way, we are able to see objects that do not give off their own light. Imagine there are no windows in the room in the picture. Would the girl be able to see objects in the room if the light went out? 4

Reflection: The bouncing back of light.

We see most objects by *reflected* light. The 5
moon is a good example. On some nights, the moon seems to be shining very brightly. Is it 6
giving off its own light? The moon reflects light from the sun.

64

4 Text Questions—Would the girl be able to see objects in the room if the light went out? *No.*

5 Skill Development—Students *compare and contrast* objects that give off their own light with those that reflect light. Use the moon and the sun as examples. The sun gives off light. The moon reflects the sun's light to the earth.

6 Text Questions—Is it giving off its own light? *No, the moon shines because the light from the sun bounces off it to our eyes on earth.*

ACTIVITY

Can we see a light beam?

A. Gather these materials: a flashlight and 2 used chalkboard erasers.

B. Work with a partner. Darken the room. Turn the flashlight on and aim it across the room.

1. Can you see the light beam?

C. Have your partner walk along the path of the light. Have your partner gently tap 2 chalkboard erasers together above the light beam.

2. What do you see now?
3. How did the chalk dust help you see the beam of light?
4. Can light be seen when there is nothing to reflect it?

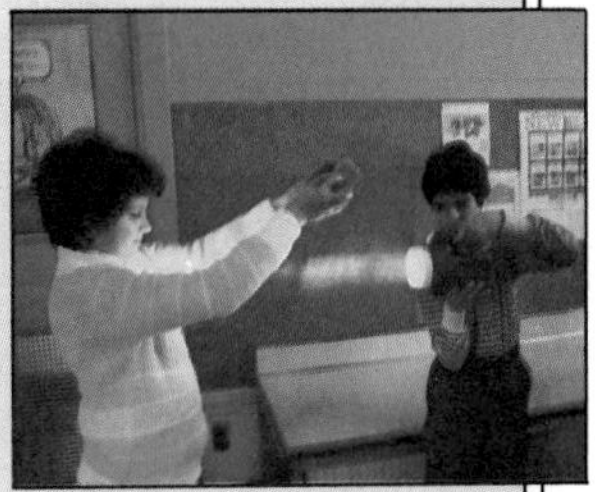

Section Review

Main Ideas: Light is a form of energy. Light sources are objects that make their own light.

Questions: Answer in complete sentences.

1. Make a chart with the words "Light Source" and "Reflector of Light" at the top. List five objects that belong in each group.
2. How is a light source different from an object that reflects light?
3. The earth and Mars are planets. A planet does not give off its own light. Why can we see planets?

EXTENSIONS

Enrichment

Research—Library

Fireflies or "lightning bugs" are light-producing beetles that are found in moist habitats in tropical or temperate climates. These insects contain chemicals called luciferins that interact with enzymes called luciferases to produce light. This change of chemical into light energy is called bioluminescence, and is characteristic of certain species of bacteria, fungi, protozoa, invertebrates, and fish. Students could research these fascinating organisms and their distinctive ability to be a light source.

ACTIVITY

Skill Development—*Observing*

Teaching Tips—This Activity makes a very nice demonstration. Have several of the students help you with it. Be sure to have the room dark.

Answers to Questions—1. The light beam should not be visible. If there is dust in the air, it will be. **2.** The beam of light is visible. **3.** The light bounces off the particles of chalk dust. **4.** No, light sources bounce their light off nonluminous objects to make those objects visible.

SECTION REVIEW

Answers to Questions

1. Light source: match, star, light bulb. Reflector: coin, leaf, book.
2. A light source gives off its own light; an object that reflects light bounces light off it so that it is visible to us.
3. Planets reflect the light of the sun.

SECTION BACKGROUND

Light travels outward in all directions from its source. It travels in straight lines at a velocity of 300,000 kps (186,000 mps). The formation of shadows, our ability to aim a ball and hit the target, and the fact that we cannot see around corners are all evidence of the straight path in which light travels. The speed of light in a vacuum is one of the most important constants in nature. Astronomers use the speed of light to measure distances to stars and galaxies. The unit they use is the light year. A light year is the distance light travels in 1 year. The speed of light is also the highest possible speed in nature.

MATERIALS

4 index cards, hole punch, clay, light source

4-2. Straight Lines

Can you imagine riding on a beam of light? It sounds like a crazy idea, doesn't it? Albert Einstein (**ine**-stine), a famous scientist, wondered what this would be like. He often used his imagination to try to find answers to his questions. Light travels very fast. If you could travel around the earth at the speed of light, you would finish seven orbits in only 1 second! If you went on a round trip to the sun on a beam of light, it would take only 17 minutes. In the space shuttle, it would take you 155 days! When you finish this section, you should be able to:

☐ **A.** Compare the speed of light with the speeds of other objects.

☐ **B.** Describe how shadows are formed.

BASIC TEACHING PLAN

MOTIVATION

Take the students on an imaginary ride on a beam of light by turning on a slide projector and clapping two used chalkboard erasers over the light. Have the students look at the beam and tell them it goes off into space for a long way. Tell them to close their eyes and imagine sitting on the beam of light, which is traveling very fast. After a minute or two, have the students open their eyes and tell about their experience of traveling as fast as light. Discuss the speed of light by comparing it to the speed of other things. Here are some speeds you can present for comparison: Apollo spaceship to the Moon—7 mps; car traveling 60 mph—1/60 mps; jet airplane—1/10 mps.

1 Light travels very fast. Blink your eyes. You probably blink your eyes once in a second. During the time that it takes you to blink once, a beam of light can travel 186,000 miles! To understand how fast light travels, consider the following example. A scientist can bounce a light beam off the moon and have it come back to earth. The round trip for the light beam would take less than 3 seconds! A trip to the moon and back in a rocket would take several days.

Light travels in straight lines. How do we know this? First, we cannot see "around the corner" of an object. Second, when light hits an object, the object casts a sharp **shadow**. A *shadow* is an area of darkness formed when light is blocked by an object. Shadows help us understand that light travels in straight lines. Let's look at some examples.

Shadow: The dark area caused when an object blocks light.

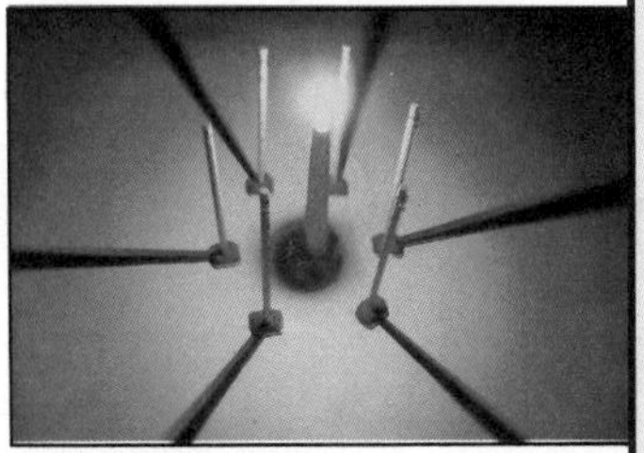

3 Look at the picture of the candle and the shadows. What do you see that shows that light travels in straight lines? How would it look if the light from the candle curved around the pencils? The shadows would disappear. Since there are shadows, the light must be traveling in straight lines.

4 Look at the shadows formed when a bright light hits these objects. The light that hits the object is blocked. Since the shadow is the same shape as the object, the light must be traveling in straight lines. If it were not, the shadows would not be the same shape as each object. The shadows would be blurred around the edges.

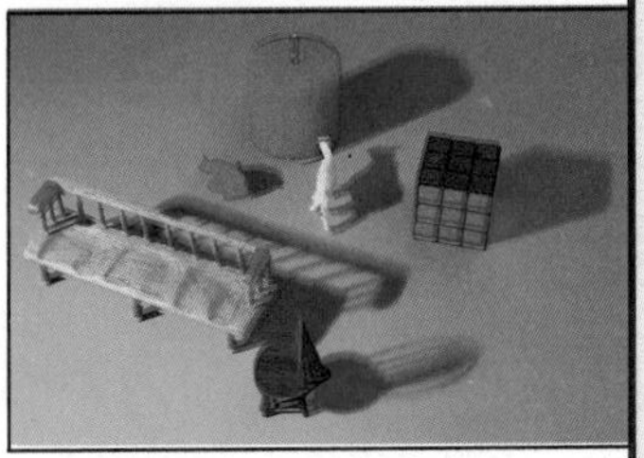

EXTENSIONS

Reinforcement

Activity

Ask the students to draw a picture showing how they are able to see the chalkboard in their classroom. Their illustrations should include a source of light (sunlight or an artificial source), the path of the beam from the source to the chalkboard, and the reflection of the beam to their eyes. This assignment could be extended by asking the class to bring in magazine pictures showing people looking at objects. Students can then draw in arrows and dotted lines to indicate the path of a light beam from its source to an object and its reflection off that object to someone's eyes.

DEVELOPMENT

1 Skill Development—Students *compare* the time it takes to blink their eyes to the time it takes light to travel a certain distance.

2 Teaching Tips—Obtain an overhead projector and a variety of three-dimensional figures: cubes, spheres, rectangular solids, oval-shaped solids. Place each object on the overhead projector and cover it with a file folder so the students cannot see it. Ask the students if they can tell from its shadow what the object is. You can also use two-dimensional shapes as well.

3 Text Questions—What do you see that shows that light travels in straight lines? *The shadows are the same shape as the objects.* How would it look if the light from the candle curved around the pencils? *There would not be any shadows.*

4 Skill Development—Students are asked to make *observations* and then to *compare and contrast* the objects with their shadows.

EXTENSIONS

Enrichment
Research—Library

Students may be interested in knowing if anything travels faster than the speed of light. Allow your students to research the speeds of all things that interest them. Be sure the speed of sound is included in their list. They will discover that nothing travels faster than the speed of light.

ACTIVITY

Does light travel in straight lines?

A. Gather these materials: 4 index cards, hole punch, clay, and light source.

B. Punch a hole as close as you can to the center of each card.

C. Use a piece of clay to stand the card up on a desk. Turn on the light and put the lamp at the other end of the desk. Look through the hole at the light.

D. Line up the next card so that you can see the light through both holes. Continue until you can see the light through the holes in all 4 cards.

1. Are the holes all in a straight line?

E. Move 1 card to the left.

2. Can you still see the light through the holes?

3. What does this tell you about how light moves?

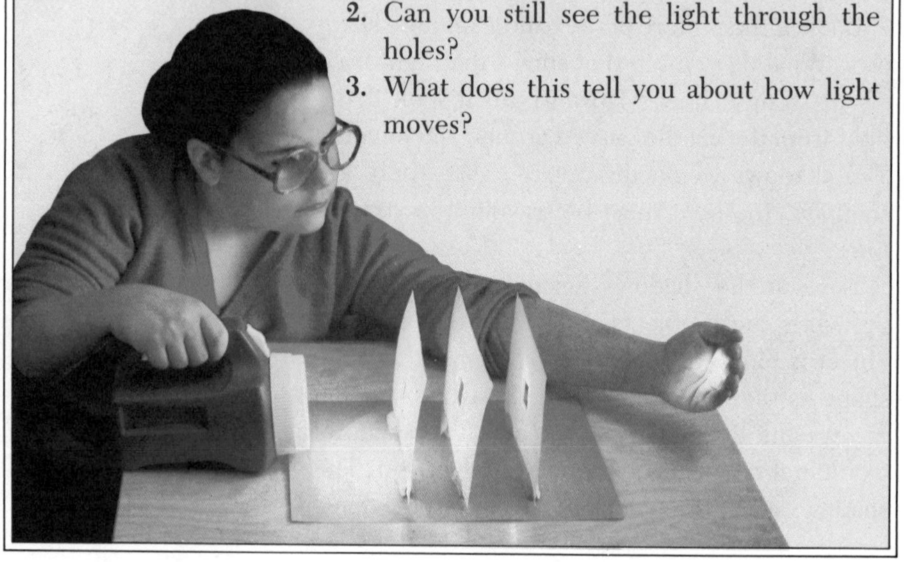

ACTIVITY

Skill Development—*Inferring*

Teaching Tips—Try to put the holes exactly in the center of each card. It would be a good math exercise to do the necessary measurements to find the exact center of the card.

Answers to Questions—**1.** Yes. **2.** No. **3.** Light travels only in a straight line.

Section Review

Main Ideas: Light travels in straight lines at a very high speed. When objects block the path of light, shadows are formed.

Questions: Answer in complete sentences.

1. Imagine you could travel at the speed of light. How long would it take you to travel (a) to the moon; (b) to the sun; (c) from school to home?
2. How is a shadow formed?
3. What would be different if light did not travel in a straight line?

People in Science

Harold E. Edgerton

Harold Edgerton was born on April 6, 1903, in Fremont, Nebraska. Dr. Edgerton developed a method of high-speed photography in 1931. At the Massachusetts Institute of Technology, he invented an electric lamp called the *electronic flash*. This lamp made a very bright light. It could be flashed on and off very rapidly. Using this flash, Dr. Edgerton was able to take "stop-action" pictures. Such pictures have been very helpful to scientists. One series of pictures shows what happens when a drop of milk falls into a saucer of milk. Another shows the moment at which a bat hits a baseball. Dr. Edgerton has also done important work in aerial and underwater photography.

EXTENSIONS

Reinforcement

Activity

Since light travels in straight lines, there is a straight line between a source of light, an object in the path of this light, and the shadow the object casts. To help students understand this concept, have them do the following:

A. Collect these materials: 1 sq ft of corrugated cardboard, 10 common pins, a flashlight, and a compass.

B. With the compass, draw a circle 8 in. in diameter on the cardboard. Stick the pins at regular intervals along the edge of the circle so that they are standing upright.

C. Hold the flashlight at different positions on the inside and outside of the circle so that the pins cast shadows of different lengths and thicknesses. Observe the directions of the cast shadows.

D. On a separate sheet of paper, draw diagrams of the location of the pins, the source of light, and the directions of the cast shadows. In each diagram, draw a straight line connecting the light source, pins, and cast shadows.

SECTION REVIEW

Answers to Questions

1. **a.** about 1 1/2 sec, **b.** about 8 min, **c.** Instantaneously
2. A shadow is a dark area where light has been blocked out.
3. You could see around corners, and there probably would not be shadows.

SECTION BACKGROUND

When light travels away from its source, it spreads out. For this reason, light is less concentrated at greater distances from its source. This means that the brightness of a light source is reduced as one travels farther way. Every time the distance is doubled, the brightness is reduced one fourth.

Light appears to have a dual nature. In some experiments, light acts like a particle. In other experiments, light behaves as if it were a wave. Scientists think that light has a dual nature. It has properties of both particles and waves.

MATERIALS

1 piece of cm graph paper, flashlight, meter stick

4-3. Spreading Light

A lighthouse can be a beautiful sight. Imagine you are the captain of a ship. You are lost at sea, but you keep heading east. Ahead you see a faint light. A little while later, the light is brighter. It's a lighthouse. Why does the light on the lighthouse get brighter? When you finish this section, you should be able to:

☐ **A.** Describe the way light travels away from its source.

☐ **B.** Describe what happens to light as it gets farther away from its source.

☐ **C.** Describe how light acts as either a particle or a wave.

BASIC TEACHING PLAN

MOTIVATION

The experience of a light source seeming dimmer or brighter as one retreats from it or approaches it may not be familiar to all your students. You might dim the lights in the room and place two lighted candles at different distances from the students. The closer one will look brighter. Ask the students why they think this is so.

The intensity or brightness of light corresponds to the square of its distance from the observer. If you move an object two times farther away than it is now, it will be four times dimmer. If you can obtain a light meter, you can demonstrate this to the class using any light source.

Text Questions—Why does the light on the lighthouse get brighter? *As one gets closer to a light source, the light appears to get brighter.*

You learned in the last section that light travels in straight lines away from its source. As light
1 travels away, it spreads out in all directions. In a way, the light gets dimmer. When the source of light is very far away, only a few light beams reach our eyes. The farther away the light source is, the dimmer the light seems.

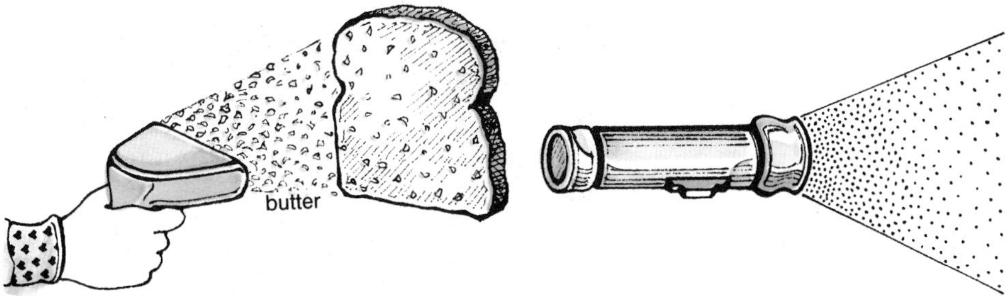

To understand this idea, look at the picture of the "butter gun." The butter spreads out as it leaves the gun. If you hold the gun far away, you can butter a lot of toast at once. But the amount of butter on each piece is very thin. Think of the butter gun as a light source like a flashlight.

Scientists have two ways of explaining how light acts. One idea is that light acts as if it were
2 made of tiny pieces of matter, or **particles** (**par-tih-kulz**). Have you ever used a spray bottle to spray water on plants? Little *particles* of water come out of the nozzle. When the water drops leave the nozzle of the bottle, they are close together. The water drops spread apart as they
3 travel away from the nozzle. Light acts in the same way. Why do you think the light is dimmer farther from a flashlight?

Particle: A very small piece of matter.

EXTENSIONS

Application

Science Skills—Comparing and Contrasting

Students can make a "brightness tester" to measure light intensity by following these steps:

A. Gather the following materials: a cardboard tube, black paper, tape, a pin, and light bulbs of various intensities (15, 30, 60 watts).

B. Wrap the cardboard tube with the black paper, covering one end of the tube with the paper. Using the pin, put about ten very tiny holes in the black paper on the end of the tube.

C. Aim the "brightness tester" at the lowest light source. Describe the intensity of the light that passes through the holes. Then stand at the same distance from the light source (about 5 m) and compare the brightness of different bulbs.

D. You can find out what happens to brightness as the distance changes. Aim the tester at a source. Describe the brightness of the light. Now double the distance and compare the brightness. It should have diminished.

DEVELOPMENT

1 Teaching Tips—You can demonstrate how light spreads by using a toy water gun or a spray bottle. Fill it with water. Direct the spray at a sheet of paper. Have the students note the area covered by the water. Now aim the gun or bottle at another piece of paper placed farther away. The area covered by the water should be greater. The water is spread out farther in the second case. Thus, there is less water per unit area. Point out that light is more concentrated closer to its source.

2 Teaching Tips—The particles of light that scientists refer to are called photons. A photon is a bundle of light energy.

3 Text Questions—Why do you think the light is dimmer farther from a flashlight? *The particles spread out as they leave the flashlight, and therefore, the light is dimmer as you move farther from the source.*

Exceptional Student

Visually Impaired/Learning Disabled

Use a butter gun or spray bottle as described on this page. Let the student feel the spray as it leaves the gun or bottle. This will help the visually impaired student to understand the concept of light rays. It will also help the learning disabled student to grasp this abstract concept.

EXTENSIONS

Application
Science Skills— Comparing and Contrasting

If you have ever looked carefully at the stars in the nighttime sky, you will know that they differ in brightness. This is due to their size and to their distance from the earth. Astronomers assign each star a number based on its brightness. It is referred to as the star's magnitude. Make copies of the map of the Big Dipper that is contained in the Interunit pages. Tell students that tonight they are to use this map with their parents' help to locate the Big Dipper. When they find the Big Dipper, they are then to determine which star is the brightest and which star is the dimmest. Have them mark these two stars on the map. The next day, use the overhead projector to point out the brightest and the dimmest star of the Big Dipper on the students' results.

ACTIVITY

How does light spread out from a source?

A. Gather these materials: centimeter graph paper, flashlight, and meter stick.
B. Place the graph paper on a flat surface. Each square measures 1 centimeter (0.4 in.).
C. Turn on your flashlight. Hold it close to the graph paper. The bright circle of light should just fill one 1-cm square. (If your light is too big, try to fill the smallest number of squares you can.)
D. Measure the distance from the flashlight to the graph paper.
E. Keep moving the flashlight away from the graph paper until the light is too dim to see. Record all your distance measurements.

1. How does this activity show that light spreads out as it gets farther from the source?
2. As the flashlight gets farther from the graph paper, what happens to the brightness of the light in each square?
3. How far must the flashlight be from the graph paper before the light is too dim to see?

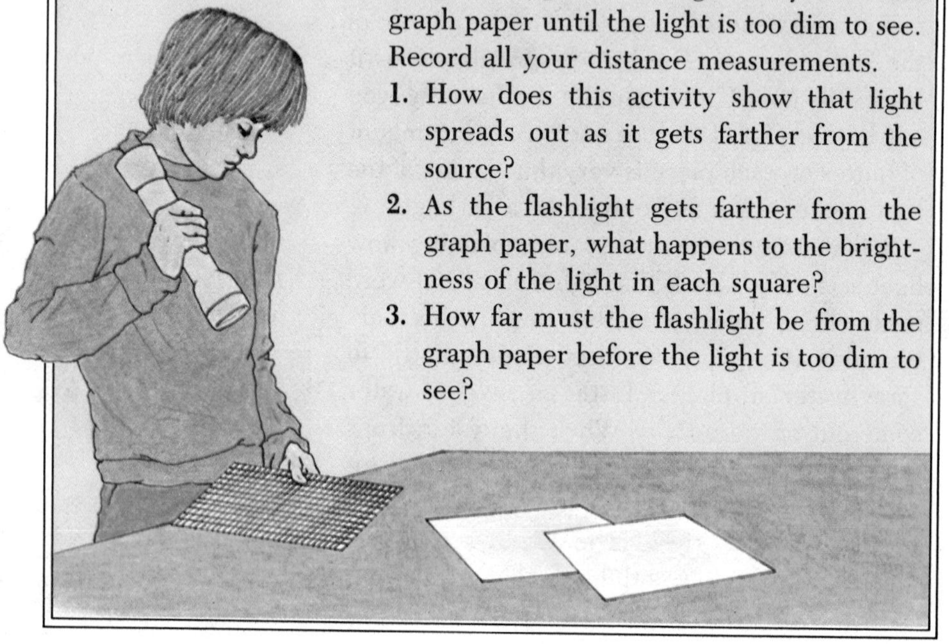

ACTIVITY

Skill Development—*Recording Data*

Answers to Questions—1. As you move the light farther away, more squares are filled by it. **2.** The brightness lessens. **3.** Answers will depend on the intensity of the light.

Have you ever dropped a stone in water? When the stone hits the water, **waves** travel away in all directions. Scientists think light also acts like *waves.* Light travels away from the source as a wave. The light wave gets weaker as it travels. Since the wave gets weaker, the light appears dimmer.

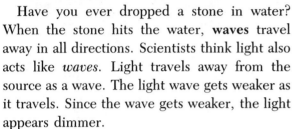

Wave: A movement like a swell of water.

Section Review

Main Ideas: As light moves away from its source, it appears to get dimmer. This happens because light spreads out as it travels. Scientists have observed that light acts like both a particle and a wave.

Questions: Answer in complete sentences.

1. Why does light from a street lamp get dimmer as you move away?
2. How does light behave like particles?
3. How does light behave like waves?

EXTENSIONS

Enrichment

Science Skills—Observing

Using the flashlight and graph paper from the Activity, the students can observe how the spreading of light is determined by the angle at which it strikes the graph paper.

A. With the graph paper on a flat surface, hold the flashlight far enough away so that its light shines on the paper at a right angle and covers 1/4 of the paper.

B. Slowly move the light so that the angle changes and observe what happens to the spot of light.

1. What happened to the size and shape of the spot of light? (The spot of light became larger and more elliptical.)
2. What happens to the brightness of the light in each square as the flashlight moves? (The brightness lessens in the squares on the far side of the spot from the flashlight.)

4 Text Questions—Have you ever dropped a stone in water? *Ask the students to describe what the water did when the stone hit the water.*

5 Teaching Tips—Set up an overhead projector and place a shallow, transparent tray of water on it. Turn on the projector and drop grains of sand into the water. Have the students watch the waves travel outward from where the sand grains hit. After the students describe what they see, explain that waves of light also travel out in all directions from the source.

SECTION REVIEW

Answers to Questions

1. The light is less concentrated the farther it is from its source. Particles are spread apart, or waves are not as intense.

2. Light and particles of water spread apart as the distance from their source is increased.

3. Light and water waves decrease in intensity as the distance from their source is increased.

SUGGESTED WORKSHEET MASTERS
p. T-59 m; for Sections 4-1 and 4-3, p. T-59 l

SECTION BACKGROUND

What happens when light hits an object depends on the nature of the material that interacts with the light. Materials are classified as transparent, translucent, and opaque. Transparent substances like glass allow light energy to pass through. Translucent materials like waxed paper bend light as it passes through them. As the light goes through these substances, it is scattered. As a result, images seen through translucent materials are blurred. Opaque objects do not allow light to pass through. The light energy is absorbed and reflected. Students will later discover that the color of an opaque object is the result of both reflection and absorption.

MATERIALS

flashlight, small samples of glass, clear plastic, tissue paper, waxed paper, fabrics, cellophane, wood, metal, rubber

4-4. When Light Strikes

These mountain climbers are crossing a snowfield. The sunlight is bright enough to hurt their eyes. The climbers are wearing sunglasses. How do the glasses protect their eyes? When you finish this section, you should be able to:

- ☐ **A.** Explain three things that can happen to light when it hits an object.
- ☐ **B.** Group objects by what happens when light hits them.

What happens to light when it hits an object? Light passes right through some objects. But it cannot pass through other objects. Let's find out how light behaves when it strikes different kinds of objects.

BASIC TEACHING PLAN

MOTIVATION

The day before this lesson, tell your students to bring pairs of sunglasses to school. Obtain some very bright lights, such as floodlights. On the day that you start this section, tell the students that they are going to make some observations with their eyes using sunglasses. Arrange the floodlights so that they reflect light off one of the walls in your room. Do not shine the lights directly into the eyes of the students. Tell the students to look at the wall without the aid of the sunglasses. Now have them look at the wall with their sunglasses on.

Text Questions—How do the glasses protect their eyes? *Sunglasses protect their eyes from the brightness of the reflected light from the snow, which could be painful and dangerous to their eyes.*

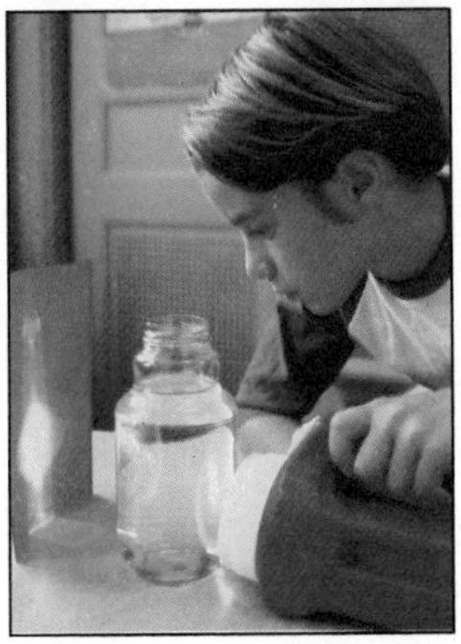

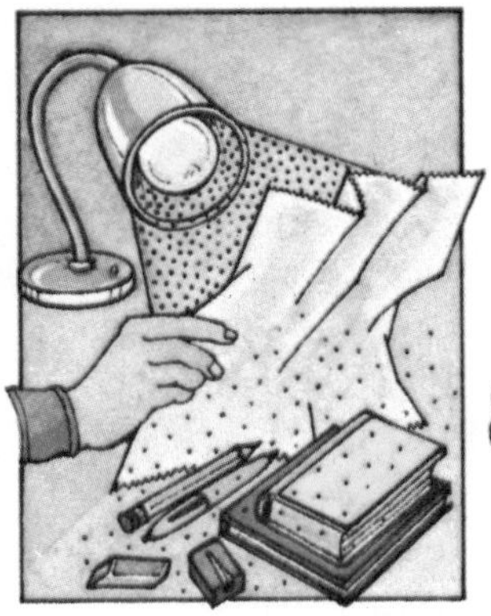

1 Some materials like glass, water, and air let light pass right through. If a flashlight is held on one side of an aquarium of water, the light can be seen on the other side. Objects through which light passes easily are called **transparent** (tranz-**pair**-ent). You can see through *transparent* objects clearly.

Transparent material: A material through which light can pass.

Sometimes when light passes through an object, things look blurred. Have you ever tried to look through a piece of waxed paper? When you do, things on the other side are not very clear. Some of the light goes through, but not enough to see clearly. The rest of the light is either bounced away or soaked up. Materials like waxed paper are called **translucent** (tranz-**loo**-sent). Think of other *translucent* materials.

Translucent material: A material that blurs light as it passes through.

What would you see if you tried to look through a piece of cardboard? You would see nothing but the cardboard. Light does not pass through some materials. Materials that block
2 light are called **opaque** (oh-**payk**). Do you think a piece of aluminum foil is *opaque*?

Opaque material: A material that blocks light.

EXTENSIONS

Reinforcement

Science Skills— Comparing and Contrasting

As a way of illustrating transparent, translucent, and opaque materials, you could do the following demonstration with your students:

A. Before class, prepare three pairs of "eyeglasses." One pair should be dark sunglasses. The other two should be made by replacing the glass in discarded glasses with waxed paper and aluminum foil.

B. Ask three students to put on the glasses and to sit in a line facing the class.

C. Have them describe the color, shape, and clarity of the objects they see.

D. Ask the class to guess why their perceptions differed. They should use the terms transparent, translucent, and opaque.

DEVELOPMENT

1 Teaching Tips—You can demonstrate how light behaves when it strikes different materials. You will need to set up an overhead projector. On a piece of clear plastic, write a word or symbol or draw a picture. Put the plastic on the overhead projector, and tell the students that you are going to place various materials over the image. The students are to predict whether or not they will be able to see the image. Gather samples of waxed paper, plastic, glass, aluminum foil, plastic wrap, and any other material with which you wish to experiment. Use the words *transparent, translucent,* and *opaque* as you do the demonstration.
2 Text Questions—Do you think a piece of aluminum foil is opaque? *Yes.*

EXTENSIONS

Enrichment
Activity

Students have experienced the greenhouse effect, although they may not be able to name it or describe it. Ask how many of them have gotten into a car in which the windows were closed on a sunny day. The air inside was much hotter than the air outside. In the greenhouse effect, light is transmitted through a material (glass), absorbed by a material (seatcovers in the car), and then trapped inside a space.

A. Ask the students to consider the causes of this phenomenon. Then have them gather a large mason jar, 2 thermometers, and 2 samples of identical fabric.

B. Tape 1 piece of fabric to the inside of the jar. Place 1 thermometer inside the jar. Put the cover on the jar and place it in the sunlight. Place the other thermometer and piece of fabric next to the jar.

C. Record the temperatures on both thermometers at 30-sec intervals for 5 min.

D. Discuss the results and how they relate to the greenhouse effect.

SUGGESTED WORKSHEET MASTER
p. T-59 n

ACTIVITY

What happens when light hits objects?

A. Gather these materials: a flashlight and a variety of materials such as glass, plastic, paper, fabrics, tape, wood, and metal.

B. Copy the chart shown here.

Materials	Opaque	Transparent	Translucent
1. Wood			
2.			
3.			

C. Shine the light at each material. Record your results in the chart.

Section Review

Main Ideas: Objects affect light in three ways.

	What Light Does	Object
Opaque	It is blocked	Paper
Transparent	Passes through	Glass
Translucent	Scatters	Waxed paper

Questions: Answer in complete sentences.

1. Is air transparent, translucent, or opaque?
2. Are sunglasses transparent, translucent, or opaque?
3. How do sunglasses protect the mountain climbers' eyes in the picture on page 74?

ACTIVITY

Skill Development—*Classifying*

Teaching Tips—Students in groups of four can share the materials. Give each group two flashlights. Dim the lights in the room, although the room does not need to be completely dark.

SECTION REVIEW

Main Ideas—You might put the skeleton of the chart on the chalkboard or the overhead projector. Invite the students to complete the chart.

Answers to Questions

1. Air is transparent.
2. Sunglasses are transparent.
3. Sunglasses absorb some of the sun's light.

CHAPTER REVIEW

Science Words: Write the meaning of each of the following words. Then give at least two examples of each word: (1) light source; (2) reflection; (3) shadows; (4) particle; (5) wave.

Questions: Answer in complete sentences.

1. Why can we see the moon? Explain your answer with a diagram.
2. Draw and label a diagram to show how a shadow is made. Include in your diagram a light source, an object, and the shadow.
3. Do transparent, translucent, or opaque objects make the best shadows? Why?
4. Look at the picture of two boats and a lighthouse. Would the light seem brighter to the captain of boat A or boat B? Explain your answer.

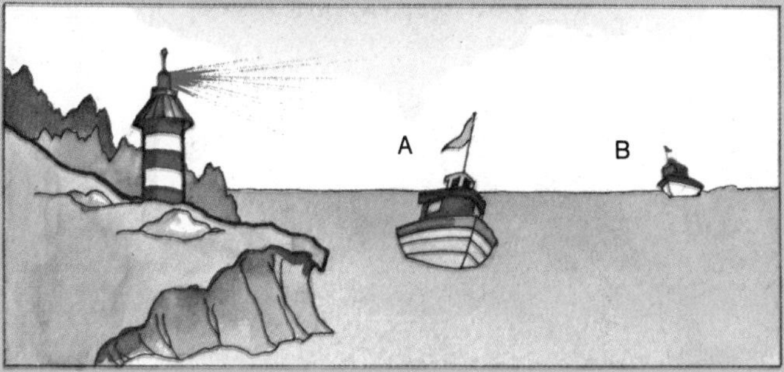

5. What will happen to light when it hits the following objects: (a) clear plastic; (b) a piece of wood; and (c) waxed paper.
6. What is the difference between a transparent and a translucent material? Give an example of each.

EXTENSIONS

Enrichment

Research—Library

Students can use the dictionary and other references to identify the following words and their relation to the concepts in this chapter.

bioluminescence
dispersion
amplitude
frequency
umbra
semiumbra
light years

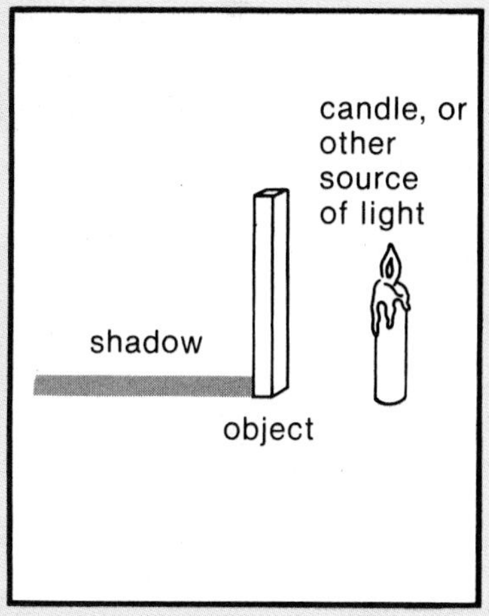

Fig. 4-1

CHAPTER REVIEW

Science Words

1. An object that produces light (sun, lamp). **2.** The bouncing back of light (mirror, wall). **3.** The dark area caused when an object blocks light (puppets, buildings). **4.** A very small object (dust, sand). **5.** One way light moves (water, sound).

Answers to Questions

1. Sunlight bounces off the moon to our eyes.
2. A shadow is made in the following way: See Fig. 4-1.
3. Opaque, because they block the most light.
4. Boat A. Boat A is closer to the source of light. It would look brighter.
5. (a) Pass through, (b). blocked, (c). pass through but be blurred.
6. A transparent material (air) allows light through without any blurring, whereas the light is blurred when it passes through a translucent material (stained glass).

SUGGESTED WORKSHEET MASTER
p. T-59 o

SUGGESTED TEST MASTERS
pp. T-59 d, e, f

Chapter Objectives

1. Explain how light reflects off of smooth and rough surfaces.
2. Describe what happens when light hits a flat reflector and explain how mirrors are used to make a periscope.
3. Describe what happens to light when it hits a curved mirror and list the uses of curved mirrors.
4. Distinguish between concave and convex mirrors.

SECTION BACKGROUND

When a beam of light falls upon a reflecting surface, the beam is turned back so that the angle of incidence (incoming) is equal to the angle of reflection (outgoing). On uneven surfaces, light still obeys the law of reflection. Microscopically, an uneven surface is a series of flat surfaces distributed at random angles. As a result, light scatters in many different directions when it hits such a surface.

MATERIALS

flashlight, 2 squares of aluminum foil (10 cm × 10 cm), piece of white paper, mirror

Exceptional Student IEP Chapter Goal

At the end of this chapter, the student will state the difference between concave and convex mirrors.

CHAPTER 5

Bouncing Light

5-1. Reflecting Light

In ancient Egypt, people used pieces of polished metal as mirrors. Why do some materials reflect light so perfectly? What kinds of materials make good mirrors? When you finish this section, you should be able to:

BASIC TEACHING PLAN

MOTIVATION

Assemble an assortment of good and poor reflectors. Hold up one obje at a time, and ask the students to predict in writing whether the object a good or poor reflector. Save their predictions and go over them at th end of the section.

Text Questions—Why do some materials reflect light so perfectly? *The have flat and shiny surfaces.* What kinds of materials make good mi rors? *Shiny materials such as glass or metal.*

☐ **A.** Describe how smooth and rough surfaces reflect light in different ways.

☐ **B.** Predict which materials will make good reflectors.

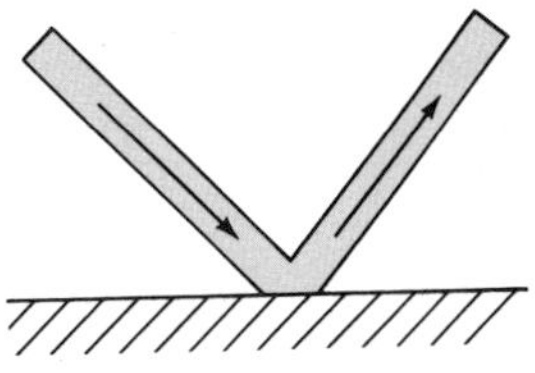

Some materials reflect light better than others. Good reflectors are usually shiny and bright when light is shined on them. If you look at a good reflector, you may see yourself clearly. If you look at a poor reflector, your reflection may be blurred or not there at all.

Imagine that you and your friends have a basketball. Where would you rather bounce the ball, on a gym floor or on a dirt road? It is easier to bounce a ball on the gym floor because the floor is smooth.

Think of a beam of light as a stream of tiny particles. In the diagram, the beam of light hits
2 the flat surface of a mirror. The beam bounces off the mirror like a basketball would bounce off a smooth gym floor.

What happens when light hits an uneven surface? The particles of light are scattered. When this happens, the light is not reflected evenly.

EXTENSIONS

Application
Activity

A kaleidoscope is a tube containing mirrors. When you turn the kaleidoscope while looking at colored glass or bits of sand, beautiful patterns are formed.

A. Gather these materials: 2 mirrors (about 10 cm × 3 cm) and a piece of cardboard the same size as the mirrors.

B. Fasten the two mirrors and the cardboard with rubber bands to form a three-sided shape.

C. Have the students look down the inside of the three-sided kaleidoscope and view pieces of broken glass or sand. If the kaleidoscope is rotated, the patterns will change. Use the kaleidoscope to look at a variety of objects. What patterns are formed?

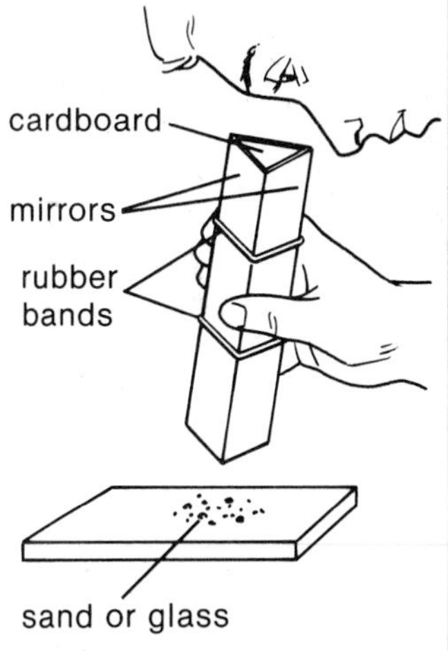

Fig. 5-1

DEVELOPMENT

1 Teaching Tips—Take the class outside where there is a smooth, hard surface and an uneven, hard surface available. Bounce a tennis ball at various angles off the smooth, hard surface. The ball should bounce at predictable angles. Now bounce it several times off the uneven, hard surface. It should bounce unpredictably. Ask the students to explain why there is a difference in the way the ball bounces.

2 Teaching Tips—Compare the bouncing of the ball to the bouncing of light off a smooth surface and an uneven surface. Demonstrate this with a flashlight, a mirror, a dull surface, and two used chalkboard erasers. Darken the room. Place the mirror on a desk. Aim the flashlight at the mirror several times at different angles. Each time you do this, clap the erasers over the beam of light to produce a cloud of chalk dust. Notice that the light bounces off at an angle. Repeat the procedure with a dull surface. The light will appear to be scattered in many directions. The beam will not be visible after it hits the dull surface.

Exceptional Student
Visually Impaired

Have the students actually bounce a ball on various surfaces, as described on this page. This will help them to understand this concept.

EXTENSIONS

Enrichment

Activity

A. Write these letters on the chalkboard exactly as shown below.

B. Tell the class that this writing is called mirror writing. If you hold a mirror in front of the writing, you will be able to read what it says.

C. Have your students try to write their own sentences in mirror writing.

D. Have students research Leonardo da Vinci's secret writing. They will discover that his secret writing was really mirror writing.

Fig. 5-2

ACTIVITY

Can you predict a good reflector?

A. Gather these materials: flashlight, mirror, 2 squares of aluminum foil, and piece of white paper.

B. Crumple 1 piece of aluminum foil until the surface is uneven. Flatten the foil out.

C. Use the mirror and each piece of aluminum foil to read the secret message.

1. With which materials were you able to read the message?
2. Which piece of foil makes a better reflector? Why?

D. Hold the mirror in one hand and the flashlight in the other. Aim the flashlight at the mirror so you bounce a reflection off the ceiling. Repeat this step with both pieces of foil and white paper.

3. With which materials were you able to bounce light off the ceiling?
4. What makes an object a good reflector?

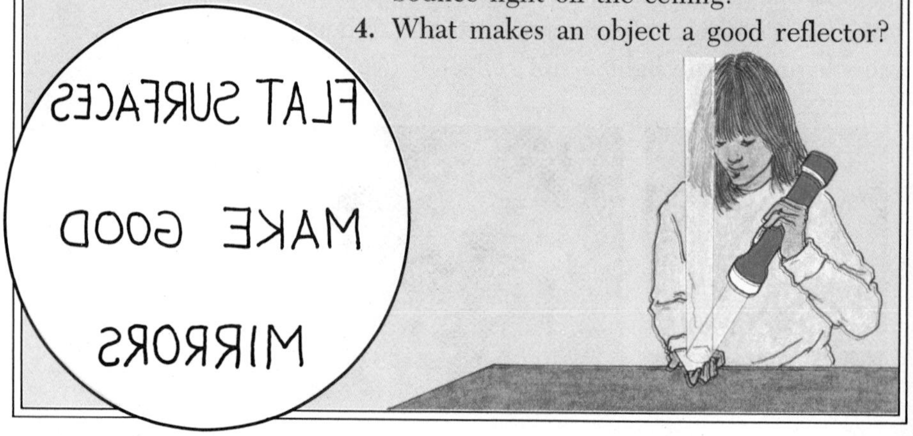

80

ACTIVITY

Skill Development—*Predicting and Inferring*

Teaching Tips—Cut out squares of aluminum foil before the Activity. Each should be about 10 cm × 10 cm. Crumpling the aluminum foil will produce an uneven surface. Shine a flashlight on the crumpled aluminum foil and on a shiny piece before you do it with the students so that you can see the difference.

Answers to Questions—**1.** The mirror and the shiny piece of aluminum foil. **2.** The flat, even aluminum foil, because all of the light reflects the same way. **3.** The mirror and flat aluminum foil. **4.** A material is a good reflector if it is flat and shiny.

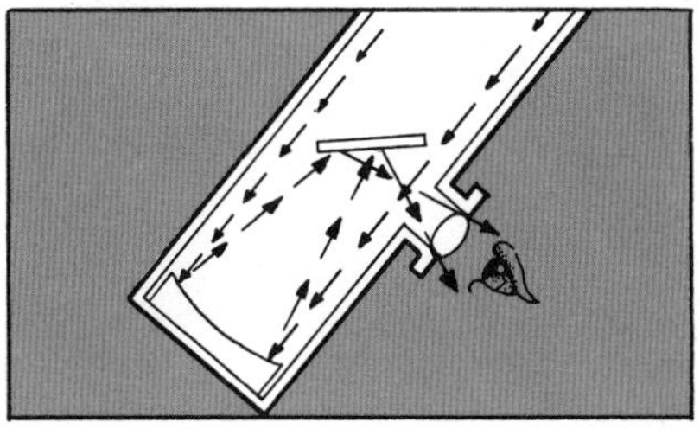

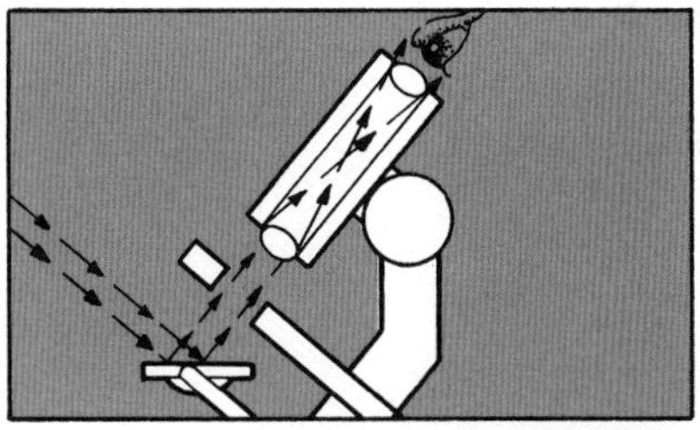

A good mirror is a very smooth reflector. Re-
3 flectors are used in cameras, flashlights, telescopes, and microscopes.

The diagram on the left shows how telescope mirrors reflect light from stars and planets. On the right, the diagram shows how light is reflected in a microscope.

Section Review

Main Ideas: When light hits an object, it can be reflected in two ways. A beam of light can bounce off the surface in a straight line. An uneven surface scatters the light particles in many directions. Flat, smooth surfaces are good reflectors. Uneven surfaces are poor reflectors.

Questions: Answer in complete sentences.

1. How is a Ping-Pong ball hitting a table like light hitting a mirror?
2. What is reflection? Give an example of a material that would give a good reflection.
3. If you wanted to make a reflector for your bike, what kind of material would you use?
4. Why do you see a good reflection in a clean mirror?

EXTENSIONS

Application

Activity

Have your students locate the Morse code in an encyclopedia.

Let them try to send a one-word message with a mirror. For a light source, use either the sun or a filmstrip projector.

3 Teaching Tips—One instrument that uses mirrors is a kaleidoscope. You can demonstrate it or have the students make it. Refer to the Extension on page T-79.

SECTION REVIEW

Answers to Questions

1. The Ping-Pong ball will bounce off the table at the same angle it hits it. Light, when it hits a mirror, also bounces off at the same angle.
2. Reflection is the bouncing back of light. A flat, shiny surface would be a good reflector.
3. A flat, shiny material would be a good reflector for a bike. Light would bounce or reflect off the material.
4. A clean mirror has a smooth, shiny surface.

SECTION BACKGROUND

According to the law of reflection, a light ray bounces off a flat surface at the same angle it hits the surface. If a mirror is pointed halfway between a light source and an intended target, a beam from the light source can be aimed at the target. A set of mirrors can be used to reflect light beams from one mirror to another and then to your eyes.

The image you see in a mirror is reversed. The apparent location of the image is behind the mirror at a distance equal to the distance of the object from the mirror.

MATERIALS

clay, light box, mirror, sheet of white paper

5-2. Flat Reflectors

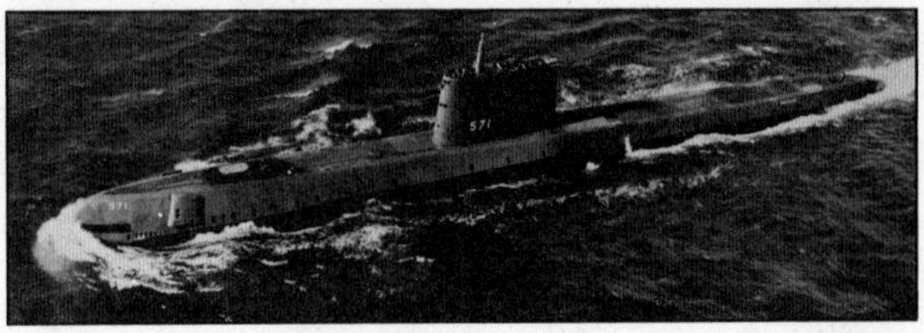

How does the captain of a submarine see what is happening above the water? A submarine uses a long tube that contains mirrors. The light from above the water is reflected down the tube. When you finish this section, you should be able to:

- **A.** Explain how a mirror changes the direction of a light beam.
- **B.** Predict the direction light will reflect when it hits a mirror.
- **C.** Explain how a *periscope* works.

If you were to throw a ball at the ground, it would bounce off the ground. The direction that it bounces depends on how it hits the ground. The direction the ball bounces is called the **angle**. The *angle* will depend on how the ball hits the ground. Light acts this way, too. Light 1 will bounce off objects at different angles.

Angle: The direction at which light bounces off something.

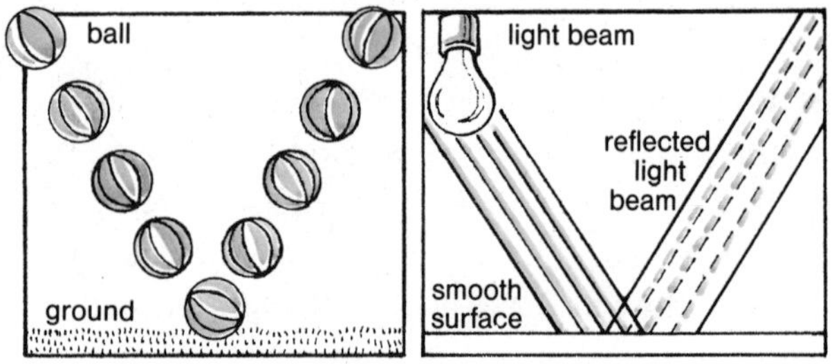

BASIC TEACHING PLAN

MOTIVATION

Make a barricade with either books or a box to separate two students. Put the students on opposite sides of the barricade in a place in the room that everyone can see. Give one of the students two mirrors. Give the other student an object to hold. The student with the mirrors is not allowed to look directly over the barricade but must use the two mirrors to find out what object the other student is holding. Give the student with the mirrors some time to orient them. It will not be easy at first. The mirrors should be used as a periscope in order to see over the barricade.

DEVELOPMENT

1 **Teaching Tips**—To demonstrate the meaning of *angle,* set a wood block on an overhead projector near the edge of the glass. Roll a Ping-Pong ball toward the wood block a few times. Ask the students to describe the path of the ball before and after it hits the wood block.

ACTIVITY

How does a mirror affect light?

A. Gather these materials: clay, light box, mirror, and sheet of white paper.

B. Turn on the light box. Place the mirror in the path of the light beam. Move the mirror so that the light hits it at different angles.

1. What happens to the light beam when it hits the mirror?
2. How can you use the mirror to change the light's direction?
3. How can you get the light beam to reflect back onto itself?

C. Bounce a beam of light off the mirror at an angle. Draw a diagram that shows the path of the light beam hitting the mirror. Show the path of the reflected beam.

4. How does the angle of the light beam compare with the angle of the reflected beam?
5. How is light affected by a mirror?

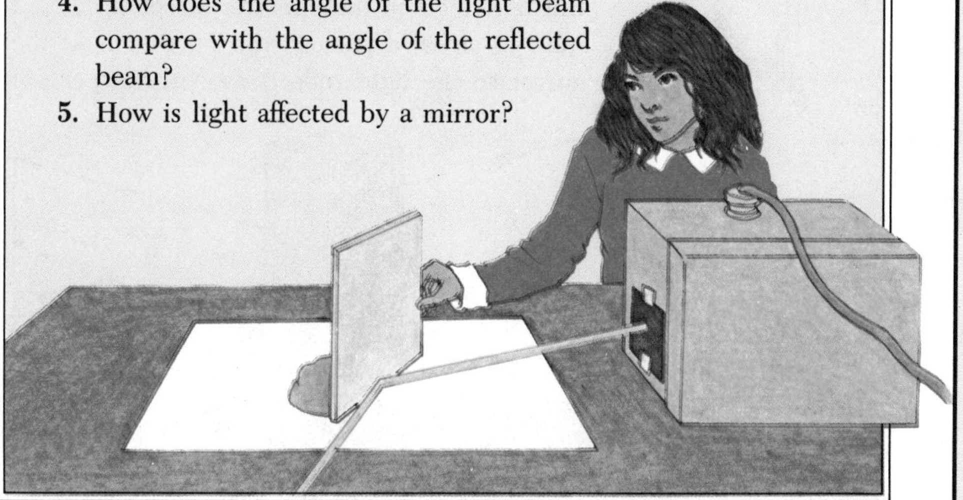

EXTENSIONS

Enrichment

Science Skills—Measuring

If students can measure angles, have them perform this task using straws and a mirror.

A. Have them use a piece of clay to stand a mirror up on a sheet of white paper. They should then place a straw on the paper to form an angle with the mirror. After they have lined up a second straw so that it forms a straight line with the image in the mirror, have them carefully draw the path of the two straws.

B. Repeat the procedure two more times, changing the angle of the straw.

C. Have the students draw a line perpendicular to the mirror. Using a protractor, they can now measure the angle between the incoming straw and the perpendicular line. This is the angle of incidence. The angle of reflection is the angle between the perpendicular and the second straw.

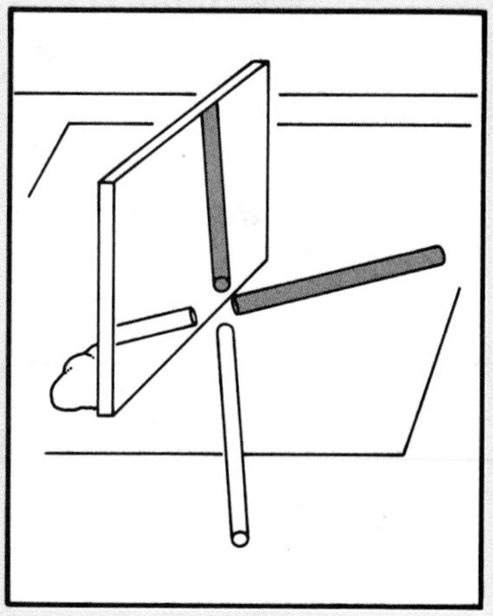

Fig. 5-3

ACTIVITY

Skill Development—*Finding Cause and Effect*

Safety Tips—Caution students about the intensity of the heat from a light bulb.

Teaching Tips—For each light box, you need a shoe box and a clear, straight-filament showcase lamp in a plug-in socket. Turn the box on its long side and cut a 5-cm square in one short end at a distance of 3 cm from the side upon which the box is resting. In the middle of what is now the top side of the box, cut a hole the size of the socket. Cover the square hole with a piece of black paper in which you have punched a hole. If you do not want to use the light box, you can use a flashlight covered with aluminum foil in which a single hole has been punched.

Answers to Questions—**1.** The light bounces off the mirror. **2.** By moving the mirror to different angles. **3.** By aiming the light straight at the mirror. **4.** The angles are the same. **5.** Light is reflected by a mirror.

EXTENSIONS

Reinforcement

Science Skills—Observing

Students can use a comb, a mirror, cardboard, and a source of light to observe reflected rays in a mirror. Place the mirror on a piece of cardboard. Shine light through the teeth of the comb. You may have to tilt the comb or the cardboard so that the beams are visible. Have the students observe the incident and reflected beams. Then have them change the angle of the incident beam and compare results.

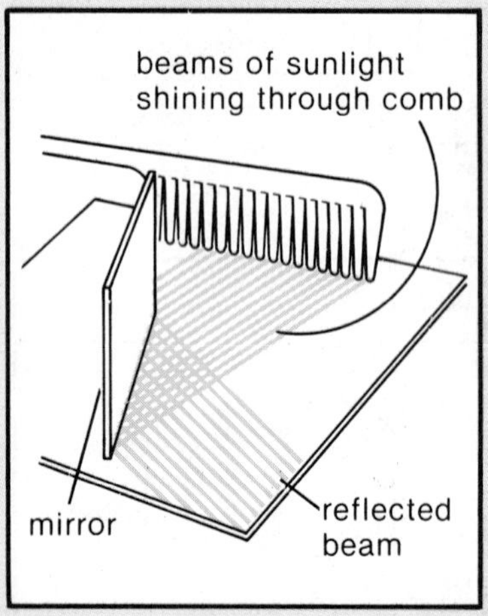

Fig. 5-4

Periscope: An instrument that uses two mirrors to see around corners.

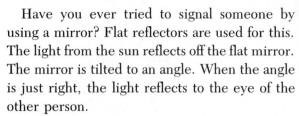

Have you ever tried to signal someone by using a mirror? Flat reflectors are used for this. The light from the sun reflects off the flat mirror. The mirror is tilted to an angle. When the angle is just right, the light reflects to the eye of the other person.

Have you ever looked through a **periscope** (**pehr**-ih-skope)? A *periscope* uses two mirrors to "see" around corners. The mirrors are placed so that one mirror reflects light beams to a second mirror. The second mirror then reflects the light beams to your eyes.

A mirror changes the direction of light. When you change the position of the mirror, the direction of the reflected light beam also changes. A light beam can be reflected back onto itself. This happens when the mirror is directly in front of a light beam. A light beam always reflects off the mirror at the same angle as it hits the mirror. But it reflects in the opposite direction. If you want to signal a person, you have to hold the mirror so the light reflects toward the person.

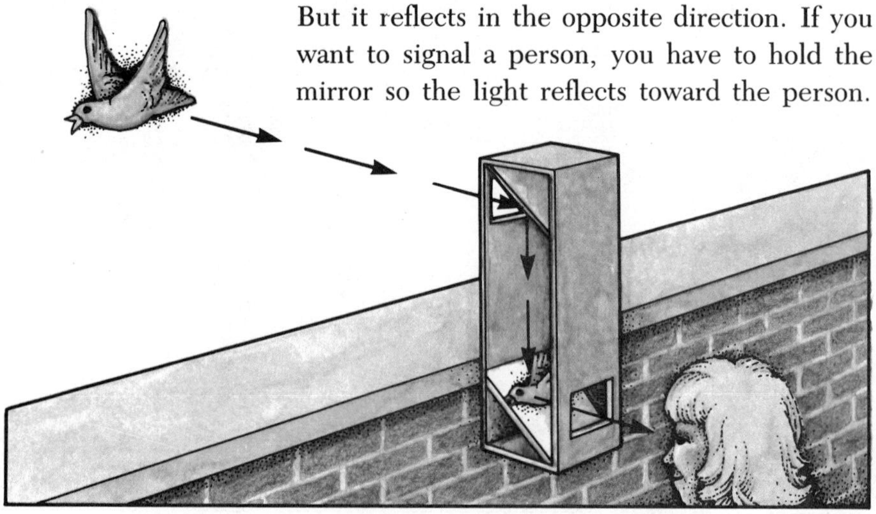

2 **Text Questions**—Have you ever tried to signal someone by using a mirror? *Have the students show how they could use a mirror to signal someone located some distance from them.*

3 **Teaching Tips**—Cover a flashlight with aluminum foil and punch a small hole in the foil to let the light out. Aim the flashlight at the mirror, and have the students observe the reflected ray. Darken the room so that the light ray is more clearly seen. Now turn off the flashlight and aim it at any angle you wish. Ask the students to predict the path of the reflected beam. Demonstrate the path by turning the light on. Discuss the predictions made by students. Ask them how they could get the beam to bounce back on itself. *They will have to aim the light directly at the mirror (perpendicular to the mirror).*

4 **Text Questions**—Have you ever looked through a periscope? *Use the question to show the students the periscope.*

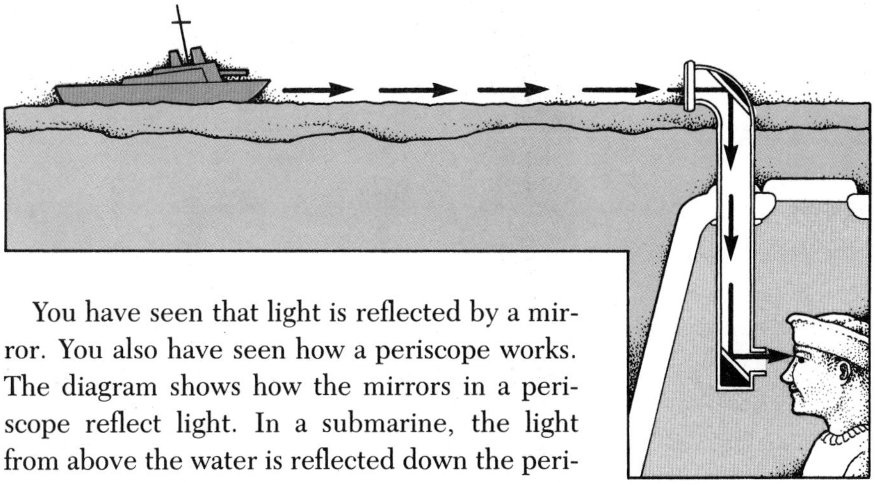

You have seen that light is reflected by a mirror. You also have seen how a periscope works. The diagram shows how the mirrors in a periscope reflect light. In a submarine, the light from above the water is reflected down the periscope. The captain sees the reflection from a second mirror.

Section Review

Main Ideas: Light beams can be reflected by mirrors. Light bounces off a mirror at the same angle that it hits the mirror. A periscope uses two mirrors to see around corners.

Questions: Answer in complete sentences.

1. How is light hitting a mirror like a ball being thrown at a flat wall?
2. How does a periscope help you see around corners?
3. Why do submarines need periscopes?
4. Copy or trace the diagrams. Each line is a light beam hitting a mirror. How will each beam bounce off the mirrors? Draw lines to show your answers.

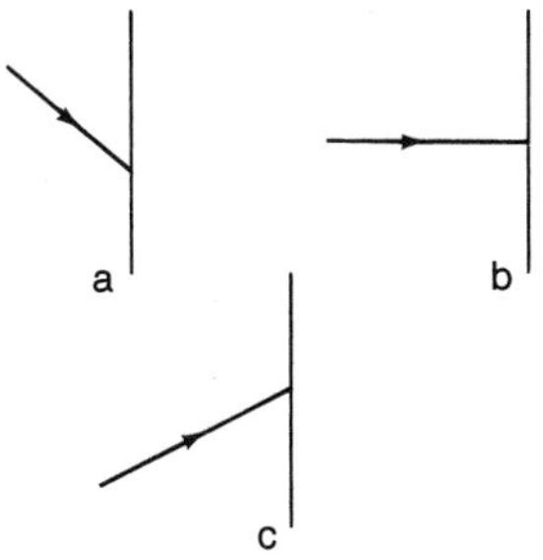

EXTENSIONS

Application

Activity

You will need a mirror and ruler to do this Activity. Fasten the mirror to the end of the ruler with some tape. Stand on one side of a door, and hold the mirror outside the door opening. Explain how the mirror enables you to see around the corner.

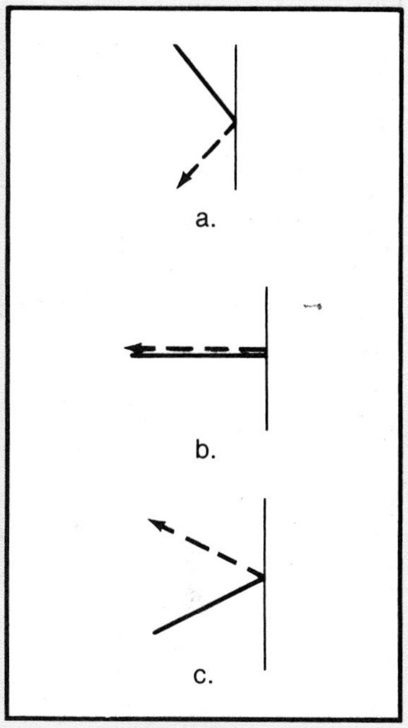

Fig. 5-5

SECTION REVIEW

Answers to Questions

1. When light hits a flat mirror, it bounces off at a predictable angle. A ball thrown against a wall will do the same.
2. The two mirrors are so placed that one mirror reflects light beams to a second mirror, and the second one reflects to your eyes.
3. Since the submarine is under the water, it needs something that will reflect the light down a tube.
4. See Fig. 5-5.

SUGGESTED WORKSHEET MASTER
for Sections 5-1 and 5-2,
p. T-59 p

SECTION BACKGROUND

Focus means to bring light together at one spot. Curved mirrors collect and focus light to a spot. This spot is called the focal point of the curved mirror. The explanation for this is again the basic law of reflection. A curved mirror might be thought of as a series of flat mirrors. Each flat mirror is tilted slightly to give a curved effect. When light strikes any point on the mirror, it is as if it were striking a flat mirror. The light is reflected at an angle equal to the angle of incidence. The effect of the curve is to reflect all the light rays to a single point—the focal point. If one places a light at the focal point of a curved mirror, then the rays of light will reflect off the mirror and form a beam of light. Curved mirrors have two shapes—concave (curves in) and convex (curves out).

MATERIALS

file card, light box or flashlight, 4 mirrors, white paper, clay

5-3. Curved Reflectors

Have you ever walked in front of a curved mirror in a museum or fun house? Some mirrors make you look tall and skinny. Other mirrors make you look short and fat. Why do you think this happens? When you finish this section, you should be able to:

- ☐ **A.** Describe the path of light when it hits a curved reflector.
- ☐ **B.** Explain how curved reflectors can bring light together.
- ☐ **C.** Identify ways curved mirrors are used.

BASIC TEACHING PLAN

MOTIVATION

If you can obtain a large curved mirror, let the students look at themselves in it. Large metal pots and pans could be used as curved mirrors.

Text Questions—Have you ever walked in front of a curved mirror in a museum or fun house? *Let several students describe experiences.* Why do you think this happens? *Because the mirrors are curved, the light is reflected at unusual angles, and images are distorted.*

Look at the photograph below of the three beams of colored light. The beams are bouncing off a curved mirror. Notice that the three beams cross each other at the same place. The blue beam is reflected back on itself. But the red and green beams hit the mirror at an angle. They are reflected off the mirror at an angle and cross each other. Mirrors with inward curves bring light beams together. These mirrors **focus** (**foh**-kus) light to a spot. Curved mirrors bend beams of light at many angles.

Focus: To bring light beams together at a spot.

The diagram shows how the light beams are reflected. You can see very clearly how the beams are *focused* on one spot.

A curved mirror is like many flat mirrors that are turned at angles to make a curve. The diagram on page 89 shows a curved mirror on the left. On the right are several flat mirrors turned slightly to make a curve. In both cases, light is focused to a spot.

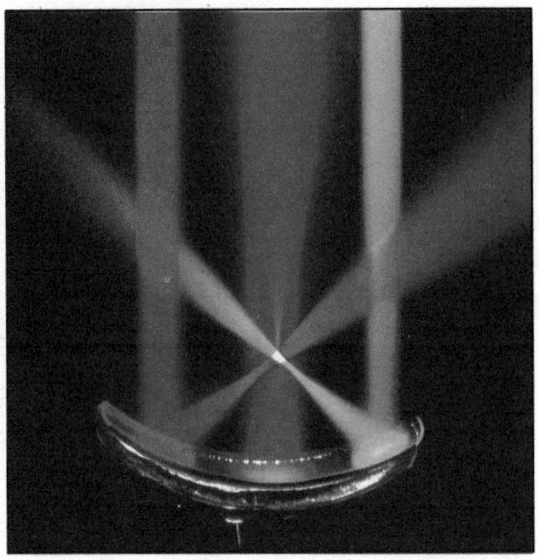

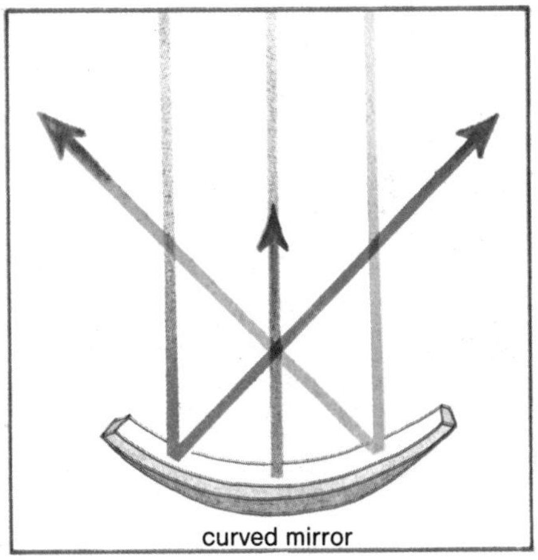

EXTENSIONS

Reinforcement

Science Skills—Comparing and Contrasting

As a way of illustrating concave and convex mirrors, distribute a spoon to each student. First ask them to look at objects nearby with the inside of the spoon (concave mirror). Things should look bigger. Next, ask them to look at things with the outside of the spoon (convex mirror). Things should look smaller. Have them compare the effects of the two surfaces.

DEVELOPMENT

1 Teaching Tips—To demonstrate a reflection from a curved mirror, tape rubber tubing in the form of a gentle curve on the surface of an overhead projector. Tell the students that this represents a curved mirror. With the overhead projector on, slowly roll a Ping-Pong ball near the top of the tubing. The ball will bounce off the tubing at an angle and roll back toward the center. Now roll the ball toward the bottom of the tube, as shown. Where the paths of the ball cross each other is the focus or focal point of the "tube" mirror. Compare the paths of the Ping-Pong ball to the paths of the light rays in the text.

2 Teaching Tips—Arrange four flat mirrors as shown in the pupil edition. Use a comb and shine light toward the four mirrors. The students should notice that the light rays are bent toward a point or area.

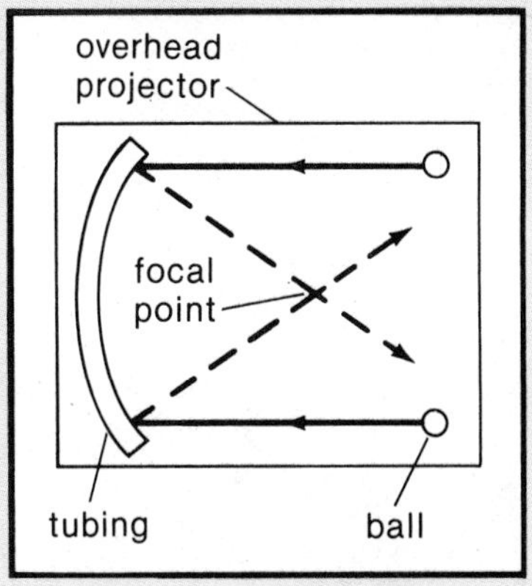

Fig. 5-6

EXTENSIONS

Reinforcement

Science Skills— Comparing and Contrasting

A. Cover the reflector of a flashlight with black paper.

B. Shine the light across the darkened room.

C. Remove the paper and shine the light across the room again.

D. Ask the students to explain the difference observed.When the mirror (reflector) on the flashlight is covered up, the light has nothing to reflect off of. Thus, there is no beam of light from the flashlight. Removing the black paper allows the light to reflect.

ACTIVITY

How can mirrors be used to focus light?

A. Gather these materials: clay, file card, light box, 4 mirrors, and white paper.

B. Place a sheet of white paper about 40 cm (16 in.) from your light box, as shown.

C. Make a screen by bending the file card. Place it at the side of the white paper.

D. Darken the room. Using the clay, stand a mirror in the path of the beam. Turn the mirror so the light is reflected onto the file card. Place another mirror next to the first one. Turn it so it also reflects light onto the card.

1. What happened to the brightness of the light when you added the second mirror?
2. What will happen to the brightness if you add a third mirror?

E. Add a third and a fourth mirror.

3. How can flat mirrors be used to focus light?

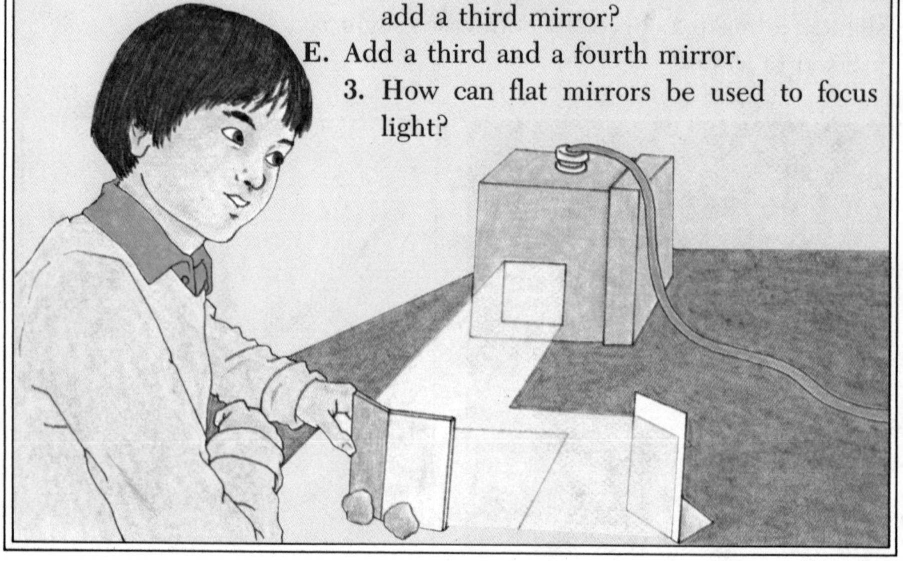

88

ACTIVITY

Skill Development–*Predicting and Inferring*

Teaching Tips—You can substitute a flashlight for the light box. Cover the light end of the flashlight with aluminum foil. Cut a 2-cm diameter hole in the aluminum foil to make a light beam. Do the Activity in a dimly lit room for best results.

Answers to Questions—1. The brightness increased. **2.** It should get brighter. **3.** By joining flat mirrors together and turning each one slightly, light can be focused on a spot.

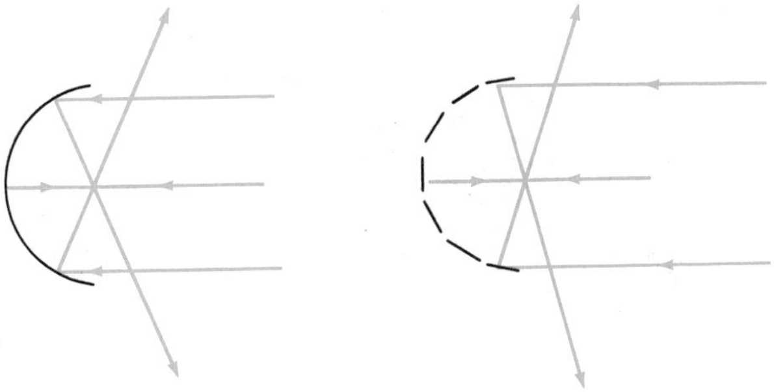

3 The inside of a spoon is like a curved mirror. If you look at the inside of a spoon, everything reflected in the spoon will look larger. Use a spoon to look at the print on this page. The reflected letters should look bigger. Mirrors like this are called **concave** mirrors.

Concave mirror: A mirror that bends in.

The outside of a spoon is also a curved mirror. But the mirror curves out. When you look at things with the outside of the spoon, they will look smaller. Mirrors like this are called **convex** mirrors. You have probably seen *convex* mirrors
4 hanging from the ceiling of stores. Why do you think convex mirrors are used for this purpose?

Convex mirror: A mirror that bends out.

EXTENSIONS

Application

Research—Library

Have your students read about the 500-cm (200-in.) mirror in the Mount Palomar telescope. The 200 in. refers to the diameter of the mirror. Such a large mirror can gather a lot of light. The more light that can be gathered, the more powerful the telescope. The light that is gathered is focused at the focal point. From this point, the light is examined with a lens. Have the students prepare a report for the class.

3 Skill Development—Students *compare and contrast* the effects of concave and convex mirrors.

4 Text Questions—Why do you think convex mirrors are used for this purpose? *The light is reflected over a larger area, allowing the store owners to view a greater area than they normally could.*

EXTENSIONS

Enrichment

Research—Library

Students can go to the library and do research on the space telescope. The space telescope is designed to orbit the earth on a satellite. Since there is no atmosphere to interfere, the space telescope can take pictures much farther out into space than ever before. These pictures can then be transmitted to earth. To guide the students' research, ask them these questions:

1. How does the size of the mirror in the space telescope compare to the size of mirrors in earthbound telescopes?
2. If the mirror is so much smaller, how can it reflect objects in space that are smaller, dimmer, and farther away?
3. How are pictures from the space telescope transmitted to earth?

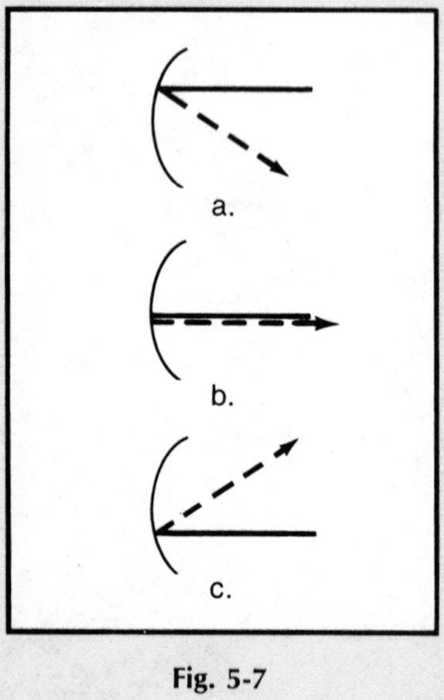

Fig. 5-7

SUGGESTED WORKSHEET MASTERS
for Sections 5-2 and 5-3,
p. T-59 q; p. T-59 r

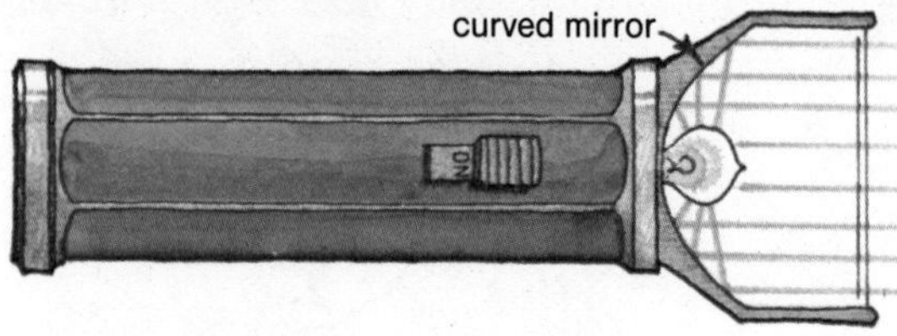

Curved mirrors have many uses. They are used in spotlights, telescopes, flashlights, and the headlights of cars. Curved mirrors focus light. When light is focused, it is brighter. In a **5** flashlight, a bulb is placed at the spot where light is focused by a curved mirror. When you turn the flashlight on, the light from the bulb reflects off the curved mirror. It travels away from the flashlight as a bright beam of light.

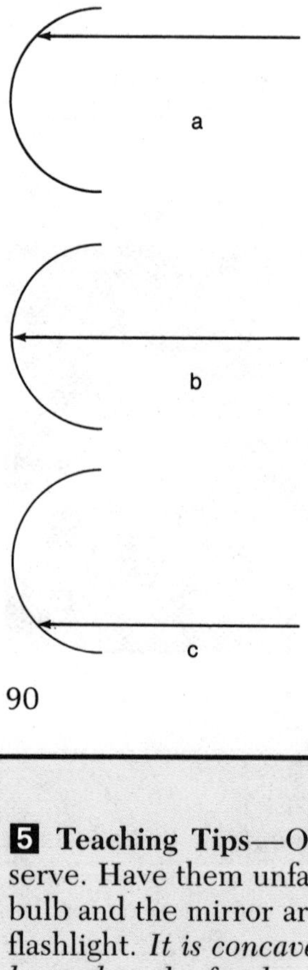

Section Review

Main Ideas: When light beams are focused, they are brought together in one spot. Mirrors turned at slight angles can be used to focus light. Curved mirrors are used in flashlights, spotlights, and headlights.

Questions: Answer in complete sentences.

1. What will be the path of the reflected light beams in the diagrams? Draw a diagram to show your answer.
2. Why does your body look bent in a curved fun house mirror?
3. When light hits a curved reflector, what happens to the light?
4. How would a flashlight be different without a curved mirror inside?

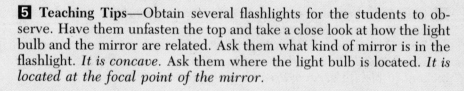

5 Teaching Tips—Obtain several flashlights for the students to observe. Have them unfasten the top and take a close look at how the light bulb and the mirror are related. Ask them what kind of mirror is in the flashlight. *It is concave.* Ask them where the light bulb is located. *It is located at the focal point of the mirror.*

SECTION REVIEW

Answers to Questions

1. See Fig. 5-7.
2. The light is reflected at angles that make you look distorted.
3. The light is focused to a point or area.
4. The flashlight wouldn't work because there would be no surface upon which the light beams could be reflected and focused to a point.

CHAPTER REVIEW

Science Words: Match the words in column A with their meanings in column B.

Column A	Column B
1. Concave mirrors	a. Used to see around corners
2. Convex mirrors	b. Direction of light reflecting off a mirror
3. Angle	c. Mirrors that curve in
4. Periscope	d. Mirrors that curve out
5. Focus	e. To bring together at one spot

Questions: Answer in complete sentences.

1. Which of the following materials would be good reflectors: (a) polished spoon; (b) mirror; (c) rock; (d) wool sweater; (e) rug; or (f) knife blade?
2. Trace or draw these mirrors. Predict the angles of reflection for the beams of light hitting these mirrors. Draw a line on your diagram to show your answer.
3. What do you think would be the path of light in the bottom diagram?
4. How does a curved mirror focus light? Show your answer with a diagram.
5. What is the purpose of a curved mirror in a flashlight and car headlight?
6. Which would be a better mirror on your bike: convex or concave? Explain.
7. How is a periscope used to see around corners?

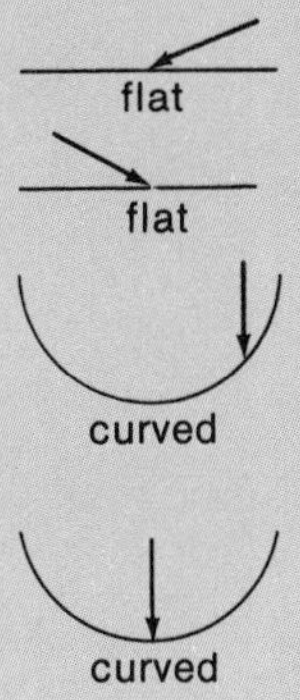

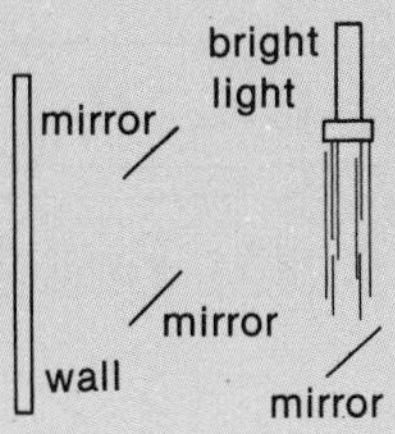

EXTENSIONS

Enrichment

Research—Library

Students can use their dictionaries and books on light to look up the meanings of these terms and to learn how they relate to the concepts in this chapter:

- virtual image—an image that cannot be projected onto a surface
- real image—an image that can be projected onto a surface; formed by a parabolic inverse
- parabolic mirror—a curved mirror
- optics—a branch of science that deals with the nature and properties of light

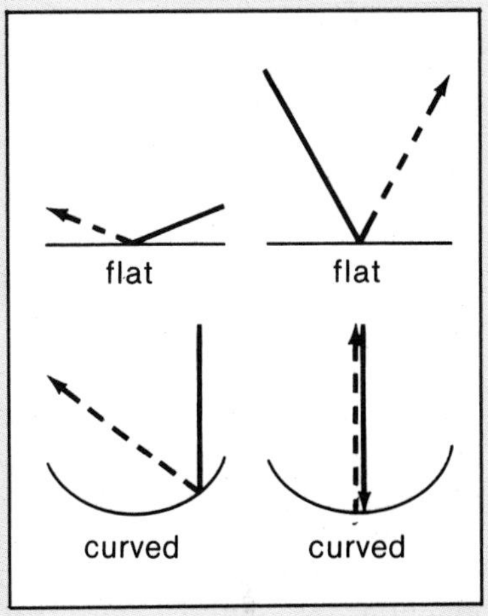

Fig. 5-8

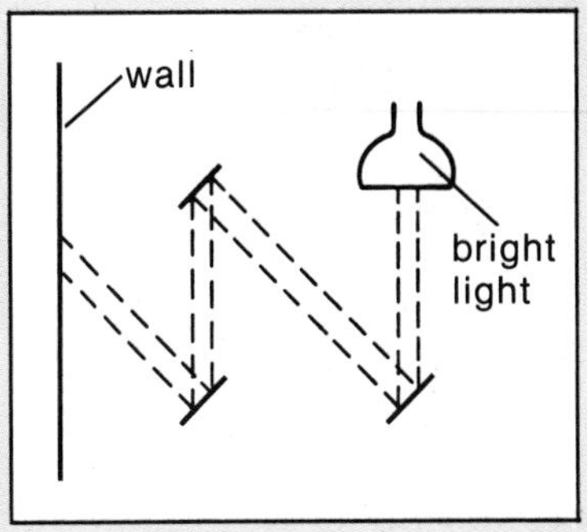

Fig. 5-9

CHAPTER REVIEW

Science Words

1. c, **2.** d, **3.** b, **4.** a, **5.** e

Answers to Questions

1. a, b, f
2. See Fig. 5-8.
3. See Fig. 5-9.
4. A curved mirror focuses light to a point. See the diagram on page 87.
5. A curved mirror in a flashlight or headlight reflects a beam of light from a bulb. The bulb is located at the focal point of the mirror.
6. A convex mirror would be better. You would be able to see a greater area with it.
7. Light is reflected from one mirror to another and then to your eye to allow you to see around corners.

SUGGESTED TEST MASTERS
pp. T-59 g, h

CHAPTER OBJECTIVES

1. Explain how light is bent when it passes from one material into another and identify phenomena caused by the refraction of light.
2. Explain what happens when light passes through a lens.
3. Explain how lenses are used in objects and instruments.
4. Describe what happens when light is refracted by a prism.
5. Explain how we see the color of an object.

SECTION BACKGROUND

Many phenomena, such as the broken appearance of a stick partly immersed in water and mirages, are due to the bending of light beams as they pass obliquely from one material (air) into another (water), or as they pass through layers of air of different densities. When light travels from air into water or glass, it is entering a different material. Its velocity in a dense material such as water or glass is slowed. Because of this, the light beam is bent. The smaller the angle at which the light beam enters the new medium, the more the light beam bends. If the beam hits the medium head on, it passes straight through.

MATERIALS

clear plastic shoe box, light box or flashlight, 4 to 5 drops of milk, sheet of black paper, water, used chalkboard eraser

Exceptional Student IEP Chapter Goal

Using paper and pencil, the student will illustrate and explain what happens when light passes from air into water.

CHAPTER 6

BENDING LIGHT AND COLORS

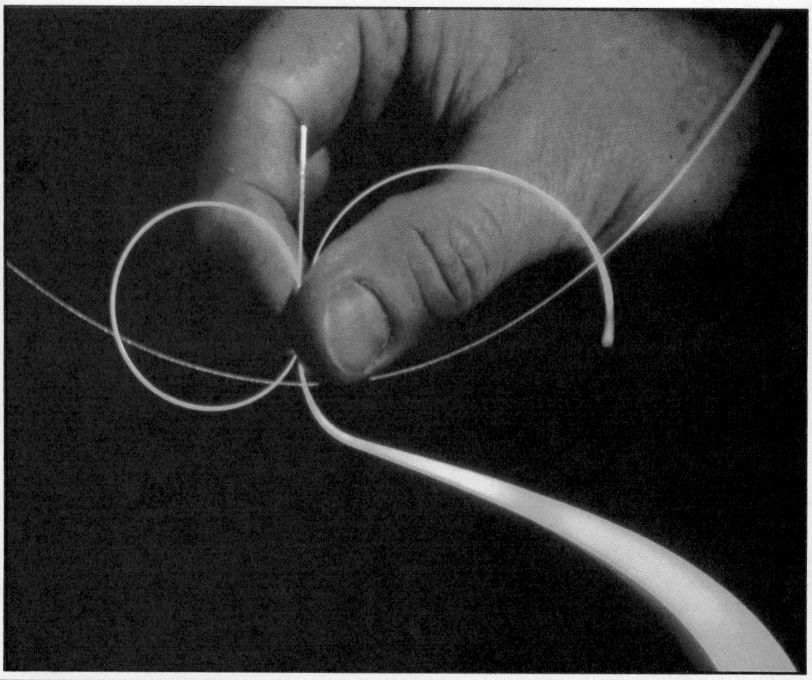

6-1. Light Bends

Imagine riding in a car on a very hot day. You look down the road and see large puddles of water. As you get closer, the puddles disappear. What are these "puddles of water" called? When you finish this section, you should be able to:

BASIC TEACHING PLAN

MOTIVATION

Some students may have experienced mirages. Ask them if they can describe their experience. Follow this by asking them to explain the cause of a mirage. Later in the section, they will have information to check their initial ideas.

Text Questions—What are these "puddles of water" called? *Mirages.*

☐ **A.** Explain what happens to a beam of light when it passes from one kind of material into another.

☐ **B.** Describe the path of light when it moves from one material into another.

Light not only bounces off materials, it goes through some of them. When light goes from air into a material like water, it bends.

1 Look at the picture of a pencil in a glass of **2** water. The pencil looks broken. Is this a trick? Light bends when it goes from air to water. Because of this bending, the pencil looks broken.

Because light bends, there are times when light plays tricks on us. Have you ever sat on the edge of a pond and tried to reach for a fish? You probably missed. You missed because the fish was not really where you grabbed. The fish was actually lower than you thought. The light reflected from the fish bends as it moves from water to air.

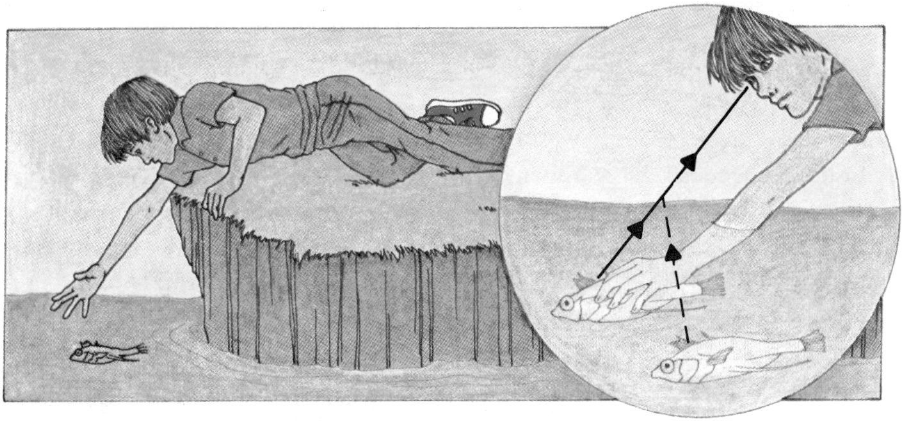

EXTENSIONS

Application
Science Skills—Inferring

A. Place a nickel in an empty bowl or cup (container should be opaque).

B. Have each student move slowly away from the bowl just until the nickel is no longer visible.

C. Slowly fill the bowl with water until the nickel can be seen again.

D. Ask why the nickel became visible. Students should infer that the water bent the light coming from the nickel to their eyes.

DEVELOPMENT

1 Skill Development—Students *observe* the demonstrations in the text and *infer* what causes these phenomena of light.

2 Text Questions—Is this a trick? *No. The pencil appears broken because the light rays are bent by the water.*

Exceptional Student
Visually Impaired/ Learning-Disabled

To teach this concept, use bent straws to reproduce the path of light as shown in the photograph.

EXTENSIONS

Reinforcement

Activity

A. Have your students put a straw in a glass half-filled with water.

B. Ask them to copy what they see onto a sheet of paper.

C. Then ask them to explain why the top of the straw does not appear to be aligned with the bottom of the straw.

ACTIVITY

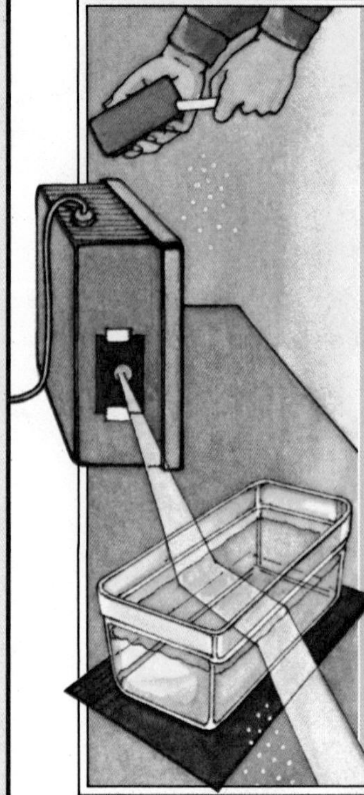

How can you bend a light beam?

A. Gather these materials: clear plastic shoebox, light box, milk, sheet of black paper, water, and used chalkboard eraser.

B. Place the plastic shoebox on the sheet of black paper. Fill the shoebox with water. Mix 4 or 5 drops of milk into the water.

C. Shine the light straight at one long side of the shoebox.

D. Scrape some chalk dust off the eraser. Sprinkle the dust into the light beam. Look down on the light beam from above.

E. Move the light box to a new position.

1. What happens to the path of the light?
2. How can you make the light bend more?
3. How does changing the angle of the light beam affect the path of the light beam in the water?

Mirage: Something we see that really isn't there.

The bending of light explains what seem to be puddles of water on roads. These puddles of water, which are not really there, are called **mirages** (muh-**razh**-ez). On a hot day, the sun heats up the road. This makes a layer of hot air just above the road. The light passing through cooler air above hits the hot air and is bent. The difference between cool and warm air is enough to bend the light as it passes through. When the light bends, you see a reflection of the blue sky.

ACTIVITY

Skill Development—*Finding Cause and Effect*

Teaching Tips—You can substitute a glass aquarium for the plastic shoe box. If you do not use the light box (see page T-83 for construction directions), a high-intensity flashlight with top covered with foil will work well.

Answers to Questions—1. It is bent. **2.** The light will bend more if the angle of the incoming light is changed. **3.** The sharper the angle at which the light enters the water, the more the beam is bent.

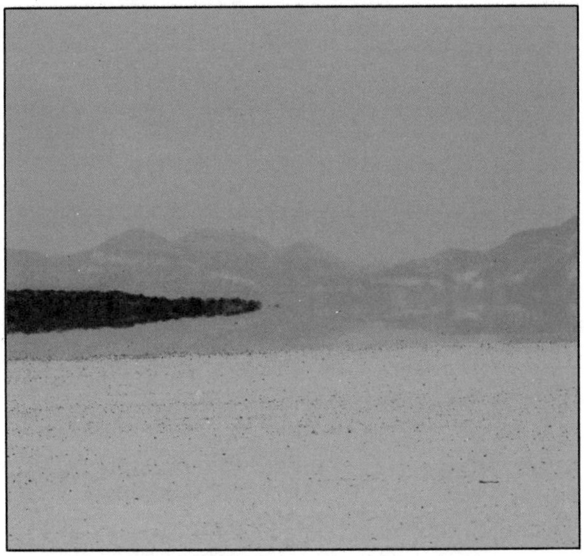

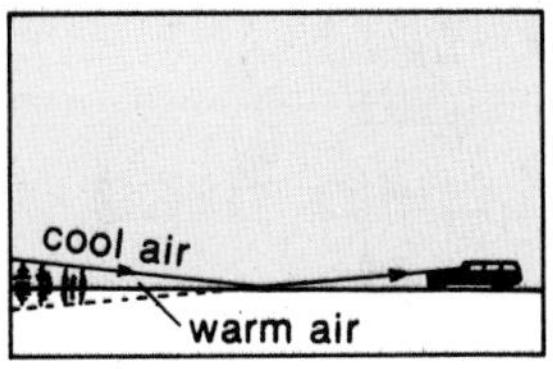

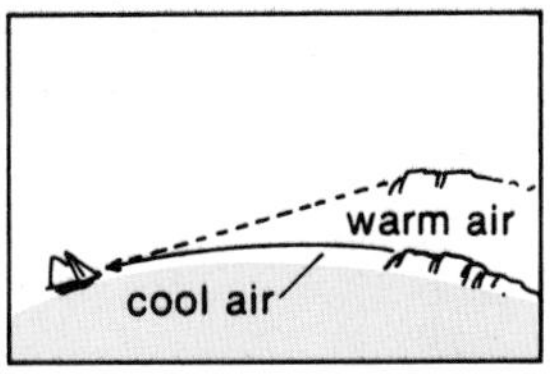

This reflection looks like a puddle of water. As the diagram shows, there are different kinds of *mirages*. Sometimes distant objects like mountains may appear to float in the air.

Section Review

Main Ideas: When light moves from one material into another, its beams are bent.

Questions: Answer in complete sentences.

1. What happens to a beam of light as it passes from one material into another?
2. Look at the picture on page 93. Why does the pencil look broken?
3. Explain one example of how the bending of light can trick your eyes into seeing something that is not really there.

EXTENSIONS

Enrichment

Research—Library

As refraction is caused by light traveling from a material of one density into a material of a different density, students could research the speed of light in various media and compare those speeds to the speed of light in air. Suggested materials are glass and water. If some speeds of light are not easily found, students could look for the densities of various substances and compare these to the density of air.

SECTION REVIEW

Main Ideas—Ask students to draw a diagram showing how light bends. Ask them to write a few sentences telling why light bends.

Answers to Questions

1. If it enters at an angle, it bends.
2. A light beam slows down as it enters the water, and the beam is bent. For this reason, the pencil appears broken.
3. In a mirage, light passing through different layers of air is bent. The bending of light causes us to see a reflection of the sky.

SECTION BACKGROUND

A lens is a piece of curved glass or plastic that refracts light passing through it. Convex lenses bulge outward. When light passes through them, it is bent to one point (the focal point). The amount of bending is due to the thickness and shape of the lens. Sharply curved lenses bend light more than slightly curved lenses. Concave lenses which have a caved-in center, spread light rays apart. They are not, however, presented in this section.

MATERIALS

1 thin jar (e. g., olive jar), 1 thick jar (e. g., mayonnaise jar), water, flashlight, aluminum foil (10 cm × 10 cm), sheet of white paper, ruler

6-2. Lenses Bend Light

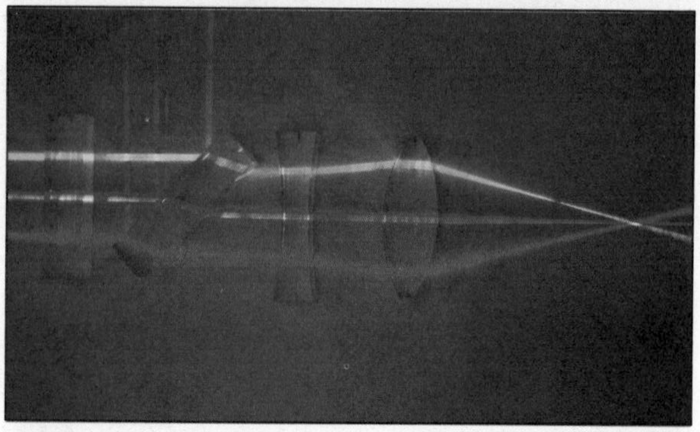

How are air and glass different? Air is a thin material and a gas. Glass is thick and solid. When light passes from air into glass, it is bent. Look closely at the picture. The light is bent so that the beams of light cross each other. Do you know why this happens? When you finish this section, you should be able to:

- ☐ **A.** Explain what happens to beams of light as they pass through a glass *lens.*
- ☐ **B.** Identify common objects that contain *lenses.*

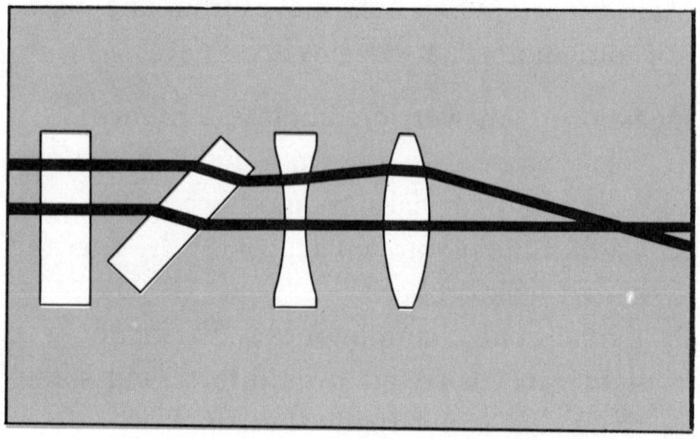

BASIC TEACHING PLAN

MOTIVATION

Give each student a small piece of waxed paper. Then put a small drop of water on the waxed paper. Next to the drop of water, put a drop of corn syrup. The drops of liquid make good lenses. Have the students look through the lenses at letters on a printed page. Which magnifies more? *The syrup will magnify more because it forms a thicker lens.* Ask the students why the letters appear to look bigger.

Some of your students may wear contact lenses. You might ask these students to describe their lenses and how they think they work.

Text Questions—How are air and glass different? *Air is less dense than glass.* Do you know why this happens? *The light beams are bent as they pass through the lens.*

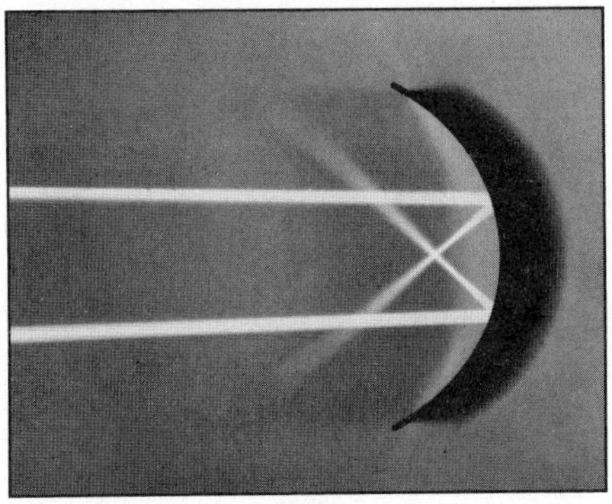

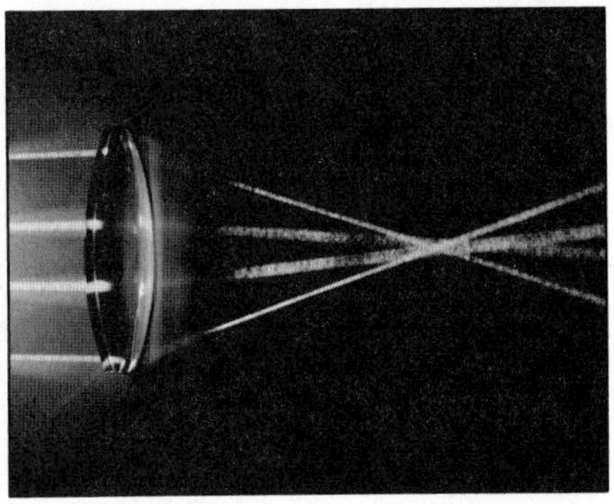

1 The picture on page 96 shows that light bends when it passes through a **lens** (lenz). A *lens* is any piece of curved glass or plastic. The lens may be curved on one side and flat on the other side. Or it may be curved on both sides. The light is bent as it moves from the air into the lens. The light is bent again as it leaves the lens and enters the air. The point where light beams meet is called the focus or **focal point** (**foe**-kul) of the lens.

Lens: A piece of curved glass that bends light.

Look at the two pictures above. One shows how a curved mirror bends light. The other shows how a lens bends light. Both focus the light to a *focal point.*

Focal point: The point at which a lens brings light beams together.

2 

EXTENSIONS

Application

Science Skills—Comparing and Contrasting

Lenses can be made using small plastic vials, test tubes, or glass jars. In this Extension, use the same size containers. Gather various liquids (water, cooking oil, corn syrup, rubbing alcohol, a clear soda pop), paper towels, one container for each liquid, and a candle.

A. Fill each container with a different liquid. Make a circle with the containers and place the candle in the center.

B. Light the candle. The light will shine through the "lenses" and will be bent. The light will be bent to a point as it passes through each jar. The distance from the jar to the point is the focal length of the "lens." Compare the various focal lengths. In general, the thicker materials should have shorter focal lengths and will bend the light more.

DEVELOPMENT

1 Teaching Tips—Obtain a large jar and fill it with water. You now have a device you can use to demonstrate how light is bent by lenses. Cover the light in a flashlight or light box with foil and cut a narrow slit in the foil. Set a screen of cardboard behind the jar. Shine the light toward the jar. If you shine the light through the side of the jar, you should be able to see the beam of light on the cardboard. Have the students observe that light is bent to a point by such a lens.

2 Skill Development—Provide your students with magnifying glasses. Let them look at a variety of objects, noting how they are magnified. If you can get magnifying glasses of different magnification, the students can *compare* them and *infer* why there is a difference.

EXTENSIONS

Enrichment

Science Skills—Measuring

Focus a lens or magnifying glass on some lined paper. Calculate how many spaces seen outside the lens equal a single space seen through the lens. For example, if four spaces are seen outside the space taken up by one space in the lens, then the lens magnifies four times.

Activity

Gather a convex lens (magnifying glass) and a piece of white paper. Darken all the windows in the room but one. Hold the lens in front of the window. Bring the piece of white paper slowly toward the side of the lens facing the inside of the room until an image of the outside is clearly seen. What do you observe about the image? (It is upside down.)

ACTIVITY

How does a lens work?

A. Gather these materials: 2 jars (1 olive jar and 1 mayonnaise jar), water, flashlight, piece of aluminum foil, sheet of white paper, and ruler.

B. Tape a sheet of white paper to your desk. Draw a straight line across the paper.

C. Fill the narrow jar with water. Place the jar on the line, as shown in the picture.

D. Put the aluminum foil over the end of the flashlight. Cut a narrow slit in the foil. Darken the room and turn on your flashlight. Aim the light at the jar as shown.

1. What happened to the light as it passed through the jar?

E. Place the wide jar of water on the line as shown. Aim the light at the jar.

2. What happened to the light as it passed through the jar?
3. How is light bent by a narrow jar compared with a wide jar?
4. How are the jars like lenses?

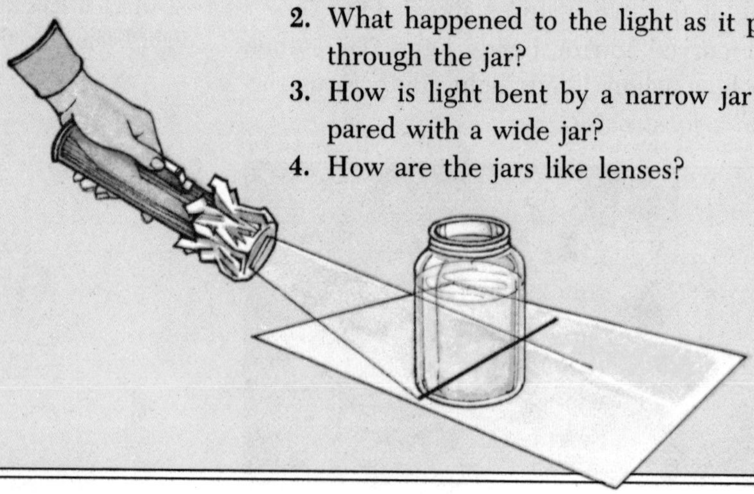

ACTIVITY

Skill Development—*Measuring and Recording Data*

Teaching Tips—Be sure that the two jars each group of students has are of different diameters. They will need a thin and a thick jar. The jars will represent lenses. You may have to help the students to measure the focal length of each jar. The measurement is the distance from the middle of the jar to the spot where the light converges. The distance will be shorter for the thick jar.

Answers to Questions—**1.** The light was bent. **2.** The light was bent. **3.** Light is bent less by a thin jar than a thick jar. **4.** The jars are like lenses in that they bend light to a point.

Lenses have many different uses. We can use lenses to get a closer look at small things, like rocks and bugs. Lenses in eyeglasses help people to see better. The lens helps the eye to focus light. This makes the object look sharper.

Lenses are also used in scientific instruments. An instrument used to make very small things
3 look larger is called a **microscope** (**my**-kruh-skope). You can see creatures with a *microscope* that are impossible to see with just your eyes.
4 Some microscopes can make an object look 1,000 times bigger than it really is! Look at the two photos of a housefly. The left picture shows how it looks using only your eyes. The right picture was taken through a microscope. What can
5 you see in the right picture that is impossible to see in the left picture?

Scientists use an instrument called a **telescope** (**tell**-uh-skope) to see things that are far away. *Telescopes* use lenses to magnify objects like

Microscope: An instrument that makes small things look large.

Telescope: An instrument that makes faraway things look closer.

EXTENSIONS

Reinforcement

Science Skills—Observing

Gather a thin wire, a nail, and water. Loop the wire around the nail to form a circle. Dip the loop into the water and look through it. The water lens will magnify as much as four times. Look at different things with it. If you tap the wire, much of the water will fall off it. The water remaining will form a lens that is very thin at the center. This is a concave lens.

3 Skill Development—You have an excellent opportunity to have the students *observe* various objects—living and nonliving—and *classify* them according to appropriate categories using a microscope.

4 Teaching Tips—Gather several microscopes so that your students can view tiny objects, such as microscopic animals and plants, cells, sand, hair, and any other objects of interest.

5 Text Questions—What can you see in the right picture that is impossible to see in the left picture? *Many more details of the fly are visible.*

EXTENSIONS

Application
***Science Skills—
Following Directions***

You can make a simple refracting telescope with just two lenses. The lens near your eye is the eyepiece. The lens closer to the objects you look at is called the objective lens.

A. Gather two lenses, one thicker than the other. Mount them on a ruler, separated by about 20 cm. The thicker lens should be the one closer to your eye.

B. Look through the eyepiece along the line of the ruler so that you can see the objective lens. Move the objective lens closer or farther away until an object comes into focus. The image of the object will be upside down.

stars and planets. Look at the two photographs.
6 Which one was taken through a telescope? What features of the moon can be seen only with the help of a telescope?

Section Review

Main Ideas: A lens is a piece of curved glass or plastic that lets light pass through. Lenses can bend light beams so that the beams come together at one place. The place where light beams come together is called the focus of the lens. Lenses can make small things look bigger or faraway things seem closer.

Questions: Answer in complete sentences.
1. What happens to light when it passes through a lens?
2. What are three objects that have lenses?
3. What is the same about the way light is bent by a lens and a curved mirror?

6 **Text Questions**—Which one was taken through a telescope? *The one on the left.* What features of the moon can be seen only with the help of a telescope? *Craters, hills, and shadows on the moon.*

SECTION REVIEW

Answers to Questions
1. The light is bent and comes to a point.
2. Telescope, microscope, magnifying glass, eyeglasses
3. Both focus light to a point.

Have you ever seen a rainbow? Why do you think rainbows only appear after a rain shower? You can hold a piece of glass in the sun to make your own small rainbow. When you finish this section, you should be able to:

- ☐ **A.** Explain why a *prism* can split light into colors.
- ☐ **B.** Identify the colors of the light *spectrum.*
- ☐ **C.** Describe how a rainbow is formed.

6-3. Prisms and Rainbows

The piece of glass shown below is called a **prism** (**priz**-um). A *prism* breaks white light into a group of colors called the **spectrum** (**spek**-
1 trum). The colors of the *spectrum* are red, orange, yellow, green, blue, indigo, and violet. An easy way to remember these colors is to imagine a boy's name, ROY G. BIV. Each letter stands for one of the colors in the spectrum.

Prism: A piece of glass that bends light and separates it into color.

Spectrum: The group of seven colors that make up white light.

SECTION BACKGROUND

Isaac Newton was the first scientist to analyze light. He found that different colors do not all bend to the same degree. As a beam of light containing all the colors enters a prism, the different colors undergo different amounts of refraction and travel through the prism along different paths. On re-emerging into air, the colors are bent further, with the result that they follow even more divergent paths. When the colors fall on a white screen, a rainbow (spectrum) is observed. The colors are arranged in the order of their degree of refraction. For example, blue light is bent more than red light.

MATERIALS

flashlight, mirror, tray of water, crayons, sheet of white paper

BASIC TEACHING PLAN

MOTIVATION

Obtain a prism for demonstration purposes. If there is plenty of direct sunlight, darken the room except for one window. Place the prism in the path of the sunlight, and direct the spectrum produced by it onto a wall.

Text Questions—Have you ever seen a rainbow? *Allow students to give accounts of their experiences.* Why do you think rainbows only appear after a rain shower? *The drops of water act like a prism, and the sunlight is split into the colors of the spectrum.*

DEVELOPMENT

1 Teaching Tips—Use a prism to help the students identify the various colors of the rainbow. Have the students draw the rainbow. You can review with them the acronym "Roy G. Biv," which can be used to remember the seven colors of the spectrum.

EXTENSIONS

Enrichment

Science Skills—Following Directions

Using a paper chromatography technique, students can find out that colors are combinations of other colors. The component colors of various inks are separated by letting water dissolve the pigments and carry them up a paper towel by capillary action.

A. Gather the following materials: strips of paper towels, various pens (ball-point, transparency, ink), water, tape, jars.

B. Cut the paper towels into small strips measuring 2 cm × 10 cm.

C. To test an ink pen, make a thick line across the narrow width of the paper about 2 cm from the end. Put this end in the water, but do not let the ink mark touch the water directly. Water will start to move upward. As it passes through the ink mark, the component colors will be separated and carried upward. Only ink that dissolves in water will work. Let the students test a variety of pens.

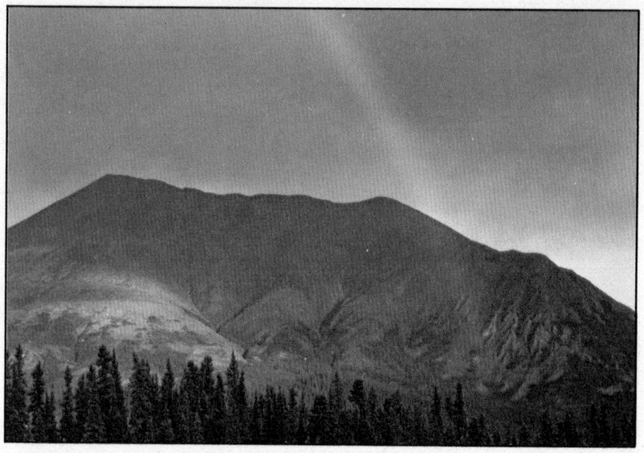

2 How does a prism split white light into the colors of the spectrum? You have already learned that light can be reflected and bent. Remember what happens when light is bent. When a beam of light passes from air into glass, it slows down. When it passes into the glass, it bends.

3 The diagram below shows white light hitting a glass prism. When the light hits the glass, it is

4 slowed down and bent. Notice that the color vio-

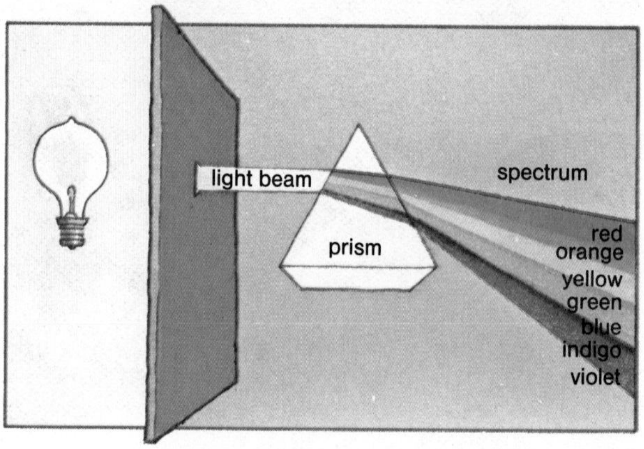

2 Text Questions—How does a prism split white light into the colors of the spectrum? *Each color in white light is bent differently in a prism. Thus, each color travels along a slightly different path.*

3 Teaching Tips—If you cannot obtain a prism, fill a jar with water and set it on a sheet of white paper on a windowsill in bright sunlight. If the light shines through the glass at the right angle, a spectrum of colors will be visible on the paper.

4 Skill Development—Students can *compare and contrast* the degree to which various colors are bent by a prism.

let is bent more than the color red. When the colors come out the other side of the prism, they are bent again. Each color is bent by a different amount. This causes the colors to be separated.

After it rains, there are millions of tiny water drops in the air. When the sun comes out, light strikes the drops of water. Each tiny droplet acts like a prism.

Sunlight enters the drop and is split into the colors of the spectrum. The colors are bounced off the other side of the raindrop. They are reflected to the front of the drop. When they leave the raindrop, the colors are bent again. This bending and reflecting happens in millions of drops at the same time.

ACTIVITY

What is white light made of?

A. Gather these materials: flashlight, mirror, tray of water, and crayons.
B. Place the mirror in the tray of water.
C. Shine the flashlight at the mirror.
D. Move the flashlight around until you can see a reflection of colors on the ceiling.
  1. What colors did you see?
E. Draw a picture of the spectrum you observed.
  2. What happened to the white light from the flashlight?
  3. What colors make up white light?

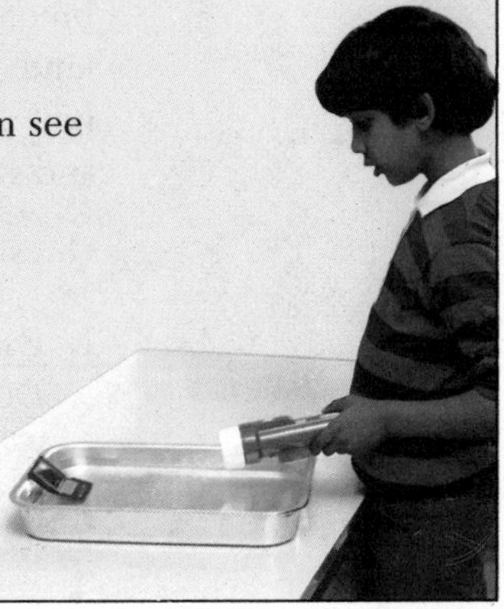

EXTENSIONS

Application
Activity

Since rainbows don't occur every day, students may wish to make their own rainbows. A common phenomenon that they probably have noticed is the rainbow effect that occurs when sunlight shines on an oil spill.

A. Gather the following materials: various oils (automobile, lubricating, and vegetable), water, crayons, white paper.

B. Students can mix oil and water, spread it on a small patch of ground, and observe and illustrate the rainbow formed. They can compare the colors and their intensity.

ACTIVITY

Skill Development—*Concluding and Generalizing*

Teaching Tips—If it is a sunny day, use sunlight rather than the flashlight. The rainbow will be much brighter. If you do not have a flat ceiling, the students can capture the rainbow by holding a piece of white paper in the path of the colors.

Answers to Questions—1. The seven colors of the spectrum.
2. The white light was split into the colors of the spectrum.
3. White light is composed of red, orange, yellow, green, blue, indigo, and violet.

EXTENSIONS

Application

Science Skills—Following Directions

Students can make a spectroscope using a piece of clear plastic called diffraction paper. Diffraction paper can be purchased from a science supply house. A piece 1 cm × 1 cm is all that is needed for each spectroscope.

A. Obtain a shoe box with a lid. In one end, cut a square about 1 cm × 1 cm. Tape the diffraction paper over the hole.

B. In the other end, cut a tiny slit about 1 cm long. This is the end of the box that will be pointed at objects. Light will come through the slit and be split by the diffraction paper.

C. Hold the end of the box with the diffraction paper up to your eye. The spectrum of colors should be visible. Use the spectroscope to look at sunlight. (CAUTION: Never look directly at the sun.) Simply point the box out the window. Students can also look at the spectra made by light bulbs and fluorescent lights.

SUGGESTED WORKSHEET MASTER
for Sections 6-2 and 6-3, p. T-59 s

5 Isaac Newton was a scientist who split light by using a prism. He held a glass prism in the path of a narrow beam of sunlight. He saw that light is broken into seven colors by a prism.

Section Review

Main Ideas: Prisms can separate white light into a group of colors called the spectrum. The spectrum is made of red, orange, yellow, green, blue, indigo, and violet. Rainbows are a special kind of spectrum. You can sometimes see a rainbow after a rain shower. Each raindrop bends and reflects sunlight like a prism.

Questions: Answer in complete sentences.

1. Explain what a prism does to white light. Draw a diagram to show your answer.
2. What are the colors that make up white light?
3. How are raindrops like a prism?
4. What happens when a prism is placed in front of a spectrum of colors?

5 **Skill Development**—Newton's thought process is a good example of a scientist *hypothesizing* and then testing the ideas.

SECTION REVIEW

Answers to Questions

1. It splits white light into the seven colors of the spectrum. See the diagram on page 102.
2. Red, orange, yellow, green, blue, indigo, and violet
3. Raindrops are like prisms in that both are able to split light into the colors of the spectrum.
4. The spectrum of colors is bent to make white light.

What colors do you see in the figure below? Cup your hands around the picture. Bring your eye close to the page and look at the picture now. Can you see colors in dim light? Can you see colors with no light? When you finish this section, you should be able to:

6-4. Seeing Colors

- ☐ **A.** Explain how we see different colors.
- ☐ **B.** Describe what happens when white light hits colored glass.
- ☐ **C.** Identify the primary colors of light.

When white light strikes an object, all the colors of white light also strike that object. If all the colors are reflected, the object will look white. For example, look at a piece of white paper. The

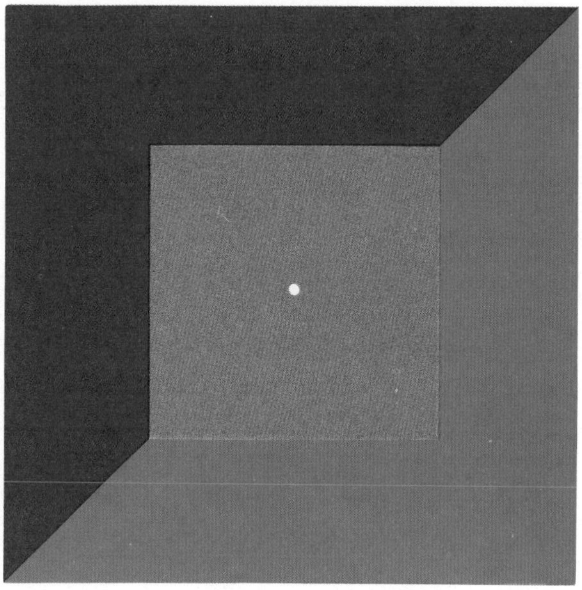

SECTION BACKGROUND

When white light strikes an object, all the colors making up white light are also striking that object. Colored objects reflect their colored portion of white light and absorb all other colors. Black objects do not reflect any light at all. White objects reflect all colors of light. Red, green, and blue are the primary light colors. If you were to mix light of these colors, the result would be white light. The primary colors of paints are red, yellow, and blue. All other colors can be made by mixing different amounts of these primary colors.

MATERIALS

flashlight; sheets of red, green, blue, and white paper

BASIC TEACHING PLAN

MOTIVATION

The sensations of color fade in dim light. You can tell if something is light or dark, but you can't tell the color. The students will discover this if they follow the directions in the Motivation.

Text Questions—What colors do you see in the figure below? *Red, green, blue.* Can you see colors in dim light? *Some students may see some color. Green will be more easily seen than red or blue. The eye is more sensitive to colors in the middle of the spectrum (green) than to colors on either end (red and blue).* Can you see colors with no light? *No.*

EXTENSIONS

Enrichment

Activity

As a class demonstration, you could make colored wax candles by melting wax and crayons. Use only crayons of red, yellow, and blue, the primary colors of pigments. Students can mix known quantities of these colors to find out what colors result.

A. Obtain wax; red, yellow, and blue crayons; and candle molds (small cans or cartons).

B. Each of the three colors should be melted with the wax in separate coffee cans that have been placed in a pan of water. The water should be heated on an electric hot plate that has an enclosed heating element.

C. Students should keep a record of the colors used for each candle. They can record their results on a chart. The chart should include the colors mixed, the quantities, and the resulting candle colors.

paper is white because all the colors are reflected to your eye.

1 Not all objects are white. Colored objects soak up some of the light that strikes them. They **absorb** (ab-**sorb**) some light. Some of the light is reflected. The apple is red because it reflects the red part of white light. The apple *absorbs* all the other colors. Grass is green because it reflects the green part of the white light. All the other **2** colors are absorbed by the grass. What color is the shirt or dress you are wearing today? Why is it that color?

Absorb: To take in and hold light.

Some objects allow light to pass through them. Colored glass, cellophane, and colored water are examples. Why do these objects have color?

Look at the picture of the stained glass. When light passes through colored glass, some of the colors in the white light are absorbed. Red glass is red because all the colors except red are absorbed. Only the red part of light passes through. A transparent material lets its own color pass through.

DEVELOPMENT

1 Teaching Tips—To demonstrate that the color of an object is determined by what portion of the spectrum it reflects, use a prism and various colors of construction paper. Hold the prism in sunlight so that the spectrum is directed at a red sheet of paper. The red end of the spectrum will be very clear, whereas the other colors will be barely visible. The red is reflected, and the other colors are absorbed. Hold a sheet of another color in the path of the spectrum. Let the students predict the color that will be clearly visible. Ask them what colors will be visible if white paper is held in the path. *All colors.* What if black is held in the path? *None of the colors.*

2 Text Questions—What color is the shirt or dress you are wearing today? *Answers will vary.* Why is it that color? *That part of the spectrum is reflected; the other parts are absorbed.*

3 Text Questions—Why do these objects have color? *Part of the spectrum passes through; the rest is absorbed.*

ACTIVITY

What happens when light hits an opaque object?

A. Gather these materials: flashlight and sheets of red, green, blue, and white paper.

B. Darken the room. Hold 1 colored sheet of paper up to the white sheet. Shine the flashlight onto the colored paper.

1. What color is reflected onto the white paper?
2. What do you think happened to other colors that make up the white light of the flashlight?

C. Repeat step B for the other colored sheets of paper.

3. What color was reflected onto the white sheet for the other 2 colors?
4. What happens when light hits an opaque object?

EXTENSIONS

Enrichment

Activity

Students will enjoy playing with colored afterimages. Here are some experiments they can try.

A. Make a large red dot in the center of a white sheet of paper. Stare at it for about 1 min. Now move your eyes to another sheet of plain white paper. You will see a green dot.

B. Make a large green dot in the center of a white sheet of paper. What do you predict the color of the afterimage will be? (Red) Now try it.

4 **Teaching Tips**—Sheets of colored cellophane, candy wrappers, glass jars, and food coloring can all be used by students to investigate what happens when light passes through colored things.

ACTIVITY

Skill Development–*Concluding and Generalizing*

Answers to Questions—1. The color of the sheet. **2.** The other colors were absorbed by the colored paper. **3.** The color of the respective sheets. **4.** Only the color of the object is reflected. The other colors are absorbed.

EXTENSIONS

Reinforcement

Science Skills— Cause and Effect

Students can discover what happens when they mix lights of different colors. Use pieces of colored cellophane or small glass bottles (baby food jars) of colored water. Provide red-, green-, and blue-colored cellophane or bottles of water. Hold one filter in front of another or one colored bottle in front of another and shine a flashlight through them. Discuss what happens when various colors are combined and when you look at various objects with colored filters.

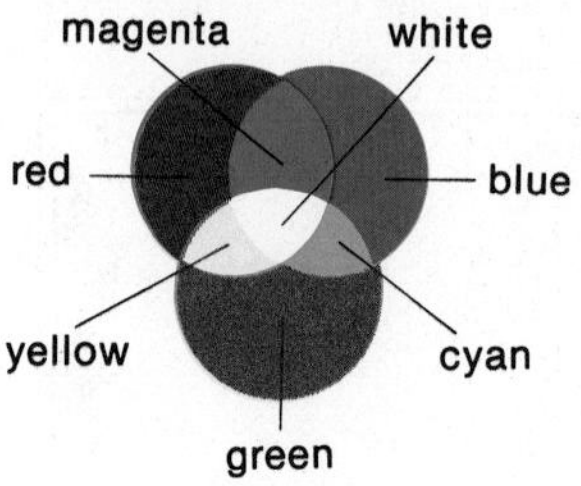

If you have ever mixed paints, you may know that the three primary colors of paints are red, yellow, and blue.

The color pictures in this book are made by the four-color printing process. Red, yellow, and blue inks are used. Black ink is the fourth color.

The primary colors of light are different from the primary colors of paints. Red, green, and blue are the primary colors of light. All colors can be made by mixing different amounts of these colors. As you can see in the diagram, red and green make yellow. Red and blue make **7** magenta. What color do green and blue make? If the three primary light colors are mixed together, white is formed.

Section Review

Main Ideas: We see colors because of what happens when light hits an object. An opaque object like a green leaf reflects green and absorbs all the other colors. A transparent object, like a blue glass vase, absorbs all the colors but blue. The blue light passes through.

Questions: Answer in complete sentences.

1. When light shines on orange paper, what happens to the white light?
2. If you shine white light through a transparent red vase, what happens to the white light?
3. If red light is reflected from an object, what is the color of the object?
4. What are the primary light colors?

5 Teaching Tips—Help the students make the distinction betwee mixing colored lights and mixing colored paints.
6 Teaching Tips—Place a petri dish or glass saucer on the overhea projector. Fill the dish half full with water. Put a few drops of red an blue food coloring in the water. Do not let them mix at first. After while, the water will heat up, and convection currents will move th water, resulting in mixing.
7 Text Questions—What color do green and blue make? *Cyan.*

SECTION REVIEW

Answers to Questions
1. The orange part of the spectrum is reflected, while the other par are absorbed by the paper.
2. The red part of the spectrum passes through the vase, while th other parts of the spectrum are absorbed.
3. Red
4. Red, green, and blue

SUGGESTED WORKSHEET MASTER
p. T-59 t

CHAPTER REVIEW

Science Words: Copy the numbered letters and spaces on paper. Use the hints to help you identify the science terms.

1. m _ _ _ _ _
2. _ _ _ s
3. _ _ i _ _
4. _ p _ _ _ _ _ _
5. _ _ _ _ _ b
6. _ _ c _ _ _ _ _ _ _
7. _ _ _ e _ _ _ _ _

Hints

1. Something you see that isn't really there
2. A curved piece of glass that bends light
3. A piece of glass that can form the spectrum
4. The seven colors of white light
5. To take in and hold light
6. An instrument that makes small things look larger
7. An instrument that makes faraway things seem close

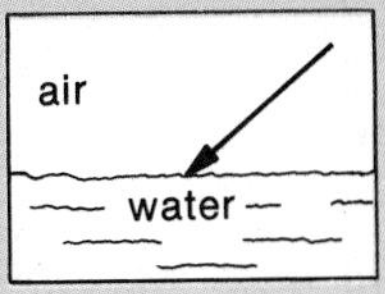

Questions: Answer in complete sentences.

1. What will be the path of light in the diagram? Draw a diagram to show your answer.
2. Light shines on the prism. What do you think will happen to the white light? Make a diagram to show your answer. You may use crayons.

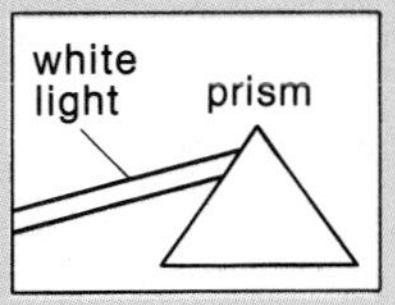

EXTENSIONS

Enrichment

Research

Students can research the lives of Antony van Leeuwenhoek and Galileo. These two famous scientists made important advances in the use of microscopes and telescopes. Have the students research the kind of instruments they used and the important discoveries they made.

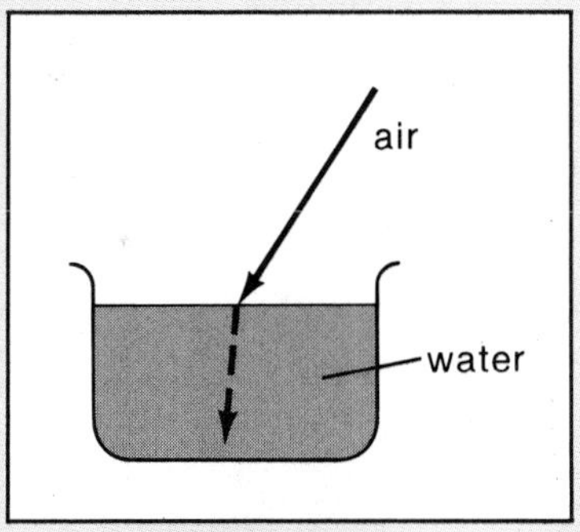

Fig. 6-1

CHAPTER REVIEW

Science Words

1. Mirage, **2.** lens, **3.** prism, **4.** spectrum, **5.** absorb, **6.** microscope, **7.** telescope

Answers to Questions

1. See Fig. 6-1.
2. The light is split into seven colors. Refer to the diagram on page 102.

SUGGESTED WORKSHEET MASTER
p. T-59 u

SUGGESTED TEST MASTERS
pp. T-59 i, j, k

EXTENSIONS

Enrichment

Activity

After the students have done the Investigation, they can use the apparatus to make colored shadows. They will need a yardstick and a textbook.

A. With all three colored lights on, so that they blend to produce white on the screen, the students should hold the yardstick edgewise and parallel to the floor in front of the lights. Have them observe the shadow formed.

B. They should then raise and lower one end of the yardstick to observe the change in the shadow.

C. Hold the book in front of the lights and observe what happens.

1. What did the shadow of the yardstick look like when it was level?
2. What did it look like when it was tipped in front of the lights?
3. What did the shadow of the book look like?
4. What happened to the shadows when the objects were moved?

INVESTIGATING

What happens when you mix the primary colors of light?

In this chapter, you learned that white light is made up of three primary colors: red, green, and blue. You will now see how you can mix these colors to produce both white light and other colors of light.

A. Gather the following materials: squares of red, green, and blue cellophane; 3 flashlights (or penlights); 3 rubber bands; and white cardboard screen.

B. Cover 1 flashlight with red cellophane. Fold over the edges and hold them in place with a rubber band. Repeat this step with the green and blue cellophane.

C. Darken the room. Shine colored spots from each flashlight on a white screen. Make sure all 3 flashlights are the same distance from the screen.

1. What color is produced when all three colors—red, green, and blue—shine on the same spot?

D. Try different combinations of the red, green, and blue lights to produce different colors. Copy the chart below and use it to record your observations.

Colors Mixed	Color Produced
1. red + blue	
2. red + green	
3.	
4.	

INVESTIGATING

Teaching Tips—If possible, use two or three layers of the cellophane to give a deeper or purer color.

Answers to Questions—1. White.

CAREERS

Photographer ►

In 1826, a Frenchman made the first photograph.

A career in photography requires that you know about light and how lenses work. You also must know when to use different kinds of film and how to develop film. Photographers can work for newspapers, public relations companies, advertising firms, and many other businesses.

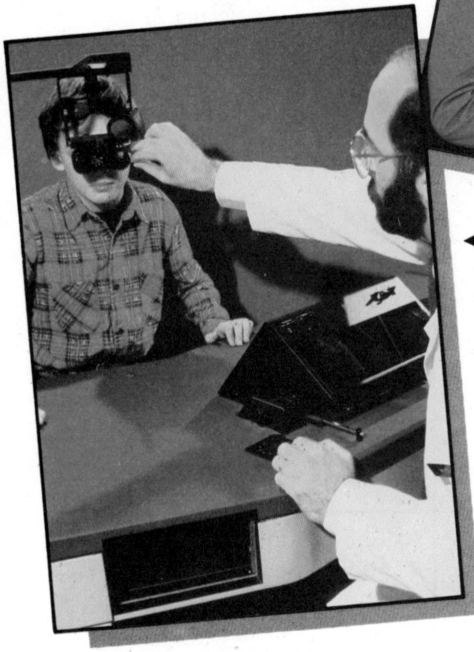

◄ Optician

The person shown in the picture is an optician. An optician makes the lenses in eyeglasses. The lens in the eyeglass helps the lens in your eye work properly. Together, they bend the light beams so that the beams focus exactly on the back of your eye. When the light beams focus this way, you see a clear picture. Opticians are skilled persons.

EXTENSIONS

Application
Research

Students may be interested in learning about other careers involving light. Astronomers use large telescopes and other instruments to study the sky. They observe the movement of stars and planets, and try to explain the phenomena they observe. An astronomer needs to know a great deal of mathematics and science, and an advanced degree is required to work in this field. To learn more about astronomers, students might want to contact the American Astronomical Society, 211 Fitzgerald Road, Princeton, NJ 08540.

Microbiologists use microscopes to learn about organisms too small to be seen with the naked eye. They discover new forms of life and learn about their structures and life cycles. Many are very interested in finding new ways to use these organisms to benefit us all. Microbiologists need to know biology, chemistry, and physics, and an advanced degree is required. More information about microbiologists can be obtained by writing to the American Society for Microbiology, 1913 I Street, NW, Washington, D.C. 20006.

CAREERS

Teaching Tips—Students who wish to find out more about a career in photography should contact the Photographic Society of America, Inc., 2005 Walnut Street, Philadelphia, PA 19103.

UNIT 3 TOMORROW'S WEATHER

CHAPTER	SECTION	BASIC SCIENCE SKILLS	ACTIVITY MATERIALS STUDENT/GROUP	EXTENSIONS
CHAPTER 7 WEATHER	**7-1** p.T-114 The Ocean of Air	*Sequencing* the layers of the atmosphere p.T-116	coat hanger, thermometer, Styrofoam cup	• Reinforcement pp.T-115, T-116, T-117 • Enrichment pp. T-118, T-118
	7-2 p.T-119 Observing the Weather	*Classifying* pictures of types of clouds p.T-121	thermometer	• Reinforcement pp.T-120, T-121 • Enrichment p.T-122
	7-3 p.T-123 Weather Forecasting	*Predicting* the weather	thermometer, weather cards	• Reinforcement p.T-125 • Enrichment pp. T-126, T-127 • Application p.T-124
CHAPTER 8 AIR ON THE MOVE	**8-1** p.T-128 Air Rises and Falls	*Finding the cause and effect* of heating air in a balloon p.T-129, from chart p.T-132	broomstick, chair, 2 large paper bags, meter stick, paper clip, string, 150-w bulb, clay	• Reinforcement pp.T-129, T-130, T-132 • Enrichment p.T-131
	8-2 p.T-133 Wind	*Observing* wind	2 bowls or Styrofoam cups, potting soil, water, 2 thermometers, watch	• Reinforcement p.T-134 • Application p.T-135
	8-3 p.T-136 Air Masses	*Classifying* air masses	2 bowls, 2 thermometers, 2 coat hangers, 2 Styrofoam cups, hot water, ice	• Reinforcement p.T-139 • Enrichment pp.T-138, T-140 • Application p.T-137
CHAPTER 9 WATER IN THE AIR	**9-1** p.T-141 Rain and Clouds	*Sequencing* the water cycle p.T-143	6 ice cubes, metal can, water, thermometer	• Reinforcement p.T-142 • Application pp.T-143, T-144
	9-2 p.T-145 Cold and Warm Fronts	*Comparing and contrasting* cold and warm fronts p.T-147	plastic shoe box or aquarium, cardboard, water, red food coloring, salt	• Enrichment p.T-148 • Application pp.T-146, T-147
	9-3 p.T-149 Weather on the Move	*Recording data* on weather	newspaper weather maps, construction paper, glue, scissors, outline map of U.S.	• Reinforcement p.T-150 • Enrichment pp.T-151, T-154 • Application pp.T-150, T-152, T-153
CHAPTER 10 WEATHER AND PEOPLE	**10-1** p.T-155 Violent Storms	*Classifying* storms		• Enrichment pp.T-156, T-159 • Application pp.T-157, T-158
	10-2 p.T-160 Hot, Wet Air	*Measuring* humidity with a hygrometer p.T-162	water	• Reinforcement p.T-161 • Application pp.T-162, T-163
	10-3 p.T-164 The Changing Atmosphere	*Observing* and *inferring* the effects of air pollution on plant growth p.T-165	4 plastic microscope slides, magnifying glass, paper towels, petroleum jelly	• Reinforcement p.T-167 • Enrichment pp.T-165, T-166, T-170 • Application pp.T-168, T-169, T-171

EXTRA ACTIVITIES/ DEMONSTRATIONS	WORKSHEET MASTERS	EVALUATIONS
• Balloons p.T-114 • Pie graph p.T-115 • Air pp.T-116, T-117		Section Review p.T-118
• Weather maps and reports p.T-120 • The size of raindrops p.T-121	• Clouds and Precipitation (SK) p.T-111 o	Section Review p.T-122
• Videotape of weather forecaster p.T-123	• Word Puzzle (SK) p.T-111 p	Sec Rev p.T-126 Ch Rev p.T-127 Test Masters pp.T-111 d, e
• Balloon p.T-128 • Air pressure p.T-129 • Bernoulli's principle p.T-131		Section Review p.T-132
• Convection p.T-133 • Balloon p.T-134	• Moving Air (AH) p.T-111 q	Section Review p.T-135
• Slides of different locations p.T-137	• Diagrams (SK) p.T-111 r	Sec Rev p.T-139 Ch Rev p.T-140 Test Masters pp.T-111 f, g, h
• Water cycle p.T-142 • Condensation of water p.T-142 • Evaporation p.T-143		Section Review p.T-144
• Slides of weather conditions p.T-145	• Weather Maps (AC) p. T-111 s	Section Review p.T-148
• Map pp.T-149, T-150 • Flip book p.T-151	• Rain (AC) p.T-111 t • Scrambled Letters (SK) p.T-111 u	Sec Rev p.T-153 Ch Rev p.T-154 Test Masters pp.T-111 i, j, k
• Pictures p.T-155 • Fronts p.T-156 • Rotation p.T-157		Section Review p.T-159
• Diagram of the water cycle p.T-160	• Storms (SK) p.T-111 v	Section Review p.T-163
• Pollution p.T-164 • Investigating p.T-170		Sec Rev p.T-168 Ch Rev p.T-169 Test Masters pp.T-111 l, m, n

KEY (AC)—Activity (AH)—At Home (SK)—Skill

BOOKS FOR STUDENTS

Alth, Max and Charlotte. *Disasterous Hurricanes and Tornadoes*, New York: Franklin Watts, 1981

Aylesworth, Thomas G. *Storm Alert: Understanding Weather Disasters*, New York: Messner, 1980

Dean, Anabel. *Up, Up, and Away! The Story of Ballooning*, Philadelphia: Westminster, 1980

Heuer, Kenneth. *Thunder, Singing Sands, and Other Wonders: Sound in the Atmosphere*, New York: Dodd, 1981

Sattler, Helen R. *Nature's Weather Forecasters*, New York: Elsevier-Nelson. 1978

Weiss, Malcolm. *What's Happening to Our Climate?*, New York: Messner, 1978

FILMS

Let's Learn to Predict the Weather, 11 min, Coronet

Weather Scientists, 14 min, Universal

What Makes Weather?, 2nd ed, 14 min, Britannica

FILMSTRIP

Air Masses and Weather Fronts, filmstrip, color, captioned, Society for Visual Education, Inc.

COMPUTER AIDS

The Weather Science Kit, Tutorial, Apple, PET, TRS-80, BASIC, 16K+ TAPE, Orange Cherry Med

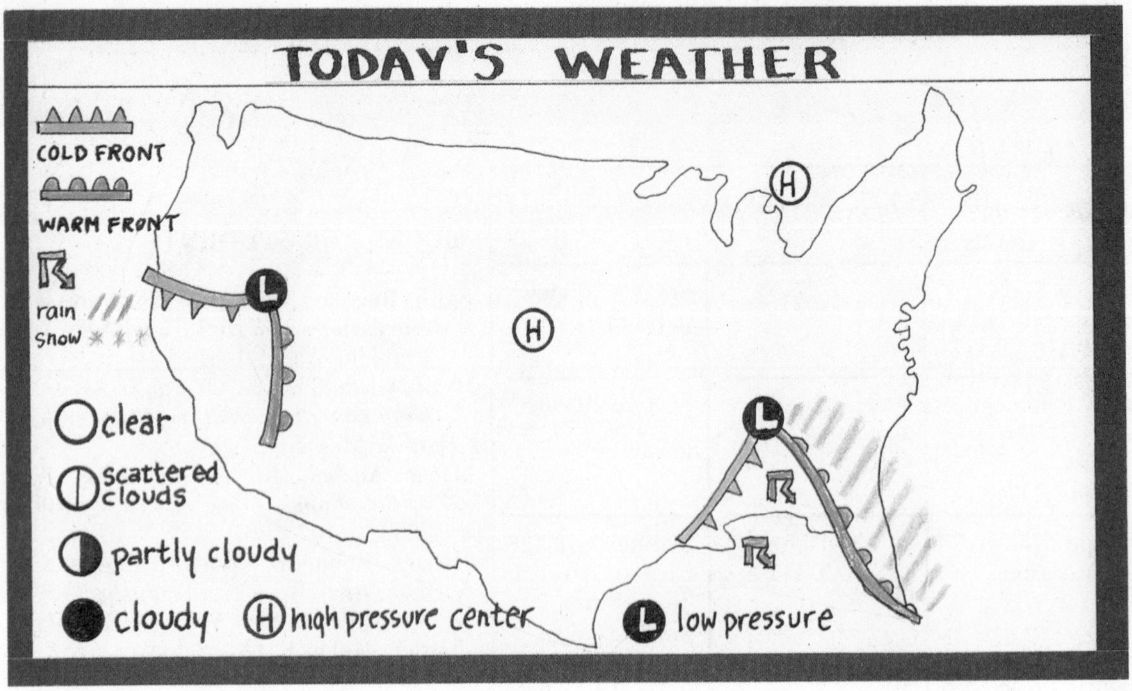

BULLETIN BOARD

Make an outline map of the United States that the students can use as a daily weather map. Make weather symbols that can be tacked to the map for such elements as cold and warm fronts, low and high air-pressure centers, snow, rain, and thunderstorms. Each day a different student could be responsible for bringing in a copy of a weather map from a newspaper. As students become more proficient, they could try their hand at some amateur weather forecasting.

FIELD TRIP IDEAS

To visit a meteorologist

Contact a nearby airport and arrange a visit to the meteorologist. This trip should be taken toward the end of the unit. Students should observe the volume and complexity of computerized equipment that is used to forecast the weather. Discuss with the meteorologist the type of weather conditions that affect the operation of the airport.

To observe how weather affects our community

To make your students better aware of how weather affects our lives, take a walking tour of your neighborhood. Before you begin, ask your students to identify any weather-related items that are used to protect us against the forces of nature. These could include such things as shades, curtains, awnings, gutters, tinted glass, fans, air conditioners, storm windows, and insulation.

Name______________________________________Date________________

Fold back answer key on line before copying.

WEATHER

TEST CHAPTER 7

Read each question. Choose the best answer from those listed. Write the letter of your choice on the line at the right.

1. In which layer of the atmosphere is the air the thinnest? **1.** ______
- **a.** the troposphere
- **b.** the stratosphere
- **c.** the mesosphere
- **d.** the ionosphere

2. Jet airplanes fly in the **2.** ______
- **a.** troposphere.
- **b.** stratosphere.
- **c.** mesosphere.
- **d.** ionosphere.

3. Most of the clouds you see are formed in the **3.** ______
- **a.** troposphere.
- **b.** stratosphere.
- **c.** ionosphere.
- **d.** mesosphere.

4. The two main gases in the earth's atmosphere are **4.** ______
- **a.** nitrogen and carbon dioxide.
- **b.** hydrogen and nitrogen.
- **c.** nitrogen and oxygen.
- **d.** oxygen and carbon dioxide.

5. Where is the air temperature the coolest? **5.** ______
- **a.** the higher up you go in the atmosphere
- **b.** the lower down you go in the atmosphere
- **c.** midway in the atmosphere
- **d.** It is the same at all levels of the atmosphere.

6. Which sentence is *not* true? **6.** ______
- **a.** Air becomes hot as sunlight passes through it.
- **b.** Sunlight can pass through the earth's atmosphere.
- **c.** The earth's surface heats up the air above it.
- **d.** The energy to warm the earth's air comes from the sun.

7. What happens to the molecules of air farther up in the atmosphere? **7.** ______
- **a.** They move farther apart.
- **b.** They move closer together.
- **c.** They move faster.
- **d.** There is no change.

CHAPTER OBJECTIVES

1. d (1)
2. b (1)
3. a (1)
4. c (1)
5. a (2)
6. a (2)
7. a (2)

Name ______________________________ Date __________

8. d (2) **8.** On a sunny day, the air temperature is highest over **8.** ______
a. a light wood patio. **c.** a patch of grass.
b. a grove of trees. **d.** a tar road.

9. a (3) **9.** Clouds that are *not* associated with precipitation are **9.** ______
a. cirrus. **c.** cumulus.
b. stratus. **d.** all of the above.

10. b (3) **10.** Which statement about stratus clouds is *not* true? **10.** ______
a. They are low in the sky.
b. They are fair-weather clouds.
c. They turn into rain clouds.
d. They are flat sheets of gray clouds.

11. c (3) **11.** When cumulus clouds get bigger and thicker, what will probably happen? **11.** ______
a. It will become hotter. **c.** It will rain.
b. It will become sunnier. **d.** It will become night.

12. a (3) **12.** Clouds that look like feathers are **12.** ______
a. cirrus. **c.** stratus.
b. cumulus. **d.** none of these.

13. c (4) **13.** The weather records show that it snowed on 6 out of 10 days with similar conditions. What is the forecast? **13.** ______
a. 10 percent chance of snow **c.** 60 percent chance of snow
b. 40 percent chance of snow **d.** 100 percent chance of snow

14. b (4) **14.** Which statement is true? **14.** ______
a. A weather forecast is always accurate.
b. A weather forecast is sometimes accurate.
c. A weather forecast is never accurate.
d. A weather forecast is accurate 50 percent of the time.

15. d (4) **15.** To predict the weather, forecasters study temperature and **15.** ______
a. wind direction. **c.** air pressure.
b. cloud types. **d.** all of the above.

16. a (4) **16.** What has had the greatest effect on the accuracy of weather forecasts? **16.** ______
a. computers **c.** fewer weather changes
b. more meteorologists **d.** new thermometers

Name______________________________ Date____________

Fold back answer key on line before copying.

AIR ON THE MOVE

TEST CHAPTER **8**

Read each question. Choose the best answer from those listed. Write the letter of your choice on the line at the right.

CHAPTER OBJECTIVES

1. When air is heated, the molecules of air **1.** _____ **1.** b (1)
a. move closer together.
b. move farther apart.
c. break up into tiny pieces.
d. remain in the same position.

2. Why does a hot-air balloon rise? **2.** _____ **2.** a (1)
a. The air outside the balloon is heavier than the air inside.
b. The air inside the balloon is heavier than the air outside.
c. The air inside and outside the balloon have equal weights.
d. There is only air inside the balloon.

3. Which of the following is *not* true about hot air? **3.** _____ **3.** c (1)
a. It is lighter than cold air.
b. The molecules are farther apart than in cold air.
c. There are more molecules than in cold air.
d. It rises through cold air.

4. If two columns of air, one cold and one warm, were weighed, **4.** _____ **4.** d (1)
a. the cold air would weigh more.
b. the cold air would push down with more pressure.
c. the warm air would weigh less.
d. all of the above are true.

5. Which of the following does *not* happen when the liquid in a barometer goes down? **5.** _____ **5.** d (2)
a. Air pressure goes down.
b. Forecasters predict rain.
c. The weather changes.
d. Air becomes heavier.

Name______________________________ Date____________

6. a (2) **6.** In a barometer that has a tube with liquid in it and that is sealed at one end, **6.** ______

a. the liquid goes up when the air pressure goes up.
b. the liquid goes up when air pressure goes down.
c. the liquid level depends on temperature.
d. air pressure has no effect on the level of the liquid.

7. c (2) **7.** What kind of weather usually follows rising air pressure? **7.** ______

a. clouds and rain
b. clouds but no rain
c. clear skies and sunshine
d. no change

8. a (2) **8.** High-pressure centers usually bring **8.** ______

a. sunshine and clear weather.
b. clouds and rain.
c. cold weather.
d. thunderstorms.

9. a (3) **9.** A wind forms when **9.** ______

a. cold air moves under warm air.
b. warm air moves under cold air.
c. warm and cold air move under each other.
d. warm and cold air stay still.

10. d (3) **10.** On a warm day at the beach, **10.** ______

a. air over the land is warmer than air over the water.
b. air over the land rises.
c. breezes blow over the land from the ocean.
d. all of the above are true.

11. b (3) **11.** What happens when there is a big difference between the air pressure in two places? **11.** ______

a. The wind blows slowly.
b. The wind blows quickly.
c. There is no wind.
d. The wind starts and stops.

12. b (3) **12.** Which sentence is true? **12.** ______

a. Water heats and cools faster than land.
b. Cool air has a higher pressure than warm air.
c. As the earth cools, the air near its surface gets hotter.
d. Air moves from areas of low pressure to high pressure.

Name________________________________Date______________

13. Which of the following is true about all air masses? **13.** ______ | **13.** c (4)

- **a.** They are hot.
- **b.** They are wet.
- **c.** They are large amounts of air.
- **d.** They are located over land.

14. An air mass located over a desert is **14.** ______ | **14.** b (4)

- **a.** hot and wet.
- **b.** hot and dry.
- **c.** cold and wet.
- **d.** cold and dry.

15. What happens when air masses meet? **15.** ______ | **15.** b (4)

- **a.** The sun shines.
- **b.** Storms form.
- **c.** The temperature rises.
- **d.** Nothing happens.

16. A mass of warm, low pressure, moist air can form **16.** ______ | **16.** d (4)

- **a.** over the desert.
- **b.** over the Poles.
- **c.** over a lake.
- **d.** over the ocean.

17. Air masses that form over land are usually **17.** ______ | **17.** c (4)

- **a.** warm.
- **b.** cold.
- **c.** dry.
- **d.** moist.

Fold back answer key on line before copying.

CHAPTER OBJECTIVES

Name______________________________ Date__________

WATER IN THE AIR

TEST CHAPTER 9

Read each question. Choose the best answer from those listed. Write the letter of your choice on the line at the right.

1. c (1)

1. Which of the following shows the order of the water cycle? **1.** ______

a. condensation, evaporation, precipitation
b. precipitation, condensation, evaporation
c. evaporation, condensation, precipitation
d. evaporation, precipitation, condensation

2. a (1)

2. What happens when the air temperature falls to the dew point? **2.** ______

a. Water forms on grass.
b. The grass becomes dry.
c. There is a heavy rainfall.
d. Water freezes.

3. b (1)

3. The change from a liquid to a gas is called **3.** ______

a. condensation. **c.** precipitation.
b. evaporation. **d.** movement.

4. b (1)

4. Water vapor changes back into a liquid **4.** ______

a. when the air temperature rises.
b. when the air temperature goes down.
c. when the air temperature stays the same.
d. when the air temperature is above 21°C (70°F).

5. c (2)

5. What type of clouds often follow a cold front? **5.** ______

a. cirrus **c.** cumulus
b. stratus **d.** no clouds

6. a (2)

6. The place where air masses meet is called **6.** ______

a. a front. **c.** a mass.
b. the jet stream. **d.** drizzle.

Name________________________________Date______________

7. Which sentence is true about cold fronts? **7.** ______ | **7.** d (2)

a. They push into warm air.
b. They often bring showers.
c. They usually pass by in a few hours.
d. All of the above are true.

8. Which of the following does *not* follow a warm front? **8.** ______ | **8.** d (2)

a. dark clouds **c.** snow
b. rain **d.** sunshine

9. What does the symbol  stand for? **9.** ______ | **9.** b (3)

a. rain **c.** low-pressure center
b. thunderstorm **d.** high-pressure center

10. Look at the symbol below. What do the points show? **10.** ______ | **10.** a (3)

a. The direction in which a cold front is moving.
b. The direction in which a warm front is moving.
c. The direction in which rain is moving.
d. The direction in which a thunderstorm is moving.

11. Which symbol stands for snow? **11.** ______ | **11.** d (3)

a. 
c. 

b. 
d. 

12. The symbol  means there will probably be **12.** ______ | **12.** b (3)

a. sunshine. **c.** soft winds.
b. a storm. **d.** a heat wave.

Name________________________________ Date______________

Use the Maps A and B to answer questions 13 through 16

Map A

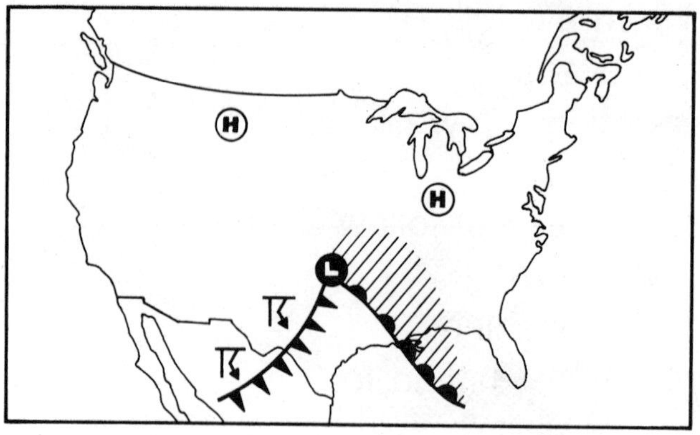

Map B

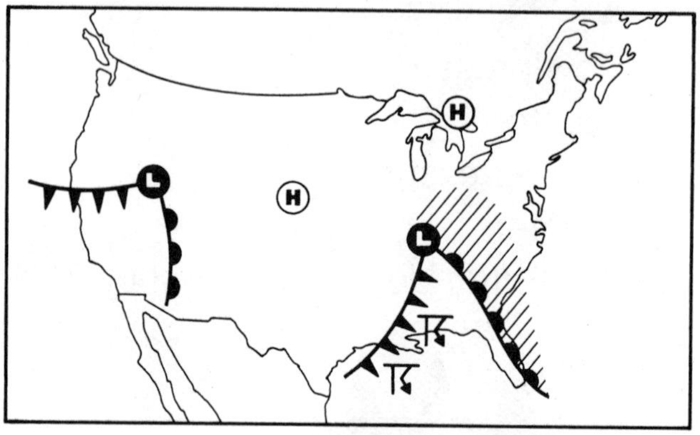

13. a (4) **13.** Look at map A. In which direction is the cold front moving? **13.** ______

a. west to east
b. east to west
c. north to south
d. south to north

14. b (4) **14.** Look at maps A and B. What type of weather is moving towards the east coast? **14.** ______

a. a heat wave
b. rain
c. snow
d. clear skies

15. b (4) **15.** Look at maps A and B. What has happened to the thunderstorm? **15.** ______

a. It has moved north.
b. It has moved out to sea.
c. It has moved inland.
d. It is staying in place.

16. a (4) **16.** Look at map B. As the low pressure centers pass they will be followed by **16.** ______

a. clear, sunny skies.
b. rain.
c. snow.
d. thunderstorms.

Name________________________________Date__________

WEATHER AND PEOPLE

TEST CHAPTER 10

Fold back answer key on line before copying.

Read each question. Choose the best answer from those listed. Write the letter of your choice on the line at the right.

CHAPTER OBJECTIVES

1. Hurricanes usually form during **1.** ______ **1.** a (1)

a. summer and fall. **c.** winter and spring.
b. fall and winter. **d.** spring and fall.

2. Small, violent storms that form along cold fronts, usually in the spring, are called **2.** ______ **2.** a (1)

a. tornadoes. **c.** blizzards.
b. hurricanes. **d.** thunderstorms.

3. Thunderstorms usually form when **3.** ______ **3.** a (1)

a. warm moist air rises quickly.
b. cold air rises over warm air.
c. winds are above 50 km per hour.
d. all of the above happen.

4. A storm in which freezing winds blow at a speed of over 70 km (45 m) per hour is a **4.** ______ **4.** c (1)

a. tornado. **c.** blizzard.
b. hurricane. **d.** thunderstorm.

5. What causes houses to collapse during a tornado? **5.** ______ **5.** c (2)

a. the difference in humidity
b. the difference in temperature
c. the difference in air pressure
d. the difference in wind direction

6. Which of the following is *not* a common result of a blizzard? **6.** ______ **6.** d (2)

a. Power lines stop working.
b. Roads become very icy.
c. People can freeze to death.
d. Houses are struck by lightning.

7. The heaviest flooding is most likely to occur because of **7.** ______ **7.** b (2)

a. tornadoes. **c.** blizzards.
b. hurricanes. **d.** thunderstorms.

Name________________________________Date______________

8. a (2)

8. In which areas of the United States are people most likely to be affected by tornadoes? **8.** ______

a. South and Midwest **c.** West and Northwest
b. North and Midwest **d.** East and North

9. b (3)

9. Humidity is **9.** ______

a. the amount of oxygen in the air.
b. the amount of water vapor in the air.
c. the amount of dust particles in the air.
d. the amount of rain that falls.

10. a (3)

10. At which reading on the THI are people the most comfortable? **10.** ______

a. less than 70 **c.** 75–80
b. 70–75 **d.** over 80

11. b (3)

11. If a dry, sunny day follows two days of rain, the hair on a human-hair hydrometer will **11.** ______

a. stretch. **c.** stay the same.
b. shrink. **d.** break.

12. c (4)

12. A natural cause of air pollution is **12.** ______

a. cars. **c.** volcanic eruptions.
b. factories. **d.** furnaces.

13. d (4)

13. How does burning coal cause air pollution? **13.** ______

a. It removes water vapor from the air.
b. It removes carbon dioxide from the air.
c. It puts oxygen into the air.
d. It puts carbon dioxide into the air.

14. a (4)

14. What is the main cause of air pollution? **14.** ______

a. humans **c.** animals
b. plants **d.** asteroids

15. a (5)

15. Factories can be productive and still reduce air pollution **15.** ______

a. by cleaning the smoke that escapes from their smokestacks.
b. by burning more coal.
c. by plugging up their smokestacks.
d. by shutting down for the winter.

Name____________________ Date__________

16. Air pollution can be lowered by elimination of all of the following except **16.** ______ **16.** b (5)

a. dust. **c.** dirt.

b. grass. **d.** chemicals.

17. Pollution from automobiles can be reduced **17.** ______ **17.** c (5)

a. by driving longer distances.

b. by using larger cars.

c. by using special cleaners in the exhaust system.

d. by burning more gas.

Name ______________________ Date ______________

Weather

SKILL WORKSHEET

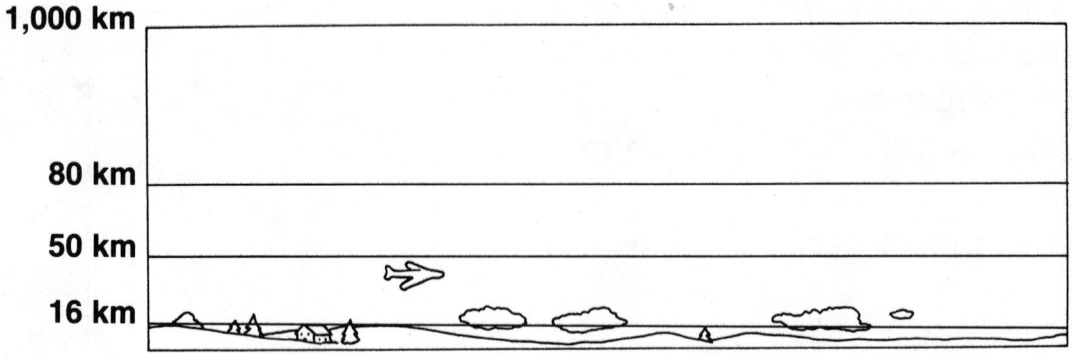

1. Which layer of the atmosphere do we live in?

   ____

2. Which layer of the atmosphere do jets fly in?

   ____

3. Label each layer of the atmosphere shown on the diagram above.

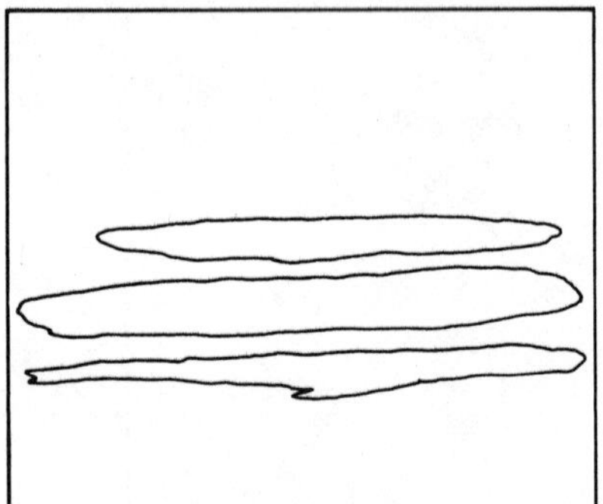

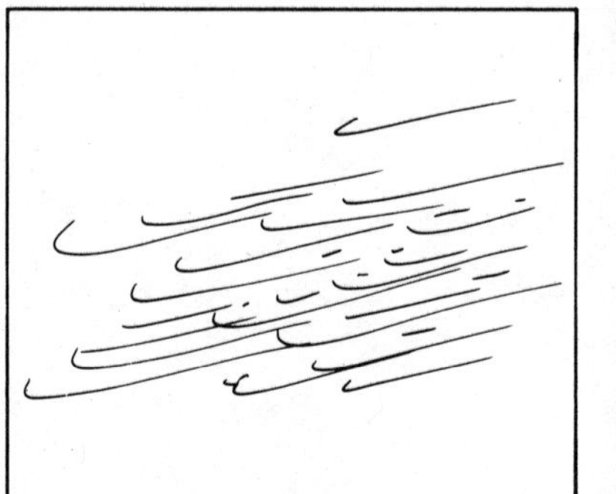

______________ ______________ ______________

______________ ______________ ______________

4. Name each cloud shown above and tell what kind of weather it brings.
5. List three kinds of precipitation: ______________

   ____

Name ______________________________ Date ______________

Weather

SKILL WORKSHEET

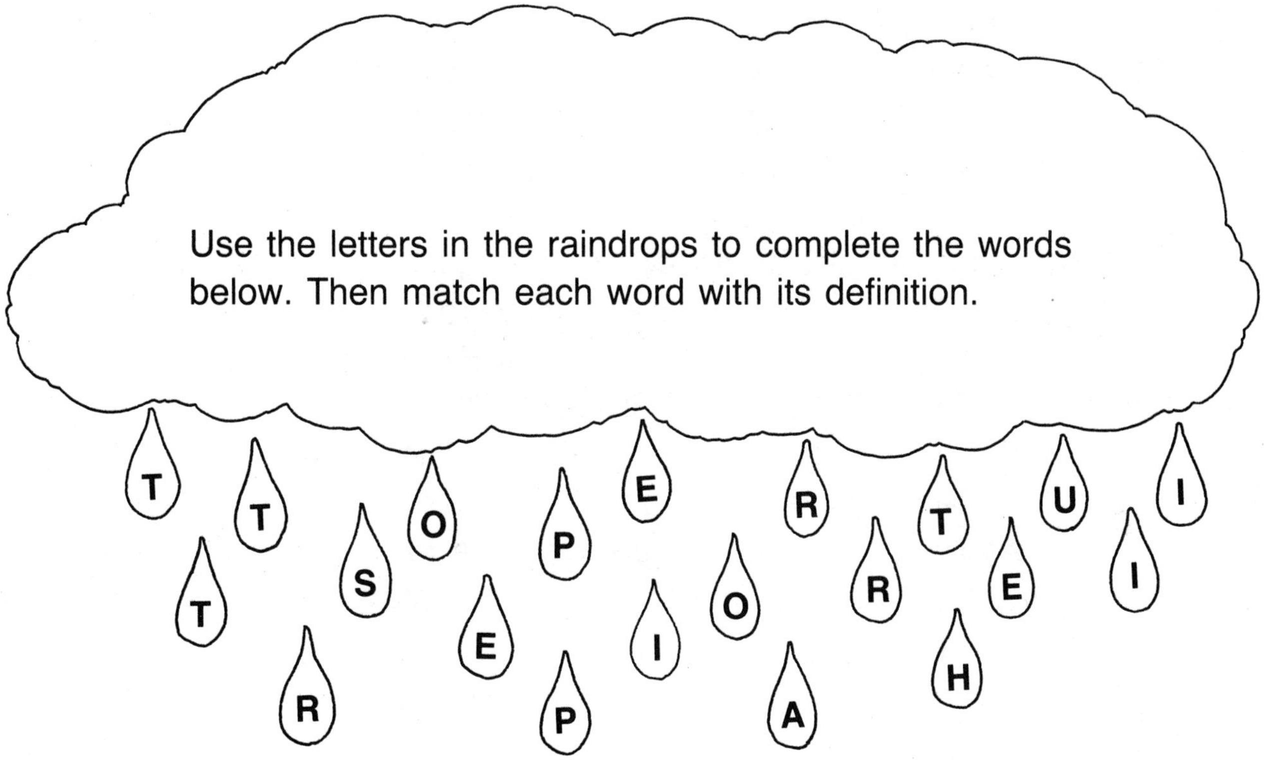

1. A _ M O _ P H _ _ E
2. M E _ E O _ _ L O G _ S T
3. _ E M _ E R _ T _ R E
4. P _ E C _ P I _ A T _ O N
5. T R _ _ O S P _ _ R _

a. The ocean of air around the earth ______________

b. The layer of air where people live ______________

c. Moisture falling from the sky ______________

d. A scientist who studies the weather ______________

e. Measured with a thermometer ______________

Name ______________________ Date ______________

Air on the Move

AT HOME WORKSHEET

You have learned that warm air rises. Cool air moves in under it. In this activity, you will see how this happens. THIS ACTIVITY MUST BE SUPERVISED BY AN ADULT.

A. Gather these materials: a narrow-mouthed glass jug, matches, 2.5 cm (1 in.) piece of hemp rope.

B. Light the piece of rope with a match. (SAFETY TIP: THIS PART OF THE ACTIVITY SHOULD BE DONE ONLY IF AN ADULT IS PRESENT.) The rope should be smoking. There should be no flame.

C. Drop the smoking rope into the jug. Observe the movement of the smoke. This shows how air moves in and out of the jug.

D. Draw a diagram to show how the air moves.

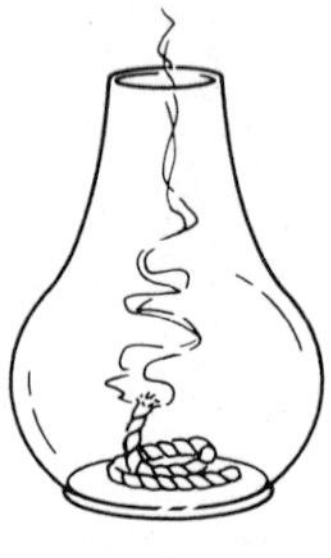

QUESTIONS:

1. What happens when air is warmed by the burning rope?

____

2. What kind of air moves into the bottle?

____

3. How is this similar to wind? ______________

____

Name ____________________ Date ____________

Weather

SKILL WORKSHEET

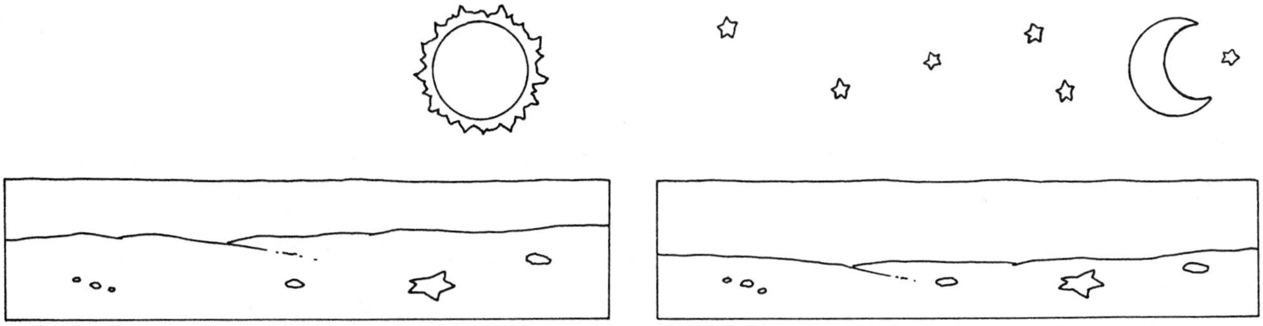

A. Draw arrows to show which way the wind would blow in each of the diagrams above.

__________________ __________________ __________________

B. What kind of air mass would form over each of the places shown above?

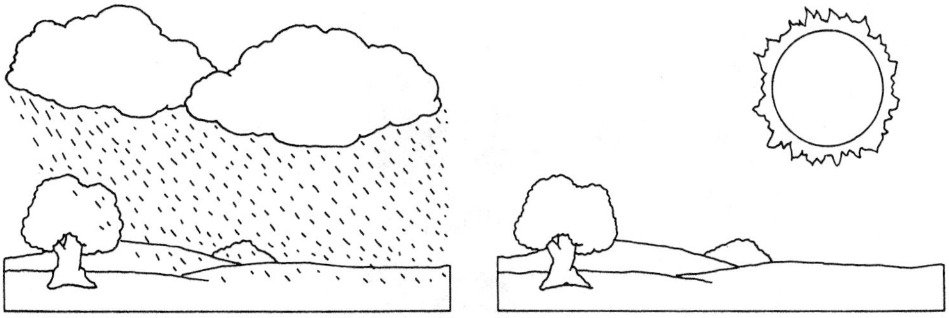

C. Use arrows to show whether a barometer would be rising or falling in each of the diagrams above.

Name________________________________ Date______________

Weather on the Move

ACTIVITY WORKSHEET

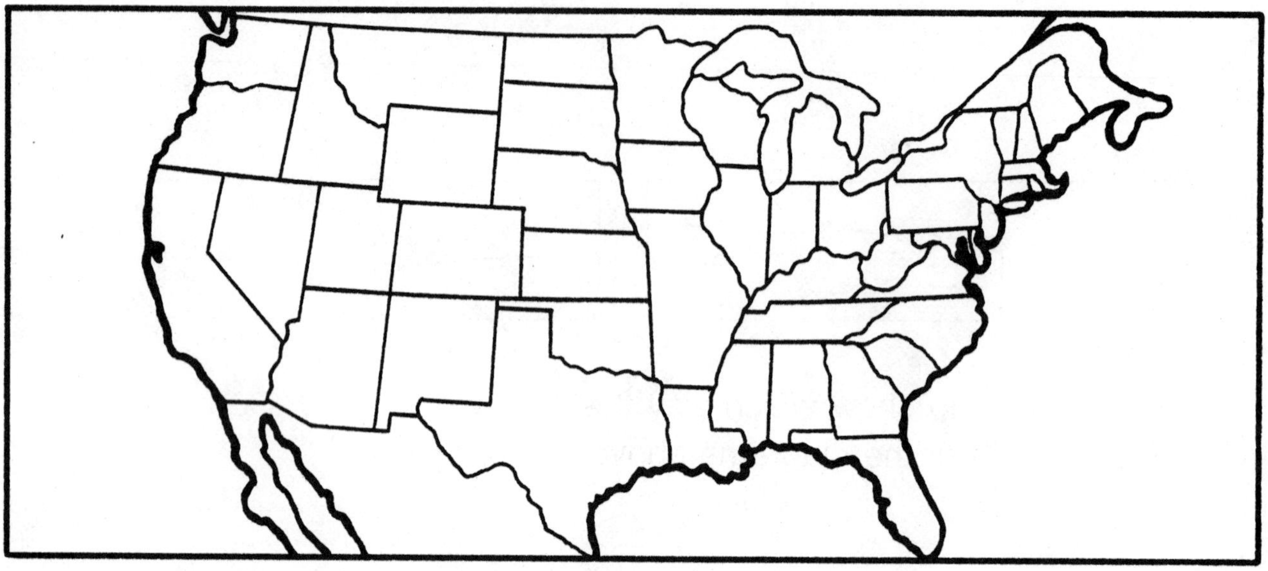

Today's weather forecast for the country is as follows:
There will be showers and thunderstorms along the East Coast from Maine to Virginia. A high-pressure center is sitting over Texas. Low pressure is moving into the Pacific Northwest, bringing snow to the Rocky Mountains.

Use the weather symbols shown below to fill in this forecast on the map.

Name ________________________ Date ____________

Rain and Clouds

ACTIVITY WORKSHEET

In this activity, you will see how surface area affects evaporation from a surface.

A. Gather these materials: glass, measuring cup, pie plate, water.
B. Pour ½ cup of water into a pie plate. Pour ½ cup of water into a glass.
C. Place the pie plate and the glass on a sunny window ledge. Leave them there for a day.
D. Pour the water left in the pie plate into the measuring cup. Record the amount on the chart.
E. Pour the water left in the glass into the measuring cup. Record the amount on the chart.

	Day 1 Amount of Water	Day 2 Amount of Water
Glass	½ cup	
Pie plate	½ cup	

QUESTIONS

1. What happened to the water in the glass and in the pie plate? ________________________
____
2. How was the surface of the water different in the glass and in the pie plate? ________________________
____
3. What does this activity show about surface area and evaporation? ________________________
____

Name ______________________ Date ______________

Water in the Air

SKILL WORKSHEET

Unscramble the letters to make science words. The circled letters will spell out another science word.

1. Water in the form of a gas — _ _ _ (_) _ (_)(_) _ _ _ — A W E R T P O V A R
2. The evaporation and condensation of water over and over again — _ _ _ _ _ _ _ _ _ _ — E R W A T L Y C E C
3. The temperature at which water condenses out of the air — _ _ _ (_)(_) _ _ _ — W E D N I P O T
4. Very small drops of slowly falling rain — _ (_) _ _ _ _ _ — Z R I L E Z D
5. Fast-moving winds high in the troposphere — _ _ _ _ _ _ _ (_) _ — T E J M E R S A T
6. Places where large air masses meet — _ _ _ _ (_) _ — S T R O N F
7. Water changing from a gas into a liquid — _ _ _ _ _ _ _ _ _ (_)(_)(_) — S O C D E N T A N I O N

The word spelled out in the circles is ______________

It means ______________________________

____

____

Name ______________________ Date ____________

Weather and People

SKILL WORKSHEET

A. Match each statement below with the picture of the right storm. Name each storm shown.

1. A storm that forms over warm oceans near the equator
2. A storm that brings thunder, lightning, heavy rains, and strong winds
3. A storm made by a spinning, funnel-shaped cloud
4. A storm that brings very cold winds and blowing snow

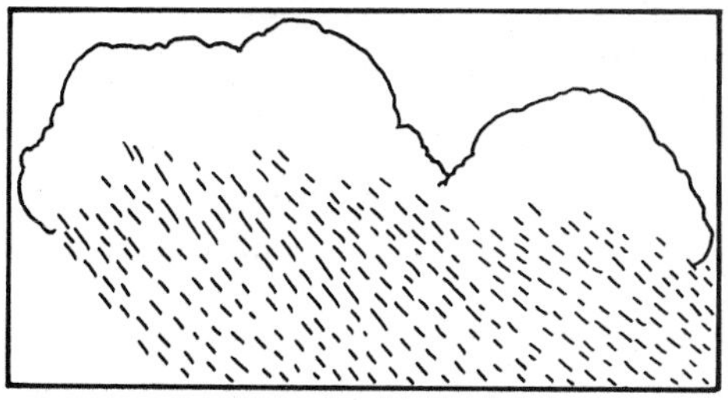

____

____

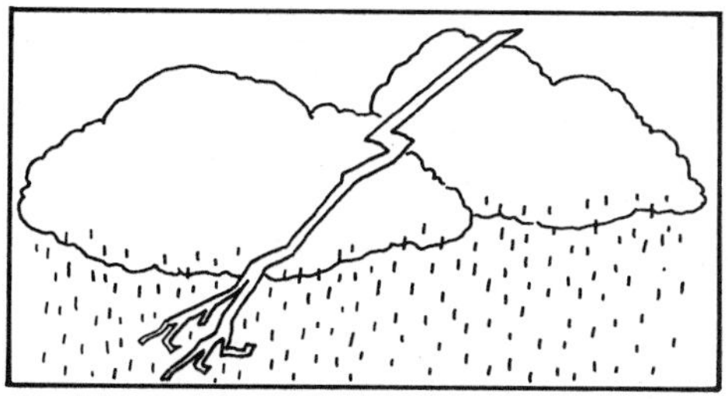

____

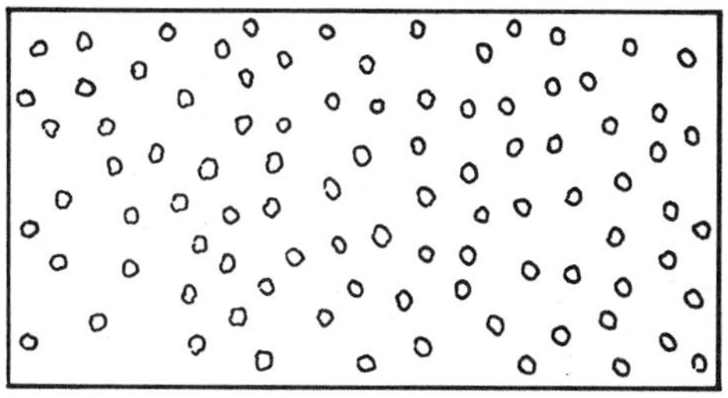

____

B. These people have been out running. They did not run very fast or very far. But they feel very hot and sticky. What does this tell you about the humidity?

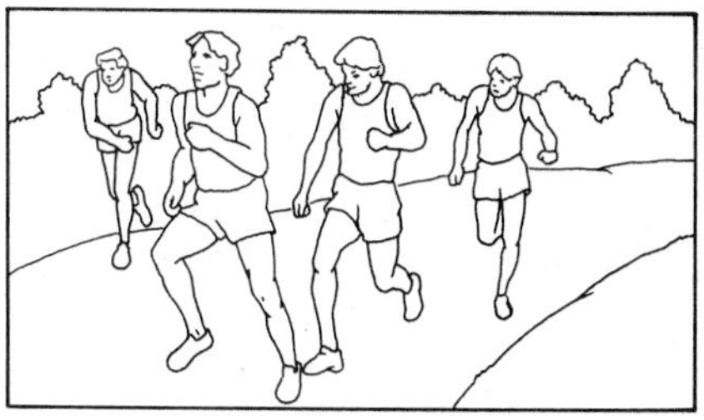

____

Name______________________ Date____________

Weather

CLASSIFYING, INFERRING — SKILL WORKSHEET

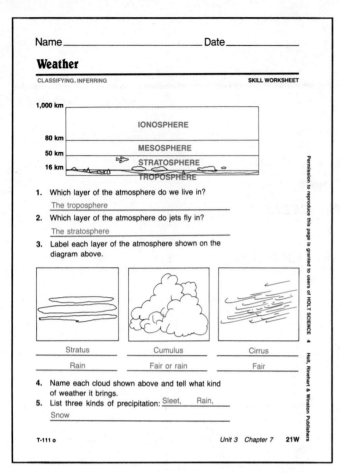

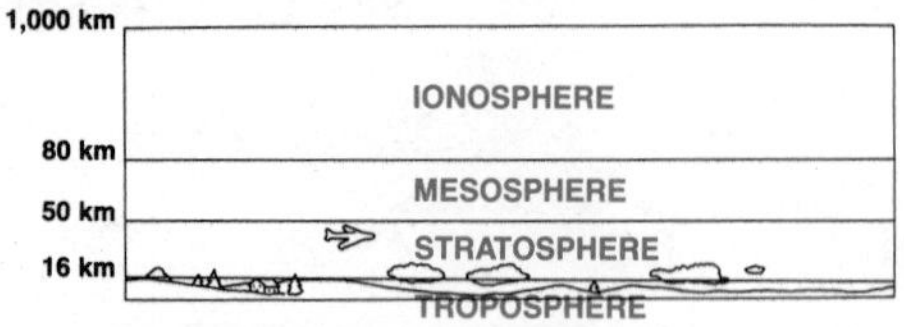

1. Which layer of the atmosphere do we live in?
   The troposphere
2. Which layer of the atmosphere do jets fly in?
   The stratosphere
3. Label each layer of the atmosphere shown on the diagram above.

Stratus	Cumulus	Cirrus
Rain	Fair or rain	Fair

4. Name each cloud shown above and tell what kind of weather it brings.
5. List three kinds of precipitation: Sleet, Rain, Snow

Name______________________ Date____________

Weather

BUILDING SCIENCE VOCABULARY — SKILL WORKSHEET

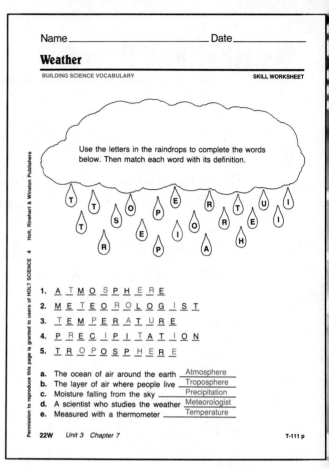

Use the letters in the raindrops to complete the words below. Then match each word with its definition.

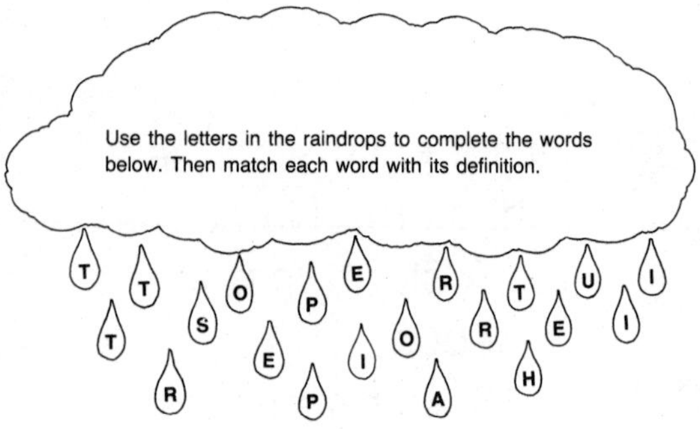

1. A T M O S P H E R E
2. M E T E O R O L O G I S T
3. T E M P E R A T U R E
4. P R E C I P I T A T I O N
5. T R O P O S P H E R E

a. The ocean of air around the earth Atmosphere
b. The layer of air where people live Troposphere
c. Moisture falling from the sky Precipitation
d. A scientist who studies the weather Meteorologist
e. Measured with a thermometer Temperature

Name______________________ Date____________

Air on the Move

AT HOME WORKSHEET

You have learned that warm air rises. Cool air moves in under it. In this activity, you will see how this happens. THIS ACTIVITY MUST BE SUPERVISED BY AN ADULT.

A. Gather these materials: a narrow-mouthed glass jug, matches, 2.5 cm (1 in.) piece of hemp rope.
B. Light the piece of rope with a match. (SAFETY TIP: THIS PART OF THE ACTIVITY SHOULD BE DONE ONLY IF AN ADULT IS PRESENT.) The rope should be smoking. There should be no flame.
C. Drop the smoking rope into the jug. Observe the movement of the smoke. This shows how air moves in and out of the jug.
D. Draw a diagram to show how the air moves.

QUESTIONS:

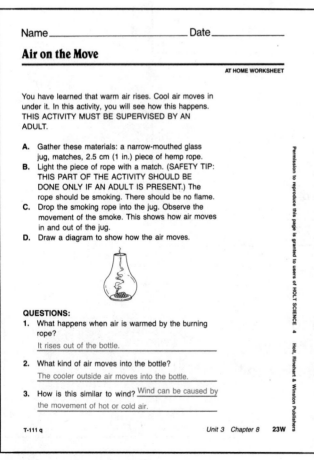

1. What happens when air is warmed by the burning rope?
   It rises out of the bottle.
2. What kind of air moves into the bottle?
   The cooler outside air moves into the bottle.
3. How is this similar to wind? Wind can be caused by the movement of hot or cold air.

Name______________________ Date____________

Weather

CLASSIFYING, INFERRING, FINDING CAUSE AND EFFECT — SKILL WORKSHEET

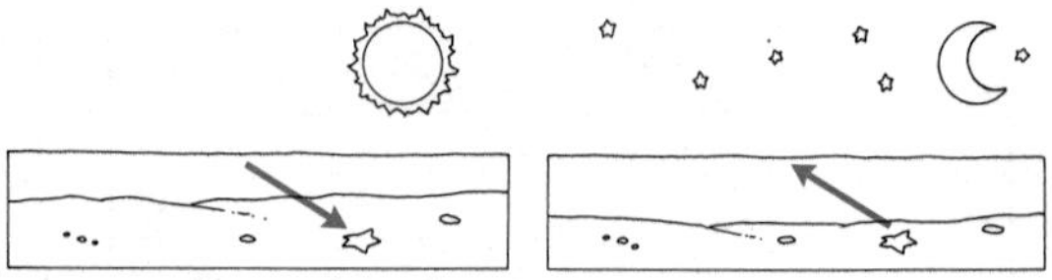

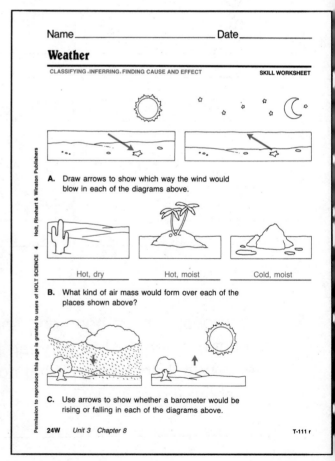

A. Draw arrows to show which way the wind would blow in each of the diagrams above.

Hot, dry	Hot, moist	Cold, moist

B. What kind of air mass would form over each of the places shown above?

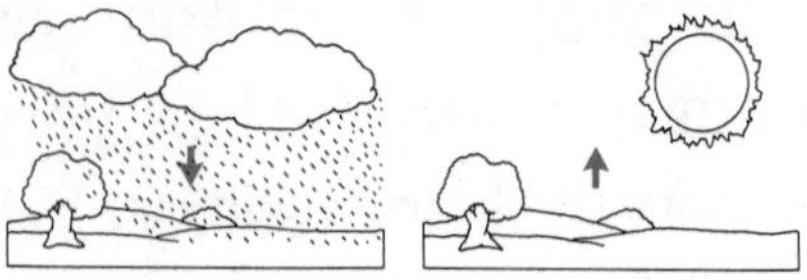

C. Use arrows to show whether a barometer would be rising or falling in each of the diagrams above.

Name______________________ Date____________

Weather on the Move

ACTIVITY WORKSHEET

Today's weather forecast for the country is as follows: There will be showers and thunderstorms along the East Coast from Maine to Virginia. A high-pressure center is sitting over Texas. Low pressure is moving into the Pacific Northwest, bringing snow to the Rocky Mountains.

Use the weather symbols shown below to fill in this forecast on the map.

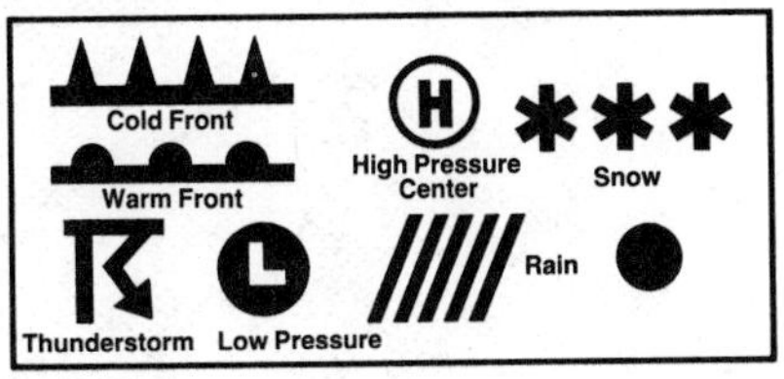

Name______________________ Date____________

Rain and Clouds

ACTIVITY WORKSHEET

In this activity, you will see how surface area affects evaporation from a surface.

A. Gather these materials: glass, measuring cup, pie plate, water.
B. Pour ½ cup of water into a pie plate. Pour ½ cup of water into a glass.
C. Place the pie plate and the glass on a sunny window ledge. Leave them there for a day.
D. Pour the water left in the pie plate into the measuring cup. Record the amount on the chart.
E. Pour the water left in the glass into the measuring cup. Record the amount on the chart.

	Day 1 Amount of Water	Day 2 Amount of Water
Glass	½ cup	
Pie plate	½ cup	

QUESTIONS

1. What happened to the water in the glass and in the pie plate? The water in the pie plate evaporated. Some water was left in the glass
2. How was the surface of the water different in the glass and in the pie plate? The surface area of the water in the pie plate was larger than in the glass.
3. What does this activity show about surface area and evaporation? The larger the surface area, the faster evaporation occurs.

Name______________________ Date____________

Water in the Air

BUILDING SCIENCE VOCABULARY   SKILL WORKSHEET

Unscramble the letters to make science words. The circled letters will spell out another science word.

1. Water in the form of a gas — W A T (E) R (V)(A) P O R — A W E R T P O V A R
2. The evaporation and condensation of water over and over again — W A T E R C Y C L E — E R W A T L Y C E C
3. The temperature at which water condenses out of the air — D E W (P)(O) I N T — W E D N I P O T
4. Very small drops of slowly falling rain — D (R) I Z Z L E — Z R I L E Z D
5. Fast-moving winds high in the troposphere — J E T S T R E (A) M — T E J M E R S A T
6. Places where large air masses meet — F R O N (T) S — S T R O N F
7. Water changing from a gas into a liquid — C O N D E N S A T (I)(O)(N) — S O C D E N T A N I O N

The word spelled out in the circles is evaporation

It means the change of water from a liquid to a gas

Name______________________ Date____________

Weather and People

INFERRING, CLASSIFYING   SKILL WORKSHEET

A. Match each statement below with the picture of the right storm. Name each storm shown.
1. A storm that forms over warm oceans near the equator
2. A storm that brings thunder, lightning, heavy rains, and strong winds
3. A storm made by a spinning, funnel-shaped cloud
4. A storm that brings very cold winds and blowing snow

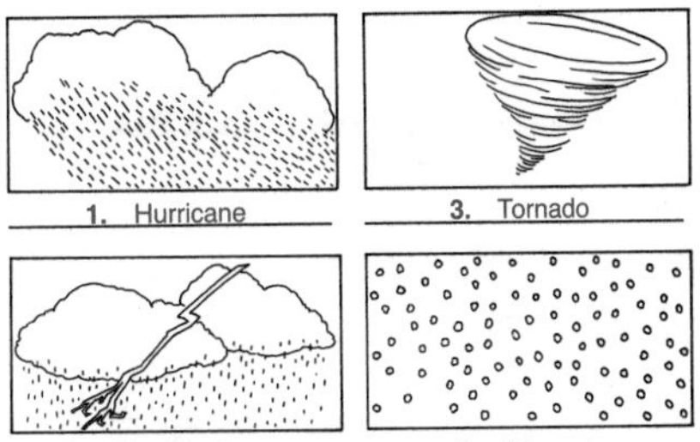

1. Hurricane   3. Tornado
2. Thunderstorm   4. Blizzard

B. These people have been out running. They did not run very fast or very far. But they feel very hot and stick. What does this tell you about the humidity?

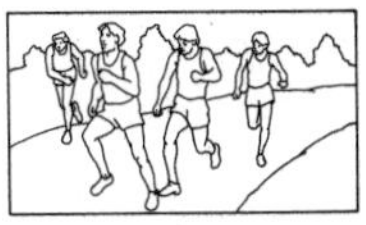

The humidity is high.

Unit Overview

This is an earth science unit about the earth's atmosphere. The atmosphere is made up of gases, mainly a mixture of nitrogen and oxygen. The layers of the atmosphere are the troposphere, the stratosphere, the mesosphere, and the ionosphere. The troposphere is the layer closest to the earth and is the cause of most of our weather.

Winds are caused by differences in temperature between air masses. When air becomes warm, it expands and exerts less pressure. Cold, dense air moves in under the lighter, warmer air, and winds are the result. All places covered by the same air mass have the same weather. When different air masses meet, a front is formed. Water circulates on the earth by the processes of evaporation, condensation, and precipitation. These are known as the water cycle. A meteorologist uses weather maps to follow and forecast the weather. People need to be warned about violent storms, such as hurricanes, tornadoes, thunderstorms, and blizzards. Humidity is a measure of the moisture in the air. Both natural and human-made pollution affect the air, the weather, and all living things.

Tomorrow's Weather

Unit Opener

This photo shows rain clouds hovering over the Pacific surf off the coast of Oregon. The climate there is mild and humid, with an annual rainfall of around 80 in.

The following questions may be asked as motivation: What kind of weather is shown in this photo? *Cloudy, windy, and damp.* What kind of weather do you expect when the clouds reach your area? *Rain.* What makes you think these are rain clouds? *Their shape and thickness.* Where do you think the water in the clouds came from? *The ocean.* How could you check your prediction of rain? *Call the weather bureau or look at a weather map.*

Exceptional Student IEP Unit Goal

At the end of this unit, the student will list five natural occurrences that affect weather.

LEARNING CENTER

A suggested title for a Learning Center for this unit is "What's the Weather?" Photos of meteorological instruments and different weather systems may be displayed.

The Extensions listed below are especially suitable for the Learning Center. They require the following materials: how some surfaces retain heat, p. T-118 (thermometer, Styrofoam cup, coat hanger); gathering snowflakes, p. T-121 (black construction paper); cloud chamber, p. T-122 (wide-mouth jar, balloon, rubber band, hot water, cup, matches); anemometer, p. T-126 (index cards, tape, scissors, straws, straight pin); air pressure, p. T-132 (plastic bag, wide-mouth jar, rubber band); weather vane, p. T-135 (straight pin, pencil, scissors, straws, clay, construction paper); water vapor in air, p. T-139 (covered jars, cotton cloth, tape, thread); mobiles, p. T-147 (coat hangers, construction paper, cotton, glue, string); size of raindrops, p. T-159 (bucket, books, comb, plastic straw, rubber tubing, aluminum pan, pin).

In addition, an index file of suggested research topics could be set up in the Learning Center, using the following Extensions: planetary atmospheres, p. T-118; weather folklore, p. T-125; the weather on your birthday, p. T-127; cloud seeding, p. T-144; weather reports from different cities, p. T-150; local weather stations, p. T-152; precipitation and mountains, p. T-154; storm safety procedures, p. T-158; humidifiers and dehumidifiers, p. T-163; air pollution, p. T-168; dinosaur extinction theories, p. T-169.

CHAPTER OBJECTIVES

1. Identify and describe the properties of the layers in the atmosphere.
2. Describe how the earth's atmosphere is heated and how to measure temperature.
3. Compare cloud types and explain what type of weather is associated with each.
4. Explain how meteorologists use observable weather conditions to predict the weather.

SECTION BACKGROUND

The earth is surrounded by a blanket of air that extends to about 1,000 km above its surface. The molecules of gas are trapped by the pull of the earth's gravity. The composition of the gas mixture in our atmosphere has evolved through time to its present values: nitrogen—78%; oxygen—21%; water vapor, carbon dioxide, and trace gases constituting the rest. Most of the gases were ejected from the earth's crust during long periods of volcanic activity. The atmosphere is separated into layers. In general, the density and temperature of the air decrease with elevation. Phenomena associated with the weather occur in the troposphere. The gases in the air are part of natural earth cycles.

MATERIALS

coat hanger (bent as shown in the Activity), thermometer, Styrofoam cup

Exceptional Student
IEP Chapter Goal

At the end of this chapter, the student will illustrate and label: (1) three types of clouds and (2) the arrangement of molecules in the four layers of the earth's atmosphere.

CHAPTER 7

WEATHER

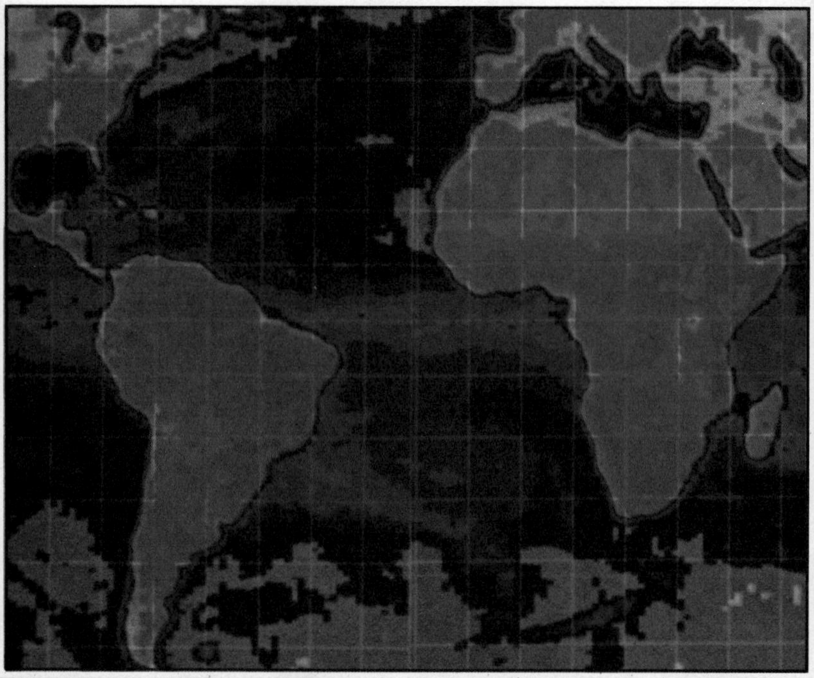

7-1. The Ocean of Air

Pretend you are orbiting the earth. You can see a blue haze around the planet. This haze is a layer of air. No living thing can survive without it. When you finish this section, you should be able to:

114

BASIC TEACHING PLAN

MOTIVATION

If possible, launch helium-filled balloons to initiate students' observations of the weather and to create an exciting activity with potential feedback. Each balloon will have a small card attached, asking the finder to return it to the school via the mail box. The following information should be included: the fact that the balloon was part of an experiment, the date and time of launch, your name, the name and address of your school, the date, time, and the place found, direction of the wind, and the condition of the balloon. If this activity is not possible, read and display the account in National Geographic's *World Magazine*, May 1982.

A. Describe and compare the layers of the *atmosphere.*

B. Explain how to measure the temperature of the *atmosphere.*

C. Explain what causes the *atmosphere* to heat up in some places more than in others.

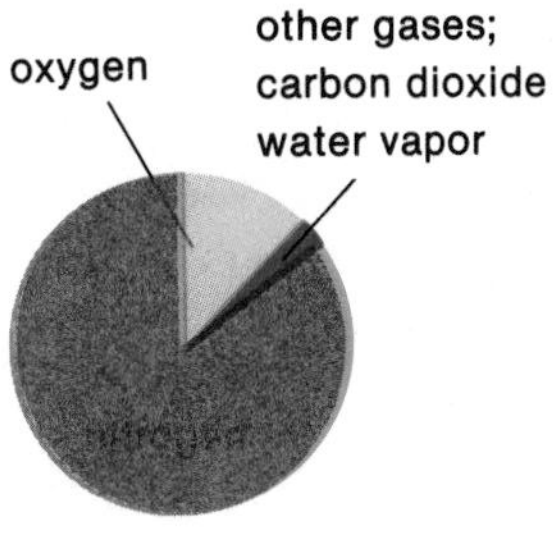

The earth's **atmosphere** (**at**-muh-sfeer) is made of air. Air contains many gases that you cannot see. There are two main gases in the air. They are nitrogen and oxygen. Without oxygen, you would not be able to breathe. The pie graph shows how much of each gas is in the air. The air also contains two other gases. They are water vapor and carbon dioxide.

Atmosphere: The air that surrounds the earth.

The *atmosphere* is made of at least four layers. The diagram on page 116 shows the four main layers of earth's atmosphere. The air is composed of tiny **molecules** (**mahl**-uh-kewls) of gas. The *molecules* in the bottom layer are tightly packed. Higher up, the molecules are spread farther apart. Let's take a closer look at each layer.

Molecule: The smallest particle of a substance.

The first layer is the **troposphere** (**trope**-uh-sfeer). This is the layer of air you breathe. The *troposphere* is between 8 and 16 kilometers (5 and 10 miles) thick. Most of the clouds you see are formed in the troposphere. The molecules of air in the troposphere at sea level are very close together. But on top of a mountain, the molecules are spread farther apart. In order to get

Troposphere: The layer of air closest to the earth (from 8 to 16 kilometers).

EXTENSIONS

Reinforcement

Science Skills—
Recording Data and Measuring

Students can use the apparatus described in the Activity to collect data on air temperature. The temperature should be measured on several days. These measurements should be taken several times a day but at the same time each day. The data gathered should be plotted on graphs and used to answer the following questions:

1. How does the temperature change during the day?
2. How does the temperature change from day to day?

DEVELOPMENT

1 Teaching Tips—Draw the pie graph on the chalkboard as students may not be familiar with such a graph. Discuss the importance of the four major gases in the air: nitrogen—essential to all plant and animal tissue; oxygen—utilized in respiration; it is the most abundant element in nature, comprising 21% of the air, 90% of water, and 50% of the earth's crust; carbon dioxide—used by plants in photosynthesis, it is incombustible; water vapor—seen in the air as clouds, rain, sleet, hail, or snow.

EXTENSIONS

Reinforcement

Science Skills—Inferring

Students can test the air they exhale for the presence of carbon dioxide by blowing into a glass of limewater. Limewater turns milky white when carbon dioxide is present.

Give each student a glass 1/4 full of limewater and a straw. Have the student blow into the glass for several seconds. What change is observed? What inference can be made about the air the student has breathed out?

Science Skills—Finding Cause and Effect Relationship

Because oxygen is needed for anything to burn, students can do a simple experiment to demonstrate the presence of oxygen in the air. They will need a candle, a pie pan, matches, clay, and a glass jar.

Have them support the candle in the pie pan with a piece of clay. They should then light the candle, cover the candle with a glass jar so no air can get in, and observe. What happens to the candle?

Exceptional Student

Visually Impaired

To reinforce the concept of the four layers of the earth's atmosphere, paste Styrofoam packing pieces onto large oaktag in an arrangement that represents the molecules in each of the four layers. The visually impaired student could feel this model.

Stratosphere: The layer of air from 16 to 48 kilometers above the earth.

Mesosphere: The layer of air from 50 to 80 kilometers above the earth.

enough oxygen, you would have to breathe more deeply.

Above this first layer is the **stratosphere** (**strat**-uh-sfeer). It goes up to about 48 kilometers (30 miles) above the earth's surface. Most jet planes fly in the *stratosphere*. There is not much weather here, so flights are smoother. The molecules in the stratosphere are far apart. Because of this, jet planes carry their own supply of oxy-

2 gen. The air in the plane is under pressure. This means that the molecules are tightly packed.

Above the stratosphere is the **mesosphere** (**mez**-uh-sfeer). The molecules are spread very far apart at this height. The *mesosphere* reaches to about 80 kilometers (50 miles) above the earth.

3

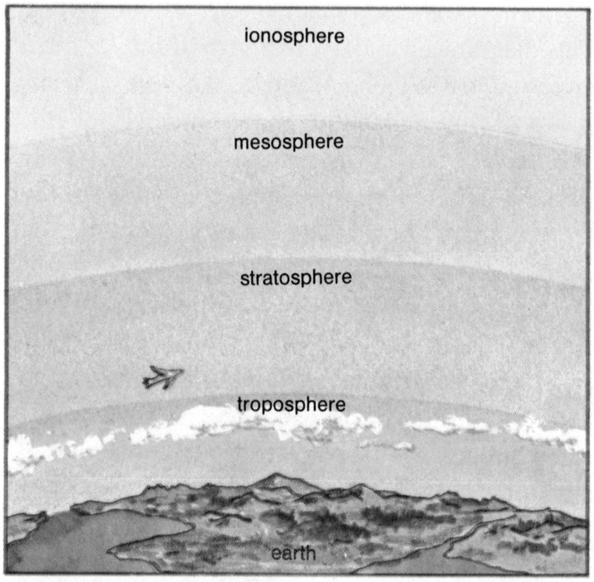

2 **Teaching Tips**—Stack Styrofoam balls (to represent molecules of air) in a glass container. Ask: What would happen if we pressed down on all these balls? *They would be compressed, or moved closer together.* You could also demonstrate this effect by blowing up about five balloons and placing them in a container.

3 **Skill Development**—Thinking about the atmosphere in layers is an example of *sequencing*. Temperature, pressure, and density are three different properties of the air that can be used to distinguish between different layers.

The last layer of the atmosphere is the **ionosphere** (eye-**ahn**-uh-sfeer). It goes to about 1,000 kilometers (620 miles) above the earth's surface. The air is thinnest in the *ionosphere*. The molecules are spread very far apart. Where does the earth's atmosphere end and outer space begin? Why is it hard to know for sure?

Ionosphere: The layer of air farthest from the earth (up to 1,000 kilometers).

The energy to warm earth's air comes from the sun. Sunlight can pass through the earth's atmosphere. The air does not heat up as the sunlight passes through it. Instead, the earth's surface heats up the air.

Sunlight passes through the air. It strikes the surface of the earth. The air over a warm patch of ground heats up. Have you ever noticed that some surfaces get hotter than others? Dark pavement feels very warm if you walk on it in bare feet on a sunny day. The air over the dark pavement will heat up faster than the air over grass or trees.

The **temperature** (**tem**-per-a-chure) of air gets cooler as you go higher up in the atmosphere. This is because the air is farther from the warm surface. Also, the molecules are spread farther apart. Molecules that are far apart hold less heat than molecules that are close together.

Temperature: The degree of hotness or coldness of the air.

The *temperature* of the air is measured with a thermometer. When the temperature is warm, the liquid in a thermometer expands. It rises up the thermometer tube. When the temperature is cool, the liquid shrinks inside the tube. The level of the liquid falls.

EXTENSIONS

Reinforcement

Science Skills—Inferring

Air, because it is matter, has weight and takes up space. The following demonstrations will illustrate this.

A. Gather these materials: two basketballs and a double-pan balance. Inflate one of the basketballs in front of your students. The other basketball should not be inflated. Flatten it by pressing it with both hands. Put a ball on each of the two pans of the balance. The balance will tip toward the side with the basketball you inflated. Ask the students to guess (infer) why the balance tipped the way it did. (Because air has mass, the ball filled with air will weigh more than the ball not filled with air.)

B. Obtain a narrow-necked glass bottle, a pitcher of water, clay, and a funnel. Put the funnel in the neck of the bottle. Plaster clay around the neck to make a tight seal. Now, slowly pour water into the funnel. The water will not pour into the bottle rapidly because the bottle is full of air. Students will see bubbles of air escaping. Ask the students to make guesses (inferences) to explain what they see.

4 Text Questions—Where does the earth's atmosphere end and outer space begin? *There is no sharp dividing line between the earth's atmosphere and outer space. When you are at a great distance from the earth's surface, molecules of gas can be very far apart.* Why is it hard to know for sure? *The space between air molecules can be extremely large at that distance from the earth, so it is difficult to define the point at which there is no air.*

5 Teaching Tips—Molecules are always in motion. When heat energy is added to molecules, they move faster. Temperature is a measurement that indicates how fast these molecules are moving. The sun heats the earth's atmosphere, which is made up of molecules. However, this happens indirectly. Solar energy for the most part passes through the air and makes contact with the surface of the earth. The energy is absorbed by materials in the earth's crust, causing them to heat up. Air coming in contact with the earth's surface is then warmed. In general, dark surfaces absorb more heat than light surfaces.

EXTENSIONS

Enrichment

Activity

Have students do a variation of the Activity. Using the thermometer, cup, and coat hanger, students can observe how some surfaces retain heat more than others.

A. Using the same locations as those in the Activity, record the temperature of the air early in the morning, at midday, and in the evening. Do this over several days at the same times each day.

B. Draw bar graphs of the air temperatures measured throughout the day and from day to day at each location. Use these graphs to compare the temperature changes at each location. Interested students may also want to try recording temperatures above different colors of oaktag. They should leave the oaktags in the sun for about half an hour, and then measure the air temperatures above each color.

1. Which surface causes the air to warm quickest?
2. Which surface causes the air to cool quickest?

Research—Library

Have students go to the library to do research on the atmospheres of other planets. They should find out the gases, temperatures, and pressures that make up these atmospheres. They may want to record their findings on a chart. Students should also speculate as to whether life is possible on any other planets in our solar system and whether or not humans could live on any other planets.

ACTIVITY

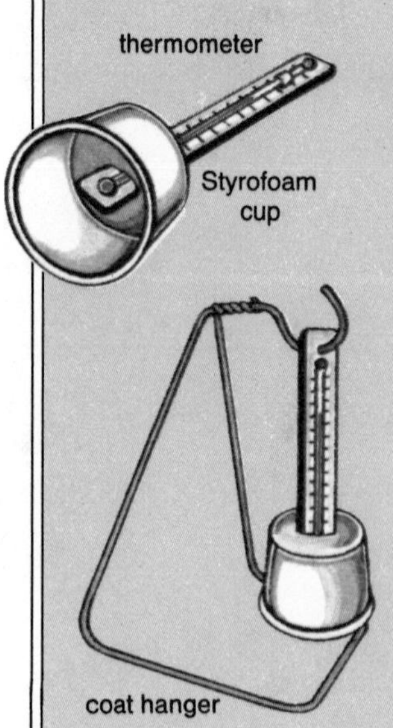

How does the surface of the earth affect air temperature?

A. Gather these materials: coat hanger, thermometer, and Styrofoam cup.

B. Bend the coat hanger, as shown. Push the thermometer through the Styrofoam cup. Hang the thermometer on the coat hanger.

C. Go outside. Measure the temperature of the air: (a) over blacktop, (b) over concrete, (c) in the shade of a tree, and (d) in the shade of a building.

1. Was the temperature higher in direct sunlight or in the shade?
2. How does the temperature differ over dark and light surfaces?
3. Why is the air warm in some places and cool in others?

Section Review

Main Ideas: The earth is covered with a blanket of air called the atmosphere. It has four layers.

Questions: Answer in complete sentences.

1. What are the two main gases in the air?
2. In which layer are most of the earth's clouds found?
3. Why does the atmosphere heat up more in some places than in others?

ACTIVITY

Skill Development—*Measuring, Recording Data, and Comparing and Contrasting*

Teaching Tips—Cut the Styrofoam cups before the Activity. They will protect the thermometers from exposure to direct sunlight, which would cause an inaccurate reading.

Answers to Questions—1. Higher in direct sunlight **2.** The temperature is higher over dark surfaces. **3.** The earth is heated more in some places than in others.

SECTION REVIEW

Answers to Questions

1. Nitrogen and oxygen
2. Troposphere
3. The sun heats the surface of the earth more in some places than in others. The air over a warm surface heats up more than the air over a cool surface.

Pretend you are hiking along a mountain ridge. It's been sunny and warm all day. But you see a dark line of clouds moving from the west. Do you think this means a storm is coming? It might help to know what kind of clouds they are. When you finish this section, you should be able to:

- **A.** Identify the elements that make up the earth's weather.
- **B.** Compare the three kinds of clouds.
- **C.** Identify the kind of weather related to each cloud type.

7-2. Observing the Weather

SECTION BACKGROUND

The science of meteorology seeks to understand the physical state of the earth's atmosphere. Of greatest concern to a meteorologist are the movement of air masses; measurements of the temperature, pressure, and density of air; the distribution of water in the air in the form of clouds; and precipitation. In recent years, meteorologists have become more concerned about the presence of chemical pollutants in the air, which come from automobiles, factories, and other sources. Until 1960, weather observations could only be made at weather observatories all around the world. Now a meteorological satellite, TIROS I, provides us with temperature and photographic data that was previously unavailable. In addition to TIROS, radar has been an invaluable tool to the weather forecaster. Students should be familiar with radar if they watch local TV weather reports. Forecasters all use radar to show the locations of rain and other forms of precipitation.

Further weather observations are taken by aircraft that fly into storms, such as the hurricane hunters. These aircraft are used to study storms as well as cloud formations and the cause of precipitation.

MOTIVATION

Most of your students are familiar with clouds, but they may not be able to tell you how different cloud formations might be used to predict the weather. Take your class outside. If it is a nice day, have them lie on their backs and watch the clouds move. If there are individual cumulus clouds, students can watch them change shape. Ask the students if they can tell by the clouds they are observing whether or not it will rain.

Text Questions—Do you think this means a storm is coming? *When clouds become darker, bigger, and thicker, this usually means a storm is coming.*

MATERIALS

thermometer

EXTENSIONS

Reinforcement

Science Skills—Observing

Students can use the school flag to make observations of the wind.

The flag outside your school is a good indicator of wind direction. Get permission from your principal to have your students draw a compass with chalk on the sidewalk near or around the flagpole. The compass should show the following eight directions: north, south, east, west, northeast, northwest, southwest, southeast. When positioning points of direction on the sidewalk, use the sun as a reference. Remind your students that the sun rises in the east and sets in the west.

Have the students set up a chart to record the wind for two weeks. Or they could use the flag to record wind direction as part of their weather observation study.

1 The following is a daily weather report:

> It will be partly cloudy and hot in the city on Friday, with a 30-percent chance of an afternoon thundershower.

2 Why is it important for people to know what the weather will be like?

Weather is the condition of the air around the earth. Clouds, rain, temperature, and wind are all parts of weather. Scientists who study the weather are called **meteorologists** (mee-tee-or-**ahl**-uh-jists). *Meteorologists* help tell what kind of weather is coming.

Meteorologist: A scientist who studies the weather.

The three main types of clouds are shown in the pictures on this page and the next. Symbols are used for each cloud type. They are shown in the lower right-hand corner of the picture.

Picture 1 shows clouds that look like feathers or curls. These clouds are found high in the sky. They are called **cirrus** (**seer**-us) clouds.

Cirrus clouds: Clouds found high in the sky that look like feathers or curls.

DEVELOPMENT

1 Teaching Tips—You might display the daily weather report and a weather map on the bulletin board. Make a different student responsible for obtaining the report from the newspaper each day.

2 Text Questions—Why is it important for people to know what the weather will be like? *The weather forecast allows us to plan our daily activities.*

Picture 2 shows low, flat sheets of gray clouds. These clouds spread out over the sky. They are called **stratus** (**strat**-us) clouds. *Stratus* clouds turn into rain clouds as they become bigger and thicker.

Stratus clouds: Low, flat sheets of gray clouds that spread out over the sky.

Picture 3 shows patches of puffy, white clouds. They look like cotton. They are called **cumulus** (**kyoom**-yoo-lus) clouds. *Cumulus* clouds are fair-weather clouds. They also become rain clouds as they get bigger and thicker.

Cumulus clouds: Patches of puffy, white clouds.

Rain is only one kind of **precipitation** (prih-sip-uh-**tay**-shun). Moisture can also fall in the form of snow, sleet, and hail. The kind of *precipitation* that falls depends on the temperature of the air.

Precipitation: Moisture that falls from the sky.

3 Skill Development—Have students bring in pictures of clouds and *classify* them.

4 Teaching Tips—Students may be aware that a hailstone can be as big as a golf ball. They may not be aware of the size of raindrops. They can observe raindrops by collecting a few on a nylon stocking sprinkled with baby powder. Stretch a nylon stocking over the top of a large can. Secure it with a rubber band. Sprinkle a small amount of baby powder on the stocking. On a rainy day, put the can in the rain for about 5–10 sec. Have the students immediately observe the spots made by the raindrops as they hit the powdered stocking. There will be some variation in raindrop size.

EXTENSIONS

Reinforcement

Activity

Tell your students to collect some snowflakes the next time it snows. Have them examine the snowflakes with a magnifying glass. They will discover that all snowflakes have six sides, yet no two snowflakes are exactly alike.

Snowflakes may be collected as follows: Put a piece of black construction paper in the freezer compartment of a refrigerator for an hour. Then place the card in the path of the falling snow. The flakes will collect on the card and their shapes will be easy to see.

Your students can draw or make paper cutouts of the snowflakes.

Exceptional Student

Visually Impaired

Paste cotton on poster board to represent the three types of clouds and their relative distances from the earth.

EXTENSIONS

Enrichment

Activity

Students can build a cloud chamber and use it to observe how clouds form. They will need a wide-mouth gallon jar, a balloon, a rubber band, 1 cup of hot water, and matches.

A. Put the hot water into the jar.

B. Stretch a balloon over the mouth and secure it with a rubber band.

C. Wait a few minutes for the air in the jar to become saturated with water vapor.

D. Light a match and blow it out quickly. Open the jar, blow the smoke from the extinguished match into the jar, and replace the balloon cover immediately.

E. Push the center of the balloon down and hold for a few seconds. Then quickly pull it up so that it is above the top of the jar. Push it down and pull it up several times. What happens in the jar? (A cloud should form when the balloon is pulled up.) Why does a cloud form in the jar? (Pulling the balloon up decreases the pressure within the jar, which causes the air in the jar to expand and cool. The water vapor in the jar then condenses on the smoke particles, causing a cloud to form.)

SUGGESTED WORKSHEET MASTER
for Sections 7-1 and 7-2,
p. T-111 o

ACTIVITY

How are weather observations made?

A. Gather this material: thermometer.

B. Copy the weather chart shown below. Complete the chart for each day of the week.

WEEK OF—				
	Day 1	Day 2	Day 3	Day 4
Cloud type				
Cloud cover				
Temperature				

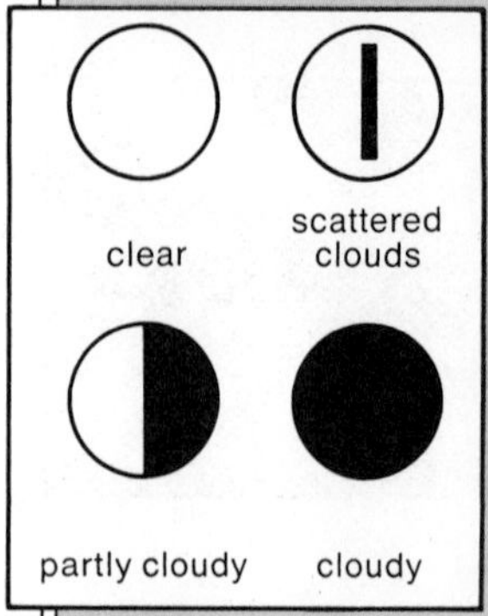

C. Record the symbols for today's cloud type and cloud cover.

D. Measure the air temperature.

E. Repeat steps C–D each day for a week.

1. What kind of clouds did you see most often?
2. What was the weather like?

Section Review

Main Ideas: Cirrus, stratus, and cumulus are three types of clouds.

Questions: Answer in complete sentences.

1. What elements make up the earth's weather?
2. What kind of cloud is described by each of the following: (a) high, feathery clouds; (b) white, puffy clouds; (c) flat sheets of gray clouds?

ACTIVITY

Skill Development—*Observing, Measuring, and Recording Data*

Teaching Tips—You might want to do this Activity as a class project. Instead of having each student make observations, make a pair of students responsible for the observations each day. The data can be recorded on a class chart on the bulletin board. The rest of the class can consult the bulletin board and put the data in their own science notebooks.

SECTION REVIEW

Answers to Questions

1. Clouds, precipitation, temperature, wind
2. **a.** Cirrus, **b.** cumulus, **c.** stratus

7-3. Weather Forecasting

Some people think groundhogs can forecast the weather. February 2 is Groundhog Day. On this day, the groundhog comes out of its hole in the ground. If the groundhog does not see its shadow, winter is over. If the groundhog sees its shadow, it jumps back into its hole. Winter will last six more weeks. By using this method, you would be right about 30 percent of the time. What are some other strange ways to forecast the weather? When you finish this section, you should be able to:

- **A.** Explain how information about the weather is recorded.
- **B.** Explain how weather forecasts are made.
- **C.** Explain how computers help to make forecasts.

1 Meteorologists collect information about the weather in order to make weather forecasts. The information includes temperature, air pressure,

SECTION BACKGROUND

Weather forecasting has been changed by the advent of computers and by new theories about the atmosphere. As a result, the quality and accuracy of weather forecasts have been greatly improved.

The basic guide for the weather forecaster is the weather map. The weather map is a synthesis of all the weather data received from weather stations around the world. Forecasters receive data on temperatures and pressure in the atmosphere, cloud patterns, air masses, fronts, precipitation, wind direction and velocity, and approaching storms.

Weather forecasting involves probabilities. A given set of weather conditions will produce a specific weather pattern a certain percent of the time. As a result, precipitation and other weather conditions are predicted in terms of percentage probabilities.

MATERIALS

thermometer, weather cards

BASIC TEACHING PLAN

MOTIVATION

What are some other strange ways to forecast the weather? *The following are some familiar forecasting expressions: (1) When windows won't open and salt clogs the shaker, the weather will favor the umbrella maker (air is very humid; it might rain). (2) Red sky at night, sailors delight (clouds are to the west, so the weather is clearing out). Red sky at morning, sailors take warning (clouds are to the east, probably moving to the west, with a chance of rain).*

DEVELOPMENT

1 Teaching Tips—Students should realize that weather forecasters are scientists who use observations to make predictions about the weather. If you can obtain a videotape of a weather forecaster giving the daily weather forecast and report, you can use it to discuss forecasting.

EXTENSIONS

Application

Science Skills—Recording Data

A wind rose is a method of recording wind direction and speed over a period of time. This recording method also reveals wind patterns, such as the prevailing winds.

A. Students should monitor the local weather report in the newspaper or on radio every day for a week. They should record the speed and direction of the wind.

B. To make a wind rose, the students should draw a dot on a piece of paper that represents the location where wind direction and speed were recorded. Above the dot is north; below, south; to the left, west; and to the right, east. The wind direction and velocity should be recorded each day, using the same dot at the center of the rose. Direction is recorded as an arrow toward the dot *from* the proper direction. The length of the arrow indicates velocity; let each centimeter represent 5 kph of wind speed.

1. What was the greatest wind speed recorded, and from what direction did it come?
2. In which direction does the wind blow the strongest and most often?

and humidity. There are over 9,000 weather stations around the world. Weather stations collect a great deal of information. The weather forecaster's job is to use this information to make a good forecast.

A weather forecast is like a guess. A forecaster might say, "There is a 70-percent chance of rain tomorrow." The forecaster has studied many weather conditions. Wind direction, cloud types, temperature, and air pressure are all studied. Past weather conditions are helpful in making forecasts. For example, weather records show that it rained seven out of ten days with similar conditions. The forecast will be a 70-percent chance of rain.

2 The modern weather forecaster must use a computer. Without the help of a computer, it would be impossible to deal with all the information. Computers can be used to make maps. They also keep track of records to make forecasts. Computers can record weather information over many years. Weather scientists use this

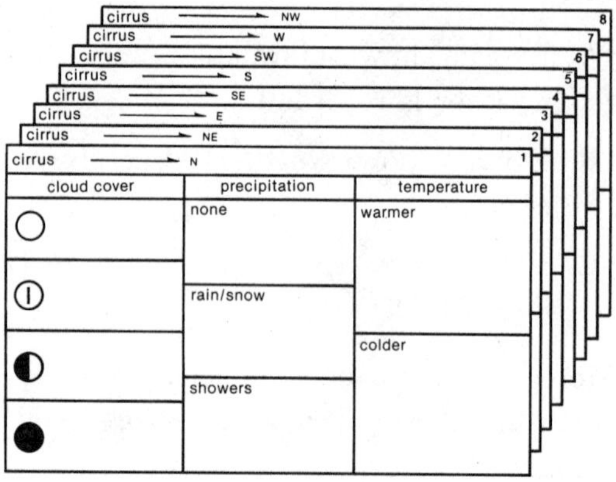

2 Teaching Tips—Meteorologists all over the world report on weather conditions at their locations every 6 h. The reports include the following: surface wind speed and direction; air pressure corrected to sea level; temperature; amount of precipitation; humidity; cloud cover and height to cloud base. At larger stations, equipment is sent up by balloon to measure conditions in the upper atmosphere. This information is put into an international code and sent to collection centers in different countries. Government agencies of different countries exchange this information. These data are the raw material from which the forecaster predicts the weather. Accurate predictions of general weather conditions are possible up to five days in advance. Detailed forecasts are not made beyond two days. Computer analysis of average movements of the atmosphere allows meterologists to make general forecasts up to 30 days in advance.

3 Text Questions—What do you think are the chances for a cloudy day? *100%*

information to predict general trends in our weather.

You can use weather cards to predict the weather. Choose the card that matches the cloud type and wind direction for the day. Suppose today is a bright, cool day. There are cirrus clouds. The wind is from the southwest. You should look at the weather card for cirrus clouds and southwest wind. You see under precipitation eight marks for rain and two for none. So the chances that it will rain tomorrow are eight out of ten, or 80 percent. Suppose ten out of ten marks for cloud cover are under cloudy sky. What do you think are the chances for a cloudy day?

ACTIVITY

How is weather predicted?

A. Gather these materials: thermometer and weather cards.

B. Find the weather card for the kind of clouds and wind direction you had yesterday. Make a mark in the column for the kind of clouds you see today. Make a mark in the column for the kind of precipitation you are having today.

C. Measure the air temperature in the shade. Record whether today is warmer or colder than yesterday.

D. Repeat steps B–C each day for a week.

EXTENSIONS

Reinforcement

Research

A. Have your students research folklore about weather. Parents, grandparents, and older neighbors are good sources of this kind of information. The *Old Farmer's Almanac* is also another good source. Students may discover some of the following:

1. A ring around the moon predicts cloudy or rainy weather.
2. Aching corns predict rainy weather.
3. Beautiful sunsets signify nice weather for the next day.

ACTIVITY

Skill Development—*Observing, Recording Data, and Predicting*

Teaching Tips—Stress that the card system is sequential. Cloud type and wind direction represent the weather for the first day of the sequence, and the tally marks record the weather on the second day of the sequence. Since this is an Activity that continues throughout the entire unit, it may be done best as a class project. Only when sufficient data are collected can the class begin to predict the weather. To predict the weather, the card with the appropriate cloud type and wind direction is located, and the weather condition with the greatest number of tallies is the most probable.

EXTENSIONS

Enrichment

Activity

Students can construct an anemometer to measure wind speed.

A. Gather these materials: 2 index cards, tape, scissors, 2 straws, and a straight pin.

B. Cut a quarter circle with a radius of 7 cm from the corner of an index card. Tape it to the end of a straw like a flag.

C. Cut a 15-cm piece from the other straw. Cut a 7-cm square from the other index card. Tape this square to one end of the straw so that the straw runs along the middle of the card. Make a pinhole at the other end of the 15-cm straw.

D. Push the straight pin through this hole, into the end of the longer straw. When the longer straw is held level, the shorter straw should hang straight down.

E. The anemometer can be calibrated by holding it out a car window on a calm day and traveling at 10, 15, 20, and 25 kph. Hold the longer straw level and let the wind hit the square card head on. Mark how much of the quarter circle is covered by the square card for each speed the car travels.

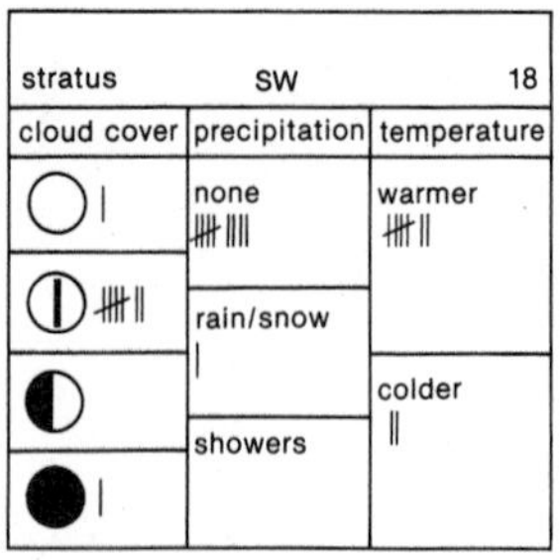

Fig. 7-1

stratus	SW	18
cloud cover	precipitation	temperature
○ |	none 𝍸 ||||	warmer 𝍸 ||
⦶ 𝍸 ||	rain/snow |	
◐	showers	colder ||
● |		

Section Review

Main Ideas: Weather records can be used to forecast the weather.

Questions: Answer in complete sentences.

1. The temperature is 13°C (55°F). It is raining. The wind is from the southwest. The clouds are stratus. Look at the card shown here. What are the chances for rain the next day?
2. What kind of information is used to make a weather forecast?
3. What are two ways in which computers help scientists forecast the weather?

People in Science

Vilhelm Bjerknes

Vilhelm Bjerknes (**byerk**-nes) was born in Oslo, Norway, in 1862. He devoted his life to the study of the weather. His dream was to be able to predict the weather just one day in advance. Weather forecasters today make predictions weeks and months ahead. Vilhelm would have been happy to make a 24-hour forecast. Around 1917, he set up a number of weather stations. These stations were located along the coast of Norway. Vilhelm studied the weather reports from all these stations. From these reports, he hoped to forecast the weather. He formed a team of scientists who began the science of meteorology.

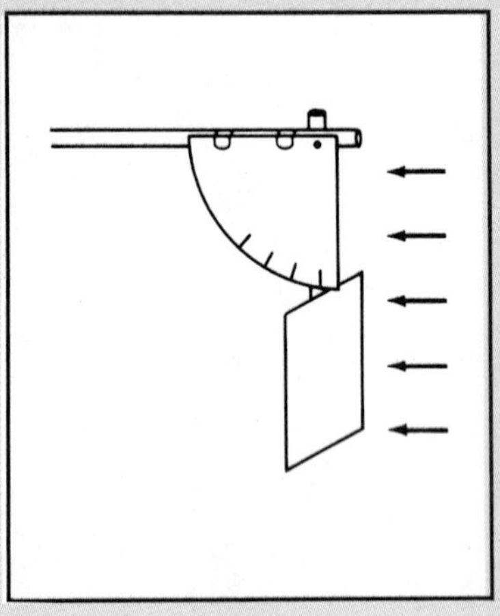

SECTION REVIEW

Main Ideas—You might have students bring in a copy of the weather report from the local newspaper. Have them identify the forecast from the report.

Answers to Questions

1. 1 out of 10, or 10% chance of rain

2. Weather forecasters use data such as temperature, pressures, wind direction and velocity.

3. Computers are able to process a large volume of data. They can easily furnish information such as average temperature, high temperature, and low temperature. They can record weather data over many years.

CHAPTER REVIEW

Science Words: Think of a word for each blank. List the letters **a** through **l** on paper. Write the word next to each letter.

The air that circles the earth is the ___a___. Air is made of small particles called ___b___. People live in the part of the air called the ___c___. The air above 16 kilometers is called the ___d___. Above this layer is the ___e___. The top layer of the air is the ___f___.

Persons who study the weather are called ___g___. They use a thermometer to observe the air ___h___. High clouds are called ___i___. Low, flat sheets of gray clouds are called ___j___ clouds. ___k___ clouds are fair-weather clouds. Rain is one form of ___l___.

Questions: Answer in complete sentences.

1. What gases make up the earth's atmosphere?
2. How does the sun heat the earth's air?
3. Where would the temperature be higher on a sunny day: (a) above a black asphalt road; (b) above a light wooden picnic table; or (c) in the shade of a tree?
4. What are three things that meteorologists observe in making a weather report?
5. Which type of clouds would you expect to find on the following days: (a) a rainy day; (b) a partly cloudy day; and (c) a fair-weather day?
6. Are weather forecasts right all the time? Explain your answer.
7. Why are computers helpful in making weather forecasts?

EXTENSIONS

Enrichment

Science Skills—Building Science Vocabulary

Students may be interested in learning the meanings of these additional vocabulary words and how they relate to the concepts taught in this chapter.

isotherms: lines on a map joining locations that record the same temperature.

isobars: lines on a weather map connecting locations of the same atmospheric pressure.

radiosonde: an electronic instrument used to take measurements of temperature, pressure, and humidity in the upper atmosphere.

weather balloon: a large helium-filled balloon used to carry radiosonde and other instruments into the upper atmosphere.

Research—Library

Interested students could go to the library to do research on weather conditions on their birthdays.

They could find temperature and precipitation records for their birthdays each year, from the year they were born to the present. Each student could make a graph of this information, plotting temperature and precipitation against year. The students could also plot their data on one large graph, which could be used to infer weather trends over the last eight or nine years.

CHAPTER REVIEW

Science Words

a. Atmosphere, **b.** molecules, **c.** troposphere, **d.** stratosphere, **e.** mesosphere, **f.** ionosphere, **g.** meteorologists, **h.** temperature, **i.** cirrus, **j.** stratus, **k.** cumulus, **l.** precipitation

Answers to Questions

1. Nitrogen, oxygen, water vapor, carbon dioxide
2. Sunlight goes through the air and is absorbed by the earth's surface. The surface is heated. The air comes in contact with the heated surface, thereby warming the air.
3. a
4. Temperature, pressure, and wind
5. **a.** Stratus, **b.** cumulus or cirrus, **c.** cumulus
6. No. A weather forecast is like a guess. No forecast is 100% correct.
7. Computers can keep track of weather records and other information needed to make forecasts.

SUGGESTED WORKSHEET MASTER
p. T-111 p

SUGGESTED TEST MASTERS
pp. T-111 d, e

AIR ON THE MOVE

8-1. Air Rises and Falls

The hot-air balloon was the first flying machine. Balloons like this one can rise thousands of feet into the air. Some rise so high that the crew has to take their own oxygen. Very soon, the balloon will rise off the ground. What causes the balloon

CHAPTER OBJECTIVES

1. Describe temperature in terms of molecular movement, and identify the relationship between air temperature and air pressure.
2. Explain how high- and low-pressure centers affect the weather.
3. Explain how the heating of the air causes wind.
4. Describe how different types of air masses are formed and what happens when air masses meet.

SECTION BACKGROUND

Heating of the earth, which in turn heats the atmosphere, is responsible for the motions and movements of air in the atmosphere. Air, like most other substances, expands when heated and contracts when cooled. For this reason, a given volume of warm air will weigh less than an equal volume of cold air. Warm air moves upward through cold air. Conversely, cold air sinks downward through warm air. Since warmer air is lighter than colder air, it exerts less pressure than an equal amount of cooler air.

Barometers are sensitive to fluctuations in the air pressure of the atmosphere and are used to predict weather conditions.

MATERIALS

broomstick, chair, 2 large paper bags, meter stick, paper clip, string, 150-w bulb, clay

Exceptional Student IEP Chapter Goal

At the end of this chapter, the student will define air pressure, air mass, and barometer.

BASIC TEACHING PLAN

MOTIVATION

You can stimulate interest by making a hot-air balloon in the classroom or outside. Use a can of Sterno and a plastic dry cleaning bag. Make sure one end is closed. Light the Sterno, and hold the open end of the bag over the Sterno can. (CAUTION: Use extreme care when lighting the Sterno.) The bag should start to inflate. When it is inflated, tie the open end firmly, and then let the bag go. It should rise into the air.

Text Questions—What causes the balloon to rise? *Heating the air inside the balloon causes it to expand and become lighter. It can then rise into the air.*

to rise? When you finish this section, you should be able to:

- **A.** Explain what happens when air is heated or cooled.
- **B.** Explain how the temperature of air affects the *air pressure.*

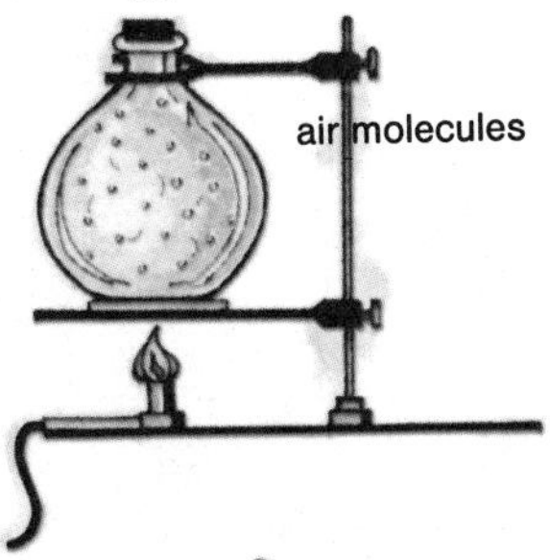

Air is made up of particles called molecules. Picture each molecule of air as a tiny, round ball. If you heat these tiny molecules, they start to move. The more you heat them, the faster they move. If you cool them, they slow down. Suppose you put popcorn kernels in a hot pan. The kernels will start to move. They bounce around the pan. As the pan cools, the kernels stop moving. Air molecules move in the same way.

We can now find out why heating the air in a balloon makes it rise. Look at the drawings below. Before they are heated, the air molecules inside the balloon are tightly packed. When the

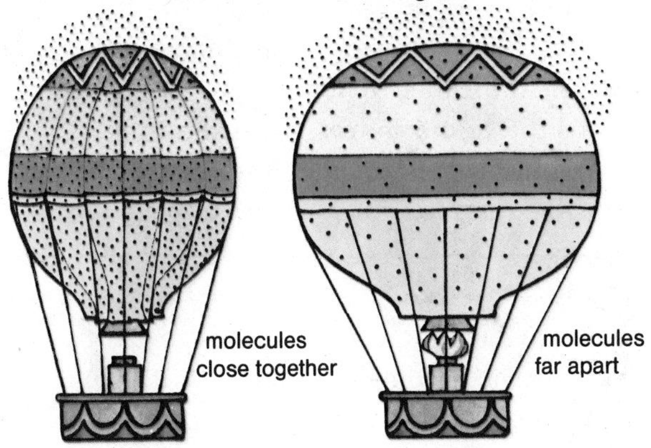

EXTENSIONS

Reinforcement

Science Skills—Inferring

This Extension should be done as a demonstration to encourage student inquiry. You will need an empty metal duplicating fluid can, water, and a hot plate. Make sure the can is empty and clean of any duplicating fluid. Put half a cup of water into the can. With the cap off, heat the water in the can until it boils. Remove the can from the hot plate, and quickly put the top back on. Keep the can away from the heat and wait. In a few seconds, the sides of the can will cave in. Because of the heating, the pressure inside the can will be less than that of the air outside. The difference in air pressure causes the can to collapse.

Ask the students to list their observations and their inferences. Give them a chance to discuss their inferences with each other.

DEVELOPMENT

1 Teaching Tips—Put a few popcorn kernels in a pan on a hot plate. Slowly heat the kernels. They should start to move and bounce around. Compare their action to that of air molecules.

2 Skill Development—Heating the air *causes* the molecules to move faster and to spread farther apart. The density of the air decreases.

EXTENSIONS

Reinforcement

***Science Skills—
Observing and Hypothesizing***

Obtain a glass jar, a pan, water, and an index card larger than the mouth of the jar. Fill the jar with water. Put the index card on top of the jar. Carefully invert the jar holding the card firmly in place. Release your hand from the bottom of the jar. The card will hold, and the water will not pour out. Ask the students if they can come up with reasons to explain this phenomenon. Have more of the above materials available so that students can conduct their own experiments as they formulate their explanations.

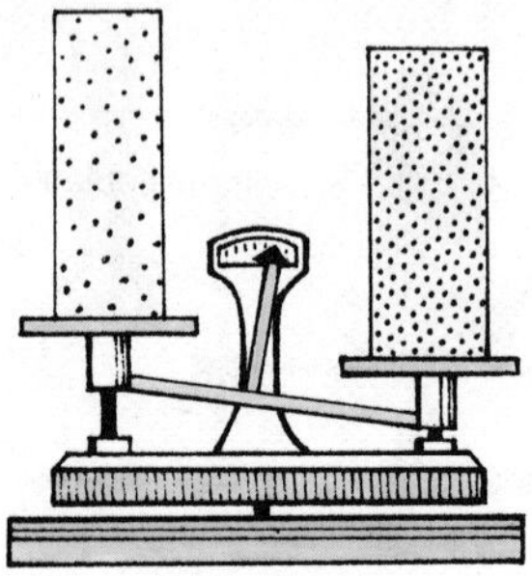

air is heated, the molecules move farther apart. They push on the inside of the balloon. This **3** makes the balloon expand. Since the molecules are farther apart, the air inside the balloon is lighter than the air outside the balloon. The lighter balloon will rise into the air.

Suppose you could weigh two columns of air as shown in the drawing. One column is cold air. The other is warm air. Would one column be heavier? Why? Which one do you think would press down harder on the balance? Air molecules in cold air are close together. There are more molecules in the cold-air column. So the cold-air column weighs more. The cold air pushes down with more force or pressure.

The force with which the air pushes down is called **air pressure**. *Air pressure* is measured
4 with a **barometer** (buh-**rahm**-uh-ter). In many *barometers*, a tube is sealed at one end. The
5 open end of the tube is placed into a jar. The jar is filled with a liquid. Air presses down on the liquid. The liquid is pushed up the tube. The greater the air pressure, the higher the liquid rises in the tube. When the air pressure goes down, the liquid moves down the tube.

Weather reports include the air pressure. Air pressure can change from day to day. Weather reports say if the pressure is rising, falling, or staying steady. You can predict the weather if you know how the air pressure is changing. The pressure may remain steady. If it does, the weather will not change very much. The chart on page 132 shows these forecasts.

Air pressure: The weight of the atmosphere caused by molecules pushing down on the earth's surface.

Barometer: An instrument used to measure the air pressure.

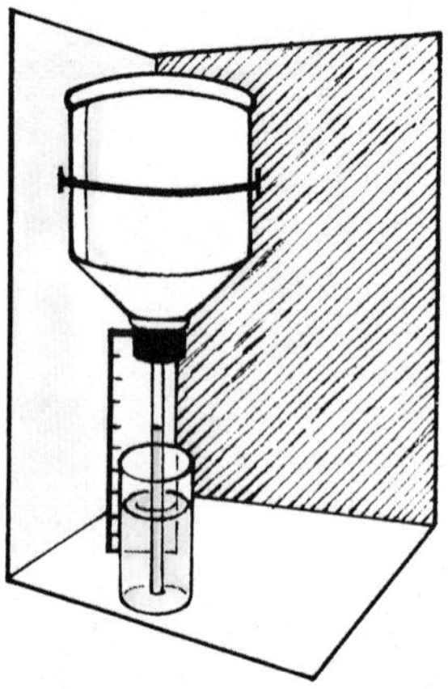

3 **Teaching Tips**—Heating the balloon causes the air inside the balloon to expand, and, therefore, the balloon becomes larger. Since the molecules are spread farther apart, the air inside the balloon is less dense than the air outside the balloon. Less-dense objects will "float" in the air and will continue to rise as long as their densities are less than that of the outside air.

4 **Teaching Tips**—If you can get a barometer (liquid or aneroid), show it to the class.

5 **Teaching Tips**—Students should understand why air pressure is reported as a measurement of length. The pressure of the air will force a column of mercury to a height of about 30 in. Less pressure means the column will fall; increased air pressure means the column will rise.

ACTIVITY

What happens to air when it is heated?

A. Gather these materials: broomstick, chair, 2 large paper bags, meter stick, paper clip, string, 150-watt bulb, and clay.

B. Make a balance like the one shown in the diagram. Bend the paper clip into a hook so the meter stick does not rub against the broomstick.

C. Hang the bags so the meter stick is level, or balanced. You can add a small amount of clay to the meter stick to make it balance.

D. Turn on the bulb. Hold it just inside 1 of the bags. Hold it there until you see a change.

1. What change did you see?
2. What do you think caused this change?
3. What happens when air is heated?

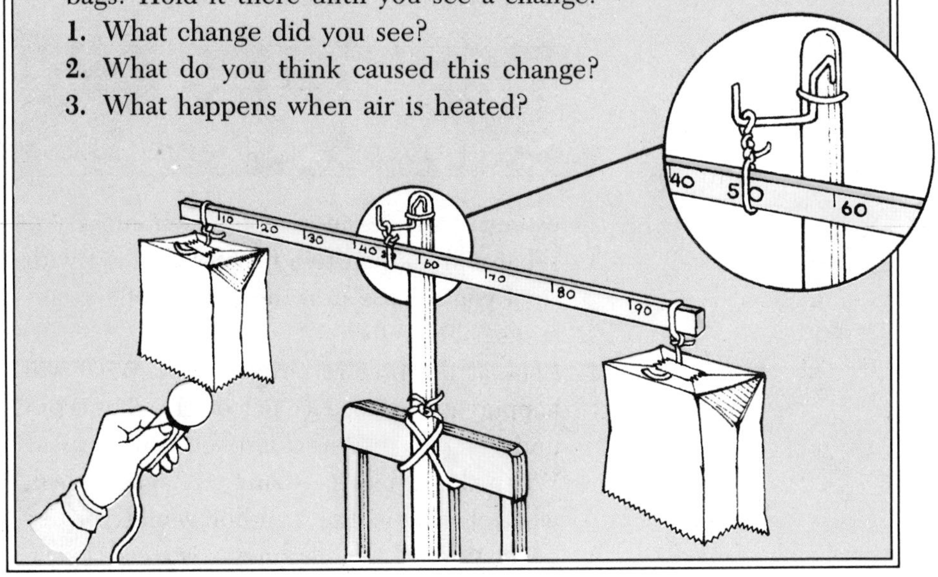

EXTENSIONS

Enrichment

Science Skills—Predicting

This Extension is a brain-teaser. Hang two apples using string so that they are about 2 cm apart. Tell the students that you are going to blow through the opening that separates the two apples. Ask them to predict what will happen to the apples when you do this. Most will think that the apples will fly apart. But some students will guess that the apples will actually bump together. This is an illustration of the Bernoulli principle. The principle says that when you increase the velocity of a fluid (air is a fluid), the pressure of the fluid decreases. When you blow between the apples, you decrease the pressure between them. Since the pressure on all other sides is greater, the apples are pushed together.

ACTIVITY

Skill Development—*Following Directions, Finding Cause and Effect*

Teaching Tips—This Activity can be done as a demonstration or by groups of about five students. The grocery bags must be large and fully open. The Activity will work with a 100-w bulb but 150 w or more are recommended.

Answers to Questions—1. The bag with the lamp under it rose upward. **2.** The air in that bag became heated and, therefore, less dense. The air in the other bag was then heavier so it fell, and the first one went up. **3.** It expands.

EXTENSIONS

Reinforcement

Activity

Students can demonstrate air pressure by doing this Activity.

A. Gather these materials: a plastic bag, a wide-mouth jar, and a rubber band.

B. Open the plastic bag and push it into the jar, so that it lines the bottom and sides.

C. Pull the edge of the bag over the rim of the jar and seal it with the rubber band.

D. Reach into the jar and grasp the bottom of the bag. Try to pull it out of the jar.

1. Could you pull the bag out of the jar? Why not? What could be holding it in? (Air pressure between the plastic and the jar is less than normal air pressure.)
2. Can you pull the bag out when holding the jar upside down or any other way? (No)

Activity

Using a jar and the materials from the previous Activity, students can discover what happens to air when it is cooled.

A. Put the paper bag right side up on the balance.

B. Leave an open jar in the refrigerator for a few minutes, and then cover and remove it.

C. Remove the cover and hold the container upside down over one of the bags.

1. What change did you see?
2. What do you think caused the change?
3. What happens when air is cooled?

SUGGESTED WORKSHEET MASTER
for Sections 8-1 and 8-2,
p. T-111 q

6

AIR PRESSURE PREDICTION CHART	
Air Pressure	**Change in the Weather**
Rising ↑	Clear, no rain
Falling ↓	Cloudy with rain
Steady	Little change

When you listen to a weather forecast, you will hear about high- and low-pressure centers. High pressure brings sunshine and clear weather. Low pressure means some form of precipitation, such as rain or snow.

Section Review

Main Ideas: The chart below shows how temperature affects weight, pressure, and the distance between air molecules.

	Weight	Pressure	Molecules
Warm Air	light	low	far apart
Cold Air	heavy	high	close together

Questions: Answer in complete sentences.

1. What will happen to a beach ball filled with air if you release it at the bottom of a swimming pool? Why?
2. Look at the picture on page 131. What will happen to a balance if a pan of ice cubes is put under one of the bags? Explain your answer.
3. When the liquid in a barometer goes down, what change in the weather would you expect? What if the barometer is steady?

6 Skill Development—Use the chart to emphasize how *predictions* can be made and *cause and effect* relationships determined. The change in air pressure is a fairly good predictor of the weather.

SECTION REVIEW

Answers to Questions

1. It would rise to the top. The air in the ball is less dense than the water.
2. The balance should tip in the direction of the bag over the pan of ice because the colder air would be denser.
3. You would expect clouds and rain. There would be little change.

8-2. Wind

Have you ever tried to fly a kite on a day when the wind was not blowing? Without wind, the kite will not fly. There are some places where a steady wind always blows. The child shown here is flying his kite at the beach. The sun is shining. Is this a good place to fly a kite? When you finish this section, you should be able to:

- **A.** Explain how changes in air pressure and temperature cause wind.
- **B.** Explain why the direction in which the wind blows at the seashore changes.

If you put an object in the path of sunlight, the object will heat up. Dark-colored objects heat up more than light-colored objects. The earth is heated by sunlight. Some places get warmer than others. For example, dark surfaces can get very hot. They absorb a lot of sunlight. Light surfaces, like water, reflect a lot of sunlight. As a result, water does not get hot very fast. It takes much longer to heat water than land. But dark objects also cool faster. At night, the land will cool faster than the water.

Heat from the earth warms the air. In the same way, heat from a radiator warms the air in a room. As the earth warms and cools, the air near the earth's surface also warms and cools. On a warm day at the beach, the air over the land is warmer than the air over the water. The daytime air heated by the land floats upward. The colder air over the water moves in under the warmer, rising air. This happens because cold air pushes

SECTION BACKGROUND

After temperature, pressure, and moisture (which is presented in the next chapter), wind rounds out the four critical elements that determine the weather. Winds blow horizontally and vertically from all compass directions.

Vertical winds are generally more gentle than horizontal winds. Vertical movements of air are very important. When air rises, its pressure is reduced, causing it to expand. As a result, the air cools.

As air cools, its ability to hold moisture decreases. When cooling air becomes saturated with moisture, clouds are formed. Most clouds result from the upward movements of air masses.

On sunny days, some surfaces (asphalt or bare soil) become warmer than other nearby surfaces, and the air over the hotter surfaces rises. The resultant air movements are called convection currents. Eventually, the air reaches the condensation level and clouds form. When there is a difference in temperature between rising air and surrounding air, the air is said to be unstable. Air will keep rising, and clouds will continue to grow and rise, producing cumulonimbus clouds.

MATERIALS

2 bowls or Styrofoam cups, potting soil (enough to fill ½ of the bowls), water, 2 thermometers, watch or wall clock

BASIC TEACHING PLAN

MOTIVATION

Kite-flying is a good way to learn about air movements firsthand. Have all the students in your class fly kites as a group. Very inexpensive ones can be purchased. Discuss how the movement of air influences kites.

DEVELOPMENT

1 Teaching Tips—Ask the students why people should wear light-colored clothing on a warm, sunny day.

2 Teaching Tips—The movements of air due to temperature differences are called convection currents. You can demonstrate convection currents in water. Heat a beaker of water, allowing one edge to get more heat. To make the current visible, put a drop of food coloring into the heated beaker. You can show the effect of cooling by filling an aquarium with water. Put two or three colored ice cubes at one end of the aquarium. As the ice melts, the colored water will sink, flow across the bottom, and begin to rise.

EXTENSIONS

Reinforcement

Activity

Inflate a balloon and let the air slowly escape. Ask: Is the air that is escaping from the neck of the balloon like wind? The students should agree that it is. Discuss what caused the air to escape. Emphasize that when the balloon was inflated, the air pressure inside the balloon was raised, making pressure outside the balloon lower than that inside.

with more pressure than warm air. Air always moves from places of high pressure to places of low pressure. The moving air is called a breeze **3** or a wind. What do you think happens at night, when the land cools faster than the water?

ACTIVITY

Which heats faster: soil or water?

A. Gather these materials: 2 bowls, potting soil, water, 2 thermometers, and watch.

B. Put water in 1 bowl. Put potting soil in the second bowl. Fill both bowls to the same depth.

C. Place thermometers in both bowls. Put both bowls in sunlight.

TEMPERATURE					
	Start	**3 min**	**6 min**	**9 min**	**12 min**
Soil					
Water					

D. Copy the chart shown here. Record the temperatures of the water and soil after 3 min, 6 min, 9 min, and 12 min.

1. Did the temperature of the soil change? How much?
2. Did the temperature of the water change? How much?
3. Which heats faster: soil or water?
4. Why do you think there is a difference in the way soil and water heat up?

3 **Text Questions**—What do you think happens at night, when the land cools faster than the water? *The flow of air will reverse itself. Air from the land will blow out to sea.*

ACTIVITY

Skill Development—*Comparing and Contrasting, Inferring*

Teaching Tips—Margarine containers make ideal plastic bowls. Keep the containers of water and soil in your classroom overnight so they will be at the same temperature when the Activity is started. The thermometer bulbs should be placed 1 cm below the surface of both substances.

Answers to Questions—1. Yes, it went up. Answers will vary. **2.** Yes, it went up. Answers will vary. **3.** Soil. **4.** Soil is darker and absorbs more heat.

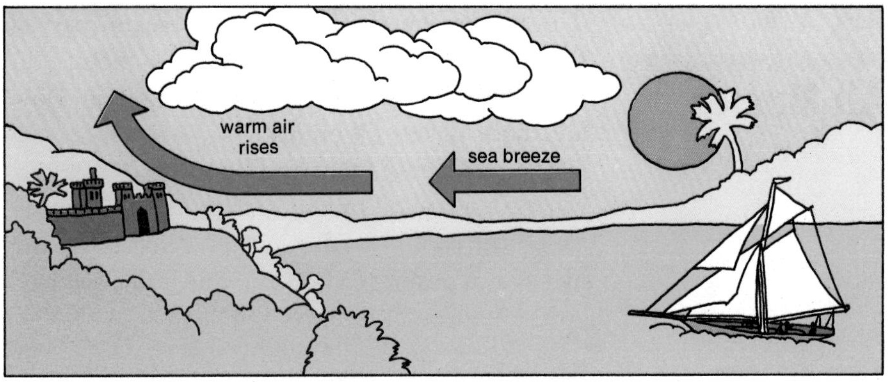

In the diagram above, the pressure over the water is higher than the pressure over the land. The greater the difference in pressure between two places, the faster the wind will blow.

Section Review

Main Ideas: As the earth warms and cools, the air near the earth's surface also warms and cools. Air always moves from places of high pressure to places of low pressure. Moving air is called wind.

Questions: Answer in complete sentences.

1. Which of these surfaces do you think will heat up the fastest: (a) gray car; (b) grassy field; (c) tar road? Explain your choice.
2. Is the kite shown flying in the wrong direction? If so, show the right direction.
3. In the picture, what is the direction of the wind?
4. Is the temperature higher at A or B?

EXTENSIONS

Application

Activity

Students might enjoy making a simple weather vane. They will need a straight pin, a pencil, scissors, straw, clay, and construction paper. Cut out an arrow shape and a tail shape from the construction paper. Make a cut at each end of the straw. Insert the arrow in one end and the tail in the other. Stick the pin through the center of the straw, and push the pin into the eraser end of a pencil. The pencil point should be pushed into a piece of clay so that it will stand upright. The weather vane will rotate and show the direction of the wind.

SECTION REVIEW

Answers to Questions

1. Tar road. It is darker, and darker objects heat up faster than light objects.
2. It is flying in the wrong direction. During the day, the wind should be blowing in from the sea. The kite should be shown moving toward land.
3. From water to land
4. The temperature is higher at A.

SECTION BACKGROUND

Air that remains stationary for a long time takes on some of the characteristics of the earth's surface lying beneath it. Air over the Caribbean becomes warm and moist; air over northern Canada becomes cold and dry.

Once an air mass has acquired its characteristics, it tends to keep them. There is a sharp boundary between different air masses. Meteorologists call these boundaries fronts. Air masses move and interact with each other. Where they interact is called the zone of mixing. The major portion of the United States is located in the zone of mixing for the western hemisphere.

MATERIALS

2 bowls, 2 thermometers, 2 coat hangers, 2 Styrofoam cups, hot water, ice

8-3. Air Masses

The picture on the left shows a barren part of the Arctic near the North Pole. The picture on the right shows a desert near the equator. How are these places different?

The air above the surface of the earth is warmed or cooled by the surface below it. Is the air hot or cool over the Arctic? What is the air like over a desert? When you finish this section, you should be able to:

- **A.** Describe what *air masses* are and where they form.
- **B.** Compare *air masses* in terms of temperature and moisture.
- **C.** Explain what happens when *air masses* meet.

BASIC TEACHING PLAN

MOTIVATION

The photographs can be used to open a discussion on what it would be like to be living in the African desert as opposed to the arctic regions of the world. Have the students make a list of the weather conditions in these contrasting areas.

Text Questions—How are these places different? *The air over the desert area is hot and very dry. There is little precipitation. The arctic area is very cold, and there is a lot of precipitation in the form of snow.* Is the air hot or cool over the Arctic? *Cool.* What is the air like over a desert? *Hot and dry.*

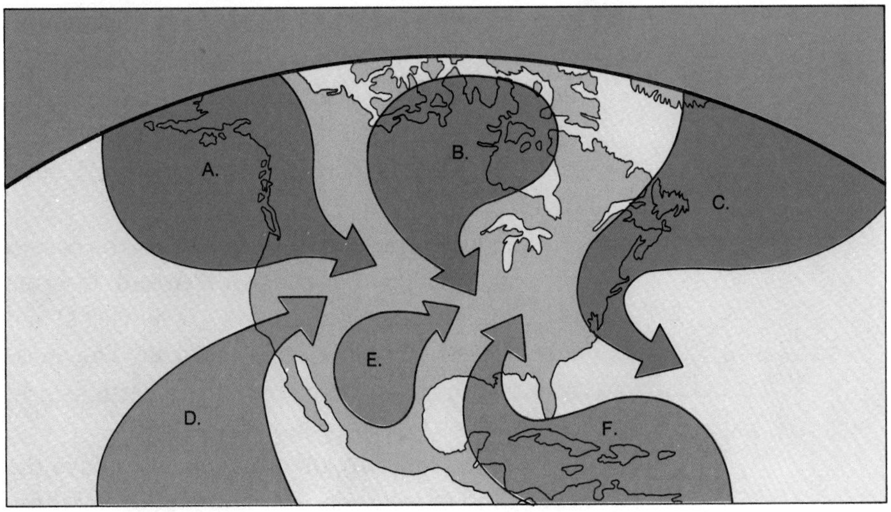

1 If air were to remain near the North Pole, it would get very cold. Air staying near the equator would get very warm. An **air mass** is a large amount of air. *Air masses* can be hot or cold. **2** What kind of air masses would you expect to form near the poles? What kind would form near the equator?

Air masses also can be wet or dry. Deserts are hot, dry places. What would the air mass over a desert be like?

3 Look at the map above. Six air masses push into each other over North America. There are three blue air masses. These are all cold air masses. There are three orange air masses. These are hot air masses. Some air masses form over land. Some form over water.

The two air masses that form over the land are dry. Dry air mass E is high-pressure air. This air

Air mass: A large volume of air that takes on the temperature and moisture of the area over which it forms.

EXTENSIONS

Application

Science Skills—Sequencing

Tell the students to collect weather maps from the local newspaper for one week. Have them mount the maps on paper in order from day 1 to day 7. They should identify one air mass, preferably at its place of origin. Have them color the air mass. They can then locate the air mass on successive days and color it on each map. In what direction is the air mass moving? When it gets to the zone of mixing, what happens?

DEVELOPMENT

1 Teaching Tips—You might use slides or pictures of different geographical locations and have students describe the climatic conditions pictured. Their descriptions need only include temperature and moisture. Air masses are described in terms of temperature and humidity.
2 Text Questions—What kind of air mass would you expect to form near the poles? *Cold.* What kind would form near the equator? *Hot.*
3 Teaching Tips—Give each student a copy of an outline map of North America. Have them identify and draw the six air masses that are described here. Put very simple descriptions of each of the six air masses on the board that tell where the air mass is located and in what direction it moves. Example: Air mass A—located in the North Pacific and Alaska, and moves southeast.

EXTENSIONS

Enrichment

Activity

In this Activity, the students will simulate the effect of the rotation of the earth on the direction of the air.

A. Place a cardboard disc on a phonograph turntable and turn the phonograph on.

B. Using a pencil, try to draw a straight line on the cardboard from the center pin outward.

C. Turn off the phonograph and look at the line you have drawn. The line curves to the left from start to finish.

D. Relate the rotation of the turntable to the rotation of the earth. Because of this rotation, air follows a curved path. You can also show this effect by spinning a globe or a basketball. Drip water from a medicine dropper on the top of the ball as it spins. The water will form a curved pattern on the turning sphere.

4 mass forms over deserts. It pushes to the north and east. It brings clear, hot, and dry weather. Dry air mass B is high-pressure air. It forms in Canada. It pushes to the south and east. It carries clear, dry, and cold weather to the United States.

5 The four air masses (A, C, D, F) over the oceans pick up moisture. Air masses A and C bring cold, high-pressure moist air. Air masses D and F bring warm, low-pressure, moist air. The moisture the air masses pick up falls to earth as precipitation.

Places covered by the same air mass have the same kind of weather. The temperature of these places is about the same. The amount of moisture in the air is about the same. Storms occur
6 where air masses meet. The picture below was
7 taken by a camera in space. Can you tell if it was sunny or cloudy where you live?

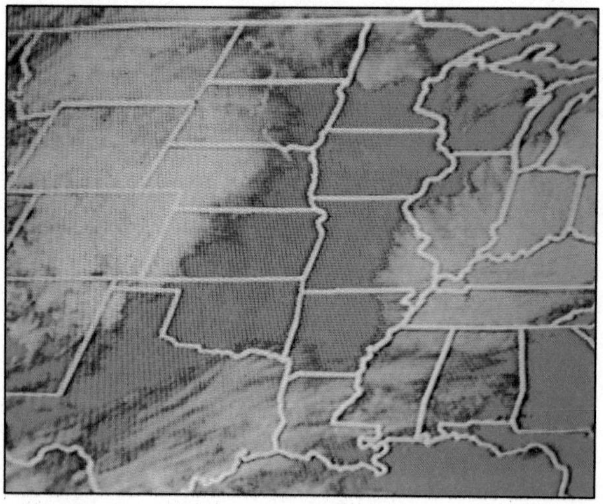

4 Teaching Tips—Air masses that form over land are known as continental air masses. Such air masses are generally dry. Point out that those that form in polar regions are therefore cold, whereas those that form in tropical areas are warm.

5 Teaching Tips—Air masses that originate over the oceans are known as maritime air masses. They are usually moist or wet. Note that maritime air masses can be either warm or cold.

6 Teaching Tips—The air masses meet in a broad zone between 30° and 65° north latitude (the zone of mixing).

7 Text Questions—Can you tell if it was sunny or cloudy where you live? You may have to help the students locate where they live on the picture.

Activity

How is an air mass formed?

A. Gather these materials: 2 bowls, hot water, ice, 2 thermometers, 2 coat hangers, and 2 plastic cups.
B. Fill 1 bowl with ice. Fill the other bowl with hot water. Put both bowls in a place where there is little air movement.
C. Hang a thermometer over each bowl.
D. Measure the temperature over each bowl each min for 5 min.
  1. Was the temperature different over the 2 bowls at the end of 5 min? Why?
  2. Compare the kind of air masses that would form over the Arctic Ocean and an ocean near the equator.

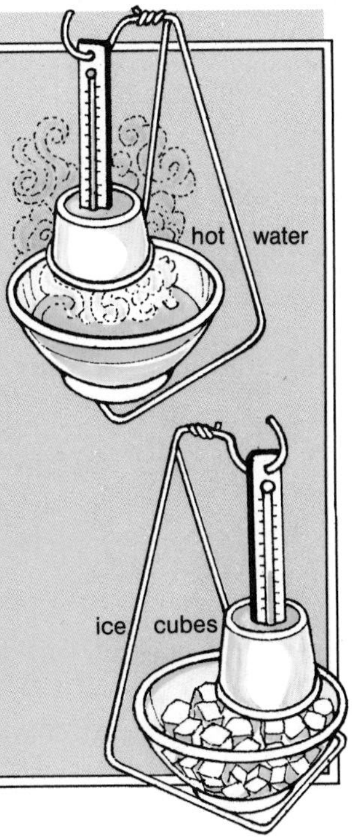

Section Review

Main Ideas: Air masses form when air remains over a cold or hot place. Six large air masses affect our weather.

Questions: Answer in complete sentences.
1. What is an air mass?
2. What kind of air mass would form over an ocean near the South Pole?
3. Where do you think a hot, moist air mass would form?
4. What type of weather would you expect where air masses meet?

EXTENSIONS

Reinforcement
Activity

By doing this Activity, students can learn which holds more water vapor—warm air or cold air.

A. Gather these materials: 2 equal-size jars with covers; 2 1-in.-sq. pieces of cotton cloth, tape, and thread.

B. Place one uncovered jar in a warm spot, such as on a radiator, for an hour. Place the other in the refrigerator.

C. Tape each cloth to a thread and the thread to the inside of a jar lid so that the cloth hangs freely. Dampen both pieces of cloth and squeeze out any extra water.

D. Screw the lids with the hanging cloths tightly onto the jars and return the jars to where they were. Check the cloths after one hour.
  1. Which cloth was drier and why?
  2. Which one held more water—the cold or the hot?

ACTIVITY

Skill Development—*Recording Data, Comparing and Contrasting*

Teaching Tips—Set up the thermometers so that they are about 2 cm above the surface of the water in each bowl.

Answers to Questions—1. Yes. The air above each bowl acquired the temperature characteristics of the water in the bowl. **2.** Cold air masses would be formed over areas like the Arctic Ocean and warm air masses over the ocean near the equator.

SECTION REVIEW

Answers to Questions
1. A large volume of air that takes on the temperature and moisture content of the place over which it forms
2. Cold and moist
3. Over the ocean near the equator
4. You would expect a storm to occur.

SUGGESTED WORKSHEET MASTER
for Sections 8-2 and 8-3, p. T-111 r

EXTENSIONS

Enrichment

Science Skills—
Building Science Vocabulary

Here are additional vocabulary words. Students can use the dictionary to learn their meanings and their relation to the concepts of this unit.

doldrums: belts of calm, low-pressure air near the equator.
horse latitudes: belts of calm, high-pressure air with light winds from 30° to 35° north and south latitude.
prevailing winds: steadily blowing winds over large regions of the earth. They blow from west to east over the United States.
wind chill effect: an effect in which moving air makes temperatures seem lower than they are.
cyclone: a large mass of low-pressure air, with winds moving toward the center in a counterclockwise whirl.
anticyclone: a large mass of high-pressure air, with winds moving out from the center in a clockwise whirl.
tradewinds: the band of prevailing winds north and south of the equator, blowing from the northeast or southwest.

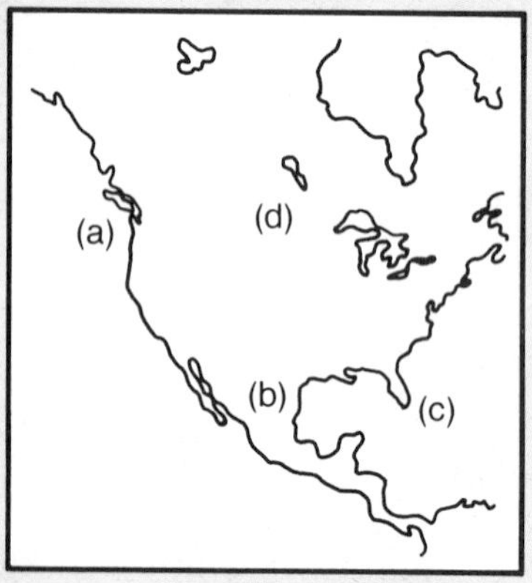

Fig. 8-1

SUGGESTED TEST MASTERS
pp. T-111 f, g, h

CHAPTER REVIEW

Science Words: Use the clues to fill in the words in the spaces below.

1. _ _ _ _ _ _ _ _ _
2. _ _ _   _ _ _ _ _ _ _ _
3. _ _ _   _ _ _ _

Clues:

1. An instrument used to measure air pressure
2. The weight of the air (two words)
3. A large amount of air (two words)

Questions: Answer in complete sentences.

1. The scale is weighing columns of hot and cold air. Which way will the balance tip? Why?
2. Which column of air is pressing down more?
3. How could you stop a hot-air balloon from rising?
4. What does a barometer measure?
5. During the day, will the wind blow (a) from land to ocean; or (b) from ocean to land?
6. What happens to the air above the ground when the sun shines?

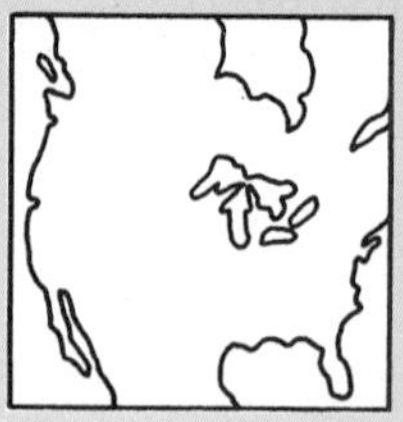

7. What kind of air masses will form over these places: (a) central Canada near the Arctic Circle; and (b) the ocean near the equator?
8. On the map to the left, show where you think these air masses would form: (a) cold, moist air; (b) hot, dry air; (c) hot, moist air; and (d) dry, cold air.
9. Make an air pressure chart showing what kind of weather you would expect if a barometer (a) remains steady, (b) rises, and (c) falls.

CHAPTER REVIEW

Science Words
1. Barometer, **2.** air pressure, **3.** air mass

Answers to Questions
1. The side with the column of cold air will tip down. Cold air is more dense than hot air.
2. The cold-air column
3. Stop heating the air in the balloon
4. Air pressure
5. b
6. It becomes warmer because the ground heats up, and this in turn warms the air above it.
7. a. Cold, dry; **b.** warm, moist
8. See Fig. 8-1.
9. See the chart on page 132.

CHAPTER 9

WATER IN THE AIR

It often rains when we are not prepared for it. Dark clouds form and rain begins to fall.

Where does rainwater come from? What causes it to rain? When you finish this section, you should be able to:

9-1. Rain and Clouds

CHAPTER OBJECTIVES

1. Describe the water cycle and the processes of evaporation, condensation, and precipitation.
2. Compare and contrast weather associated with warm and cold fronts.
3. Identify symbols on a weather map.
4. Predict the weather using a series of weather maps.

SECTION BACKGROUND

The water cycle describes the way water circulates on earth. Essentially, there are three stages in the cycle. Water evaporates from the ocean reservoir into the atmosphere. The atmosphere transports water over the land, where it forms clouds and then falls to the ground as precipitation. Rivers and underground transport systems carry the water over the land back to the ocean. The water cycle involves the processes of evaporation, cloud formation, and precipitation. Also, running water in rivers is the major force of erosion on the surface of the planet. As the water is making its way back to the sea, it is sculpturing the landscape.

MATERIALS

6 ice cubes, metal can, water, thermometer

BASIC TEACHING PLAN

MOTIVATION

If there is dew on the grass, take the students outside and have them feel the grass. Tell them it did not rain last night, and then ask them where the water came from. As a demonstration put a small amount of water in the bottom of a gallon glass jar. Seal the jar, and place it on the windowsill or under a light source. Let the students observe what you do. The next day, the water should have evaporated. Show the jar to the students, and ask them what they think happened.

Text Questions—Where does rainwater come from? *They may say it comes from clouds or lakes and oceans. All answers are correct.* What causes it to rain? *When water vapor begins to condense in the atmosphere, the drops of water become larger and larger until they fall to the earth as rain.*

Exceptional Student
IEP Chapter Goal

At the end of this chapter, the student will predict what happens when water condenses in the air and when a cold front and a warm front meet.

EXTENSIONS

Reinforcement

Science Skills—Observing

You can make a simple model of the water cycle for the class. Have the students watch this demonstration, and then discuss with them what they observed. Finally, encourage them to trace in a diagram the path that individual molecules of water take.

A. Place a pan of water on a hot plate, and bring the water to a boil.

B. Fill a pie plate with ice cubes, and hold the plate in the steam rising from the boiling water. Droplets of steam will condense on the underside of the pie plate. The drops will become larger and larger and begin to drip back into the pan of boiling water.

C. Ask the students to use the words *evaporation, condensation,* and *precipitation* when they describe the demonstration.

D. Give them drawing paper and have them draw a picture showing the path of water. They should label the processes of evaporation, condensation, and precipitation.

A. Explain what the *dew point* is.

B. Explain how *water vapor* gets into the air.

C. Describe how water moves through the *water cycle.*

Water moves back and forth between the air and the ground. Suppose you place a saucer of water on a windowsill. Later, you see the water **1** is gone. Why? When the water dried up in the saucer, it changed to a gas. This change from a liquid to a gas is called **evaporation** (ee-vap-uh-**ray**-shun). The gas goes into the air. Water in the form of a gas is called **water vapor**.

Evaporation: The change of a liquid into a gas.

Water vapor: Water in the form of a gas.

Water vapor in the air can change back into a liquid. This happens if the air is cooled. The water vapor will condense on a surface such as a **2** blade of grass. **Condensation** (kahn-den-**say**-shun) happens when water vapor changes to liquid water. The temperature at which water vapor *condenses* is called the **dew point**. When the temperature of the air falls to the *dew point*, water forms on the grass.

Condensation: The change of a gas into a liquid.

Dew point: The air temperature at which water condenses.

DEVELOPMENT

1 Teaching Tips—Give the students a piece of slightly wet paper towel. Ask them how they could make the paper towel dry. They may suggest fanning it, blowing on it, or putting it in the sun. Give them time to try their experiment. You can talk about which was the most effective way to evaporate the water.

2 Teaching Tips—If you don't do the Activity in this section, you might want to demonstrate condensation by using a large metal can filled with water and ice. Let the students feel the water that condenses on the outside of the can. They should realize that the water comes from the air.

Water vapor needs an object to condense on. Clouds form when water vapor condenses on dust in the air. Without dust, there would be no clouds.

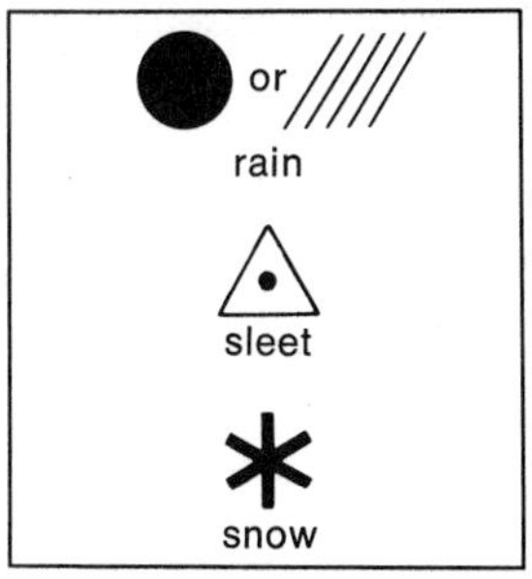

As more water vapor condenses, the drops of water become larger and heavier. They fall to the earth as precipitation. The symbols in the margin are used for the kinds of precipitation. Use them on your daily weather chart.

What do you think happens to the water that falls as precipitation? First, it evaporates. Next, it condenses into clouds. Then it falls to the ground as precipitation again. The evaporation and condensation of water is called the **water cycle** (sy-kul). A *cycle* describes something that happens over and over again in the same order. The drawing below shows these steps in the water cycle.

Water cycle: The evaporation and condensation of water over and over again.

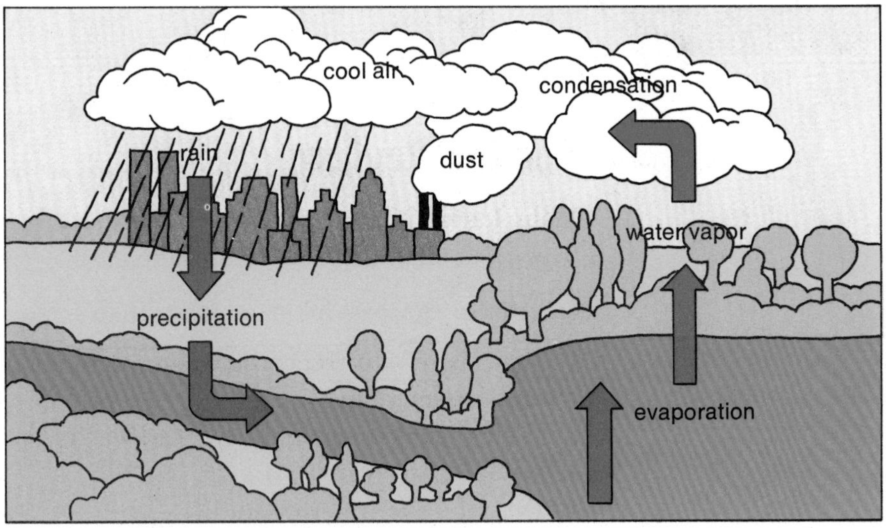

EXTENSIONS

Application

Science Skills—Observing

In this Activity, you can demonstrate how water evaporates from plants. You will need a plant in a pot and a plastic bag.

A. Place a well-watered potted plant in a large, clear plastic bag.

B. Inflate the bag, seal it with an elastic band, and place it on the windowsill. Eventually, water will evaporate from the soil and plant. The air inside will become saturated. With more time, water will begin to condense on the inside of the bag.

C. Ask the students to make inferences about why the water appeared and where it came from.

3 **Teaching Tips**—If there is snow available or if you can shave ice very finely, do a demonstration to show that it takes a large volume of snow to make an inch of rain. Fill a 46-oz juice can with ice or snow. After it melts, measure the depth of the water.

4 **Skill Development**—Students should be able to name the parts of the water cycle in *sequence*. Have several students describe each process within the cycle.

EXTENSIONS

Application

Research

Students can do research on the development of cloud-seeding techniques. Materials such as carbon black, dry ice, and silver nitrate are used to cause rain to fall where it will be most beneficial and to prevent rain from falling where it might cause flooding. Students should investigate the methods and problems of cloud seeding and find out whether it has been used in their area.

ACTIVITY

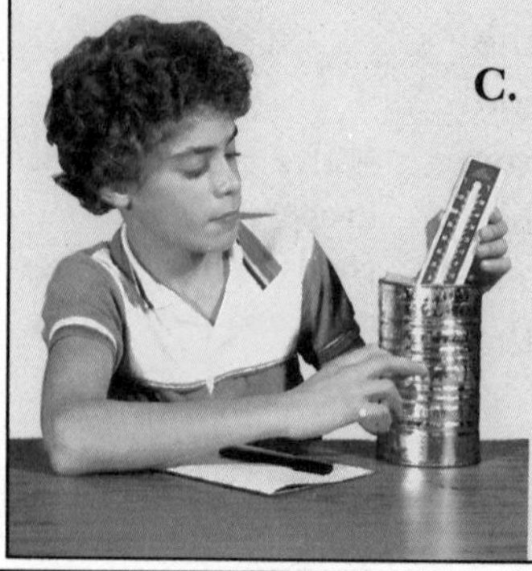

What happens to water vapor when the air is cooled?

A. Gather these materials: ice cubes, metal can, thermometer, and water.

B. Place the ice cubes in a metal can half filled with water. Put the thermometer in the can. Stir the ice slowly with the thermometer. Watch the outside of the can. When water forms on the outside, read the temperature.

C. Repeat step B outside.

1. What was the temperature of the ice water when dew formed on the can inside?
2. What was the temperature of the ice water when this happened outside?
3. What was the dew point inside and outside?

Section Review

Main Ideas: Water moves back and forth between the air and the surface of the earth.

Questions: Answer in complete sentences.

1. What is the difference between evaporation and condensation?
2. If air is cooled enough, what happens to the water vapor in it?
3. Describe the water cycle.

ACTIVITY

Skill Development—*Recording Data, Finding Cause and Effect*

Teaching Tips—The time to take the temperature reading is when water first appears on the can. The temperature at that point is called the dew point. If you are in an air-conditioned building and it is humid outside, you will see quite a difference between the inside and outside readings.

Answers to Questions—1. The answers will vary according to the temperature and moisture content of the air. **2.** Answers will vary as above. **3.** The dew point is the temperature at which water condensed.

SECTION REVIEW

Answers to Questions

1. Evaporation is the changing of a liquid into a gas, whereas condensation is the changing of a gas into a liquid.
2. It might condense.
3. See the diagram on page 143.

9-2.

Cold and Warm Fronts

Pretend you are the pilot of an airplane. You are flying into the clouds shown here. You will be going from one air mass to another. Do you think this change will affect the people on your plane? When you finish this section, you should be able to:

- **A.** Describe how the weather changes when a cold *front* moves across an area.
- **B.** Describe how the weather changes when a warm *front* moves across an area.

1 You learned that cold and warm air masses move away from the place over which they form. The air masses move toward each other. They meet in an area called the zone of mixing. The
2 small map shows the zone of mixing. Do you live in this zone?

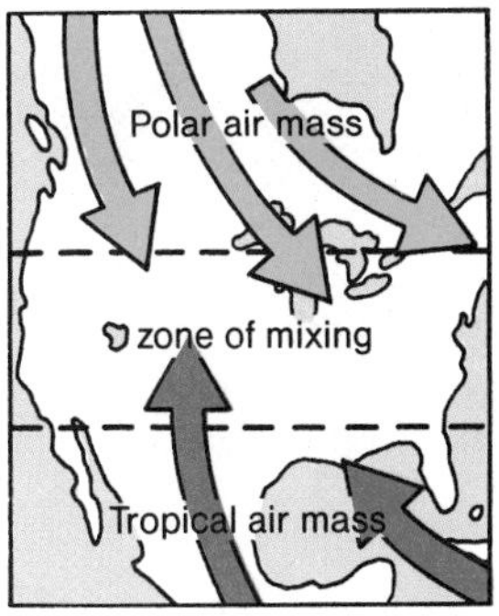

SECTION BACKGROUND

The air masses discussed in the last chapter converge along a line known as the polar front. Quite frequently, a wave develops along the front. This is an area of low pressure. The forward part of the wave is a warm front. Following this leading front is a front of cold air.

The first sign of a warm front will be wisps of clouds high in the sky. With time, the clouds thicken and eventually get lower and hide the sun or moon. Usually, rain follows. The rain is light at first but becomes heavier. Then it tapers off. It will feel muggy. Finally, thick clouds bearing lots of rain and sometimes thunder and lightning arrive. This is the approach of the cold front. The cold front moves rapidly, and within hours the storm has passed and the weather has cleared. The humidity has also dropped, as well as the temperature. The illustration on page T-147 shows this sequence.

MATERIALS

plastic shoe box or aquarium, piece of cardboard, water, red food coloring, salt

BASIC TEACHING PLAN

MOTIVATION

Obtain slides or pictures showing different weather conditions. Ask the students what it is like in these different situations.

Text Questions—Do you think this change will affect the people on your plane? *Yes. It will be darker, maybe rainy and bumpy.*

DEVELOPMENT

1 Teaching Tips—Use a large map to supplement the map in the text. If the students live between 30° and 65° north latitude, they should realize they live in the zone of mixing. Review with them the origin of polar and tropical air masses.

2 Text Questions—Do you live in this zone? *For most students, the answer is yes.*

EXTENSIONS

Application

Science Skills—Recording Data

Your students can make a rain gauge and then use it to record data on precipitation. They should perform the following steps:

A. Gather these materials: a large jar, a small jar (olive jar), a metric ruler, and masking tape.

B. Pour water into the large jar until it is 1 cm deep. Pour this water into the small jar. The water will come up higher than it was in the large jar.

C. Put the masking tape on the small jar to form a vertical scale. Mark the topmost spot the water reaches. This shows the 1-cm mark. Repeat this step until you reach the 5-cm mark. Now divide the space between each mark you made into ten equal divisions. Each division will be 1 mm of rain.

D. Put the large jar outside in an open area. This jar will be used to collect precipitation. After the next rain, pour the water into the smaller jar. This will tell you how much rain fell.

E. Use the rain gauge to collect data on precipitation.

ACTIVITY

What happens when a cold air mass meets a warm air mass?

You will make a model of the air using water. Models let you see a part of nature in the classroom.

A. Gather these materials: plastic shoe box, piece of plastic or cardboard, water, red food coloring, and salt.

B. Fill the box with water. Using a piece of plastic, divide the box into 2 sides.

C. Quickly pour salt into one half of the tank. Stir gently. Add red food coloring to this side. The salt water is heavier. It is a model for cold air. The water in the other side is lighter. It is like warm air.

1. What do you think will happen when you lift the plastic between the 2 sides?

D. Lift the plastic.

2. What did you see when the 2 kinds of water met?

3. How is this like a front? What kind of front?

Jet stream: Fast-moving winds high in the troposphere.

3 High in the troposphere is a fast-moving stream of air. This is called the **jet stream**. It moves from west to east. It goes through the zone of mixing. The *jet stream* helps to mix warm and cold air masses. It also helps to move them from west to east.

Exceptional Student

Visually Impaired

Have these students perform the same Activity using hot and cold water instead of salted and nonsalted water. The students should have their hands in the plastic container while the divider is being removed. They will be able to feel the warm and cold fronts meeting.

ACTIVITY

Skill Development—*Hypothesizing, Observing, Comparing and Contrasting*

Teaching Tips—This Activity might be done as a demonstration. The line separating the different densities is the front. You could also use liquids of different densities such as water and cooking oil. To see the front more clearly, color the water with food coloring.

Answers to Questions—1. Answers will vary. **2.** The salt water flowed along the bottom, forcing the less-dense water up. **3.** It is like a front because two substances with different characteristics are colliding with each other. It is like a cold front.

3 Teaching Tips—The jet stream is a west–east current of strong winds that circle the earth between 3 and 6 mi above the ground. These winds control the movement of lows and highs in the lower atmosphere. For example, a low situated under an eastward-moving jet stream will follow the path of the jet stream.

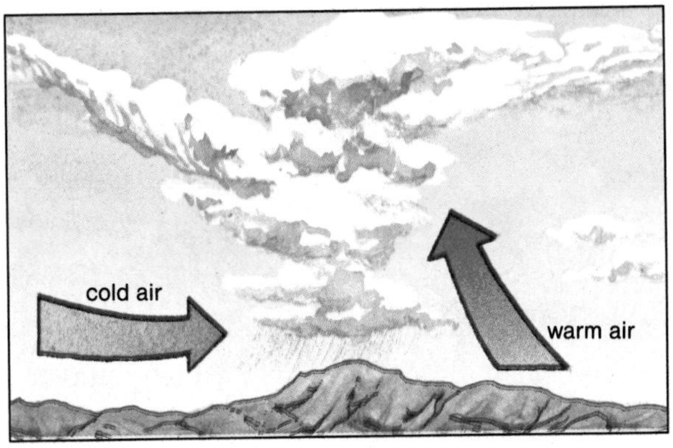

The places where cold and warm air masses meet are called **fronts**. If cold air is pushing into warm air, it is a cold *front*. If the warm air is doing the pushing, it is a warm front.

Fronts: The places where cold and warm air masses meet.

4 Look at the drawing of the cold front. The front edge of the cold air mass is steep. It pushes the warm air up off the ground quickly. The rising warm air cools. Clouds form. Cold fronts often bring showers. There may be thunder and lightning with the shower. The air behind a cold front is clear and cooler. Fair-weather cumulus clouds are carried by the clear, cooler air.

The drawing on page 148 shows that a warm 5 front is long and sloping. The warm air rides up over the cold air and pushes it away. As a warm front moves in, many kinds of clouds form. High feathery cirrus clouds are seen first. In the next 12 to 24 hours, the clouds thicken. They drop lower in the sky. They change to stratus clouds. Then they change to rain clouds. Warm fronts almost always bring rain or snow.

EXTENSIONS

Application

Activity

Students can find out in more detail how warm fronts differ from cold fronts. These are the two basic classifications of fronts.

A. Gather coat hangers, construction paper, cotton, glue, and string.

B. Have the students make mobiles of each kind of front. They can bend the coat hanger to form the shape of each front.

C. They can use cotton and construction paper to create the types of clouds associated with each front.

D. Have them write a brief description of each front and hang it and the mobiles from the ceiling with string.

4 Skill Development—Help the students *compare and contrast* cold and warm fronts. Ask them to describe the differences between the two fronts shown in the figures on pages 147 and 148.

5 Teaching Tips—Students can understand how a front moves by making a flip book. Make a master scene in which you show hills and other markers, such as building or trees. These will serve as reference points. The students should draw the front moving gradually from left to right using a series of five to ten cards. Stack the cards and staple them together. When the students flip the cards, they will see the front move and the weather change at points along the card. Include gradually darkening clouds and precipitation.

EXTENSIONS

Enrichment

Science Skills—Classifying

Ask the students to bring in four or five pictures of clouds from magazines. Use these for this Activity.

A. Have the students work in small groups and share the pictures they have brought in. They should identify each type of cloud as cumulus, stratus, or cirrus.

B. Have them subdivide their groups into clouds associated with warm fronts and with cold fronts. They can mount the clouds on large sheets of newsprint or poster board.

C. Ask the students to describe the kind of weather associated with each type of front, and tell how the clouds are related to it.

Drizzle: Very small drops of slowly falling rain.

Very small drops of slowly falling rain are called **drizzle** (**driz**-ul). Dark stratus clouds bringing *drizzle* may follow a warm front. Warm fronts may take up to two days to pass. Cold fronts usually pass in a few hours.

Warm fronts can move quickly. If cumulus clouds follow cirrus clouds, the warm front is moving fast. You may have heavy rain within 12 hours. There may even be thunder and lightning.

Section Review

Main Ideas: There are two types of fronts: cold and warm.

Questions: Answer in complete sentences.

1. Storms were followed by clear, cooler air. What kind of front passed?
2. The clouds changed from cirrus to stratus. What kind of front passed?
3. What type of front travels very fast?
4. The temperature is forecast to drop quickly. What type of front do you think will pass through?

SECTION REVIEW

Answers to Questions

1. Cold front
2. Warm front
3. Cold front
4. Cold front

SUGGESTED WORKSHEET MASTER
p. T-111 s

The Harrison family is looking at a weather map. They are planning a trip from St. Louis to Denver. They want to know what the weather will be like as they drive west. The weather map will tell them what kind of weather to prepare for. When you finish this section, you should be able to:

- **A.** Identify the direction in which weather moves across the United States.
- **B.** Read a weather map.
- **C.** Forecast the weather a day or two ahead by using a weather map.

9-3. Weather on the Move

A weather map is a tool to a weather forecaster. Daily newspapers often print a weather map of the whole country. The map uses symbols to describe the weather. These symbols are shown on the next page. What symbol is used for a high pressure center? How can you tell a cold front from a warm front? How are thunder-

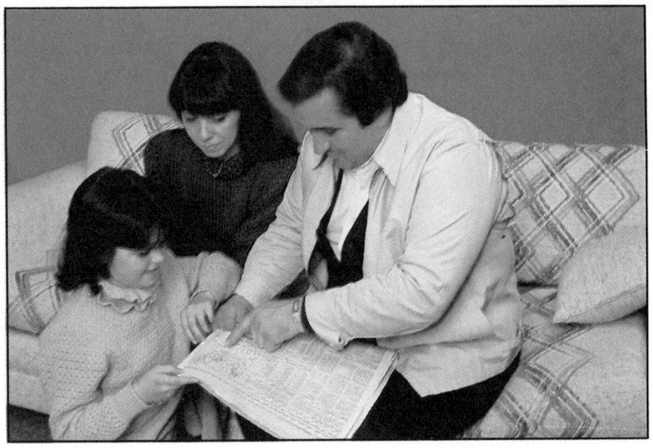

SECTION BACKGROUND

The weather map or chart is indispensable to the weather forecaster. Meteorologists use it to compile and show the data they have collected on the weather. The key factors that are recorded on weather maps include temperature, precipitation, cloud type and cover, wind speed and direction, and air pressure. All these data are used to trace the growth and decline of major weather systems often referred to as highs or lows.

The weather maps that are shown in the local newspaper can serve as useful instructional tools. The maps use symbols to represent different aspects of the weather. Fronts are shown with heavy lines, and geometric shapes are used to differentiate warm and cold fronts. Lighter lines are used to show pressure. These pressure lines are called isobars. Temperature and precipitation type are also shown.

MATERIALS

outline map of the United States, weather maps from a newspaper for three successive days, construction paper, glue, scissors

BASIC TEACHING PLAN

MOTIVATION

Obtain today's weather map. Make an overhead transparency of it. Ask the students to point out some of the weather conditions of several cities. Ask questions such as, Is it raining? What is the temperature? What might the weather be tomorrow?

DEVELOPMENT

1 Teaching Tips—Give each student a copy of today's weather map. Ask the students to circle each of the following on their maps: high- and low-pressure areas, cold fronts, warm fronts, thunderstorms, rain or snow. They should make use of the symbols printed on page 150 of their text.

2 Text Questions—What symbol is used for a high-pressure center? How can you tell a cold front from a warm front? How are thunderstorms shown on the map? *See the symbols on page 150.*

Exceptional Student
Visually Impaired

The teacher should make a three-dimensional replica of a weather map for the student.

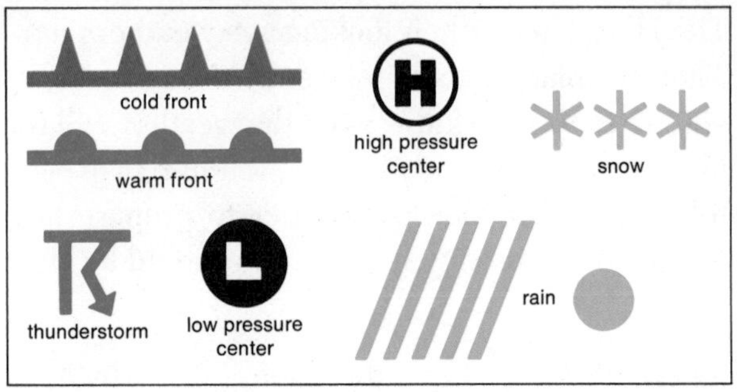

3 storms shown on the map? How is the symbol for rain different from the symbol for snow?

4 The map below is a weather map for a Monday. Study this map. Then answer these ques-
5 tions. Over what state is the low-pressure center on the map? What do the red and blue lines with the bumps and points show? Suppose the map were printed in black and white. How could you tell the warm front from the cold front? The points on the cold front show the direction the cold front is moving. Cold air is behind the cold front. Where is the warm air? How do you know?

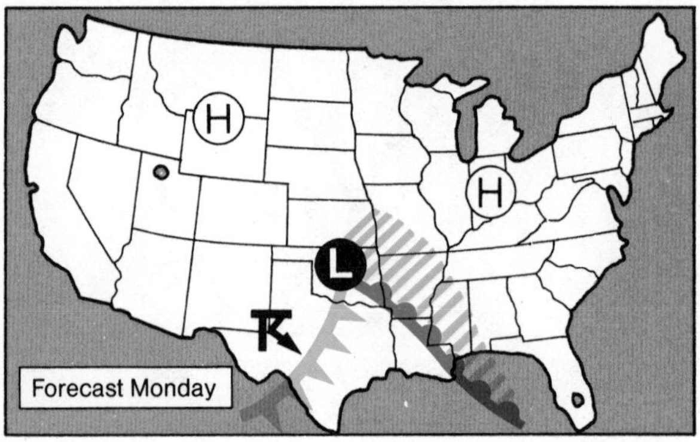

EXTENSIONS

Application

Research—Library

Interested students could go to the library to obtain daily weather reports from other cities. They could record the temperature, precipitation, cloud cover, wind speed and direction, air pressure, and humidity on the same day in several different cities of the world.

The students can then compare the weather reports from the different cities with the local weather report.

Reinforcement

Science Skills—Sequencing

Have your students collect weather maps from the daily newspaper each day for two weeks. Fasten them to a bulletin board in chronological order, making one continuous strip. Have the students observe the motion of weather systems on the maps. Use blank maps of the United States to plot the path of the storm centers. Draw a long arrow to represent the path of each low indicated on the weather maps. Identify the principle storm tracks.

3 Text Questions—How is the symbol for rain different from the symbol for snow? *See the symbols on this page.*

4 Teaching Tips—Make overhead transparencies of the maps on the student text pages. By laying the transparencies on top of one another, the students will see the path of the storm. Use a fourth transparency, and draw a line connecting the storm centers. This is the path of the storm.

5 Text Questions—Over what state is the low-pressure center on the map? *Oklahoma.* What do the red and blue lines with the bumps and points show? *Warm and cold fronts.* Suppose the map were printed in black and white. How could you tell the warm front from the cold front? *The warm front has the bumps or half-circles, while the cold front has points.* Where is the warm air? *Behind the warm front.* How do you know? *The half circles show the leading edge of the front. Warm air is behind this leading edge.*

Now look at the map for Tuesday. You can see that the low-pressure center has moved. In which direction did it move? Did the high-pressure centers move in the same direction? There is rain ahead of the warm front. Most of the rain is near the low-pressure center. Low-pressure centers are usually the centers of storms. What kind of storms are along the cold front?

The map for Wednesday shows a new low-pressure center. The old one has moved farther east. Low-pressure centers are followed by high-pressure centers. The highs and lows travel mainly from west to east. Look at the warm front and the cold front. They have been on the map for three days. The cold front has almost caught up with the warm front. Cold fronts move faster than warm fronts.

All weather forecasters use pictures of the earth. These pictures are made by satellites in outer space. The patterns of the clouds help forecast the weather. The pictures show how patterns of clouds move.

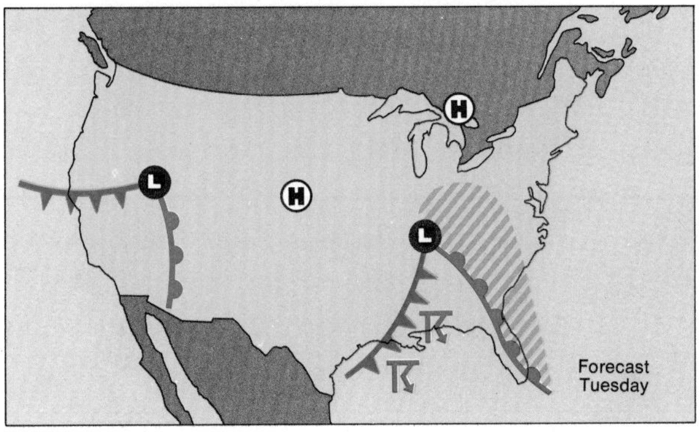

EXTENSIONS

Enrichment

Science Skills—Sequencing

A flip book is a very good way to show the dynamics of the weather. You will need about ten consecutive newspaper weather maps. Depending on the size of the maps in your newspapers, you can mount them on index cards or file folders cut to size.

A. Cut out the weather maps for the desired sequence.

B. Glue the maps on cards or file folders cut to size.

C. Stack the maps in the sequence. Staple the stack together.

D. Flip the maps to create motion. Do this several times so that students can see the weather move.

Ask the following questions: How does the weather move? What is the general direction?

6 Text Questions—In which direction did it move? *East.* Did the high-pressure centers move in the same direction? *Yes.* What kind of storms are along the cold front? *Thunderstorms.*

7 Teaching Tips—Use the overhead projector to discuss the movement of weather across the United States. Ask the students what the general direction of movement is for storms.

8 Teaching Tips—Weather satellites are placed in two types of orbits: polar and geosynchronous. Satellites in polar orbits circle the earth every 100 min. Geosynchronous satellites orbit the earth at the same speed that the earth rotates. Once in orbit, they stay fixed above the same position. Their pictures show a continuous flow of the cloud patterns over time.

EXTENSIONS

Application
Research

Students should contact their local weather bureau to find out how and where local weather readings are taken. They could find out why the weather stations are located where they are and what readings are taken at different stations. The students should be able to explain why these sites are good places to take readings. Most weather stations are located in areas that have good exposure to the elements and are free from outside influences that would disturb the recording devices.

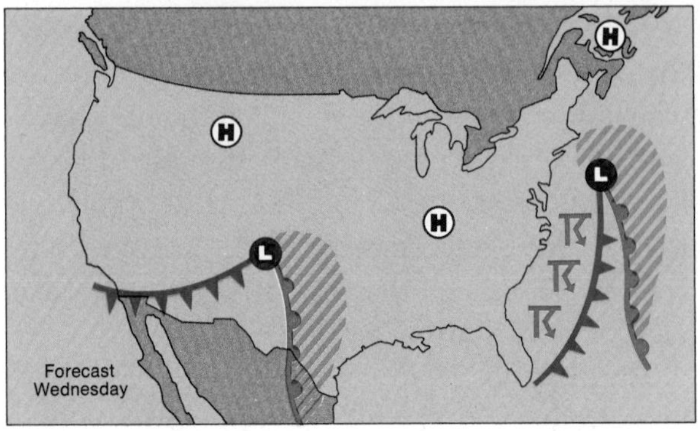

ACTIVITY

How does weather move across the United States?

A. Gather these materials: outline map of the United States, weather maps from a newspaper for 3 days in a row, construction paper, glue, and scissors.

B. Glue the 3 U. S. weather maps on a piece of construction paper. Find a low or a high pressure on the first of the 3 maps. Mark the high or low on the outline map.

C. Find the same high or low pressure on the next 2 maps. Mark them on your outline map.

1. In what direction did the high- or low-pressure center move?
2. In what direction does weather seem to move across the United States?

ACTIVITY

Skill Development—*Reading Illustrations, Inferring*

Teaching Tips—Choose maps that clearly show low- and high-pressure centers. Make copies of these for students to work with.

Answers to Questions—1. In general they should move from west to east. You could have movements to the northeast as well. **2.** It moves from west to east.

 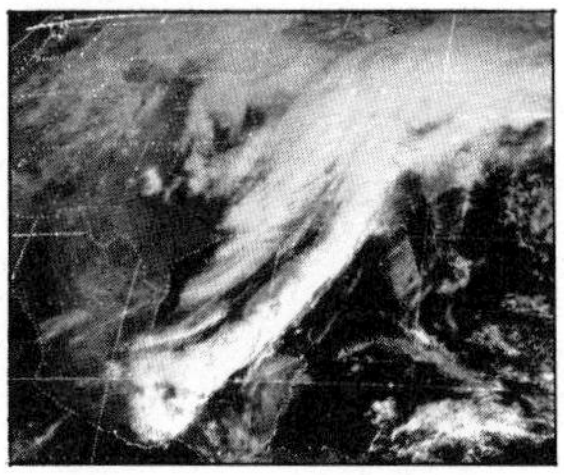 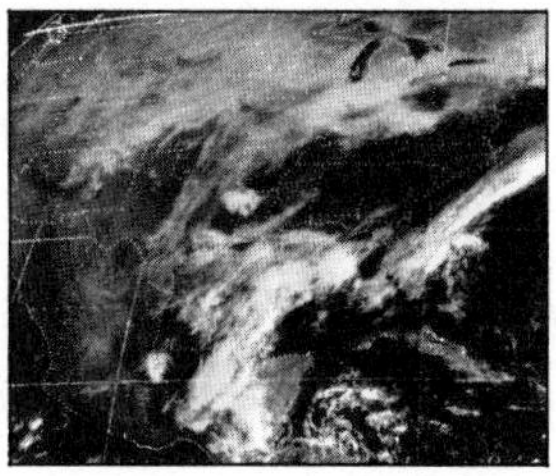

Low-pressure centers show up as swirls of clouds. Forecasters can watch these swirls move. They compare pictures taken on different days. Computers show how fast and in what direction the weather is moving. The forecasters use this information to predict where the storm will move next.

Section Review

Main Ideas: Symbols on weather maps show kinds of weather. High- and low-pressure centers travel from west to east. Satellite pictures show how weather moves across the earth.

Questions: Answer in complete sentences.

For questions 1–3, look at the map on page 150.

1. Where do you think the low-pressure center above Oklahoma will move during the next day?
2. What kind of weather is Tennessee having?
3. What kind of weather do you think Tennessee will have on Thursday?
4. In what direction does weather move across the United States?

EXTENSIONS

Application
Activity

Students can use the weather symbols they have learned to write coded weather messages to each other. Have each student write a message on a piece of paper and pass it to another student, who must read it. The messages can be similar to this example:
When a (symbol for warm front) moves quickly and hits a (symbol for cold front), there can often be a (symbol for thunderstorm).

SECTION REVIEW

Main Ideas—Give the students a weather map, and ask them to identify highs, lows, cold and warm fronts, and areas of rain.

Answers to Questions
1. To the east
2. Clear
3. Rain and clouds
4. From west to east

SUGGESTED WORKSHEET MASTER
p. T-111 t

EXTENSIONS

Enrichment

Research—Library

Students can go to the library to research how mountains affect precipitation and climate. As air moves up and over a mountain range, it expands and cools. Water vapor in the air condenses and forms rain. As the air moves down the other side of the mountains, it contracts and warms. Moisture in the air becomes water vapor. The air becomes very dry, since most of the moisture in the air fell as rain on the windward side of the mountains. Thus, there is heavy rainfall and lush growth on the windward side of the mountains and a desert on the leeward side.

Ask students the following questions to guide their research:

1. What happens to air as it rises up the side of a mountain?
2. What happens to air as it descends the other side of the mountain?
3. What happens to the water in the air as it rises and then descends over mountains?
4. What kind of climate would you expect to find on the windward and leeward sides of mountains?

SUGGESTED WORKSHEET MASTER
p. T-111 u

SUGGESTED TEST MASTERS
pp. T-111 i, j, k

CHAPTER REVIEW

Science Words: Complete the crossword puzzle on a separate sheet of paper.

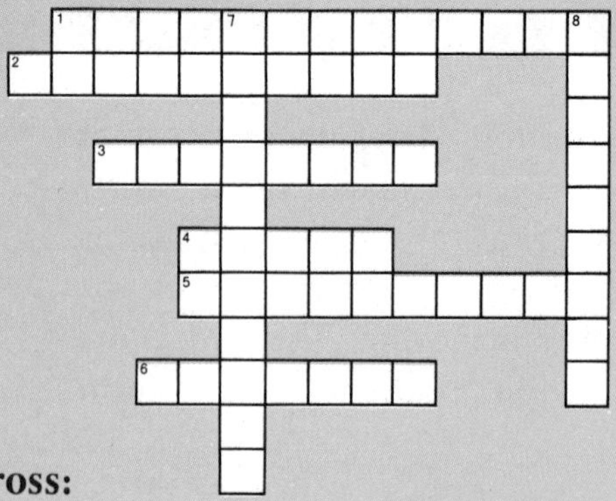

Across:

1. The change of a gas into a liquid
2. Water in the form of a gas (two words)
3. The air temperature at which water condenses (two words)
4. A place where cold and warm air masses meet
5. The evaporation and condensation of water over and over (two words)
6. Very small drops of slowly falling rain

Down:

7. The change of a liquid into a gas
8. Fast-moving winds high in the troposphere (two words)

Questions: Answer in complete sentences.

1. Draw a diagram of the water cycle. Label each part. Explain the cycle.
2. The weather report says a cold front will be moving into the city. What do you think the weather will be?

CHAPTER REVIEW

Science Words

1. Condensation, **2.** water vapor, **3.** dew point, **4.** front, **5.** water cycle, **6.** drizzle, **7.** evaporation, **8.** jet stream

Answers to Questions

1. Refer to diagram on page 143. Water evaporates from the oceans and is drawn up into the atmosphere. It condenses and forms clouds. The clouds move over the land. Water in the clouds falls to earth as rain or other forms of precipitation. Rain water collects in streams and rivers, and eventually reaches the ocean again.

2. Cold fronts often bring showers. There may be thunder and lightning. This will be followed by clearing and cooler temperatures.

CHAPTER 10

WEATHER AND PEOPLE

Storms like tornadoes and hurricanes are violent. They can destroy homes. They cause flooding. People and wildlife may be harmed. How are tornadoes formed? When you finish this section, you should be able to:

10-1. Violent Storms

CHAPTER OBJECTIVES

1. Compare and contrast the kinds of weather associated with tornadoes, hurricanes, thunderstorms, and blizzards.
2. Describe the effects of these storms on people and property.
3. Explain what humidity is and how it is measured.
4. Identify sources and causes of air pollution.
5. Describe ways to reduce air pollution.

SECTION BACKGROUND

Blizzards, thunderstorms, and tornadoes are storms that are created when polar and tropical air masses meet to form fronts. Blizzards are storms that can drop over 6 cm of snow with sub-freezing and high-wind conditions.

Thunderstorms and tornadoes are associated with cold fronts. Tornadoes, whirling masses of air with intense low pressure at the center, are caused by a strong updraft of air that sucks in lower air, causing the entire mass to swirl. Winds of over 300 mph have been reported for some tornadoes. Thunderstorms occur along cold fronts. Huge cumulonimbus clouds develop in the presence of high-velocity up- and down-drafts of air.

Hurricanes are intense areas of low pressure that are born in tropical oceans. Air is sucked into the center and spins around a central region known as the eye. The eye of the storm is usually marked by clear skies and low winds.

MATERIALS

none

Exceptional Student IEP Chapter Goal

At the end of this chapter, the student will state one factor that contributes to each of the following: storms, humidity, and air pollution.

BASIC TEACHING PLAN

MOTIVATION

Have old magazines available so that the students can look through them to find examples of violent storms. Discuss why they think their choices show examples of violent storms. If you have access to slides of tornadoes, hurricanes, thunderstorms, and blizzards, you might show them with music to set the stage for this section.

Text Questions—How are tornadoes formed? *They are formed when polar and tropical air masses meet.*

EXTENSIONS

Enrichment

Science Skills—Observing

To show what happens when warm and cold air meet, have students do the following Activity individually, or else demonstrate it to the class.

A. Gather these materials: a gallon jar, a baby food jar and lid, a small nail, hammer, a string, hot water, cold water, and food coloring.

B. Fill the gallon jar with cold water.

C. Punch a hole in the center of the baby food jar lid with a nail. Make two smaller holes on either side of the first hole near the edge.

D. Fill the baby food jar with very hot water. Add food coloring. Put the lid on the jar.

E. Tie a string around the baby food jar and lower it into the large jar of cold water. The hot water will start to come out of the jar, and the jar will spin.

Ask the following types of questions: Where does the hot water go? When does it stop? How is this like air rising?

- **A.** Identify four kinds of violent storms.
- **B.** Compare the kind of weather each violent storm causes.
- **C.** Describe the effects of violent storms on people.

Hurricane: A storm that forms over warm oceans near the equator.

1 Storms that form over the warm oceans near the equator are called **hurricanes** (**her**-uh-kaynz). *Hurricanes* are the strongest storms on earth. They bring heavy rains and very strong winds. They form between June and November. During these months, the sun is above the equator. It is so hot that large amounts of ocean water evaporate. The warm, moist air rises quickly. Then it condenses. A violent storm forms. The picture below shows what happens when a hurricane hits land.

DEVELOPMENT

1 Teaching Tips—Show on a map of the western hemisphere places where hurricanes are born. This is a region between 5° and 20° north latitude. Hurricanes tend to travel first to the west and then to the northeast. Most hurricanes occur between August and November. In the region near the Philippines, China, and Japan, hurricanes are called typhoons. In the southern hemisphere, near Australia, they are known as cyclones.

Storms with thunder and lightning, heavy rains, and strong winds are called **thunderstorms** (**thun**-der-stormz). These storms often form when warm, moist air rises quickly. The water droplets in the clouds may become charged. Electric charges jump from cloud to cloud or from a cloud to the ground. We see lightning. The picture above shows lightning striking the ground during a thunderstorm.

Thunderstorm: A storm that brings thunder, lightning, heavy rains, and strong winds.

Thunderstorms can cause small storms called **tornadoes** (tore-**nay**-dohz). A *tornado* is a spinning, funnel-shaped cloud. It touches the earth as it moves along. The picture on page 158 shows a tornado. Tornadoes are very violent storms. They can destroy things in their path.

Tornado: A storm that produces a spinning, funnel-shaped cloud.

Tornadoes occur in the spring from April to June. The weather is changing during this time of year. Many fronts move across the United

EXTENSIONS

Application

Activity

You or the students can create a model that illustrates the rotating or whirling motion of air associated with tornadoes and hurricanes.

A. Gather these materials: a large can, a pail of water, a nail, a hammer, a ring stand, a catch pail, and pencil shavings.

B. Punch a hole in the center of the bottom of the can with the nail and hammer.

C. Set the can on a ring stand. Put a catch pail under the metal can.

D. Quickly fill the can with water. Sprinkle pencil shavings on the water. Let the water run out of the hole into the catch pail.

E. Repeat the above steps. Ask questions such as, What pattern does the water take as it runs out of the can? How is the water-can system like a tornado or hurricane?

2 **Teaching Tips**—You might ask the students why we see the flash of lightning before we hear the thunder. *The reason is because light travels much faster than sound.* You might also let the students know that you can tell how far away the storm is by watching and listening. By counting "a thousand-one, a thousand-two, a thousand-three, etc." after the lightning is seen, one can estimate the distance of the storm from the lightning flash. Each count is a second. It takes the sound about 1 sec to travel 1,000 ft. Therefore, every five counts is about 1 mi.

EXTENSIONS

Application
Research

Students could write to the Washington Science and Information Center, 60-10 Executive Road, Rockville, MD 20852, for information on safety procedures during violent storms.

The class should be divided into groups so that each can report on the safety procedures for a specific type of storm.

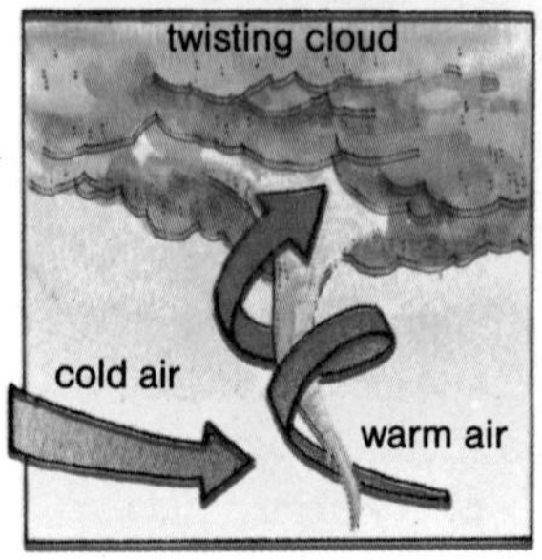

States. Tornadoes have occurred in all states in the country. But most of them occur in the South and Midwest.

Tornadoes form along cold fronts. Cold fronts move very fast. As the cold front pushes forward, it forces warm air to rise quickly. The rising air may twist. When this happens, a funnel-shaped cloud forms.

The winds inside a tornado can be as high as 800 kilometers (500 miles) per hour. As the tornado moves, it skips and jumps across the land. It is very hard to guess exactly where it will touch down. When a tornado touches down, it can destroy objects in its path.

The air pressure inside the tornado is very low. As the tornado comes close to buildings, a strange thing happens. If the windows and doors are closed, the air inside a building is trapped. As the tornado comes close, the air pressure outside the building gets very low. Inside the building, the pressure is high. The difference in pressure causes the air to rush from inside to outside. As a result, windows break and walls collapse.

Blizzard: A storm that brings cold winds and blowing snow.

Some storms bring cold winds and heavy, blowing snow. These storms are called **blizzards** (**bliz**-erdz). *Blizzards* are dangerous storms. The freezing winds blow at a speed of over 70 kilometers (43 miles) per hour. A blizzard can drop
5 over 60 centimeters (2 feet) of snow. Roads be-
6 come icy and slippery. Power lines may fall. People become stranded. The heating systems

3 Teaching Tips—You might ask the students if they have ever seen a tornado or been in an area where one occurred. Ask them to describe their experiences.

4 Teaching Tips—Tornado winds are severe. Some have actually been able to carry objects aloft for many miles. A piece of straw was found driven into a telephone pole after one tornado passed.

5 Teaching Tips—During the 1977 and 1978 blizzards in the northeast, 18 in. of snow fell within 24-hour periods. Drifts between 10 and 20 ft were not uncommon. Although many people die of exposure to the cold, more die from heart attacks associated with shoveling snow or asphyxiation from exhaust fumes while sitting in cars stranded on highways.

6 Teaching Tips—Ice storms are another type of severe storm you might discuss. Freezing rain hits cold surfaces, covering roads, trees, buildings, and cars with sheets of ice.

in homes or other buildings may fail. People may freeze to death.

Section Review

Main Ideas: Hurricanes, thunderstorms, tornadoes, and blizzards are violent storms.

Questions: Answer in complete sentences.

1. What type of storm might form in each of these cases: (a) a fast-moving cold front moves into hot, humid air; (b) a front moves north, the temperatures are below freezing, and there are high winds; and (c) it is September, with high winds and heavy rain?
2. What effect could a tornado have on homes and buildings?
3. Why could buildings explode if a tornado passed?

SECTION REVIEW

Answers to Questions

1. **a.** Tornado or thunderstorm, **b.** blizzard, **c.** hurricane
2. It could lift the roofs off, knock down walls, blow out windows.
3. The pressure inside the building is higher than the pressure in the tornado. The difference in pressure results in the air rushing from the inside to the outside.

EXTENSIONS

Enrichment

Activity

The electricity in thunderstorms causes raindrops to become larger. The charged particles in the cloud, known as ions, attract water around them to form large drops. You or some interested students may want to demonstrate the following Activity to the class.

A. Gather these materials: a bucket, books, a comb, a plastic straw, rubber tubing, an aluminum pan, and a pin.

B. Assemble the device as shown in the figure below.

C. Punch a hole in the straw, and suck on the hole to get the water to start spraying.

D. When the water is coming out as tiny drops, rub the comb on your clothing and bring it near the water spout. Observe what happens. (The drops will get larger.)

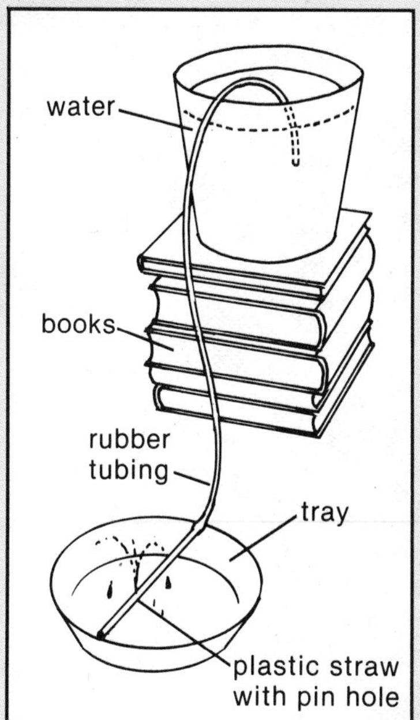

Fig. 10-1

SECTION BACKGROUND

The amount of moisture in the air is called humidity. Humidity and temperature often affect the way people feel. On hot, moist days, perspiration evaporates more slowly because the air is closer to being saturated with moisture. Since evaporation has a cooling effect and moisture in the air slows down the rate of evaporation, you feel very warm. Some weather reports speak of a temperature-humidity index, or the THI. The higher the THI is above 80, the more uncomfortable you feel.

MATERIALS

water

10-2. Hot, Wet Air

The inside of a greenhouse is very hot. The air is full of moisture. On some days, the outside air feels just like the inside of a greenhouse. When you finish this section, you should be able to:

- **A.** Explain what *humidity* is.
- **B.** Describe how the amount of *humidity* in the air affects people.
- **C.** Explain the effect of air temperature on *humidity*.

1 You learned that one path in the water cycle is evaporation. Water that falls to the ground as

BASIC TEACHING PLAN

MOTIVATION

Ask the students to describe the weather conditions when they feel sticky. You may have to give an example: Imagine you have been outside playing a game that involves a lot of running. You feel yourself sweating quite a bit. When you stop playing, you just can't seem to get cool. Have the students imagine what it might be like to walk inside a greenhouse of tropical plants.

DEVELOPMENT

1 Teaching Tips—You might make a diagram of the water cycle, and review the path that water follows as it circulates in the atmosphere.

rain goes back into the air. When water evaporates, it becomes water vapor. The air can hold only a certain amount of water vapor.

Water vapor in the air affects the way we feel. The amount of water vapor in the air is called **humidity** (hyoo-**mid**-ih-tee). On a hot summer day when the *humidity* is high, the air feels sticky. The air is holding a great deal of water. When the humidity is high, water condenses on the grass at night.

Humidity: The amount of water vapor in the air.

The weather service predicts hot, moist days using a *temperature-humidity index*. They call it *THI* for short. The higher the THI, the more uncomfortable you feel. Most people are uncomfortable if the THI is over 80. But if the THI is less than 70, most people feel comfortable.

On hot, humid days, the liquid you perspire is not easily evaporated. The air cannot hold much more moisture. This is part of the reason you feel hot and sticky. What effect does evaporation have on your body?

EXTENSIONS

Reinforcement

Science Skill—
Comparing and Contrasting

This experiment will help the students understand what factors affect humidity.

A. Gather these materials: 3 drinking glasses of the same size, a marking pen, and water.

B. Fill all three glasses about ¾ full of water.

C. Line the glasses up and add or subtract water from them until they all have the same amount.

D. With the marker pen, draw a line at the water level on the outside of each glass.

E. Put one glass in a warm place, one in a cold place, and one in a place that is at room temperature.

F. For two or three days, check the water levels in the glasses. You can mark the levels each day with the marking pen. Which glass lost the most water? Which glass lost the least water? Where did the water go? Where does water in the atmosphere come from?

2 Teaching Tips—Ask the students to give evidence that air holds water. Some evidence includes water forming on the outside of a glass of ice water, dew on the grass in the morning, and dew and frost on cars in the morning.

3 Teaching Tips—If it is hot and humid, the THI is high. When the air is humid, it means that there is a lot of moisture in the air. Because evaporation does not proceed very rapidly when humidity is high, perspiration does not leave our skin, and you feel uncomfortable. Fanning yourself helps because it tends to move the air around you, and this increases the rate of evaporation. The result is that you feel cooler.

4 Text Questions—What effect does evaporation have on your body? *Evaporation of a liquid from the skin cools the body.*

EXTENSIONS

Application

Science Skills—Measuring

As mentioned in the student text, meteorologists use an instrument called a hygrometer to measure the humidity in the air. In this Activity, students can make and use a simple hygrometer.

A. Gather these materials: 2 thermometers, a piece of flat shoelace (3 cm), a rubber band, and water.

B. Slip the shoelace tubing over the bulb of one of the thermometers. Fasten it with the rubber band. Wet the shoelace with water.

C. Go outside and measure the air temperature with the dry-bulb thermometer.

D. Gently wave the thermometer with the wet bulb for about 3 min. Waving the thermometer allows the water to evaporate more rapidly. As it evaporates, the temperature will drop. The difference between the dry-bulb temperature and the wet-bulb temperature provides a measurement used by meteorologists to determine relative humidity. In general, the greater the difference in temperature, the lower the humidity. The less the difference, the greater the humidity. When the air is dry, evaporation can proceed at a greater rate than when the air is humid.

ACTIVITY

What happens to the temperature when water evaporates?

A. Gather this material: water.

B. Moisten the back of your hand. Wait a few seconds. Then blow across the wet spot.

1. How did the wet spot feel?

C. Moisten the back of the same hand. Blow across the wet spot. Also, blow across the back of your other hand.

2. How did the wet hand feel compared with the dry hand when you blew across them?
3. What happened to the moisture when you blew across it?
4. What happened to the temperature of your hand when you blew across the wet spot?

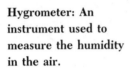

Hygrometer: An instrument used to measure the humidity in the air.

5 Meteorologists measure humidity with a **hygrometer** (hy-**grahm**-uh-ter). One type of *hygrometer* uses a strand of human hair. Human hair stretches when it is humid. A homemade **6** hygrometer is shown on page 163. On a damp and cloudy day, the hair will stretch. The pointer will move. On a dry, sunny day, the hair will shrink. The pointer will move the other way.

A second type of hygrometer uses two thermometers. One of them is wet. The hygrometer is then whirled around. If the temperature on

ACTIVITY

Skill Development—*Comparing and Contrasting, Finding Cause and Effect*

Teaching Tips—After you do the Activity with water, you might want to try the Activity with rubbing alcohol.

Safety Tips—Do not let students who are allergic to alcohol do the above.

Answers to Questions—**1.** It felt cool. **2.** Much cooler. **3.** It evaporated. **4.** It lowered.

5 Skill Development—The process of *measuring* is reinforced here. You might set up a simple "hair hygrometer" as a demonstration.

6 Skill Development—Students find out how to draw *conclusions* about the humidity by observing a hygrometer. The Extension on this page could be used here to help the students see the relationship between humidity and the temperatures obtained using the wet-bulb thermometer.

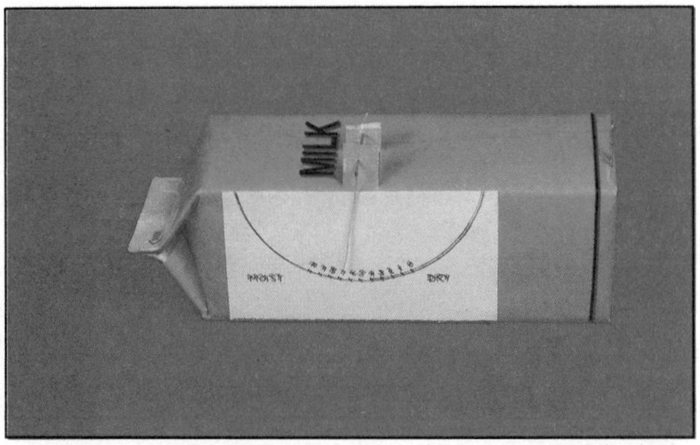

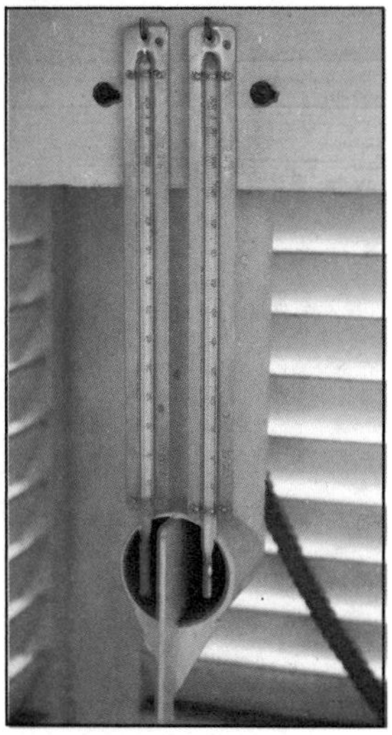

the wet bulb drops sharply, the humidity is very low. If the temperature does not drop much, the humidity is high.

Section Review

Main Ideas: The moisture in the air is called humidity. Humidity is measured with a device called a hygrometer.

Questions: Answer in complete sentences.

1. Why do you feel hot and sticky on humid days?
2. What happens to the temperature when water evaporates?
3. How does perspiring help you cool off on a hot day?
4. Why do you think dogs have to pant to stay cool?
5. Why does a room fan make you feel cool on a hot, humid day?
6. How can you measure humidity?

EXTENSIONS

Application
Research

Students can visit an appliance store to learn about humidifiers and dehumidifiers. They should ask about how each device works, where they are used, and why they are used. They could do research to discover how humidity was controlled in homes before the invention of these electronic devices.

SECTION REVIEW

Answers to Questions

1. Because the air is saturated on hot, moist days, very little evaporation occurs. Evaporation is a cooling process. Without evaporation, you feel sticky and hot.
2. It drops.
3. As perspiration evaporates, the body is cooled.
4. Dogs are not able to perspire as effectively as humans.
5. The air near you never gets a chance to get too humid because the fan moves it around.
6. We can use a hygrometer.

SUGGESTED WORKSHEET MASTER
for Sections 10-1 and 10-2,
p. T-111 v

SECTION BACKGROUND

The atmosphere can be polluted by a variety of things. Dust or fine moisture particles can cause a haze. Volcanic eruptions can put tons of dust into the air, which can create hazes that last for several months or even years. Haze can also result from fine sand lifted by the wind and from forest fires.

Another form of pollution is smog, which is a mixture of smoke and fog. Smog is dangerous because it reduces visibility and may contain dangerous chemicals. A very dangerous form of smog is called photochemical smog. This type of smog occurs in hot, sunny weather when chemicals produced by car exhaust fumes are changed by sunlight into substances that are dangerous to our health. The smog in Los Angeles is an example of photochemical smog.

The federal regulations governing pollution abatement in industrial areas are very strict. The auto industry and industrial factories have had to improve their exhaust systems so that chemicals are recycled rather than vented into the air.

MATERIALS

4 plastic microscope slides, hand lens (magnifying glass), paper towels, petroleum jelly

10-3. The Changing Atmosphere

The city scene above shows how humans have affected the air in Los Angeles. Compare this picture to the one of mountain air. Why is the air so different in these two places? When you finish this section, you should be able to:

BASIC TEACHING PLAN

MOTIVATION

About a week before starting this section, put squares of clean white paper (about 10 cm × 10 cm) at sites around the school. These could include inside a windowsill, outside a windowsill, spots near a parking lot, and near a road. On the day that you begin this section, compare the "test" papers to a clean one.

Text Questions—Why is the air so different in these two places? *Factories and cars have added dust and smoke to the air in Los Angeles.*

■ **A.** Identify causes of *air pollution.*

■ **B.** Explain how both human and natural causes can change the atmosphere.

■ **C.** Identify some things we can do to reduce *air pollution.*

1 People need clean air to live. When we breathe, whatever is in the air enters our lungs. Some things in the air are harmful to us. People with breathing problems would be in danger if

they lived in a polluted area. **Air pollution** (pol-**oo**-shun) damages the lungs. It also hurts the eyes. It can even cause death.

Air pollution: The presence of dirt, dust, and chemicals in the air.

People are not the only living things harmed by *air pollution.* Plants need sunlight in order to grow and remain healthy. If the air is polluted,
2 less sunlight reaches plants' leaves. Also, dust and dirt in the air settle on the leaves. If too much dirt gets on the leaves, the plant could die from lack of sunlight.

EXTENSIONS

Enrichment

Science Skills—Observing and Inferring

Students can find out what effect the settling of dust and smoke has on the growth of plants.

A. Gather these materials: 2 potted plants of the same kind and size, dust (collected from the windowsill and other places), and water.

B. Moisten the leaves on one plant. Apply dust to the leaves.

C. Set both plants together on a windowsill and observe them for the next three or four days. What differences did you observe? What caused the differences?

DEVELOPMENT

1 Teaching Tips—To show how much air we inhale with each breath, fill a gallon jar with water. Invert it and place it in a pan that will also hold a gallon of water. Slide a narrow rubber tube into the mouth of the jar. Ask one of your students to exhale at a normal rate into the hose. Make sure he or she does not inhale. Mark the level of the water. The amount of water pushed out is the amount of air exhaled, which is about the same as the amount inhaled. Emphasize that we breathe in everything that is in the air.

2 Skill Development—The processes of *observing* and *inferring* can be encouraged by watching plants that have dust on their leaves grow.

EXTENSIONS

Enrichment

Science Skills— Observing and Inferring

With the help of an adult, the students can use the slides from the Activity to demonstrate the pollution control devices on newer automobiles. Under adult supervision, the students should place the prepared slides near the end of the exhaust pipes of first an old and then a new car. After the cars have been running for a while, the students should remove the slides and examine them. The slide from the older car should show more pollution.

ACTIVITY

How can you see air pollution?

A. Gather these materials: petroleum jelly, 4 plastic microscope slides, hand lens, and paper towels.

B. Put a small amount of petroleum jelly on each of the 4 slides. Use your finger. Any pollutants in the air will stick to the petroleum jelly.

C. Put slide no. 1 away in a safe, clean place.

D. Put the other slides in these places.
Slide no. 2: on the windowsill inside your classroom.
Slide no. 3: on the windowsill outside your classroom.
Slide no. 4: on the ground near a parking lot.

E. Leave the slides for 24 hours.

F. Collect all 4 slides. Compare each slide.

1. Which slide showed the most traces of air pollution?
2. What could be the source of air pollution in each place?

Air pollution has many causes. Humans are **3** the major cause of air pollution. The pictures on page 167 show some of the ways humans pollute the air. What do you think is polluting the air in each picture?

ACTIVITY

Skill Development—*Observing, Comparing and Contrasting, Recording Data*

Teaching Tips—It might help to tape each of the slides to individual index cards. Students can use the cards to label the slides and make notes about them. The data collection period can be extended. The students can observe the slides each day. If you have a microscope, you might have the students look at the particles on their slides. Put a cover slip over the slides so that the microscopes are not smeared with petroleum jelly. The students can make drawings of the particles.

Answers to Questions—1. Slide no. 4 should show the most pollution. **2.** Sources include dust, smoke from factories or fires, and auto emissions.

3 Text Questions—What do you think is polluting the air in each picture? *Auto exhaust, smoke from an industrial smokestack, a volcano.*

Exceptional Student

Visually Impaired

If the students cannot use a microscope, have them record the intensity of odors in the classroom and school yard, and on the highway and local street.

Cars are a major cause of air pollution. Cars put many kinds of gases into the air. Air pollution is worse in large cities than in the country. Factories also pollute the air. Many of them burn coal. Coal-burning makes gases such as car-
4 bon dioxide. Too much carbon dioxide in the air causes air pollution.

Humans are not the only source of air pollution. Nature also pollutes the air. These two examples show how natural causes can pollute the air.

5 A volcanic eruption like the one shown can pollute the air. When a volcano erupts, it throws fine dust and gases into the air. The dust blocks some sunlight from reaching the earth's surface. The air temperature drops.

The atmosphere has also changed in the past.

EXTENSIONS

Reinforcement

Science Skills—Observing

When a volcano erupts, throwing fine dust into the atmosphere, the dust will float around in the air for a long time. Students can simulate this by letting a mixture of sand and silt settle in a jar of water.

A. Gather these materials: a glass gallon jar, water, and sand-silt-clay mixture.

B. Fill the jar with water. Pour a half cup of the sand-silt-clay mixture into the jar. Cover the jar. Shake the mixture, and then set the jar down.

C. Observe the settling of the mixture. The sand will settle immediately, but the silt and clay will stay in suspension for hours. Have the students observe the jar once per hour for several hours. They can examine it the next day to see if anything is still in suspension.

4 Teaching Tips—Carbon dioxide acts like the glass walls of a greenhouse. It allows the sunlight to pass through the air, but it absorbs the heat radiating from the earth. The result is a rise in temperature.
5 Teaching Tips—You might find pictures, slides, or a film on a recent volcanic eruption.

EXTENSIONS

Application

Research

Students should contact local industries, utilities, and environmental protection agencies to learn about any local air pollution problems and what is being done about them. They should investigate the regulations and standards pertaining to air pollution in their area, and the devices and methods used to meet them. They might also be interested in knowing how those standards were established.

Asteroid: An object made of rock and metal from outer space.

Dinosaur: An animal that lived on the earth a long time ago.

6 Some scientists believe the earth was once hit by a giant **asteroid** (ass-ter-oyd). They think this took place a long time ago. When the *asteroid* hit, dirt and dust were thrown into the air. A dark cloud covered the whole earth. This cloud may have caused the temperature of the earth to drop. Many plants would have died because of the lower temperature. Since most **dinosaurs** 7 (**dine**-uh-sorz) ate plants, this might explain why the *dinosaurs* died.

8 Clean air is important to life on earth. There are ways to keep the air clean. Cars can use special cleaners in their exhaust systems. This keeps unsafe gases and fumes from getting into the air. Factories can clean the smoke that goes out of their smokestacks by using special filters.

It costs a lot of money to reduce air pollution. Many people think it is too expensive. But in many ways, our lives depend on clean air.

Section Review

Main Ideas: Dust, dirt, and chemicals in the air are all air pollutants. Humans and natural events, like volcanoes, can pollute the air.

Questions: Answer in complete sentences.

1. What is air pollution?
2. How have humans polluted the air?
3. What effect does too much dust have on the atmosphere?
4. How can a volcano pollute the air?
5. How can air pollution be reduced?

6 **Skill Development**—This discussion of the collision of the earth with an asteroid is a good example of *hypothesizing*.
7 **Teaching Tips**—This is only one of many theories proposed to explain the extinction of the dinosaurs.
8 **Teaching Tips**—This is a good place to mention the concept of conservation as it pertains to the atmosphere. Regulations limiting toxic chemicals, smoke, and dust are examples of air conservation practices.

SECTION REVIEW

Answers to Questions

1. Making air unclean by putting dirt, dust, and chemicals into it
2. Humans have put auto emissions, smoke, dust, and chemicals into the air.
3. It lowers visibility, covers plant leaves, and irritates some people's eyes and lungs.
4. It puts dust into the air, which blocks sunlight and lowers temperatures.
5. By making cars and factories reduce the gases they emit

CHAPTER REVIEW

Science Words: Find the words that are hidden in the puzzle below. Write the meaning of each word that you find.

H	U	R	R	I	C	A	N	E	O	P	L	V	S	O	P	H
U	D	I	T	H	U	N	D	E	R	S	T	O	R	M	P	Y
M	I	O	T	O	R	N	A	D	O	K	L	M	Y	U	O	G
I	N	K	L	I	O	B	L	I	Z	Z	A	R	D	I	O	R
D	N	A	S	T	E	R	O	I	D	D	E	R	T	U	O	O
I	O	O	P	O	L	L	U	T	I	O	N	J	Y	T	U	T

Questions: Answer in complete sentences.

1. What type of weather may occur with these storms: (a) tornado; (b) hurricane; (c) thunderstorm; and (d) blizzard?
2. What happens to the air temperature when water evaporates?
3. An air conditioner removes moisture from the air. Why does this make you feel cooler?
4. What is humidity?
5. What are some causes of air pollution?
6. In what way does a volcano pollute the air?
7. How can air pollution harm people?
8. Would the air be safer to breathe while jogging in the city or in the mountains? Explain.
9. How can air pollution from cars and factories be reduced?

EXTENSIONS

Application
Research

The asteroid theory is just one of the many theories proposed to explain the disappearance of the dinosaurs.

Interested students might do research to learn about the other theories. They could compare the evidence for each, the plausibility of the theory, and its acceptance in the scientific community. They might want to report their findings to the class.

CHAPTER REVIEW

Science Words
Hurricane, thunderstorm, tornado, blizzard, asteroid, pollution. See the definitions in the chapter margins.

Answers to Questions
1. **a.** High winds, low pressure, **b.** heavy rains, strong winds, **c.** heavy rain, thunder and lightning, **d.** cold wind, heavy snow
2. It is lowered.
3. With lower humidity, moisture can evaporate from your skin readily. Evaporation cools you.
4. The amount of water in the air
5. Smoke from fires, dust from volcanoes and dirt, chemicals from autos and factories
6. It puts dust into the air. This blocks sunlight and lowers temperatures.
7. It can damage our lungs and irritate our eyes.
8. In the mountains; the air is cleaner.
9. By reducing the output of dust, smoke, and chemicals

SUGGESTED TEST MASTERS
pp. T-111 l, m, n

EXTENSIONS

Enrichment

Science Skills—
Building Science Vocabulary

Here are additional vocabulary words. Students can use the dictionary to learn their meanings and their relation to the chapter's concepts.

squall line: a long line of violent storms often 80–320 km ahead of a fast-moving cold front.
monsoon: seasonal wind that is more pronounced over large continental areas near the equator. Usually accompanied by heavy rains.
typhoon: a hurricane that originates in the Pacific Ocean.
acid rain: precipitation with a high acid content, caused by water falling through polluted air.
relative humidity: the amount of water vapor in the air compared with the amount of water vapor the air could hold at that temperature.

Activity

Students can use the barometers they have made to observe the effect that altitude has on air pressure.

A. Place one barometer on the ground floor of a tall building where it will not be disturbed and where the temperature doesn't change.

B. Place another barometer on the top floor of the building under similar conditions.

C. Record and compare the air pressure reading from both barometers.

1. What do you observe about the two barometer readings?
2. How do you account for this observation?

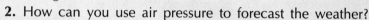

INVESTIGATING

How can you use a barometer to forecast the weather?

You can make your own barometer to measure the air pressure. You will then be able to forecast the weather.

A. Gather these materials: 2 olive or baby food jars, balloon, ice cream stick, glue, plastic straw, 2 rubber bands, and scissors.

B. Cut a large section from the balloon. Stretch it tightly over 1 jar. Fasten it with a rubber band.

C. Cut a point on the straw. Glue the other end to the center of the balloon.

D. Fasten the stick to the other jar with a rubber band. Put the point of the straw next to the stick.

E. For the next week, call the weather bureau each day. Record the air pressure on the scale.

F. Put your barometer in a place where the temperature does not change. Do not move it once you have set it up.

1. How does the air pressure change when the weather changes?
2. How can you use air pressure to forecast the weather?

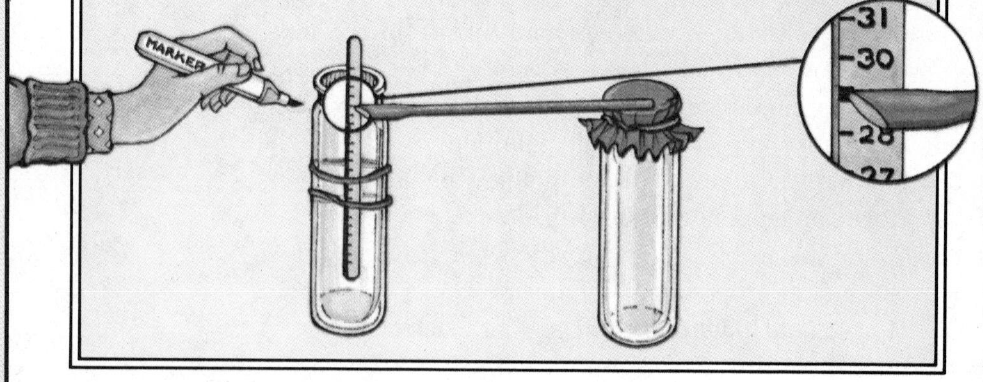

INVESTIGATING

Teaching Tips—The stick will serve as the scale. Each day, mark the point where the straw touches the stick. Do this the same time each day. Record the barometric reading you obtain from the weather bureau next to the mark made that day. In a notebook, have the students record the date, the barometric pressure, and the weather conditions for that day. The students should note that the barometer reading is lowest on wet, rainy days. They should also notice that the pressure begins to drop before the rain actually starts.

Answers to Questions—**1.** The air pressure becomes lower when the weather becomes cloudy and rainy. **2.** If you record air pressure readings daily, you will be aware when the pressure is dropping. You will be able to forecast rain. If the pressure is going up, you will be able to forecast fair weather.

CAREERS

Television Weather Forecaster ▶

Each day people give weather reports and forecasts on television. Meteorologists use computers, instruments at the TV station, radar, and satellite pictures. All this information helps them predict the weather. Weather forecasters have studied meteorology in college.

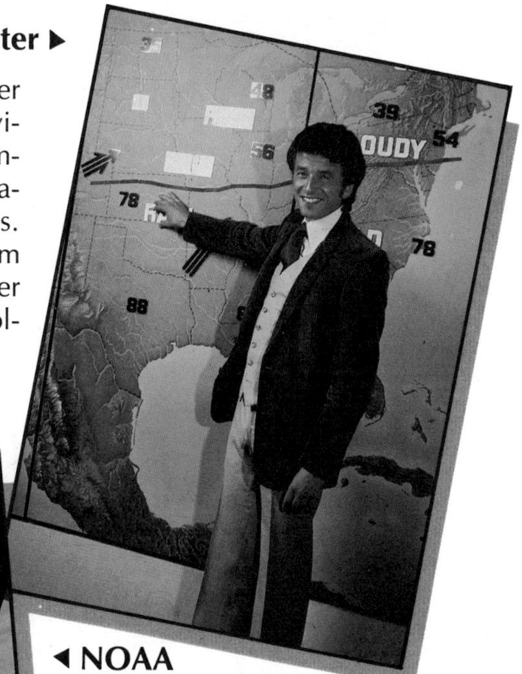

◀ NOAA

The National Oceanic and Atmospheric Administration (or NOAA) is in Boulder, Colorado. Scientists work for the NOAA in many ways. Some operate the satellites that observe the earth's environment. Others study the earth's atmosphere and oceans. They also study the effects of pollution around the world. The National Weather Service reports the weather and gives forecasts.

EXTENSIONS

Application

Research

Students may be interested in doing research on additional careers such as meteorologist and instrumentation specialist. Studying the phenomena of the earth's atmosphere enables the meteorologist to learn about the weather, the physical and chemical composition of the atmosphere, the laws governing atmospheric motion, and long-term climatic trends. A person interested in meteorology should be good at mathematics, should like to work with computers, and should be very interested in the weather. An advanced degree is often required. Additional information can be obtained by writing to the American Meteorological Society, 43 Beacon Street, Boston, MA 02108.

Instrumentation specialists develop, operate, and improve the devices used by meteorologists. Much of this work now involves designing weather-recording devices for satellites. A person interested in this field should have a good understanding of electronics and meteorology. Additional information may be obtained by writing to the American Geophysical Union, 2100 Pennsylvania Ave., NW Washington, D.C. 20037

CAREERS

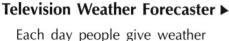

Teaching Tips—To obtain additional information about television weather forecasters, students could contact their local television stations. Students may wish to contact the local branch of NOAA to find out what kinds of careers are available in their area.

UNIT 4 MACHINES

CHAPTER	SECTION	BASIC SCIENCE SKILLS	ACTIVITY MATERIALS STUDENT/GROUP	EXTENSIONS
CHAPTER 11 MACHINES AND WORK	**11-1** p.T-174 What Is Work?	*Observing* if work is done or not p.T-175 *Comparing and contrasting* work p.T-175	metric ruler, string, medium rubber band, paper clips, index card, scissors, books, chalk	• Enrichment p.T-176 • Application pp.T-175, T-177
	11-2 p.T-178 Machines	*Comparing and contrasting* force on inclined planes p.T-180	force measurer, 1-m board, toy car or truck, 3 books	• Reinforcement p.T-179 • Enrichment pp.T-180, T-182 • Application p.T-181
	11-3 p.T-183 Hidden Inclined Planes	*Comparing and contrasting* straight and curved inclined planes p.T-184	2 screws, 2 triangles, 2 pencils, tape, screwdriver, crayon, wood block	• Enrichment pp.T-184, T-185, T-186, T-187
	11-4 p.T-188 The Lever	*Comparing and contrasting* moving an object with and without a lever p.T-189 *Observing* levers and *predicting* which will move heaviest load p.T-189	paper clips, flat-sided pencil, 2 paper cups, small box, tape, 30-cm wooden ruler	• Enrichment pp.T-189, T-191, T-192 • Application p.T-190
CHAPTER 12 MACHINES WITH WHEELS	**12-1** p.T-193 Pulleys	*Comparing and contrasting* fixed and movable pulleys p.T-195	small pulley, meter stick, string, pail, sand, spring scale	• Enrichment pp.T-194, T-195, T-196 • Application p.T-197
	12-2 p.T-198 The Wheel and Axle	*Inferring* differences between screwdrivers p.T-200	2 screwdrivers, 2 screws, wood block, metric ruler	• Reinforcement p.T-199 • Enrichment pp.T-200, T-201 • Application p.T-199
	12-3 p.T-202 Gear Wheels	*Finding the cause and effect* of movement of gears p.T-203	crayon, egg beater	• Enrichment pp.T-203, T-205 • Application p.T-204
	12-4 p.T-206 Compound Machines	*Observing* simple machines in compound machines p.T-209	scissors, hand drill, toy crane, pencil sharpener	• Reinforcement p.T-210 • Enrichment p.T-209 • Application pp.T-207, T-208
CHAPTER 13 FRICTION AND WORK	**13-1** p.T-211 What Is Friction?	*Finding the cause and effect* of friction and surfaces pp.T-212, T-213	shoe box, sand, sandpaper, wax paper, spring scale	• Reinforcement p.T-214 • Enrichment p.T-213 • Application pp.T-212, T-215
	13-2 p.T-216 Friction and Wheels	*Inferring* how wheels reduce friction	shoe box, 4 books, 3 round pencils, string, spring scale	• Reinforcement p.T-217 • Enrichment p.T-218
	13-3 p.T-219 Reducing Friction	*Observe* and *infer* effects of water on friction p.T-220	4 marbles, liquid soap, paper towels	• Enrichment pp.T-220, T-222, T-223 • Application pp.T-221, T-224, T-225

EXTRA ACTIVITIES/ DEMONSTRATIONS	WORKSHEET MASTERS	EVALUATIONS
• Tug-of-war p.T-174 • Pull books with a spring scale p.T-176		Section Review p.T-177
• Inclined plane p.T-179		Section Review p.T-182
• Hammer and chisel p.T-185		Section Review p.T-187
• Seesaw lever p.T-188 • First-class lever p.T-189 • Hammer and nails p.T-191	• Machines (SK) p.T-171 k • Survey (AH) p.T-171 l • Word Puzzle (SK) p.T-171 m	Section Review p.T-191 Chapter Review p.T-192 Test Masters pp.T-171 d, e
• Classroom shades p.T-193	• Model Windmill (AC) p.T-171 n	Section Review p.T-197
• Doorknob p.T-199 • Pencil sharpener p.T-199		Section Review p.T-201
• Bicycle gears p.T-202 • Bicycle p.T-205	• Gears (SK) p.T-171 o • Wheels (AC) p.T-171 p	Section Review p.T-205
• Simple machines in a bicycle and other compound machines p.T-207 • Projector p.T-209		Sec Rev p.T-209 Chapter Review p.T-210 Test Masters pp.T-171 f, g, h
• Three grades of sandpaper p.T-213		Section Review p.T-215
• Science toy car race p.T-216		Section Review p.T-218
• Hovercraft p.T-219 • Lubricate p.T-220 • Oil p.T-222 • Investigating p.T-224	• Friction (SK) p.T-171 q • Machine Vocabulary (SK) p.T-171 r	Sec Rev p.T-222 Chapter Review p.T-223 Test Masters pp. T-171 i, j

KEY (AC)—Activity (AH)—At Home (SK)—Skill

BOOKS FOR STUDENTS

Ackins, Ralph. *Energy Machine*, Milwaukee: Raintree, 1980

Adkins, Jan. *Heavy Equipment*, (illus.), New York: Scribner, 1980

Ciupik, Larry A. & Seevers, James A. *Space Machines*, Milwaukee, Raintree, 1979

Girard, Pat. *Flying Machines*, Milwaukee: Raintree, 1980

Kiley, Denise. *Biggest Machines*, Milwaukee: Raintree, 1980

Milton, Joyce. *Here Come the Robots*, New York: Hastings, 1981

Richards, Norman. *Tractors, Plows, and Harvesters: A Book About Farm Machines*, Garden City: Doubleday, 1978

Stone, William D. *Earth Moving Machines*, illus. by Jerry Scott, Milwaukee: Raintree, 1979

Wade, Harlan. *Gears*, Milwaukee: Raintree, 1977

Zubrowski, Bernie. *Messing Around with Water Pumps and Siphons: A Children's Museum Activity Book*, Boston: Little, Brown & Co., 1981

FILMS

Energy and Work, 11 min, Britannica

How Levers Help Us, 11 min, Coronet

How Ramps Help Us, 11 min, Coronet

Simple Machines: Inclined Planes, 6 min, Coronet

Simple Machines: Lever, 6 min, Coronet

Simple Machines: Pulleys, 5 1/2 min, Coronet

FILMSTRIPS

Machines Around Us: How They Work Series, sound filmstrips, National Geographic

——— *Simple Machines*, 15 min.

——— *Trucks, Trains, and Airplanes*, 17 min

Machines Do Work, filmstrip and cassette, 6 min, color, Britannica

What Is Friction?, filmstrip and cassette, 6 min, Britannica

The Work of Simple Machines, filmstrip and cassette, 10 min, Britannica

COMPUTER AIDS

Simple Machines, Apple, BASIC, 32K + disk, Micro Power & Light

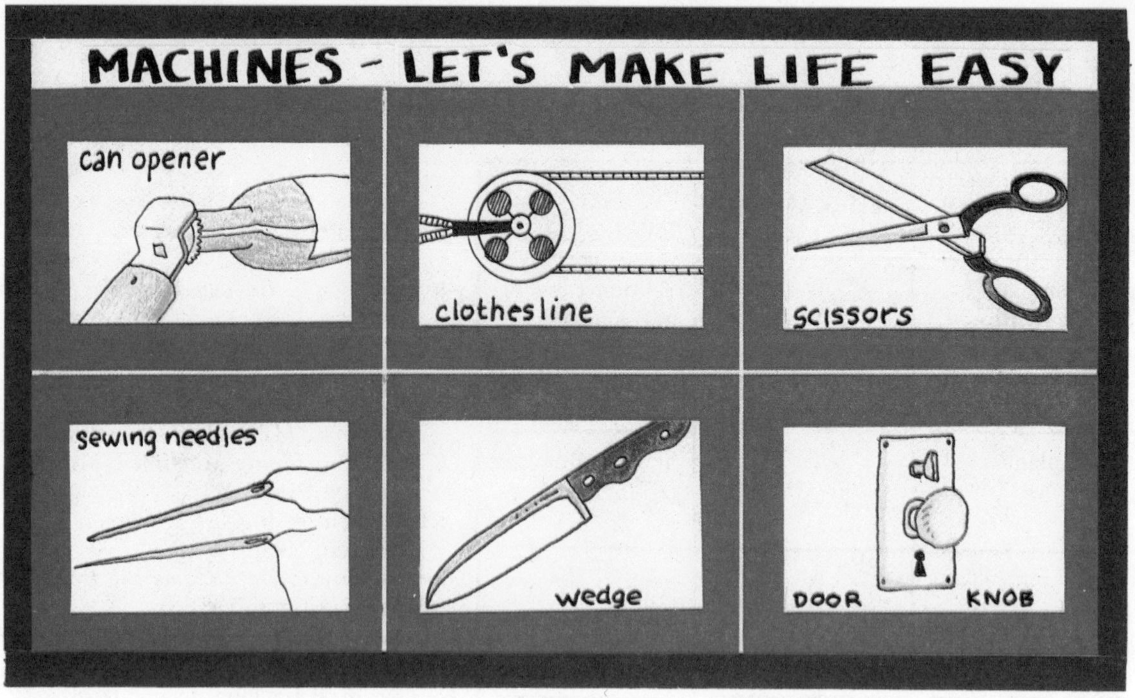

BULLETIN BOARD

This bulletin board illustrates different simple machines and could be developed as the unit progresses. If possible, have students bring in household items that are examples of simple machines. Otherwise, have the students draw pictures of them. Items that might be included are can openers, scissors, nutcrackers, forks, pliers, hammers, sewing needles, small wedges, and doorknobs. Fasten the items to the bulletin board with string and thumbtacks. As an alternative, cut out pictures of the different items from magazines, and post them on the board.

FIELD TRIP IDEAS

To visit a construction site

Take your class to a construction site, such as a house-remodeling project. Have the students draw pictures of the tools that the construction workers use and find out how they work. Among the tools and equipment that could be identified are hammers, saws, nails, crowbars, wheelbarrows, and cement mixers.

To investigate the tools and equipment used in your school

Ask one of your school custodians to take your class on a tour around the school to learn about the machines that are used to clean the school, maintain the grounds, and do repairs. Ask the custodian to demonstrate how the machines are used and how they are cared for. Ask the students to point out the simple machines that comprise the compound machines they see.

Name_________________________________Date______________

MACHINES AND WORK

TEST CHAPTER 11

Fold back answer key on line before copying.

Read each question. Choose the best answer. Write the letter of your choice on the line at the right.

CHAPTER OBJECTIVES

1. Which of the following is *not* an example of work? **1.** ______ **1.** b (1)
   - **a.** a woman opening a door
   - **b.** a man watching a movie
   - **c.** a girl pushing a lawnmower
   - **d.** a boy pulling a wagon
2. Work is done when **2.** ______ **2.** b (1)
   - **a.** a force does not move an object.
   - **b.** a force moves an object.
   - **c.** a person uses energy.
   - **d.** a person does not use force.
3. Which of the following would make the spring on a spring scale stretch the most? **3.** ______ **3.** d (1)
   - **a.** a pencil
   - **b.** a feather
   - **c.** a spoon
   - **d.** a hammer
4. Pitchers use energy when they **4.** ______ **4.** d (1)
   - **a.** swing a bat.
   - **b.** throw a baseball.
   - **c.** pick up a baseball.
   - **d.** do all of the above.
5. When an inclined plane is used, the amount of work done **5.** ______ **5.** a (2)
   - **a.** stays the same.
   - **b.** increases.
   - **c.** decreases.
   - **d.** depends on the angle of the plane.
6. Ramps are examples of **6.** ______ **6.** b (2)
   - **a.** wedges.
   - **b.** inclined planes.
   - **c.** levers.
   - **d.** screws.
7. A road that curves from side to side going up a mountain **7.** ______ **7.** a (2)
   - **a.** saves force but increases distance.
   - **b.** saves force and decreases distance.
   - **c.** has no effect on force.
   - **d.** decreases the amount of work.

Name________________________Date________

8. c (2) **8.** Less force is needed to move an object up an inclined plane as **8.** ______
- **a.** the ramp gets shorter.
- **b.** the angle increases.
- **c.** the angle decreases.
- **d.** the object gets larger.

9. d (3) **9.** An example of a simple machine that is a screw is **9.** ______
- **a.** a knife.
- **b.** an axe.
- **c.** a straight ladder.
- **d.** a winding stairway.

10. b (3) **10.** Wedges are used to **10.** ______
- **a.** stick things together.
- **b.** break things apart.
- **c.** lift things.
- **d.** lower things.

11. c (3) **11.** Which of the following is *not* a wedge? **11.** ______
- **a.** a fork
- **b.** a needle
- **c.** a can opener
- **d.** a nail

12. a (3) **12.** Where is force focused on a wedge? **12.** ______
- **a.** on the sharp edge
- **b.** on the flat side
- **c.** on all edges
- **d.** on none of the edges

13. d (4) **13.** The turning point of a seesaw is called the **13.** ______
- **a.** lever.
- **b.** inclined plane.
- **c.** screw.
- **d.** fulcrum.

14. a (4) **14.** Levers are used to move things by **14.** ______
- **a.** pushing down on one end of a bar.
- **b.** rolling things down a ramp.
- **c.** keeping things level.
- **d.** not using any force.

15. c (4) **15.** A hammer is an example of **15.** ______
- **a.** a wedge.
- **b.** a fulcrum.
- **c.** a lever.
- **d.** an inclined plane.

16. a (4) **16.** The least amount of force is used with a lever when **16.** ______
- **a.** the fulcrum is close to the load.
- **b.** the fulcrum is far from the load.
- **c.** the fulcrum is close to the force.
- **d.** there is no fulcrum.

Name_________________________________Date_______________

MACHINES WITH WHEELS

TEST 12
CHAPTER

Fold back answer key on line before copying.

CHAPTER OBJECTIVES

Read each question. Choose the best answer. Write the letter of your choice on the line at the right.

1. What is a pulley? 1.______ 1. d (1)
   a. a wheel with a rope that does not move
   b. a wheel that does not turn
   c. a wheel with teeth
   d. a wheel with a rope that moves around it
2. When you pull down a fixed pulley, 2.______ 2. a (1)
   a. only the load is lifted.
   b. the load and pulley are lifted.
   c. only the pulley is lifted.
   d. nothing is lifted.
3. A movable pulley 3.______ 3. c (1)
   a. is fastened to one spot.
   b. changes the direction of the force.
   c. moves with the load.
   d. increases the amount of force needed.
4. Look at the picture below. The clothesline is an example of a 4.______ 4. b (2)
   a. movable pulley. **c.** lever.
   b. fixed pulley. **d.** wheel and an axle.

Name________________________________Date__________

5. c (2)

5. A crane is a machine that 5. ______

a. uses only a fixed pulley.
b. uses only a movable pulley.
c. uses a fixed and a movable pulley.
d. uses levers.

6. c (2)

6. It would be easiest to lift a brick 6. ______

a. using a machine with one movable pulley.
b. using a machine with one fixed pulley.
c. using a machine with a movable and a fixed pulley.
d. by not using any machine.

7. a (3)

7. Which machine is *not* an example of a wheel and axle? 7. ______

a. scissors
b. a screwdriver
c. a pencil sharpener
d. a doorknob

8. a (3)

8. A large handle makes a screwdriver easier to use because 8. ______

a. it is easier to turn a larger wheel.
b. it fits in your hand better.
c. it does not slip.
d. it fits more screws.

9. b (3)

9. Which of the following is an axle? 9. ______

a. a doorknob
b. the rod of a doorknob
c. the doorknob and its rod
d. a door

10. b (4)

10. An egg beater is a machine that uses a 10. ______

a. wedge.
b. gear.
c. lever.
d. pulley.

11. d (4)

11. What prevents the gear wheels of a bicycle from turning in opposite directions? 11. ______

a. the pedal
b. the front wheel
c. the back wheel
d. the chain

12. a (4)

12. When you turn the large wheel on an egg beater, 12. ______

a. the small blades make more turns.
b. the small blades make fewer turns.
c. the small blades turn more slowly than the wheel.
d. the small blades stop turning.

Name________________________________Date______________

13. Compound machines are made of **13.** ______ **13.** c (5)

a. one simple machine.
b. not more than two simple machines.
c. two or more simple machines.
d. only wheels and axles.

14. Scissors are made up of **14.** ______ **14.** a (5)

a. two levers and two wedges.
b. two levers and a pulley.
c. two inclined planes and two screws.
d. two wheels and two axles.

15. Which of the following is *not* a compound machine? **15.** ______ **15.** d (5)

a. a hand drill **c.** a movie projector
b. a bicycle **d.** a screwdriver

Fold back answer key on line before copying.

CHAPTER OBJECTIVES

Name______________________ Date__________

FRICTION AND WORK

TEST CHAPTER 13

Read each question. Choose the best answer. Write the letter of your choice on the line at the right.

1. a (1)

1. As the friction between two objects decreases, **1.** ______
- **a.** the objects move more easily.
- **b.** the objects move with more difficulty.
- **c.** the objects stop moving.
- **d.** there is no difference in how the objects move.

2. c (1)

2. On which surface would a person find the least amount of friction while walking? **2.** ______
- **a.** a dirt path
- **b.** a gravel road
- **c.** an icy sidewalk
- **d.** a sandy beach

3. c (1)

3. Which of the following does *not* increase friction? **3.** ______
- **a.** wearing sneakers
- **b.** stepping on car brakes
- **c.** polishing the floor
- **d.** putting chains on tires

4. a (2)

4. What effect do ball bearings have on a machine? **4.** ______
- **a.** They reduce friction.
- **b.** They increase noise.
- **c.** They reduce efficiency.
- **d.** They have no effect.

5. a (2)

5. A wheel reduces friction because **5.** ______
- **a.** only a small part of it touches the ground.
- **b.** it goes faster.
- **c.** it can go backwards.
- **d.** it doesn't need oil.

6. a (2)

6. Ball bearings are used in machines because they **6.** ______
- **a.** make wheels turn more smoothly.
- **b.** make less noise.
- **c.** increase friction.
- **d.** decrease efficiency.

Name________________________________Date____________

7. A lubricant allows two surfaces to — 7. ____ — 7. a (3)
   a. rub smoothly against one another.
   b. stick together.
   c. increase friction between them.
   d. retain heat.

8. All of the following are lubricants except — 8. ____ — 8. d (3)
   a. oil. **c.** liquid soap.
   b. grease. **d.** sand.

9. The best way to reduce friction in a car engine is — 9. ____ — 9. b (3)
   a. to clean the engine.
   b. to lubricate the engine.
   c. to remove oil from the engine.
   d. to turn on the engine.

10. When the amount of work done by a machine is compared to the amount of work put in, we are measuring — 10. ____ — 10. c (4)
   a. force. **c.** efficiency.
   b. friction. **d.** energy.

11. To overcome friction, a machine — 11. ____ — 11. b (4)
   a. will do less work.
   b. will do more work.
   c. will stop working.
   d. will do a different kind of work.

12. A machine becomes more efficient — 12. ____ — 12. b (4)
   a. as the friction increases.
   b. as the friction decreases.
   c. as the parts wear out.
   d. as the machine produces less.

Name ______________________________ Date ______________

Machines and Work

SKILL WORKSHEET

There are many simple machines in the picture. Find as many of them as you can and write down their names, what types of machines they are, and how they make work easier.

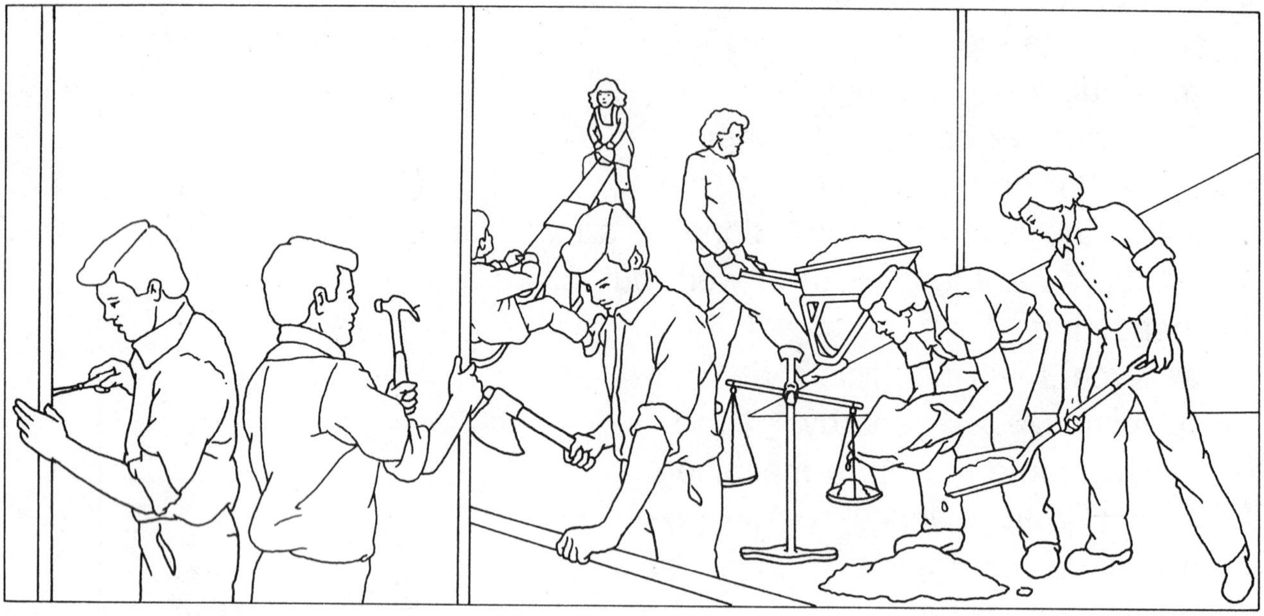

____

____

____

____

____

____

____

____

____

____

Name ______________________ Date ______________

Machines and Work

AT HOME WORKSHEET

You are learning about simple machines and work. You can better understand how we use simple machines in our homes by completing this activity.

Take a simple-machine survey of your home. Find as many simple machines as you can. List each one you find in the table below. Tell what kind of simple machine it is and what work it does.

Simple Machine	Type of Simple Machine	Work It Does

Name ______________________ Date ____________

Machines and Work

SKILL WORKSHEET

Find the science words hidden below. They may be spelled forward, backward, up, down, or diagonally. Match each word you find with its meaning.

Q	H	G	E	U	L	K	C	T	A	B	O	F	T	B
B	I	C	A	L	B	A	F	I	T	A	T	H	C	L
V	R	N	Z	W	H	Y	H	O	X	Q	O	I	K	T
F	O	R	C	E	I	S	J	K	L	S	H	L	E	A
U	S	D	X	L	L	P	C	Y	K	V	E	P	M	S
L	N	H	V	U	I	U	H	I	K	L	M	U	R	M
C	E	K	Q	T	O	N	D	Z	W	R	A	H	D	I
R	O	N	O	P	N	A	E	O	T	I	P	A	X	F
U	Y	P	L	N	I	L	N	D	O	P	M	T	W	V
M	L	O	C	D	T	K	I	H	P	Q	R	S	W	Y
H	M	N	A	O	Q	N	H	Y	D	L	E	V	E	R
K	A	Z	H	Y	Z	S	C	R	E	W	A	I	D	T
P	C	W	B	T	W	O	A	N	K	X	Z	N	G	R
U	I	N	R	I	C	T	M	B	C	M	O	T	E	Q
X	C	D	A	N	F	R	I	L	J	U	Z	O	R	P

QUESTIONS

1. A push or pull on something ______________
2. Anything that makes work easier ______________
3. A slanted surface, which is sometimes called a ramp ______________
4. An inclined plane that winds around a spiral ______
5. Two inclined planes joined together to make a sharp edge ______________
6. A bar resting on a turning point ______________
7. The turning point of a lever ______________

Name ______________________ Date ______________

Machines with Wheels

ACTIVITY WORKSHEET

You are learning about simple machines. In this activity, you will build a model windmill and see how it works as a simple machine.

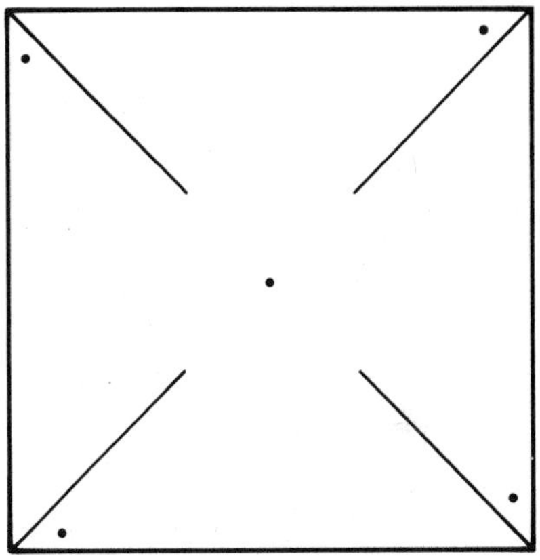

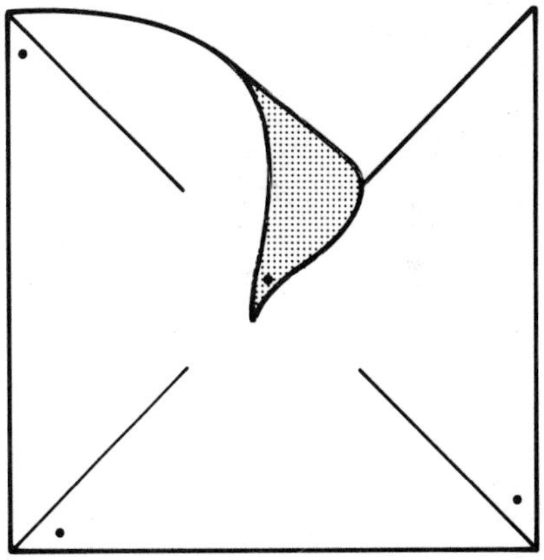

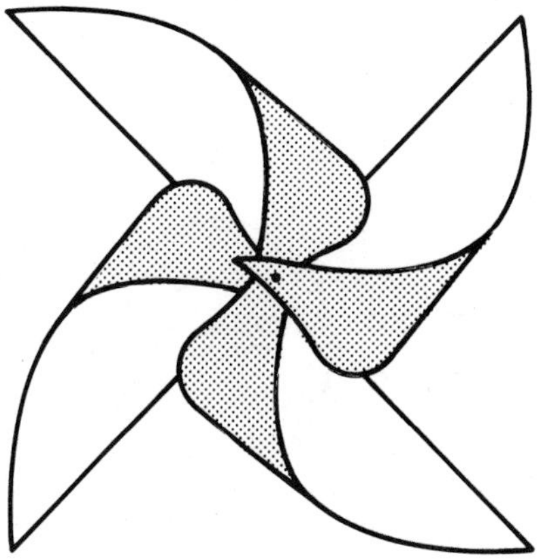

A. Gather these materials: paper, pencil, ruler, scissors, straight pin. SAFETY TIP: BE VERY CAREFUL WHEN USING THE SCISSORS AND THE STRAIGHT PIN.

B. Draw a 13 cm (5 in.) square on a piece of paper. Make lines and dots on the square as shown in the drawing.

C. Cut the square. Cut along each line you drew on the square.

D. Fold over each corner so that the corner dot is over the center dot.

E. Stick the pin through the dots. Push the end of the pin into the eraser of the pencil.

1. What makes a pinwheel and a windmill turn?

____

2. What kind of simple machine is a windmill? Explain. ______________________________

____

____

____

3. What kind of work is done by a windmill?

____

____

Name________________________________ Date______________

Machines with Wheels

SKILL WORKSHEET

Show the answers on the diagrams below.

1. If gear wheel A turns once in the direction shown, how many times and in which direction will gear wheel C turn?

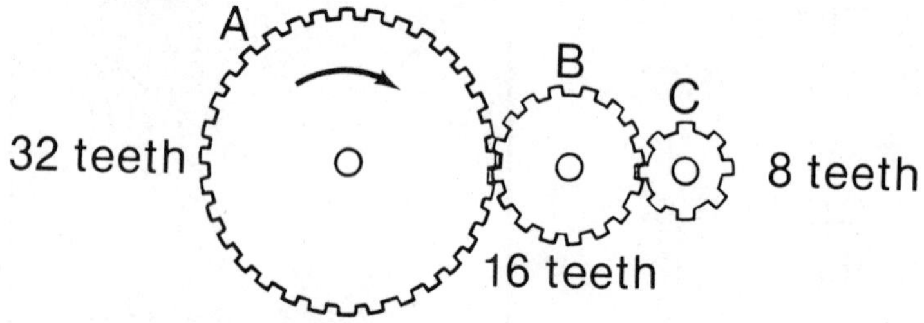

2. If gear wheel A turns in the direction shown in each of the drawings below, in which direction will gear wheel B turn?

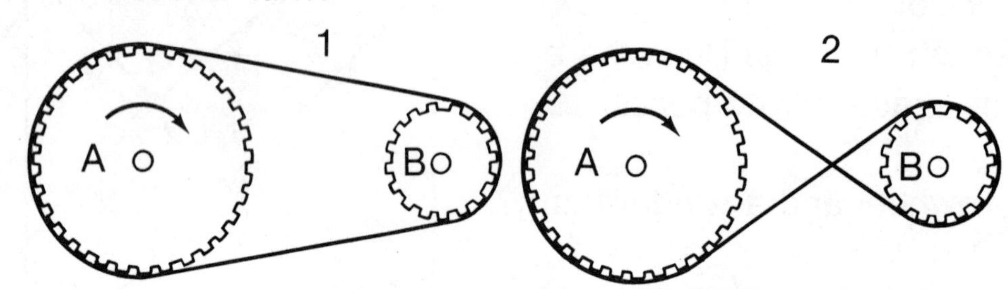

3. Gear wheels B and C are joined, so they move together. If gear wheel A turns 10 times in the direction shown, how many times and in which direction will gear wheel D turn?

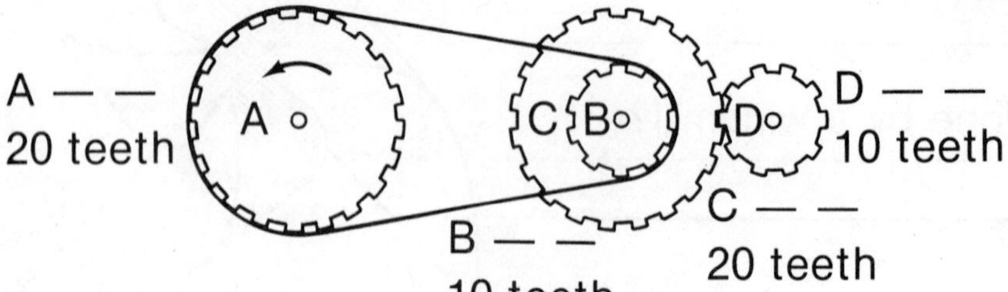

Name ______________________ Date ______________

Machines with Wheels

ACTIVITY WORKSHEET

You are learning about how wheels are used. In this activity, you will see how one wheel can be used to turn another wheel.

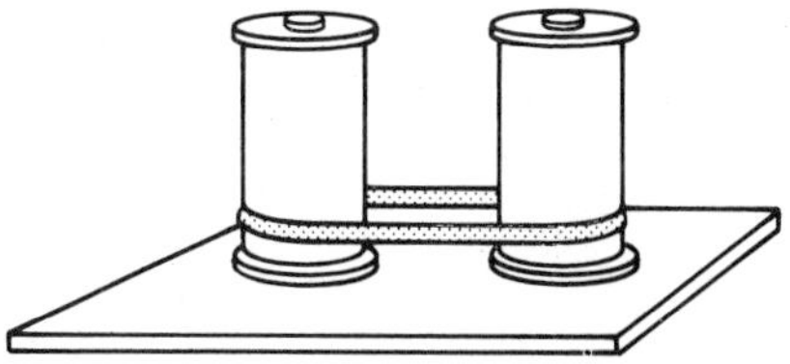

A

A. Gather these materials: hammer, 2 nails, rubber band, 2 large spools, 1 small spool, piece of wood. SAFETY TIP: BE CAREFUL WHEN USING THE HAMMER AND NAILS.

B. Hammer the nails into the wood so that they are about 1 cm (2.5 in.) apart. Place a large spool over each nail. Place the rubber band around the spools as shown in Fig. A. Make a pencil mark at the same spot on each spool.

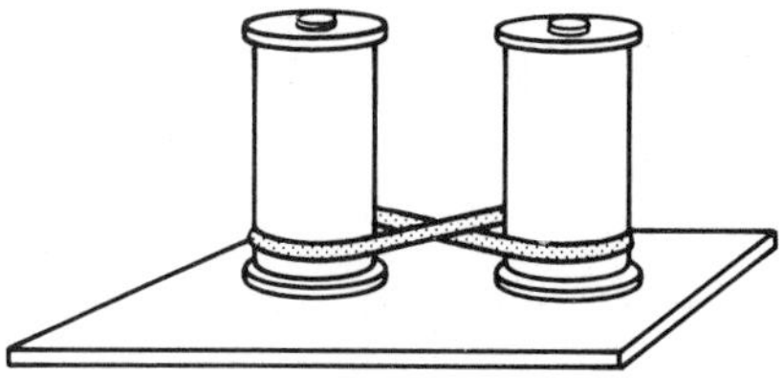

B

C. Slowly turn one spool until it makes one complete turn. Watch both spools.

D. Arrange the rubber band as shown in Fig. B. Repeat Step C.

E. Replace one of the large spools with the small spool as shown in Fig. C. Repeat Step C.

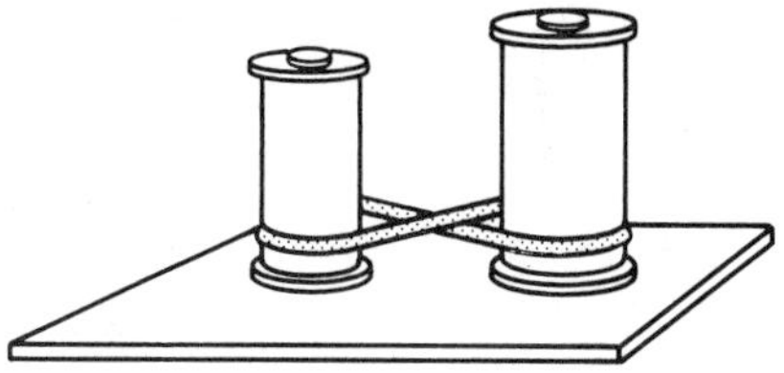

C

QUESTIONS

1. How many turns and in what direction did the spools move in step C? ______________________

____

In step D? ______________________

____

In step E? ______________________

____

Name ______________________ Date ______________

Friction and Work

SKILL WORKSHEET

If you wanted to move a heavy crate, which method would you use? List the drawings below in order of decreasing friction. ______________________

QUESTIONS

1. In which of the drawings above is the most friction present? ______________________
2. Which drawing shows the least amount of friction?

   ____
3. Why do wheels reduce friction? ______________________

   ____
4. Why does a polished floor reduce friction? ______________________

   ____

Name ______________________ Date ______________

Friction and Work

SKILL WORKSHEET

Write in the science word shown in each of the drawings below and the number to the matching definition.

____

____

____

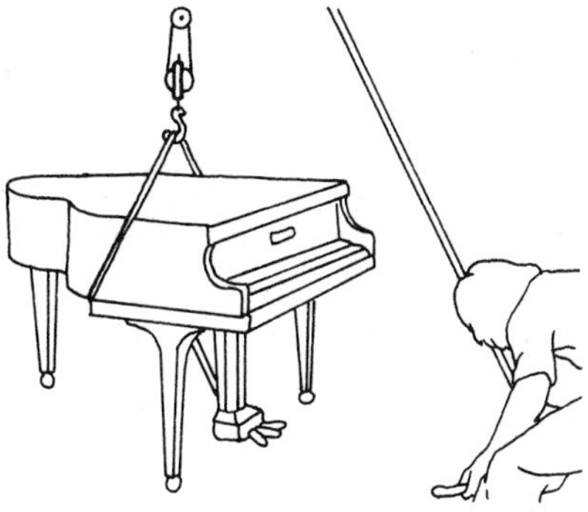

____

____

1. A force caused when two objects rub or slide over one another
2. Small metal balls used to reduce friction
3. The amount of work done by a machine compared to the amount of work put into it
4. A boat that rides on a cushion of air to reduce friction with the water
5. A way to reduce friction by using a liquid on the moving parts of a machine

Name ______________________ Date ____________

Machines and Work

OBSERVING, CLASSIFYING — SKILL WORKSHEET

There are many simple machines in the picture. Find as many of them as you can and write down their names, what types of machines they are, and how they make work easier.

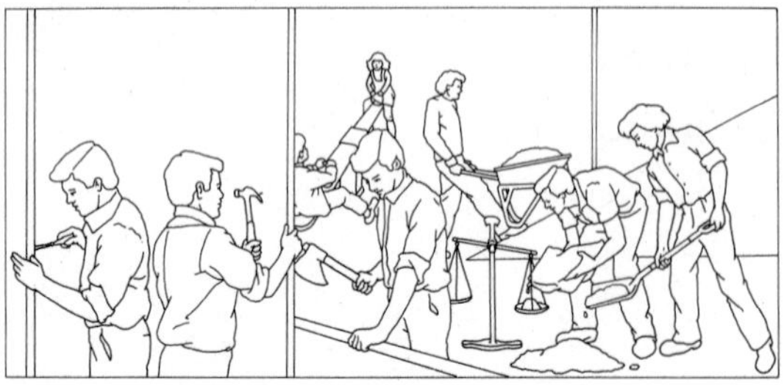

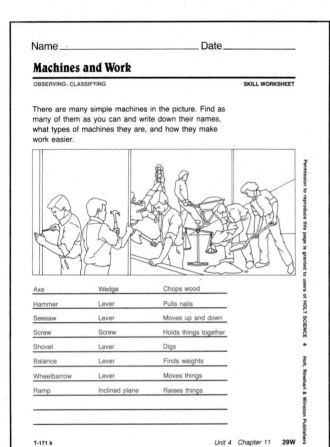

Axe	Wedge	Chops wood
Hammer	Lever	Pulls nails
Seesaw	Lever	Moves up and down
Screw	Screw	Holds things together
Shovel	Lever	Digs
Balance	Lever	Finds weights
Wheelbarrow	Lever	Moves things
Ramp	Inclined plane	Raises things

Name ______________________ Date ____________

Machines and Work

AT HOME WORKSHEET

You are learning about simple machines and work. You can better understand how we use simple machines in our homes by completing this activity.

Take a simple-machine survey of your home. Find as many simple machines as you can. List each one you find in the table below. Tell what kind of simple machine it is and what work it does.

Simple Machine	Type of Simple Machine	Work It Does

Name ______________________ Date ____________

Machines and Work

BUILDING SCIENCE VOCABULARY — SKILL WORKSHEET

Find the science words hidden below. They may be spelled forward, backward, up, down, or diagonally. Match each word you find with its meaning.

Q H G E U L K C T A B O F T B
B I C A L B A F I T A T H C L
V R N Z W H Y H O X Q O I K T
F O R C E I S J K L S H L E A
U S D X L L P C Y K V E P M S
L N H V U I U H I K L M U R M
C E K Q T O N D Z W R A H D I
R O N O P N A E O T I P A X F
U Y P L N I L N D O P M T W V
M L O C D T K I H P Q R S W Y
H M N A O Q N H Y D L E V E R
K A Z H Y Z S C R E W A I D T
P C W B T W O A N K X Z N G R
U I N R I C T M B C M O T E Q
X C D A N F R I L J U Z O R P

QUESTIONS

1. A push or pull on something Force
2. Anything that makes work easier Machine
3. A slanted surface, which is sometimes called a ramp Inclined plane
4. An inclined plane that winds around a spiral Screw
5. Two inclined planes joined together to make a sharp edge Wedge
6. A bar resting on a turning point Lever
7. The turning point of a lever Fulcrum

Name ______________________ Date ____________

Machines with Wheels

ACTIVITY WORKSHEET

You are learning about simple machines. In this activity, you will build a model windmill and see how it works as a simple machine.

A. Gather these materials: paper, pencil, ruler, scissors, straight pin. SAFETY TIP: BE VERY CAREFUL WHEN USING THE SCISSORS AND THE STRAIGHT PIN.
B. Draw a 13 cm (5 in.) square on a piece of paper. Make lines and dots on the square as shown in the drawing.
C. Cut the square. Cut along each line you drew on the square.
D. Fold over each corner so that the corner dot is over the center dot.
E. Stick the pin through the dots. Push the end of the pin into the eraser of the pencil.

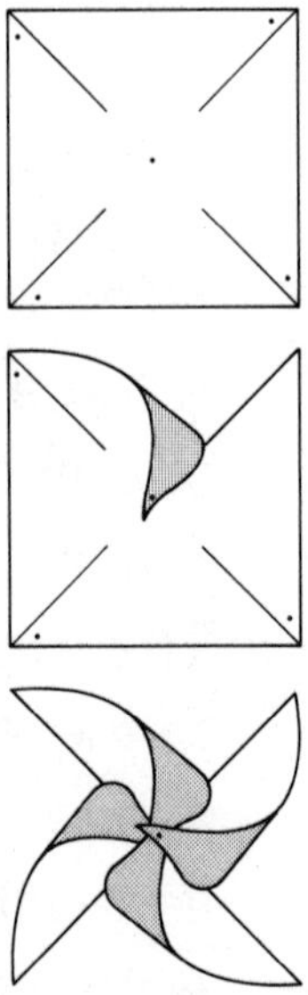

1. What makes a pinwheel and a windmill turn? The wind
2. What kind of simple machine is a windmill? Explain. A windmill is a wheel and axle. The blades of the windmill turn like a wheel. A rod, or axle, is connected to the center of the blades.
3. What kind of work is done by a windmill? A windmill can be used to pump water, grind grain and produce electricity.

Name______________________ Date____________

Machines with Wheels

OBSERVING, PREDICTING — SKILL WORKSHEET

Show the answers on the diagrams below.

1. If gear wheel A turns once in the direction shown, how many times and in which direction will gear wheel C turn?

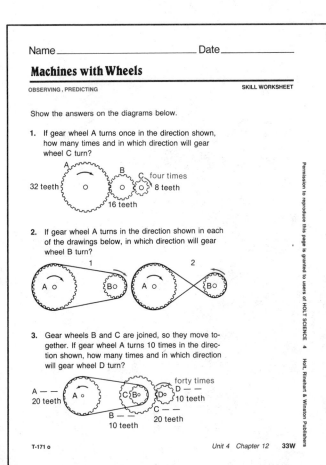

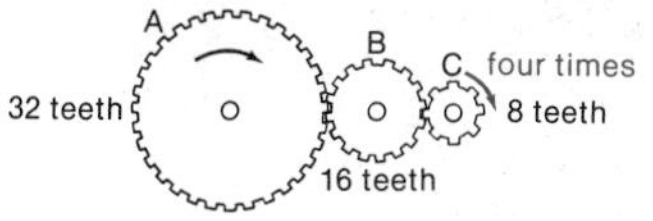

2. If gear wheel A turns in the direction shown in each of the drawings below, in which direction will gear wheel B turn?

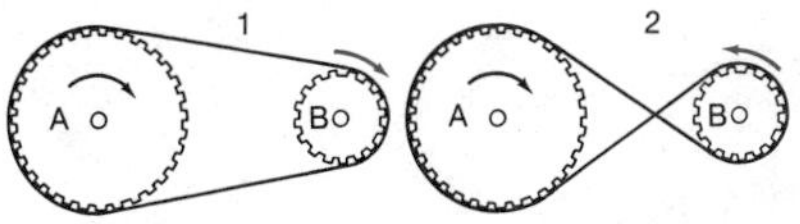

3. Gear wheels B and C are joined, so they move together. If gear wheel A turns 10 times in the direction shown, how many times and in which direction will gear wheel D turn?

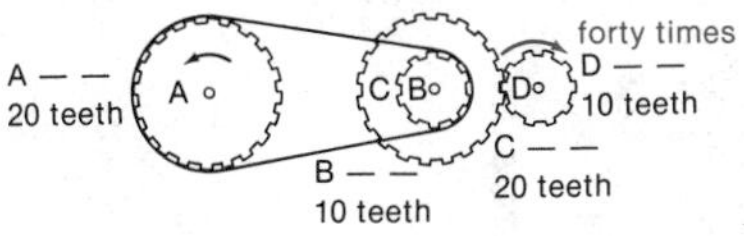

Name______________________ Date____________

Machines with Wheels

ACTIVITY WORKSHEET

You are learning about how wheels are used. In this activity, you will see how one wheel can be used to turn another wheel.

A. Gather these materials: hammer, 2 nails, rubber band, 2 large spools, 1 small spool, piece of wood. SAFETY TIP: BE CAREFUL WHEN USING THE HAMMER AND NAILS.

B. Hammer the nails into the wood so that they are about 1 cm (2.5 in.) apart. Place a large spool over each nail. Place the rubber band around the spools as shown in Fig. A. Make a pencil mark at the same spot on each spool.

C. Slowly turn one spool until it makes one complete turn. Watch both spools.

D. Arrange the rubber band as shown in Fig. B. Repeat Step C.

E. Replace one of the large spool with the small spool as shown in Fig. C. Repeat Step C.

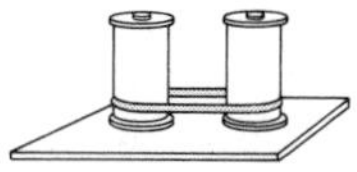

A

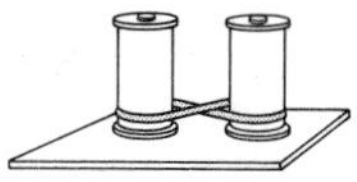

B

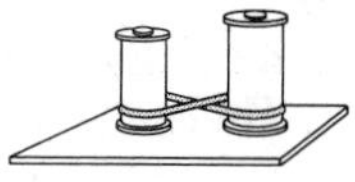

C

QUESTIONS

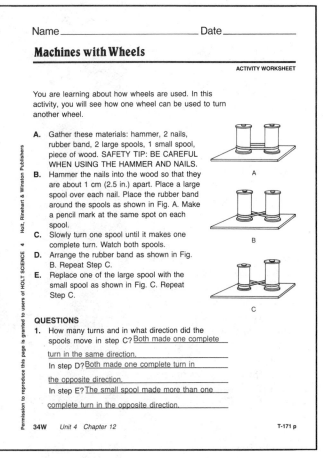

1. How many turns and in what direction did the spools move in step C? Both made one complete turn in the same direction.

   In step D? Both made one complete turn in the opposite direction.

   In step E? The small spool made more than one complete turn in the opposite direction.

Name______________________ Date____________

Friction and Work

COMPARING AND CONTRASTING, INFERRING — SKILL WORKSHEET

If you wanted to move a heavy crate, which method would you use? List the drawings below in order of decreasing friction. 2, 4, 3, 1

QUESTIONS

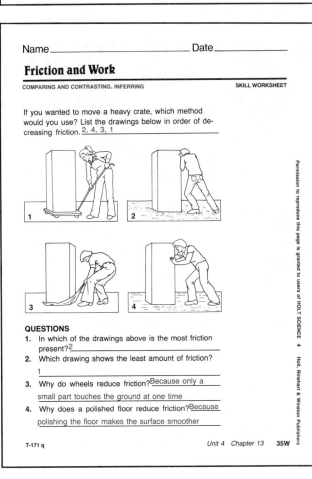

1. In which of the drawings above is the most friction present? 2
2. Which drawing shows the least amount of friction? 1
3. Why do wheels reduce friction? Because only a small part touches the ground at one time
4. Why does a polished floor reduce friction? Because polishing the floor makes the surface smoother

Name______________________ Date____________

Friction and Work

BUILDING SCIENCE VOCABULARY — SKILL WORKSHEET

Write in the science word shown in each of the drawings below and the number to the matching definition.

4. Hovercraft

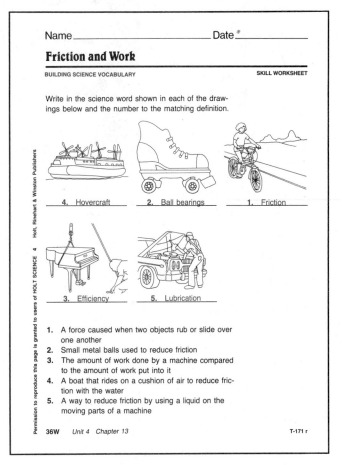

2. Ball bearings

1. Friction

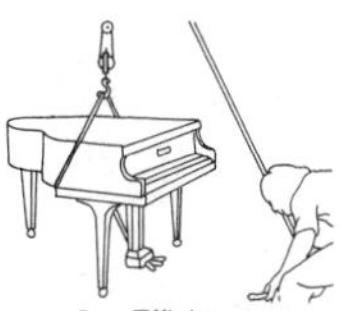

3. Efficiency

5. Lubrication

1. A force caused when two objects rub or slide over one another
2. Small metal balls used to reduce friction
3. The amount of work done by a machine compared to the amount of work put into it
4. A boat that rides on a cushion of air to reduce friction with the water
5. A way to reduce friction by using a liquid on the moving parts of a machine

Unit Overview

This is a physical science unit on work and machines. In science, work has only one meaning: Work is done when a force causes an object to move over a distance. Machines are used to make work easier. A machine reduces the amount of force required to do work.

An inclined plane is a surface set at an angle against a horizontal surface. Screws and wedges are modified inclined planes.

A lever is a bar that rests on a turning point called a fulcrum. There are three parts to a lever: the fulcrum, the effort arm, and the resistance arm.

A pulley is a wheel with a rope moving around it. Fixed pulleys make work easier by changing the direction of the force exerted. Movable pulleys make work easier by decreasing the force needed to move an object.

A wheel that turns on a rod is called a wheel and axle. Turning the wheel causes the axle to rotate. Likewise, turning the axle causes the wheel to rotate. A wheel with teeth or notches is called a gear wheel. Large gear wheels turning smaller gear wheels make work easier by increasing distance and speed at the expense of force.

Most machines we use every day are compound machines, made up of two or more simple machines.

When we attempt to roll or slide one object over another, we find that there is a force that opposes the motion. This force is called friction. Wheels and ball bearings reduce friction. Lubricants also reduce friction.

Exceptional Student IEP Unit Goal

When shown ten household objects, the student will identify what type of machines they are.

Machines

Unit Opener

This is a photograph of the gear wheels in a watch. Using the photo, a the students the following questions: How is energy provided to tu the gear wheels? *When the watch is wound, energy is stored in t mainspring.*

How can the movement of the hands in a circle be made even a steady? *A train of wheels transmits the power to devices that regula the flow of power so that it is even and can be registered on a di*

How can the energy stored in the mainspring be used to turn the ho hand, the minute hand, and the second hand, all at different speed *The energy is used to turn a series of wheels that, because of differenc in diameter and tooth spacing, cause the hands to turn smoothly different speeds.*

What is the main function of the wheels in the picture? *They change t direction and speed of a force.*

UNIT 4

LEARNING CENTER

A suggested title for the Learning Center could be "Let's Go to Work." Pictures of machines of all types could be displayed. There could be sections for heavy industrial machines, construction equipment, and household machines. You may wish to create a file for copies of worksheet masters and Extensions that students can work on independently.

Materials for the following Extensions should be available in the Learning Center: predicting needed force, p. T-180 (board for inclined plane, ruler, brick or book, force measurer); effect of position of fulcrum, p. T-191 (yardstick, book, force measurer, lump of clay); comparing fixed and movable pulleys, p. T-195 (two pulleys, cord, force measurer, pail, sand); path of the outside of a wheel, p. T-201 (wheel, roll of paper, marker or crayon that can be attached to the outside of the wheel); measuring the effect of lubrication, p. T-222 (1-m board, large wood block, petroleum jelly, force measurer); measuring work, p. T-224 (spring scale, string, meter stick, 3 pencils, milk carton, sand, 50-cm board, 2 books).

In addition, an index of suggested research topics could be set up in the Learning Center, using the following Extensions: objects that are screws and inclined planes, p. T-184; Archimedes's screw, p. T-186; how do elevators work?, p. T-197; automotive gear systems, p. T-205; perpetual motion machines, p. T-221.

Chapter Objectives

1. Explain how force is measured, how force is related to work, and what happens when a force is applied to an object.
2. Explain what an inclined plane is, and give examples of machines that are inclined planes.
3. Explain why screws and wedges are inclined planes, and give examples of machines that are screws and wedges.
4. Explain what a lever is and identify machines that are levers.

SECTION BACKGROUND

The term *work* has a scientific definition that differs from its conventional meaning. In order for work to be done, a force must move an object over a distance. A force is a push or pull on an object. The equation for work is Work = Force × Distance ($W = F \times d$). Force is measured in newtons; distance is measured in meters; and work is measured in joules or newton-meters.

A spring scale is used to measure force. The greater the force that is exerted on it, the farther its spring will stretch. Grocery stores use spring scales to weigh produce.

MATERIALS

30-cm metric ruler, 15-cm string, medium-sized rubber band, 4 paper clips, index card, scissors, 5 books, box of chalk

Exceptional Student IEP Chapter Goal

At the end of this chapter, the student will give one example of how each of the following helps us work: inclined planes, wedges, and screws.

CHAPTER 11

MACHINES AND WORK

11-1. What Is Work?

Many state fairs have a competition between teams of horses. The team that can move the heaviest load wins. Suppose they cannot move the load? When you finish this section, you should be able to:

BASIC TEACHING PLAN

MOTIVATION

If you are adventuresome, start the unit by taking the class outside to play tug-of-war. You will need a long rope, a marker, and a goal line. Tie a marker around the center of the rope and mark off a goal line. Each side should try to pull the other side across the line. You can also demonstrate tug-of-war by inviting two students to the front of the class to pull against you in a mini-tug-of-war. Use the demonstration to talk about work and force. If neither team could pull the other, then the forces on both sides were balanced. With balanced forces, there is no movement and no work being done.

Text Questions—Suppose they cannot move the load? *The horses will pull until the force they exert is not balanced by the load and the load moves. If that point is not reached, the load does not move.*

- ☐ **A.** Explain what happens when a *force* is applied to an object.
- ☐ **B.** Identify examples of work being done.
- ☐ **C.** Describe how *force* is measured.

A **force** is a push or a pull on something. Scientists say that a *force* is only part of what is
1 needed to do work. Work is done only when a force moves something. If you push on a wall,
2 you are not doing any work because the wall is not moving. But if you push a chair and the chair moves, you are doing work.

3 The girl in picture 1 is not doing any work. She is holding a large rock. Her arms may get tired. But the rock is not moving. Work is done only when an object is moved. Look at the picture of the baseball player. He is about to throw the baseball. Is he doing work? As in picture 1,
4 the answer depends on both force and motion. Now let's look at another example.

Force: A push or a pull on something.

EXTENSIONS

Application

Science Skills—Measuring

Obtain a bathroom scale that is thin enough for the students to grip. Also try to obtain hand grips from your physical education department or from a sporting goods store. Hand grips are used by people to strengthen the muscles in their hands.

Have students do an experiment to see the effect of using hand grips on the strength of their grips.

A. Have each student squeeze on the bathroom scale. Record the force of each student's grip.

B. Have the students exercise the muscles in their hands by using the strength grip for the next five days. Each student should squeeze the grip the same number of times each day. (You might tell the students to squeeze it 20 times in each hand, twice a day.)

C. On the fifth day, have each student squeeze the bathroom scale. Record the force of each person's grip. Determine the change, if any, in the force of each student.

1. What effect did exercise have on the strength of their grips?
2. Is the strength the same in each hand?
3. Is work being done when they are squeezing on the grip?

DEVELOPMENT

1 Teaching Tips—Demonstrate when work is being done and when it is not. Have a student push a chair across the room. Ask the students if work is being done. *Yes, because a force is being applied to an object, and it moves.* Have the same student push against the wall. In this case, no work is being done because the wall is not moving.

2 Skill Development—Students will *observe* whether or not a force on an object makes it move, thereby causing work to be done.

3 Skill Development—Students will *compare and contrast* the photographs illustrating work being done and not being done. To reinforce this skill, demonstrate each situation by using your students.

4 Text Questions—Is he doing work? *His arm is still for a moment before he starts the forward motion, so at this instant, he is not doing work. He will be doing work when he actually throws the ball.*

EXTENSIONS

Enrichment

Research

Most sports involve the application of force to move something. Athletes, therefore, do work. Students can research the names and records of the following people and explain what work they do.

1. Strongest man
2. Strongest woman
3. Person who has hit the longest home run
4. Person who has thrown a football the farthest
5. Person who has jumped the highest from a standing position
6. Person who has jumped the longest distance from a standing position

In the third picture, the boy is reading a book. He probably is studying hard, but a scientist would say that the boy is not doing any work.
5 Why would the scientist say this?

Scientists can measure the amount of work being done. To do this, they must know how
6 much force is being used. A *spring scale*, like the one shown here, is used to measure force. If you pull on the scale, the spring will stretch. The harder you pull, the more the spring will stretch.

A spring scale can also be used to measure weight. When we measure weight, we are really measuring a force. Each object that we weigh pulls with a certain force on the spring. A heavy object pulls with more force than a light object. So a heavy object will stretch the spring more than a light object. A 1-kilogram (2-pound) book would stretch the spring twice as far as a 0.5-kilogram (1-pound) book.

5 Text Questions—Why would the scientist say this? *The boy is not doing any work because the book is not moving. He's just holding it.*
6 Teaching Tips—It would be helpful throughout the unit to have a coiled-spring balance similar to the one shown in the student's text. Use it to measure the force of different pulls. Pull some books across the table. Point out that the amount of stretch in the coiled spring is related to the force exerted.

Exceptional Student

Learning Disabled

Have the student cut out ten pictures from a magazine. Five should illustrate work being done, and five should illustrate no work being done.

ACTIVITY

How can force be measured?

A. Gather these materials: 30-cm (12 in.) ruler, 15-cm (6 in.) string, medium-sized rubber band, 4 paper clips, index card, scissors, 5 books, and box of chalk.

B. Make a scale to measure force using the ruler, paper clips, and a rubber band. Tape a piece of the index card on the ruler. Mark off the card in cm.

C. Pile 5 books on your desk. Tie string around a box of chalk. Attach the box of chalk to the force scale. Lift the box straight up to the top of the book pile.

1. What was the force needed to lift the box?
2. What was the distance the box moved off the table?

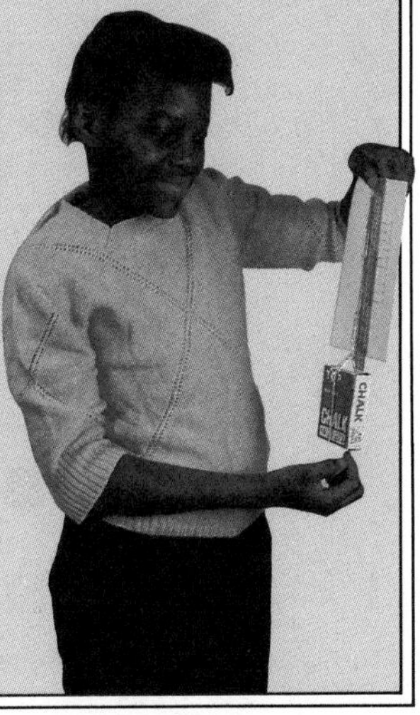

Section Review

Main Ideas: Work is done when a force is used to move an object. Scientists define a force as a push or pull on something. A spring scale can be used to measure force.

Questions: Answer in complete sentences.

1. What is meant by a force?
2. What two things are needed to do work?
3. How do scientists measure force?
4. Find pictures in this chapter that show people doing work.

EXTENSIONS

Application
Activity

Students do not have step-by-step instructions in their texts for making the force measurer. Follow these directions:

A. Hang a rubber band on a paper clip. Wedge the paper clip on the end of the metric ruler. Bend another paper clip slightly open. Hang it on the free end of the rubber band.

B. Tie about 15 cm of string to the paper clip hanging from the rubber band. Wedge another paper clip on the free end of the ruler. Slide the string through the clip. This simply keeps the string aligned. Tie the free end of the string to another paper clip. You can hook objects to the paper clip.

C. Cut a narrow strip of the index card 10 cm long, and mark off 1-cm marks. Mount the card on the ruler. The zero reading of the card should be aligned with the pointer of the paper clip when the rubber band is hanging freely. If you pull slightly on the string, the pointer will move.

ACTIVITY

Skill Development—*Measuring*

Teaching Tips—See the Extension on this page for directions for making the force measurer for the Activity.

Answers to Questions—1. Answers will vary with the weight of the box. **2.** The box moved a distance equal to the height of the books.

SECTION REVIEW

Answers to Questions
1. A force is a push or a pull on something.
2. Force and motion.
3. With a spring scale.
4. See photos on pages 178, 179, 180, 181, 182, 189.

SECTION BACKGROUND

Machines are used to make work easier. A machine reduces the amount of force required to do work at the expense of increased distance. Machines do not save work. The same amount of work is done, but it is easier to do.

The reduction of force provided by a machine is called its mechanical advantage. For example, if it takes 50 lbs of force to lift a box 1 m but only 25 lbs to pull it along an inclined plane, the mechanical advantage of the inclined plane is 2. Another way to find the mechanical advantage of an inclined plane is by dividing the length of the incline by its height.

MATERIALS

force measurer (from Activity in Section 1); board, 1 m long; toy car or truck; 3 books

11-2. Machines

Have you ever driven on a steep mountain road? When a road is built over a mountain, it is not straight. As shown in the picture, the road curves from side to side. This curving makes the road longer. But it also makes it easier for cars to get over the mountain. Why? When you finish this section, you should be able to:

☐ **A.** Explain how a *machine* makes work easier.

☐ **B.** Explain how an *inclined plane* is used to do work.

Each day we do work of many kinds. We carry out the trash. We turn on the faucet in the
1 kitchen sink. Can you name some other examples of work? The pictures that follow show work
2 being done. What do you think makes the work easier in each case?

BASIC TEACHING PLAN

MOTIVATION

Have available several simple machines—scissors, can opener, doorknob, crowbar, hammer, screw, and wedge. Ask students how work is made easier by each of these machines. Discuss how the same work would be done without these machines and how much more force it would take.

Text Questions—But it also makes it easier for cars to go over the mountain. Why? *The steepness of the road is much reduced when the road winds around the mountain or curves from side to side.*

DEVELOPMENT

1 **Text Questions**—Can you name some other examples of work? *Have students think of examples of work from their own experience, e.g., riding a bicycle, throwing a ball, lifting and carrying objects.*

Anything that people use to make work easier is called a **machine**. Perhaps when you hear the word *machine*, you think of a crane or a car engine. Do you also know that many of the things you use every day are simple machines? The bottle opener in the picture above is a simple machine. When you use a tilted board to move a
3 box, you are using a simple machine. How many kinds of simple machines are there? How do machines make work easier? Let's find out!

Machine: Anything that makes work easier.

The person loading the car is using a simple
4 machine called an **inclined plane** (inn-**klind plane**). An *inclined plane* is a slanted surface. It is often called a ramp, a slope, or a hill.

Inclined plane: A slanted surface, which is sometimes called a ramp.

Inclined planes make doing work easier. The inclined plane shown above makes the work of lifting the barrel easier. You have to push the barrel farther, but you don't need as much force.

EXTENSIONS

Reinforcement

Science Skills—Measuring

Set up several inclined planes of various heights. Use the force-measurer to determine the force needed to pull an object (such as a brick or a book) up the different inclined planes.

Some students may want to determine the mechanical advantage of each inclined plane. Lift the brick straight up with the force measurer. This is the object's resistance to movement. Divide the resistance by the effort required to move the brick up the inclined plane to find the mechanical advantage.

2 Text Questions—What do you think makes the work easier in each case? *In the first photo, the clippers; in the second photo, the ramp; and in the third photo, the bottle opener.*
3 Text Questions—How many kinds of simple machines are there? *There are six—inclined plane, wedge, screw, lever, wheel and axle, and pulley.* How do machines make work easier? *They reduce the amount of force needed at the expense of increased distance.*
4 Teaching Tips—Bring in a long board to use as an inclined plane. Demonstrate how much easier it is to lift objects with it. Fill a large box with books. Make it heavy enough so that it is difficult for any of your students to lift. Ask for a volunteer to lift the box to the table. Show students the proper way to lift heavy objects to avoid hurting their backs. When lifting, they should bend their knees and use their thigh muscles rather than their back muscles. After a few students have tried to lift the box, ask the same students to push the box up the inclined plane. Ask them if this made the task easier.

EXTENSIONS

Enrichment
Science Skills—Predicting

Students can predict the force needed to move an object along an inclined plane by first measuring the mechanical advantage of the plane.

A. Have the students set up an inclined plane, then measure its length and height. To calculate the mechanical advantage of the inclined plane, divide length by height.

B. Using a brick or other standard mass and a force measurer, the students can find the resistance force by lifting the brick straight up for the height of the plane.

C. After finding the mechanical advantage and the resistance force, have the students predict the force needed to pull the brick up the incline. Divide the resistance by the mechanical advantage.

D. Have the students pull the brick up the incline and compare the force needed with their predictions.

If you have to use a lot of force, you get tired. A machine, like the inclined plane, helps you use less force to do work. Even though it might take a little longer to do the work, you won't be as tired. Pushing an object up a ramp is easier than lifting it straight up. Inclined planes are all around you. Ramps are used to make it easier for people in wheelchairs to enter buildings. The mountain road shown on page 178 is also a type of inclined plane.

The angle of an inclined plane affects the force
5 needed to move an object. Look at the two ramps shown below. A spring scale is shown attached to each brick. Notice that less force is being used to move the brick on the left. The
6 angle or slant of this inclined plane is less. Since the inclined plane is not as steep, it takes less force to move the brick.

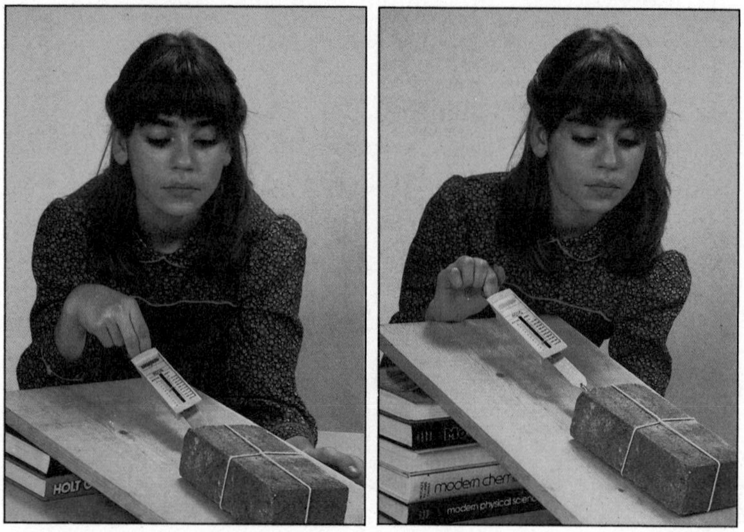

5 **Skill Development**—Students can *compare and contrast* the force needed to move an object up inclined planes at different angles.
6 **Teaching Tips**—Set up two inclined planes at different angles. Make sure both inclines are the same height. They will be different lengths. Have students move heavy objects up the two inclines and compare the efforts needed.

ACTIVITY

How does an inclined plane help you move an object?

A. Gather these materials: a spring scale, 1 board, toy car or truck, and 3 books.

B. Copy the chart shown. Use it to record your results.

C. Make an inclined plane by placing the board on 1 book.

D. Use the spring scale to pull the toy car up the inclined plane. Record the force needed to move the car.

E. Change the angle of the inclined plane by adding the second book. Repeat step D.

F. Make the angle of the inclined plane steeper by adding the third book. Repeat step D.

1. How does the angle of an inclined plane affect the force needed to move an object?

Number of Books	Force
1	
2	
3	

When work is done, the object is moved through a distance. Look at the truck on page 182. There are two ways for the driver to get the barrel into the truck. The driver can lift the barrel straight up. In this case, the distance is 1

EXTENSIONS

Application
Research

Have your students explore careers that involve some aspect of machine design, repair, or usage. They can research the following occupations:

1. mechanical engineer
2. machinist
3. mechanic
4. heavy-equipment operator

Enrichment
Research—Library

Some students may wish to do some research to find out how inclined planes were used to build the great pyramids of Egypt. Your students should be able to find drawings of workers pulling immense stone blocks up inclines.

ACTIVITY

Skill Development—*Measuring and Recording Data*

Teaching Tips—Make sure the toys you use are heavy enough to get a reading on the force measurer. If not, get heavier ones or add a weight, such as a brick, to the toys. Make sure the force measurers are in good working order.

Answers to Questions—1. The steeper the angle of an inclined plane, the greater the force needed to move an object up it.

EXTENSIONS

Enrichment

Science Skills—Comparing and Contrasting

The students can compare and contrast the force needed to move an object along inclined planes with different surfaces.

A. Have the students set up inclined planes with the same height and slant but with different surfaces, such as waxed paper, sandpaper, or polished and unpolished boards.

B. Move the same object up each incline and measure the force needed. Compare the values obtained for the different surfaces.

1. Which surface needed the least force?
2. Which surface needed the most force?
3. Which inclined plane has the greatest mechanical advantage?

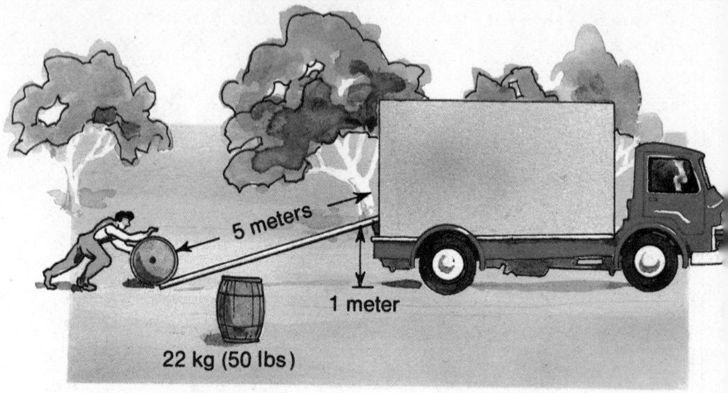

7 meter (3 feet). But to do this, he must use a lot of force. The other way to get the barrel into the truck is to use the ramp. The ramp is 5 meters long (about 15 feet). The driver moves the barrel a longer distance but uses less force.

Section Review

Main Ideas: Machines make work easier. They do not change the amount of work done. Inclined planes are simple machines that make work easier.

Questions: Answer in complete sentences.

1. How does a machine affect the work done?
2. What difference would it make if you walked up a flight of stairs instead of a ramp?
3. How could an inclined plane make moving a chair into a truck easier?
4. Suppose you have to walk up a very steep hill. What path would you take to make it easier going up the hill?

7 Teaching Tips—Ask: Is the barrel moved farther when it is lifted straight up or when it is moved up the ramp? *When it is moved up the ramp.* Which requires more force—lifting it or moving it up the ramp? *Lifting it.* Which requires more work—lifting it or moving it up the ramp? *They require the same amount of work. Lifting it requires more force, and moving it up the ramp requires more distance. Work = Force × Distance.*

SECTION REVIEW

Answers to Questions

1. A machine does not affect or change the amount of work done. It makes it easier to do.
2. More force is needed to climb steps, but the distance will be shorter.
3. Pushing the chair up an inclined plane into a truck would require using less force than lifting the chair straight up.
4. A path that curved from side to side would make the walk easier than one that went straight up.

11-3. Hidden Inclined Planes

Look at the picture of the winding staircase. There are over a hundred steps in this staircase. If you had a ladder the same height as the winding staircase, which would you rather climb: the staircase or the ladder? Why? When you finish this section, you should be able to:

☐ **A.** Explain why a *screw* and a *wedge* are kinds of inclined planes.

☐ **B.** Identify objects that are kinds of *screws* and *wedges*.

SECTION BACKGROUND

A screw is an inclined plane that winds around and around in a spiral. The edge or ridge of the screw is called the thread. The thread moves through the wood as the screw is turned. Screws decrease the force you use, but increase the distance.

Wedges are two inclined planes joined together to form a sharp edge. Knives and axes are wedges. A wedge concentrates applied forces on one point. This gives the effect of a gain in force, so your work is made easier.

MATERIALS

2 screws of different pitch, 2 sheets of paper cut into triangles of different height, 2 pencils, tape, screwdriver, crayon, wood block

BASIC TEACHING PLAN

MOTIVATION

Give groups of students three or four screws, and ask them to tell how they are different and how they are similar. Have them carefully follow the path of the plane around the screw. The pitch of screws will vary. A lower-pitch (angle) screw will have more turns, while a higher-pitch screw will have fewer turns. Lower-pitch screws have a higher mechanical advantage. It is easier to turn the screw, but you have to make more turns to get it in.

Text Questions—If you had a ladder the same height as the winding staircase, which would you rather climb: the staircase or the ladder? *The staircase.* Why? *Because, although you would have to cover a longer distance on the staircase, you would use less force.*

EXTENSIONS

Enrichment

Research

Make a list of objects that are screws or inclined planes: animal claws, rake, plow, teeth, bird beaks, can opener, fork, hoe, etc. Ask the students to look through magazines to find pictures of objects that are screws, inclined planes, or wedges. Have them mount the pictures on paper and then answer these three questions:

1. How are the machines similar?
2. How are the machines different?
3. How do the machines make work easier?

Many of the things in your home are held together with inclined planes. Also, many of the tools that we use to make and build things are hidden inclined planes.

The stairway in the picture on page 183 is a simple machine. It is a curved inclined plane. Do you recall how inclined planes make work easier? Instead of lifting an object up, the inclined plane allows you to move it along a slope. It is much easier to walk up a curved stairway than to climb straight up a ladder. You walk farther, but you use much less force.

Screw: An inclined plane that winds around in a spiral.

A winding stairway is a type of simple machine. It is called a **screw**. A *screw* is an inclined plane that winds around in a spiral. As a screw is pushed and turned into a board, its inclined plane moves through the wood.

Imagine being small enough to walk up a screw's winding edge. Wouldn't that be like walking up a winding stairway or a winding mountain road? What other types of screws can you think of? You cannot lift a car using only your arms. But a jackscrew can lift a car easily. As you turn the handle, the screw lifts the car.

DEVELOPMENT

1 Skill Development—*Compare and contrast* straight inclined planes with curved inclined planes. Help the students recall what they learned about inclined planes in the last section.

2 Teaching Tips—You might have the students actually imagine themselves small enough to walk along the inclined plane of a screw. They should relax and imagine the slope of a screw. Then have them imagine being very tiny and walking up the screw. Ask: What kind of screw is easiest to walk up? The students should share their experiences with the class.

3 Text Questions—What other types of screws can you think of? *Hand or power drill, screw propeller, pencil sharpener.*

4 Another kind of inclined plane that is a simple machine is the **wedge** (**wej**). A *wedge* is two inclined planes joined to form a sharp edge. Wedges are used to cut or break things apart. Knives and axes are wedges.

Look at the picture below. Imagine hitting the flat side of the wedge. Follow the path of the arrows. You see that your force becomes focused at the sharp edge of the wedge. Wedges focus forces to their sharp edges the way lenses focus light to one point. This makes it easier to force the wood apart. When you hit the wedge with a hammer, the hammer acts as a lever.

A nail is a pointed wedge that forces wood apart. Forks and needles are also wedges. When a wedge, such as an ax, is used, the wood moves along the wedge. A thinner ax will go into wood easier. It is like a shallow inclined plane. You do not use as much force to move objects along it.

Wedge: Two inclined planes joined together to form a sharp edge.

EXTENSIONS

Enrichment

Activity

Have students identify the inclined planes hidden in different tools.

A. Gather these tools: a small hand rake, a chisel, a pocket knife, and a scissors.

B. Ask the students to make a drawing of each tool.

C. Have them label each inclined plane that they can observe in each tool.

1. How does the inclined plane make work easier?
2. What are some other tools that use inclined planes?

4 Teaching Tips—Do a demonstration of how a wedge works. Obtain a chisel, a hammer, and a cut log. Hammer the chisel into the end of the log. Now hit the chisel until the log splits. Ask the students why using a chisel makes splitting a log easier than just using a hammer. Ask them what would happen if you used a chisel that was thicker.

Exceptional Student

Visually Impaired

Bring in examples of various types of screws and wedges. This will help the student to understand straight and spiral inclined planes.

EXTENSIONS

Enrichment

Research—Library

Students can go to the library to do research on Archimedes's water screw. This screw does not hold things together. It is used to draw water from one level to another. Students should find out how the pitch and turning direction of the water screw affect how much and how fast water is carried by it.

ACTIVITY

How is a screw like an inclined plane?

A. Gather these materials: 2 screws, 2 sheets of paper cut into triangles, crayon, 2 pencils, tape, screwdriver, and a wood block.

B. Look at the two screws.

1. Which one will be easier to screw into the wood?

C. With the screwdriver, turn each screw into the wood.

2. Which one was easier to screw in?

D. With the crayon, make a line along the slanted edge of each triangle. Note that both look like inclined planes.

E. Wrap each triangle around a pencil. Fasten each with tape. Count the number of turns on each pencil.

3. Which one has more turns or threads?
4. Which inclined plane had a smaller angle?
5. How is a screw like an inclined plane?

186

ACTIVITY

Skill Development—*Comparing and Contrasting*

Teaching Tips—Do this Activity in two parts. Let the students experiment with different screws to discover that the pitch of the screw will affect the ease with which the screw goes into the wood. Students can find the pitch of the screws by counting the number of turns on them. Then they can compare the effort needed to screw them into the wood by counting the number of turns it takes to do it. Go to a hardware store and pick out the screws. You should have two screws of the same length and thickness but of different pitch for the Activity.

Cut the two triangles in advance. One should have a steeper angle than the other.

Answers to Questions—**1.** The one with the lower pitch. **2.** The one with the lower pitch (has more turns). **3.** The one with the narrower slope. **4.** The one with more turns. **5.** A screw is an inclined plane that winds around in a spiral instead of being a straight surface.

Section Review

Main Ideas: The screw and the wedge are both simple machines. Both are inclined planes.

Questions: Answer in complete sentences.

1. How is a screw like an inclined plane?
2. Identify each of the following as either a screw or a wedge: (a) nail; (b) fork; (c) ax; (d) needle; and (e) winding staircase.
3. Which of the wedges shown in the diagram would be easier to drive into a block of wood? Explain.

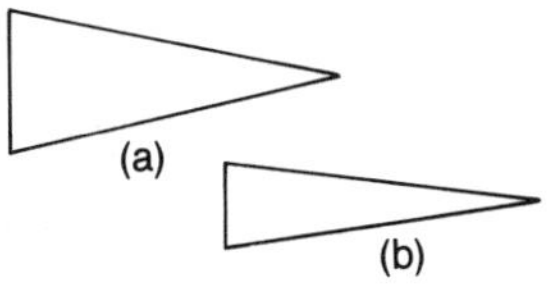

People in Science

Seol Man Taik

Seol Man Taik is a Korean inventor. He has made a new kind of bicycle. It is called the lever bike. Bicycle pedals usually move in circles. But the pedals on the lever bike move up and down. This means that the rider's legs move less. The rider uses less force to pedal. The force of the rider's feet on the pedals is carried to the rear wheel by levers. The rider can change speeds on hills by changing the length of the levers. Most bicycles have 10 speeds. The lever bike has 29 speeds!

The earliest bicycle was built in about 1816 in Germany. In 1886, a modern bicycle was built in England. Bicycles have not changed much from that time up until the invention of the lever bike.

EXTENSIONS

Enrichment

Science Skills—
Comparing and Contrasting

We use two different kinds of modified inclined planes to hold things together—screws and nails. Students can compare how both of these work. They will need a screw and a nail of the same length and thickness, a hammer, a screwdriver, and four blocks of wood.

A. Have the students join two blocks of wood together with the nail and another two blocks with the screw. Note how much effort is needed to do this.

B. Using the claw end of the hammer, pry the blocks of wood apart and compare which are harder to pull apart.

1. Which was easier to drive into the blocks of wood?
2. Which held them together better?
3. When would you use a nail? A screw?

SECTION REVIEW

Answers to Questions

1. A screw has an inclined plane wrapped around it.
2. a. Wedge, b. wedge, c. wedge, d. wedge, e. screw
3. b. It has a narrower slope.

SECTION BACKGROUND

A lever is a bar that rests on a turning point called the fulcrum. The object that the lever lifts is called the load. There are three parts to a lever: fulcrum (the turning point), effort arm (the part on which the force is exerted), and resistance arm (the part that bears the load to be raised).

Levers are grouped into three classes, based on how the three parts are arranged and where the weight is. Crowbars, seesaws, and can openers are examples of first-class levers. The resistance arm moves in the opposite direction to the effort arm. The fulcrum is between the weight and the effort arm. A wheelbarrow is an example of a second-class lever. The weight is between the fulcrum and the effort arm. The human arm is a third-class lever. The effort arm is between the weight and the fulcrum. The elbow is the fulcrum, your biceps provides the effort, and your fist represents the load.

MATERIALS

box of paper clips, flat-sided pencil, 2 small paper cups, small box, tape, wooden ruler (30 cm)

11-4. The Lever

The board in the picture is resting on a small log. The smaller person wants to lift the larger person off the ground. She can stand either on the spot marked *x* or the spot marked *y*. Where do you think she should stand? Why? When you finish this section, you should be able to:

- ☐ **A.** Identify objects that are *levers.*
- ☐ **B.** Explain what a *lever* is and how it can make work easier.
- ☐ **C.** Show where to put the *fulcrum* when you want to move a heavy load.

Can you guess where the girl in the picture should stand? She should stand on the spot marked *y*. How will this make it easy for her to lift the other person off the ground? **1**

BASIC TEACHING PLAN

MOTIVATION

Tell your students to think about playing on a seesaw to help them predict what should happen in the motivational picture. If there is a playground nearby, use a seesaw to demonstrate the principles of a lever. If it is not possible to go outside, bring in a long board and a fireplace log. Use the log as the fulcrum. Stand on one end of the board, and ask a student in the class to stand on the other end of the board so that you are lifted.

DEVELOPMENT

1 Text Questions—How will this make it easy for her to lift the other person off the ground? *To overcome the resistance (weight of the large person), the small person must increase the distance from the fulcrum.*

2

A simple machine with a bar resting on a turning point is called a **lever** (**lee**-ver). The bar may be a stick, a rod, or a board. A seesaw is a *lever*. The turning point of a lever is called the **fulcrum**
3 (**ful**-crum). Can you find the *fulcrum* on the seesaw? Let's find out how levers make work easier.

Lever: A bar resting on a turning point.

Fulcrum: The turning point of a lever.

The girls in the picture above are using a lever to move a heavy rock. The tree branch is the bar. The spot where the branch rests against the box is the fulcrum. The girls push down on one end of the branch. The other end moves up and
4 lifts the rock. Suppose the girls tried to move the rock without the lever. They would need a great deal of force to move the rock. They might not be able to move the rock at all. What happened when they used the lever? They pushed the lever down a great distance but used very little force. Like inclined planes, levers allow you to use less force to move things.

5 You can lift heavy loads with a lever. To do so, you need to know where to put the fulcrum. The
6 diagram shows three levers. With which lever could you lift the heaviest load?

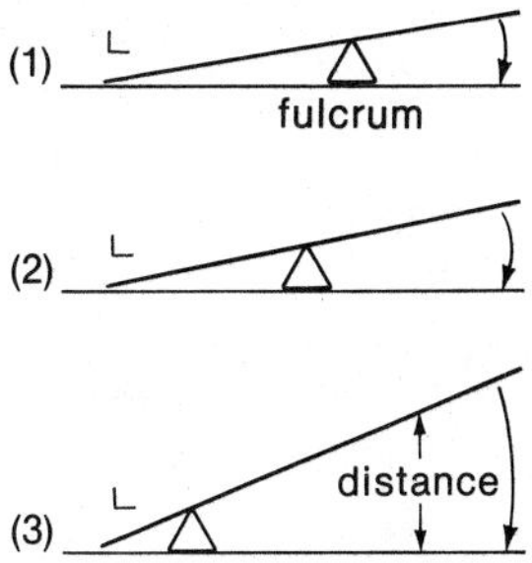

EXTENSIONS

Enrichment

Research—Library

Some students may wish to explore levers in greater depth. Have them research and find examples of first-, second-, and third-class levers. They can report their findings in a chart, including the type of lever, a diagram of it, and examples. They should discover the following: On first-class levers, the fulcrum is located between the applied force and the load. On second-class levers, the load is between the applied force and the fulcrum. On third-class levers, the applied force is between the load and the fulcrum. Pliers and scissors are first-class levers. Nutcrackers and bottle openers are second-class levers. Brooms, fishing poles, and shovels are third-class levers.

2 **Teaching Tips**—Set up a first-class lever, as shown in the photo. A broomstick handle, a box, and an object for a load are all that is needed. Ask the students how this setup is like a seesaw. *They are both first-class levers.*

3 **Text Questions**—Can you find the fulcrum on the seesaw? *It is located between the effort force and the load.*

4 **Skill Development**—Students will *compare and contrast* the force needed to move an object with and without a lever.

5 **Skill Development**—Students will *observe* the levers and *predict* which will lift the heaviest load.

6 **Text Questions**—With which lever could you lift the heaviest load? *With lever no. 3.*

EXTENSIONS

Application
Activity

Challenge students to design a way to increase the mechanical advantage of a lever. You will need a lever-type can opener; a clean, empty tin can; two 30-cm rulers; and masking tape.

Give the can opener to the students and ask them to experiment to find a way to use the can opener so that it is easier to open the can. Give them the additional materials. Students who can solve the problem will realize that they must increase the length of the lever. Taping the rulers to the can opener will increase its length, thus increasing the mechanical advantage of the can opener.

ACTIVITY

How is the force of a lever related to the location of the fulcrum?

A. Gather these materials: box of paper clips, flat-sided pencil, 2 small paper cups, small box, tape, and wooden ruler (30 cm).

B. Label 1 cup L for load. Label the other cup F for force.

C. Tape a cup to each end of the ruler. Place a pencil on top of a small box.

D. Put 10 paper clips into cup L. Place cup L 8 cm from the fulcrum. Put enough paper clips into cup F to balance the load. Record your results in a chart like the one shown here.

1. How many paper clips did it take to balance the load?

E. Remove the paper clips from cup F. Repeat step D with the fulcrum at 12, at 15, and at 18 cm.

2. Did you use more or less paper clips as the fulcrum got farther from the load?
3. How does the location of the fulcrum affect the load a lever can lift?

Fulcrum at	Force*
8 cm	
12 cm	
15 cm	
18 cm	

*(Number of paper clips)

ACTIVITY

Skill Development—*Observing, Finding Cause and Effect*

Teaching Tips—The students will have to work carefully on this Activity. It will take a steady hand and patience to balance the cups. Tape the cups to the rulers. If the rulers are wood, push a thumbtack through the cup into the ruler. In step D, make sure the students place the pencil 8 cm from the edge of the cup. For example, if the cup is 5 cm in diameter, then place the pencil at the 13-cm mark.

Answers to Questions—1. It should only take around one or two clips to balance ten clips. **2.** More. **3.** The closer the fulcrum is to the load, the less the force needed to lift it.

A hammer can also be used as a lever. You can use a hammer to pull a nail out of a wall. The fulcrum is at the head of the hammer. The whole handle length is the lever. You can grasp the hammer at any spot along the handle. Where would you grasp it to make pulling the nail out easiest?

Remember that the closer the fulcrum is to the load, the less force you have to use.

Section Review

Main Ideas: Levers decrease the force needed to move things. The closer the fulcrum is to the load, the less force you need to move the load.

Questions: Answer in complete sentences.

1. Which of the levers shown will make lifting a load easier?
2. Make a diagram showing the fulcrum, lever, load, and force. Label each part.
3. The drawing shows two can openers. Which one would make it easier to open a can?
4. Where is the fulcrum on the can opener?

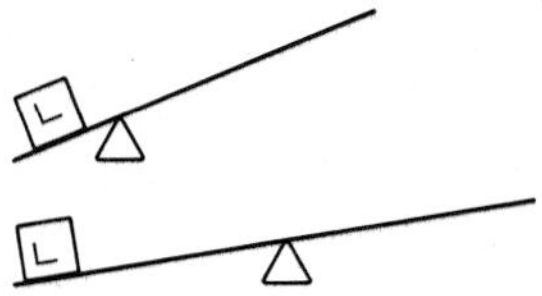

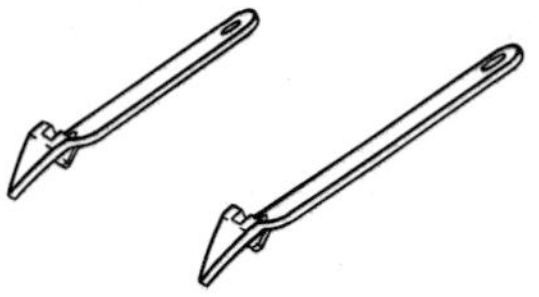

EXTENSIONS

Enrichment

Activity

How does the position of the fulcrum change the force needed to lift an object?

A. Gather these materials: a yardstick, a book, a force measurer, and a mass such as a lump of clay.

B. Attach the mass to one end of the yardstick. At the other end of the yardstick attach the force measurer so that it can measure downward force.

C. Set a book on the table so that the covers form a triangle with the table and the binding can be used as a fulcrum.

D. Place the fulcrum halfway between the mass and the force. Note the distance between the fulcrum and the mass. Measure the force needed to lift the mass.

E. Move the fulcrum toward the mass and again measure the force needed to lift the mass. Then move the fulcrum in the other direction and measure the force. Each time, measure the distance between the fulcrum and the mass.

F. Graph force against distance of fulcrum from mass.

7 Teaching Tips—Obtain a hammer, board, and nails. Hammer several nails into the board. Ask the students how they would grasp the hammer to make it easier to pull the nails out. Let the students test their predictions. Grasping the hammer on the end increases the mechanical advantage of the hammer to its maximum and should make pulling the nail out easier.

8 Text Questions—Where would you grasp it to make pulling the nail out easiest? *At the end.*

SECTION REVIEW

Answers to Questions

1. The first lever
2. Students could illustrate any of the examples given in the text. You can refer to the diagram on page 189.
3. The longer opener
4. At the edge of the can

EXTENSIONS

Enrichment

Activity

Students can compare the work done by the three classes of levers.

A. Gather a ruler, a pencil, clay, and a force measurer.

B. Assemble a first-class lever by placing the clay (the load) at one end of the ruler and the pencil as a fulcrum in the middle. Apply a downward force at the other end of the ruler. Use the force measurer to determine the amount of force needed. Notice how far the clay was moved.

C. Assemble a second-class lever by placing the clay in the middle of the ruler and lifting one end. The end that remains on the table is the fulcrum. Measure the force and distance.

D. Assemble a third-class lever by placing the clay load at one end of the ruler and lifting from the center. The other end of the ruler is the fulcrum. Measure the force and distance.

1. Which lever required the most force?
2. Which moved the load the farthest?
3. Which did the most work?

CHAPTER REVIEW

Science Words: Match the terms in column A with the definitions in column B.

Column A	Column B
1. Screw	a. The turning point of a lever
2. Lever	b. Two inclined planes
3. Force	c. A winding inclined plane
4. Fulcrum	d. A push or a pull
5. Machine	e. Makes work easier
6. Wedge	f. A bar resting on a point
7. Inclined plane	g. A slanted surface

Questions: Answer in complete sentences.

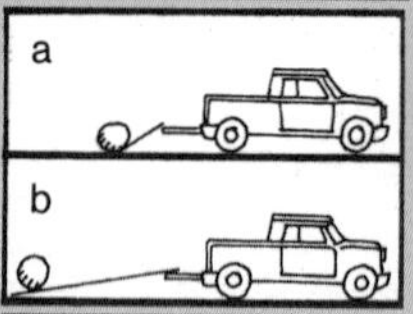

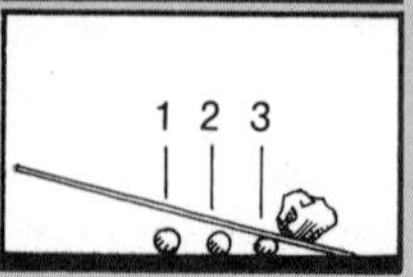

1. What is work?
2. In which of the following examples is work *not* being done: (a) pushing on a wall that does not move; (b) lifting a box off the floor; (c) watching television; and (d) throwing a basketball?
3. How can force be measured?
4. How does a machine help us do work?
5. The picture shows the path cows take over a steep hill. Why do the cows choose a longer, zig-zag path?
6. On which inclined plane will it be easier to push a barrel up to a truck? Explain.
7. How are screws and wedges alike?
8. How is a screw like a winding staircase?
9. At which spot would you put a fulcrum to make lifting the rock easiest? Why?
10. What are two examples of levers that you might use at home?

CHAPTER REVIEW

Science Words

1. c, **2.** f, **3.** d, **4.** a, **5.** e, **6.** b, **7.** g

Answers to Questions

1. Work is done when a force is used to move an object.
2. a, c
3. With a force measurer, such as a spring scale
4. It makes work easier. It requires less force.
5. They are walking on inclined planes at low angles. It is easier to walk up a slope that is not steep.
6. b. The angle is less steep.
7. They are both made from inclined planes.
8. They are both turning inclined planes.
9. At 3. It increases the length of the lever the most.
10. Scissors, hoe, rake, fishing pole, can opener

SUGGESTED WORKSHEET MASTERS
pp. T-171 k, l, m

SUGGESTED TEST MASTERS
pp. T-171 d, e

CHAPTER 12

MACHINES WITH WHEELS

Machines with wheels can help you do many jobs. One kind of machine is made of wheels and ropes. This machine helps people lift heavy loads. Do you know what this machine is? When you finish this section, you should be able to:

12-1. Pulleys

CHAPTER OBJECTIVES

1. Define a pulley and explain how it makes work easier.
2. Give examples of machines using fixed and movable pulleys.
3. Explain how a wheel and axle make work easier, and give examples of machines that use them.
4. Explain how gears work, and give examples of machines that use them.
5. Identify the simple machines in a compound machine.

SECTION BACKGROUND

A pulley is a wheel with a rope moving around it. There are two types of pulleys—a fixed pulley and a movable pulley. The fixed pulley is fastened to one spot. It makes work easier by changing the direction of force. You pull down to lift up. Fixed pulleys are used on flagpoles and window shades. The movable pulley is attached to and moves with the load. It makes work easier by reducing the amount of force you need to lift something. A block and tackle is a single pulley and a movable pulley used together. This changes direction and increases force at the same time.

MATERIALS

small pulley, meter stick, string, pail, sand, spring scale

BASIC TEACHING PLAN

MOTIVATION

Ask your students if they have ever used a pulley. Most students probably have, although they may not be aware of it. Your classroom shades may have pulley systems. If so, demonstrate how they work. By pulling down on the shade cord, the shade can be pulled up. Ask students why this is an advantage. Is it easier to pull down than to pull up? Pulleys are also commonly used on clotheslines, sailboats, cranes, and flagpoles.

Exceptional Student
IEP Chapter Goal

At the end of this chapter, the student will give one example of how each of the following helps us to do work: pulleys, gears, wheels and axles.

EXTENSIONS

Enrichment

Activity

Have your students assemble a homemade pulley system that can be used for display purposes. They can use empty thread spools, nails, and a board.

A single pulley can be made by placing a nail through a spool and then hammering the nail and spool to a board. The spool will spin freely when a string is passed over it. A number of such pulleys can be placed on the board and connected by string to make an interesting pulley system. A load attached to one end of the string can be moved by pulling on the other end.

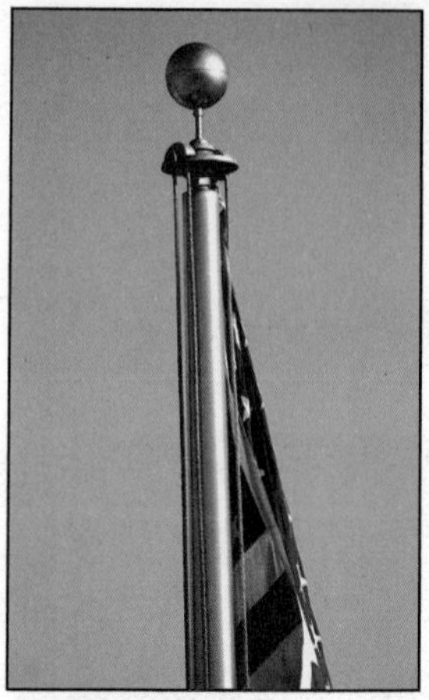

- ☐ **A.** Explain what a *pulley* is and give some examples.
- ☐ **B.** Explain why a *fixed pulley* makes work easier.
- ☐ **C.** Explain why a *movable pulley* makes work easier.

Pulley: A simple machine that is a wheel with a rope moving around it.

Fixed pulley: A pulley that stays in place as the load moves.

Movable pulley: A pulley that moves with the load.

A **pulley** is a simple machine that is a wheel 1
with a rope moving around it. The rounded edge of the wheel usually has a groove in it. The groove keeps the rope from slipping off the *pulley*. The picture above shows a pulley being used to raise a flag. The person raising the flag is pulling down on the rope. The rope moves around the wheel and pulls the flag up. This pulley stays in place as the load moves because the wheel is fastened to one spot. A pulley that does not move is called a **fixed pulley**.

A *fixed pulley* changes the direction of the force used. You pull down and the load is pulled up. The amount of force used to lift the load is the same needed to lift it straight up. The work is easier because, as with the lever, pushing or pulling down is often easier than pulling something up.

The pulley shown in the margin is not fastened to one spot. It is attached to the load. It moves with the load. As the load is lifted, the pulley is also lifted. A pulley that moves is called
a **movable pulley**. When you use a *movable pul-* 2
ley, you pull up to lift the load. But your work is easier. You use less force to do the lifting.

DEVELOPMENT

1 Teaching Tips—You can purchase inexpensive pulleys from a hardware store. Sash cord is recommended for use with the pulleys. Set up a fixed-pulley system. Have the students make a diagram of it. Lift an object using the fixed pulley. Ask how this is similar to the pulley on a flagpole.

2 Teaching Tips—Set up a movable-pulley system and have the students make a diagram of it. Lift an object with the movable pulley.

Often, a fixed pulley and a movable pulley are used together. This makes the force needed to lift a load even less. The ropes between the pulleys share the force. You can pull on one rope with less force, but for a longer distance. The crane in the picture below uses fixed and movable pulleys.

Eight ropes are moving between the pulleys. They share the load among them. Each rope lifts only one eighth of the load. The crane must then pull 8 meters (26 feet) of rope to lift the load 1 meter (3 feet). Suppose the crane lifts the load 15 meters (50 feet). How much rope would it have to pull?

EXTENSIONS

Enrichment

Science Skills—
Comparing and Contrasting

A. Gather these materials: a pulley, a cord, a pail, sand, and a metric ruler.

B. Set up a fixed-pulley system. Lift the pail at least 1 m. Measure the length of the cord used to pull the pail up.

C. Set up a movable-pulley system. Lift the pail the same distance off the table as you did with the fixed system. Measure the distance. Measure the amount of cord you pulled while lifting the pail.

1. Which pulley system used more cord?
2. Which pulley system made it easier to lift the pail?
3. Do you think there is a relationship between the amount of cord used and the ease of lifting?

3 **Teaching Tips**—Draw both pulley systems on the chalkboard. Tell the students that these two systems are often used together. Have two pulleys and cord on a table. Ask the students to suggest how they could be fastened together to make a block and tackle. (See the picture on the right on page 197 for the setup.)
4 **Skill Development**—Students will *compare and contrast* the advantages and uses of the fixed- and movable-pulley systems.
5 **Text Question**—How much rope would it have to pull? *120 m (396 ft).*

Exceptional Student

Orthopedically Disabled

Students who have received physical therapy may wish to explain how pulleys can be used to exercise muscles.

EXTENSIONS

Enrichment
Activity

This is an Extension of the Activity. Students can set up both fixed and movable pulleys and determine the effort needed to raise a load.

A. Gather these materials: 2 pulleys, a cord, a force measurer, a pail, and sand.

B. Set up a fixed pulley. Half-fill the pail with sand. Lift the pail using the single fixed pulley.
1. What effort is needed to raise the load?

C. Set up a movable pulley and use it to lift the pail.
2. What effort is needed to raise the load?

D. Set up a system that contains a fixed and a movable pulley. Run the cord through the system and lift the load.
3. What effort is needed to raise the load?
4. How do the three pulley systems compare?
5. How much cord was pulled to lift the pail in each case?

ACTIVITY

How do pulleys make work easier?

A. Gather these materials: small pulley, meter stick, string, pail, sand, and spring scale.

B. Fill the pail about 1/4 full of sand. Lift the pail with the spring scale.
1. What force was needed to lift the pail?

C. Attach 1 end of the string to the meter stick, as shown. Run the string through the pulley. Attach the free end of the string to the spring scale. Hook the pail onto the pulley and lift the pail.
2. What was the force needed to lift the pail using the pulley?
3. How does this force compare to the force needed to lift the pail without the pulley?
4. How does a pulley make work easier?

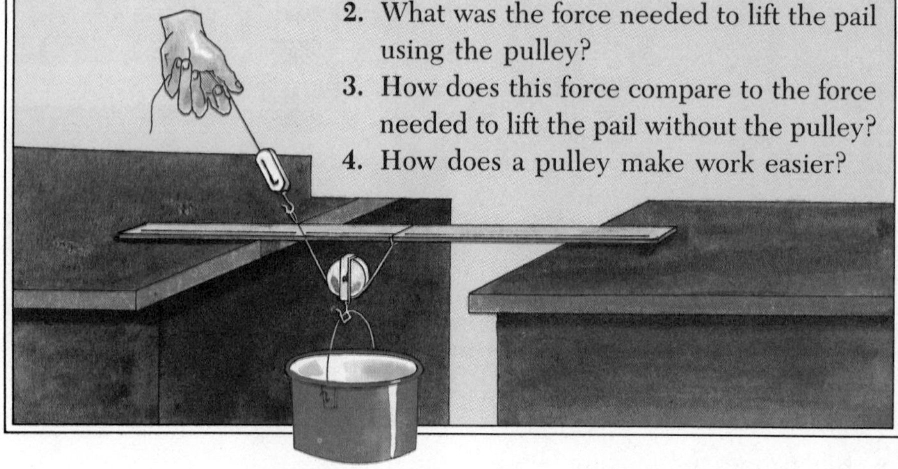

6 The drawing on page 197 shows two pulley systems. The one on the left has only one pulley. The other system has two pulleys. Without looking **7** at the scales, guess which pulley system uses less effort to lift the same load. As you can probably guess, two pulleys use less effort.

196

ACTIVITY

Skill Development—*Comparing and Contrasting*

Teaching Tips—Students will have to fasten their pulleys to some kind of support. A board or meter stick connecting two tables will do. The fixed pulley can be tied to the board with strong string. Try to obtain good pulleys. Inexpensive ones can be purchased from a hardware store. Have the class work in small groups.

Answers to Questions—1. Answers should be in spring-scale units. **2.** Answers should be in spring-scale units. **3.** It was less. **4.** The pulley makes it easier to lift a load, since less force is needed to lift the same load.

6 Teaching Tips—You might set up both pulley systems in your classroom. Lift a load with each system. Record the force each system requires to lift the load by using a force measurer.
7 Skill Development—Students will *predict* which pulley system requires less force to lift the same load.

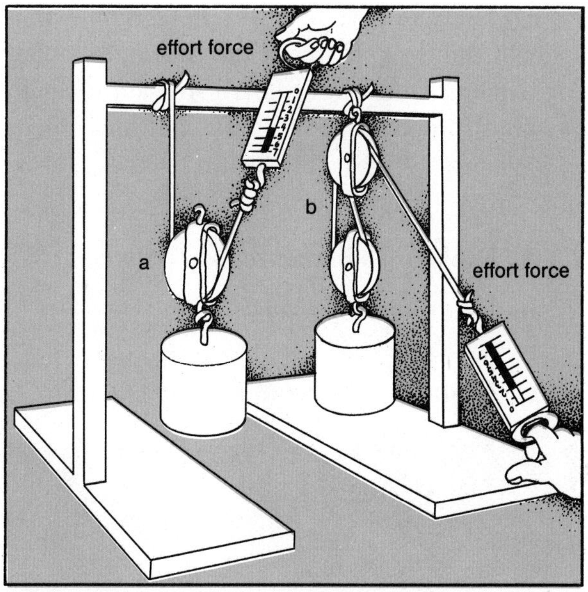

Section Review

Main Ideas: Fixed pulleys make work easier by changing the direction of force. Movable pulleys make work easier by making the force less. Often, fixed pulleys and movable pulleys are used together.

Questions: Answer in complete sentences.

1. Draw a picture of a pulley. Explain how it can be used to lift a heavy load.
2. What is a fixed pulley and a movable pulley?
3. Draw a picture to show how a fixed pulley and a movable pulley could be used together.
4. Which of the pulley systems shown at the top of this page makes work easier? Why?

EXTENSIONS

Application
Research

Elevators use complex pulley systems to work. Students can research how elevators operate. They should look for the following information:

1. What kinds of pulleys are used on an elevator?
2. What is the force used to move the elevator?
3. What allows the elevator to stop and change directions once it is moving?
4. What kind of safety devices are used in elevators?

SECTION REVIEW

Main Ideas—You might have students make diagrams of fixed and movable pulley systems.

Answers to Questions

1. Students can draw a diagram of a fixed pulley or a movable pulley.
2. A fixed pulley is a pulley that is attached to some object, such as a pole. A movable pulley is a pulley that moves with the load.
3. Diagrams should show two pulleys, either arranged as a block and tackle or with one pulley to the side of the other.
4. The double pulley system. Using more pulleys increases the mechanical advantage of the system.

SUGGESTED WORKSHEET MASTER
p. T-171 n

SECTION BACKGROUND

A wheel that turns on a rod is called a wheel and axle. Turning the axle causes the wheel to rotate. Likewise, turning the wheel causes the axle to rotate. By turning the axle, force is sacrificed to gain speed and distance on the outside of the wheel. By turning the wheel, an advantage in force is gained, whereas speed and distance are sacrificed.

Some examples of the wheel and axle include a doorknob, a pencil sharpener, a screwdriver, and a windlass. A windlass is a crank with a handle used to lift loads.

One can change the mechanical advantage of a wheel and axle by altering the diameter of the wheel and/or the axle.

MATERIALS

2 screwdrivers with handles of different diameter, 2 screws of same size and pitch, wood block, metric ruler

12-2. The Wheel and Axle

A doorknob is part of a simple machine that unlocks the door. Without the doorknob, opening a door would be very hard. In fact, it would be almost impossible. Why do you think this is so? When you finish this section, you should be able to:

☐ **A.** Explain what a *wheel and axle* is.

☐ **B.** Describe how a *wheel and axle* makes work easier.

☐ **C.** Identify examples of a *wheel and axle.*

BASIC TEACHING PLAN

MOTIVATION

If you can unscrew the tiny set screws holding the doorknob on your classroom door, take off the knob. Ask the students if they know what kind of machine a doorknob is. Have someone try to open the door by using only the axle. Now have them try it with the knob. Ask the students to explain why the axle turned when the doorknob was attached.

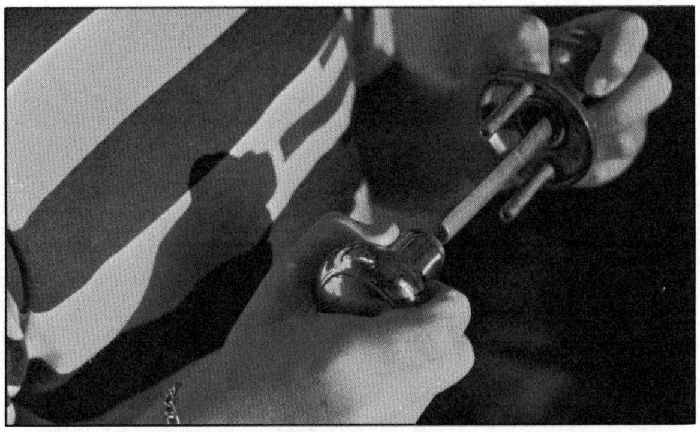

1 Look at the picture above. Have you ever taken a doorknob apart? The round knob is attached to a rod. It is very hard to turn the rod without turning the knob. Why do you think this is so?

A wheel that turns on a rod is called a **wheel and axle** (**ak**-sell). A doorknob and the rod it is attached to is a *wheel and axle*. The doorknob is the wheel. The rod is the axle. An axle usually goes through the center of a wheel. When the wheel turns, the axle turns. When the axle turns, the wheel turns.

Wheel and axle: A simple machine that is a wheel that turns on a rod.

When you turn a doorknob, you are using force to turn the wheel part of a wheel and axle. You move your hand more than you would if you just turned the rod. But you turn with a lot less force. Your work is made easier.

2 The wheel of a wheel and axle may be hard to recognize. You can't always see the wheel. The handle of a food grinder is a type of wheel and axle that does not seem to have a wheel. The wheel is the circle made in the air when you turn the handle.

DEVELOPMENT

1 Teaching Tips—Demonstrate how a doorknob works. Show the axle attached to the wheel. Illustrate how your hand turning the knob moves a greater distance than the axle does.

2 Teaching Tips—Take the cover off a pencil sharpener, and have students point out the wheel and axle. You could also bring in an old meat grinder, a windlass, or other examples of wheels and axles. Identify the wheel and axle in each machine. Have the students explain how each machine makes the work it does easier.

EXTENSIONS

Reinforcement

Science Skills—
Comparing and Contrasting

Your students can use the class pencil sharpener to determine how the wheel and axle can decrease the force needed to lift things.

A. Have them tie two books together with a string and note the force needed to lift the books with the string. Use a force measurer to measure the force.

B. Tie the string around the axle of the pencil sharpener. Have them turn the handle of the pencil sharpener to lift the books. Less force is needed to lift the books. Since the crank had to be turned around many times to lift the books, less force was used over a greater distance.

Application

Activity

Have the students obtain a copy of a large department-store catalog. They can use it to investigate types of machines.

List the simple machines that they are studying:

- Inclined plane
- Screw
- Wedge
- Pulley
- Wheel and axle
- Lever

Tell the students to look through the catalog to find one example of each machine. Have them cut a picture of the machine from the catalog and paste it to construction paper.

For each machine, they should make a small diagram showing the parts and write a very brief description of how the machine makes work easier.

EXTENSIONS

Enrichment

Activity

Have your students find one wheel-and-axle machine at home and bring it to class. Use the machines for a display. Have each student make a diagram of his or her machine on a small card that identifies the wheel and axle and tells how it makes work easier.

Activity

A crank is a wheel and axle. It changes the direction of motion. Students can perform the following Activity to observe how a crank does this.

A. Have the students bend a paper clip so that it has a small, square bulge in the middle and the two sides are level.

B. Punch a hole in a small index card, and slide it to the center of this bulge.

C. Twirl the paper clip while holding both ends, and observe the motion of the card.

1. How is the paper clip moving? (In a circular motion)
2. How is the top edge of the card moving when you are looking edge on? (Up and down)
3. How is the side edge of the card moving when you are looking edgewise? (Back and forth)

D. Have someone hold the ends of the paper clip and move the index card up and down.

4. When you moved the index card, how did the paper clip move? (When the card moved up and down, the clip turned in a circle.)
5. What examples of cranks can you think of? (Bicycle pedals, pencil sharpener, crank shaft in an automobile)

ACTIVITY

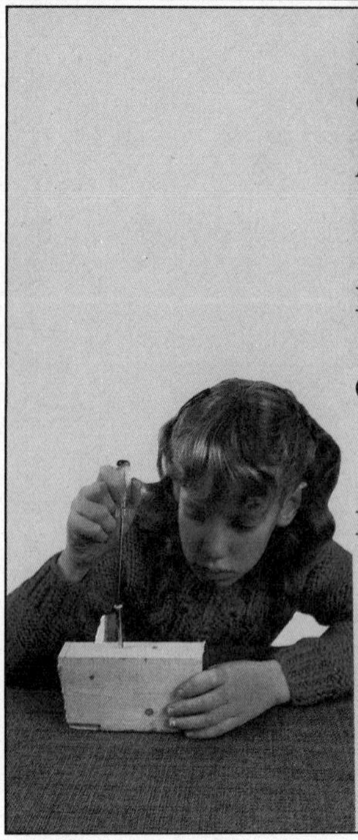

How does a wheel and axle make doing work easier?

A. Gather these materials: 2 screwdrivers with different-size handles, 2 screws (same size), wood block, and metric ruler.

B. Measure the thickness of the handle of each screwdriver.

C. Use the screwdriver with the thinner handle to screw one of the screws into the wood.

1. How many turns did you make?

D. Use the screwdriver with the thicker handle to screw in the second screw.

2. How many turns did you make?
3. With which screwdriver was it easier to turn the screw?
4. Why was there a difference between the 2 screwdrivers?

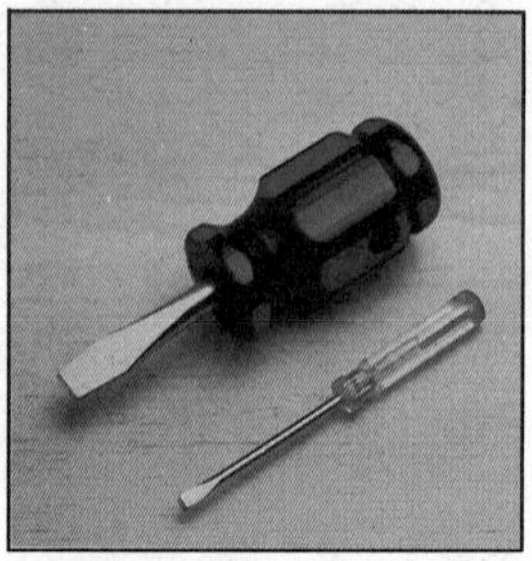

3 There are many other examples of the wheel and axle. Look at the two screwdrivers shown here. They are both the same length. But the handles are different sizes. The handle of a screwdriver is the wheel. The metal part is the axle. Which screwdriver would be easier to use? Since it is easier to turn a larger wheel, the screwdriver with the larger handle is easier to use. You have to turn it more, but each turn is easier to make.

ACTIVITY

Skill Development—*Comparing and Contrasting*

Teaching Tips—Starter holes should be either drilled or hammered into the blocks of wood to make it easier to turn the screws. Use soft rather than hard wood. Give each group of students two screwdriver handles that have different diameters.

Answers to Questions—**1.** Answers will vary, depending on the pitch of the screw and on how well students can use a screwdriver. **2.** The number of turns should be the same. **3.** The screwdriver with the larger handle. **4.** The larger handle sacrifices the distance the hand turns for force. You have to turn the screwdriver more, but each turn is easier to make.

3 Skill Development—Students should be able to make *inferences* about the differences between various screwdrivers.

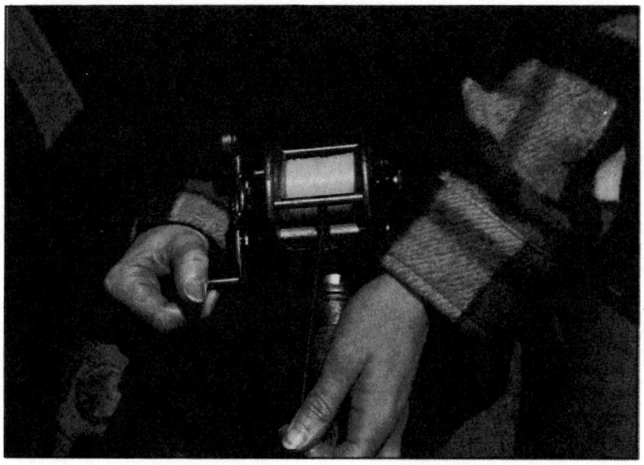

Some other examples of the wheel and axle are shown above. Look at each one. You should be able to find the wheel and axle shown in each of the pictures.

Section Review

Main Ideas: A wheel turning on a rod, or axle, is a kind of simple machine. The axle usually goes through the center of the wheel.

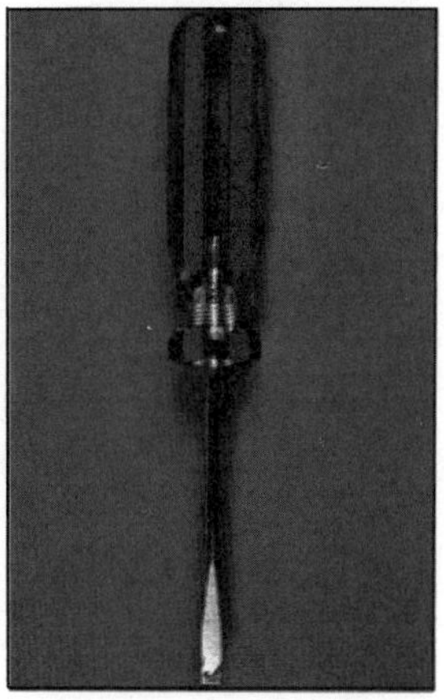

Questions: Answer in complete sentences.

1. What are two examples of a wheel and axle in your home?
2. Why is unlocking a door easier with a doorknob than without it?
3. Why do you think buses have very large steering wheels?
4. Look at the screwdriver shown in the margin. Which part can be thought of as a wheel? Which part is an axle?

EXTENSIONS

Enrichment

Activity

What path does a point on the outside of a wheel follow? To find out, have students do this Activity.

A. Gather these materials: a wheel, a roll of paper, and a marker or crayon that can be attached to the outside of the wheel.

B. Tape about 6 ft of paper to the wall, along the floor.

C. Attach a marker or crayon to the outside of the wheel so that the wheel is still free to roll. The marker tip should be at right angles to the direction the wheel rolls.

D. Place the wheel next to the paper, so that the marker tip traces the path of the outside of the wheel as you roll it along the floor.

1. What path does the point on the outside of the wheel take? (Semicircles)

E. Place the marker at the center of the wheel and see what path it follows.

2. What path does the center of the wheel take? (A straight line)

4 Teaching Tips—Suggest that the students make a sketch of each wheel and axle in the photographs. Have them label the wheel and axle on each sketch and tell how the machine makes work easier. They could also draw sketches of other wheels and axles or look through magazines for pictures of them.

SECTION REVIEW

Answers to Questions

1. Doorknob, screwdriver, windlass on toys
2. The handle is a wheel, which makes turning the axle easier.
3. Bigger wheels are easier to turn than smaller ones.
4. The handle is the wheel; the rod is the axle.

SECTION BACKGROUND

A wheel with teeth or notches is called a gear or gear wheel. Gear wheels are usually connected to other gear wheels. A bicycle has gear wheels that are connected by a chain. Gear wheels connected by a chain move in the same direction. Gear wheels that fit directly together move in opposite directions. Larger gear wheels turning smaller gear wheels make work easier by increasing distance and speed at the expense of force.

MATERIALS

crayon, egg beater

12-3. Gear Wheels

These children are riding 10-speed bicycles. They can change gear by using a gear shift. If they are going up a steep hill, they change to a gear that will make it easier to pedal. What speed should they use to go up a steep hill? When you finish this section, you should be able to:

- ☐ **A.** Identify machines that contain *gears*.
- ☐ **B.** Explain how *gears* make work easier.
- ☐ **C.** Explain why chains are used to connect *gear wheels*.

When you ride a bicycle, you are doing work. The pedals are attached to a large wheel that has

202

BASIC TEACHING PLAN

MOTIVATION

Have a bicycle in the classroom, and make sure that students know where the gears are. Demonstrate shifting the gears using the bike. Turn the bicycle upside down to do this.

Text Questions—What speed should they use to go up a steep hill? *Low speed.*

points, or teeth. The back wheel is attached to another toothed wheel. A wheel with teeth is called a **gear** or **gear wheel**. *Gear wheels* are usually attached to other gear wheels. On bicycles, the gears are joined by a chain. The teeth fit into open places in the chain. When you pedal, you turn the larger gear wheel. This turns the chain, which turns the smaller gear wheel. Your bicycle goes forward.

Gear wheel: A simple machine that is a wheel with teeth.

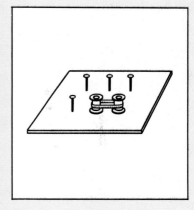

The boy in the picture is using a machine called an egg beater to mix frosting. The turning handle is attached to a larger gear wheel. The mixing blades are attached to a smaller gear wheel. The larger gear wheel turns the smaller gear wheel. In an egg beater, the gear wheels fit without a chain. How is work made easier when large gear wheels turn small gear wheels?

Gear wheels, like the one on an egg beater, make work easier. When you turn the large wheel around, the smaller wheel makes more turns. The blades also turn faster than the larger wheel.

EXTENSIONS

Enrichment

Science Skills—Observing and Predicting

You can make a gear board by hammering a nail into a 2.5-cm board that is about 30 cm square. Separate the nails by about 6 cm. Empty sewing-thread spools can be used as the gears, and rubber bands can be used to link the gears. You should have at least two different-diameter spools.

Let the students experiment with observing both the speed and direction of linked gears. After some initial experimentation, they should be able to predict the behavior in terms of the speed and direction of the gears.

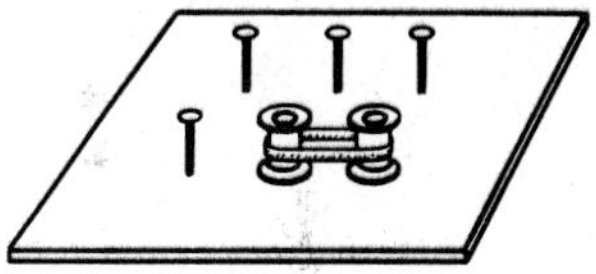

Fig. 12-1

DEVELOPMENT

1 Skill Development—Students should be able to explain the following *cause and effect* relationship: The movement of one gear affects the movement of the connected gear.

2 Text Questions—How is work made easier when large gear wheels turn small gear wheels? *The small gear wheels turn faster than the large wheels. Distance is sacrificed for speed.*

EXTENSIONS

Application
Activity

Have your students explore the gear-wheel system used in 10- and 15-speed racing bicycles. They will discover that those bicycles have a number of gear wheels connected to the front and back wheels. The rider can move the connecting chain from one wheel to another by using a device called a derailleur. Your students can find out the following:

1. How do different sizes of the two gear wheels affect the speed at which the wheel moves?
2. Which gear wheels are used to pedal uphill?
3. Which gear wheels are used to ride downhill?

ACTIVITY

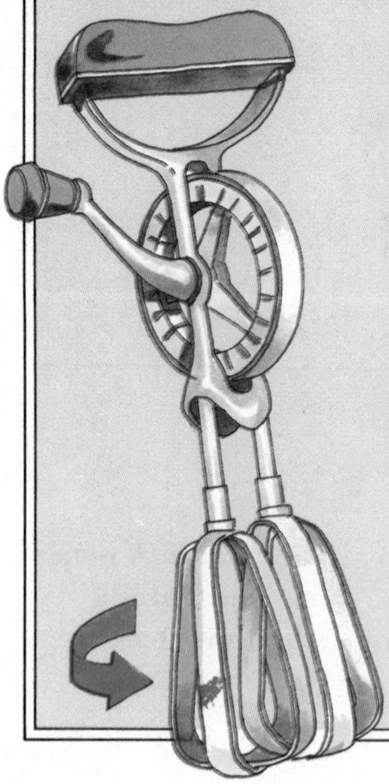

How does a gear wheel work?

A. Gather these materials: crayon and egg beater.

B. Put a crayon mark on 1 blade of an egg beater.

C. Slowly turn the large gear wheel 1 complete turn. Use the mark on the blade to count how many turns the blade made.

D. Repeat step C, turning the gear wheel 2 times, and then 3 times.

1. How many times did the blade turn each time?
2. Did the blade turn faster or slower than the large gear wheel?

3 Do you know why the gear wheels on a bike are joined by a chain? Look at the drawings below. The gear wheels without the chain turn in opposite directions. Wheels with the chain turn in the same direction. If the gear wheels on a bicycle were joined without a chain, you would have to pedal backward to go forward.

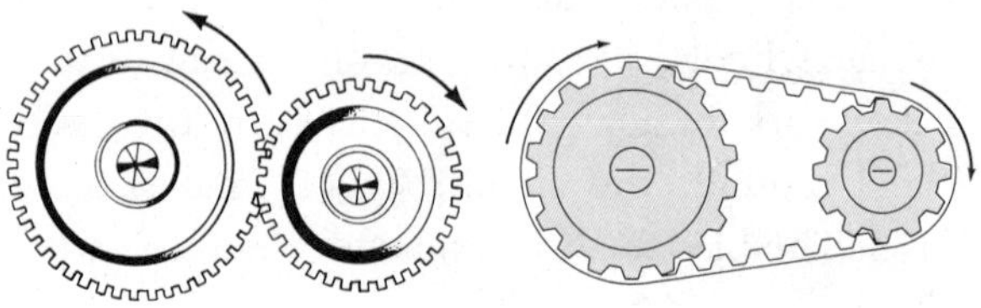

204

ACTIVITY

Skill Development—*Observing, Finding Cause and Effect*

Teaching Tips—The day before the Activity, ask students to bring in a hand egg beater similar to the one in the picture. Make sure the crayon mark on the blade is dark enough to see while turning the beater. It will be used to count the number of times the blades turn around. You might have the students count the number of notches on the large and small wheels. The ratio of large to small will determine the speed of the blades. If there are 20 notches on the large gear and 10 on the smaller one, then the smaller gear (and therefore the blades) will turn twice as fast as the large wheel.

Answers to Questions—1. Answers will vary, depending on the ratio of the number of notches on the large gear to the number of notches on the small gear. **2.** It turned faster than the large gear wheel.

These pictures show a close-up of the gear and wheels on a bike and those inside a watch. The gear wheels on the rear wheel of the bike are of different sizes. The watch also has different-size gear wheels. Why do you think the watch has different-size wheels?

Section Review

Main Ideas: Large gear wheels that turn small gear wheels make work easier. They increase the speed of the small gears and the number of times they turn. Two gear wheels that are joined by a chain turn in the same direction.

Questions: Answer in complete sentences.

1. How do gear wheels make work easier?
2. How can two gear wheels be made to turn in the same direction?
3. In the picture of the bike, which size gear wheel would make pedaling easier?
4. What does it mean when we say a bicycle has 10 speeds?

EXTENSIONS

Enrichment

Research—Library

Automobiles and trucks have complicated gear systems. Students can do research on what kinds of gear systems they use and how they work. They should try to answer these questions:

1. What do the gears in the automobiles and trucks do?
2. What is the difference between standard and automatic gear systems?
3. Why do cars sometimes have three, four, or five different gear systems?
4. Why do some large trucks have as many as 18 different gear systems?

3 Teaching Tips—If you have a bicycle available, let the students observe the motion of both gear wheels. Turn the bike upside down and pedal the bike by hand. The students will see that the chain connecting the gear wheels allows both gears to turn in the same direction. Ask the students which gear should be used in going up a steep hill. *The lower gear.* Show how the chain shifts to a lower gear, which makes it easier to pedal. Make an overhead transparency of the drawing of the two sets of gears on page 204. Leave the arrows off. Have the students predict the direction in which each gear wheel will move in both setups.
4 Text Questions—Why do you think the watch has different-size wheels? *The different-size wheels create different speeds.*

SECTION REVIEW

Answers to Questions
1. They increase the speed at which connected gears move.
2. Connect the toothed wheels with a chain.
3. The smaller one
4. Ten different adjustments in the gears can be made.

SUGGESTED WORKSHEET MASTERS
pp. T-171 o, p

SECTION BACKGROUND

A machine made up of two or more simple machines is a compound machine. Most machines that we use every day are compound machines. A bicycle is a compound machine made of wheels and axles, gear wheels, and screws. A hand drill is a compound machine made of a wheel and axle, a screw, and a wedge. A compound machine increases force more times than any of its simple machines used alone.

MATERIALS

scissors, hand drill, toy crane, pencil sharpener

12-4. Compound Machines

Have you ever taken your bike apart to clean or repair it? If you have, then you know that it is not as simple as it looks. A bicycle is a machine. Most machines are made of two or more simple machines that work together. What are other examples of such machines in your home? When you finish this section, you should be able to:

- ☐ **A.** Identify and give examples of *compound machines.*
- ☐ **B.** Identify the simple machines that are in a *compound machine.*

BASIC TEACHING PLAN

MOTIVATION

Challenge students to list as many simple machines as they can think of that are in a bicycle or some other machine, such as a pencil sharpener or hand drill.

Text Questions—What are other examples of such machines in your home? *Answers could include coffee grinder, hand drill, movie projector, pencil sharpener, etc.*

A machine made up of two or more simple
1 machines is called a **compound machine** (**kom**-pound). A bicycle is a *compound machine*. The
2 word *compound* means to mix or put together. A bicycle is made of many simple machines. The front and back wheels are wheel and axles. The handlebar and pedals are also wheel and axles. The screws that hold the seat and handlebar in place are hidden inclined planes. The toothed wheels joined by the chain are gear wheels.

Compound machine: A machine made of two or more simple machines.

The tool shown above is a compound machine called a hand drill. A hand drill is made of three simple machines. Do you know what they are? The handle of the drill is a wheel turning on an axle. When you turn the handle, you are turning a rod that moves in a circle. The tip of the drill is spiraled like a screw. It is an inclined plane. The sides of the tip are wedge-shaped. They are sharp and cut like knives.

EXTENSIONS

Application

Activity

Challenge your students to bring a machine (simple or complex) that is small enough to fit into a small box. The size is up to you. It could range from shoe-box size to a hat-box size. Ask students to bring the machine inside the box to school. Have them describe the machine without actually naming it or telling what it is.

They should describe its shape, where it is used, and so forth. If it is a compound machine, they might list the simple machines that make it up as clues. Let the other students write on a sheet of paper what they think the machine is. After everyone has had an opportunity to do this for each box, let each student open his or her box and show the machine to the class.

DEVELOPMENT

1 Teaching Tips—Tell the students to find a compound machine at home. They can either bring it in to school the next day or discuss the machine with their parents. With their parents' help, they can make a drawing of the machine and list the simple machines that make it up. The drawings and machines can be used as a display in the classroom.
2 Teaching Tips—Stand a bicycle up on a desk so that everyone can see it. Give the students a few minutes to observe the bike and identify all the simple machines that they can find.

EXTENSIONS

Application
Activity

In this Activity, you will challenge pairs of students to use the materials provided to create a compound machine that has some function. They will not only make the machine but also include a set of the "blueprints" that they drew before actually building it.

A. Gather these materials: Erector sets, Tinkertoy sets, string, straws, tape, glue, paper, screws, nails, bolts, wire, Styrofoam, rubber bands, empty sewing spools, wood, hammers, screwdrivers, and anything else you think would be useful.

B. Announce to the class that they are going to invent a compound machine. You might explore the possibilities with the whole class. Just list them on the board. Let the students make use of these ideas for their own creations.

C. Let the students work in pairs. Encourage them to experiment with ideas. When they think they know what they are going to build, have them make a drawing or "blueprint" of their machine. They can use it as a guide and for display purposes.

D. When the machines are completed, let each pair of students demonstrate their machine to the rest of the class. Then set up the machines in your classroom for all the students to enjoy.

ACTIVITY

What are the parts of compound machines?

A. Gather these materials: scissors, hand drill, toy crane, and pencil sharpener.

B. Copy the chart shown below. Use it to record your observations.

Compound Machine	Inclined Plane	Screw	Wedge	Lever	Pulley	Wheel and Axle
Scissors						
Hand drill						
Toy crane						
Pencil sharpener						

C. Look at each compound machine. Find as many simple machines in each as you can. Describe each in your chart.

1. What are compound machines made of?
2. How many simple machines did you find in each compound machine?

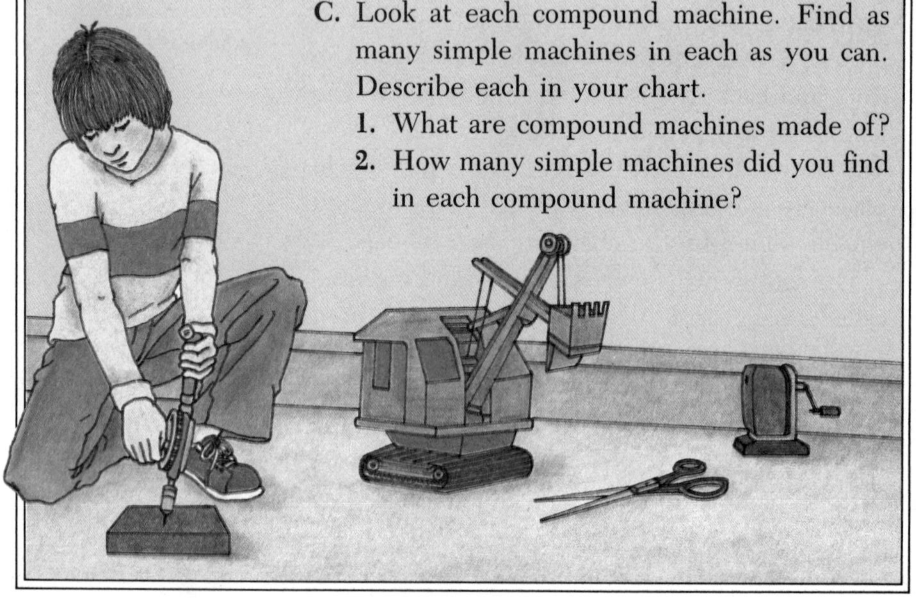

208

ACTIVITY

Skill Development—*Observing*

Teaching Tips—We have listed several compound machines from which you can choose. Use the ones that you can obtain and substitute for ones you cannot find. This is an observation-type Activity. Students will apply what they learned in Chapter 11 as well as in this chapter.

Answers to Questions—**1.** Simple machines. **2.** Scissors—wedge, lever; hand drill—wheel and axle, screw, wedge; toy crane—wheel and axle, pulley; pencil sharpener—wedge, wheel and axle.

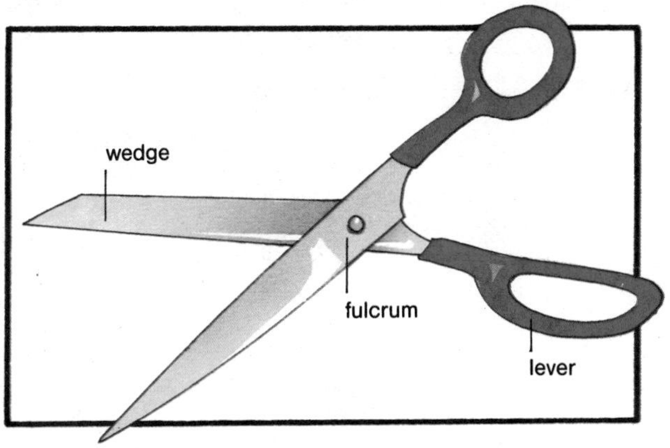

3 Scissors are also compound machines. A pair of scissors is made of two levers. The fulcrum is the place where the levers are joined. Each lever also has a wedge-shaped cutting edge.

4 Another example of a compound machine is a
5 movie projector. How many simple machines can you find in the movie projector?

Section Review

Main Ideas: Compound machines are machines made of two or more simple machines. Bicycles, hand drills, and scissors are examples of compound machines.

Questions: Answer in complete sentences.

1. What simple machines can you find in the machine shown in the margin?
2. What are three examples of compound machines?
3. What is the advantage of a compound machine over a simple machine?

EXTENSIONS

Enrichment

Science Skills— Comparing and Contrasting

Students can compare and contrast the force needed to lift an object by using no machines, a simple machine, and a compound machine. Students will need string; a standard mass, such as a block of wood; an inclined plane; a pulley; and a force measurer.

A. Have the students set up the inclined plane and measure its height.

B. Lift the mass to the height of the incline, and measure how much force it takes.

C. Then pull the object up the incline, and measure the force needed.

D. Mount the pulley on the top of the inclined plane. Measure the force needed to pull the object up the incline using the pulley.

1. Which method required the least force?
2. Can you devise a compound machine that requires even less force?

3 Skill Development—Students will *observe* the simple machines in different compound machines.

4 Teaching Tips—Have a movie projector in the classroom. Pair students off, and let them list the simple machines that they see in the projector.

5 Text Questions—How many simple machines can you find in the movie projector? *Wheel and axle, gears, pulleys, inclined planes (screws).*

SECTION REVIEW

Answers to Questions

1. Wheel and axle, wedge, screw
2. Hand drill, movie projector, bicycle, pencil sharpener
3. It is able to apply more force than the individual simple machines of which it is composed.

EXTENSIONS

Reinforcement

Activity

Principles of machines can be demonstrated with playground equipment. Send students to the playground with these questions to answer:

1. What kind of simple machine is a seesaw? (A lever)
2. Draw a seesaw and label its parts. (Drawing should include fulcrum, load, and force.)
3. If a heavy child is on one end of the seesaw and a light child is on the other end, which way does each child have to move to get the seesaw to go down on the end that the light child is sitting on? (The light child moves back; the heavy child moves forward.)
4. Why is a slide smooth? (So that you can slide easily) How do different materials affect the speed at which you slide? (The materials with more friction slow down the slide.)
5. What kind of simple machine is the ladder going up a slide? (An inclined plane)

SUGGESTED TEST MASTERS
pp. T-171 f, g, h

CHAPTER REVIEW

Science Words: Copy the numbered letters and spaces on paper. Use the clues to help you identify the science terms.

1. ___ u ___ ___ ___ ___
2. ___ ___ x ___ ___   ___ ___ ___ ___ ___ y
3. ___ ___ v ___ ___ ___ ___   ___ ___ l ___ ___ ___
4. w ___ ___ ___ ___   ___ ___ ___   ___ ___ ___ e
5. ___ e ___ ___   ___ ___ e ___ ___
6. ___ ___ ___ p ___ ___ ___ ___
   ___ ___ ___ ___ i ___ ___

Clues

1. A wheel with a rope moving around it
2. A machine that stays in place as the load moves (two words)
3. A machine that moves with the load (two words)
4. A wheel that turns on a rod (three words)
5. A wheel with teeth (two words)
6. A machine made of two or more simple machines (two words)

Questions: Answer in complete sentences.

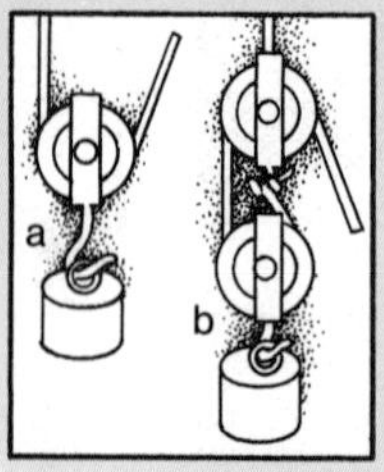

1. Draw a picture showing the difference between a fixed and a movable pulley.
2. Which of the pulleys shown here would make work easier to do?
3. How does a wheel and axle make work easier?
4. Draw a picture showing how the gear wheels on a bike are joined with a chain.

CHAPTER REVIEW

Science Words

1. Pulley, **2.** fixed pulley, **3.** movable pulley, **4.** wheel and axle, **5.** gear wheel, **6.** compound machine

Answers to Questions

1. Diagrams should show a fixed pulley that does not move with its load and a movable pulley that does.
2. b
3. Turning the larger wheel increases the force applied to the axle.
4. Diagram should show front and back gear wheel with chain around both.

CHAPTER 13

FRICTION AND WORK

In January 1973, a freezing storm struck Atlanta, Georgia. This storm was later called the "Great Atlanta Ice Storm." Cars, trucks, and buses slid all over the icy streets. When you finish this section, you should be able to:

13-1. What Is Friction?

CHAPTER OBJECTIVES

1. Explain how friction affects the force needed to move objects, and give examples of the effects of friction.
2. Explain and give examples of how wheels and other round objects reduce friction.
3. Explain and give examples of how lubrication reduces friction.
4. Explain the effect of friction on the efficiency of machines.

SECTION BACKGROUND

When we attempt to roll or slide one object over another, we find that there is a force that opposes the motion. This force is called friction. Without friction, an object like a spaceship would continue moving in a straight line until it hit something. Newton's first law of motion explains that every object remains at rest or moves at a constant speed unless acted upon by some outside force. In other words, if there is a change in the motion of an object, then an outside force must have acted on it. When you are driving a car and you take your foot off the accelerator, the car will slow down and eventually stop. The outside force acting on the car is friction.

BASIC TEACHING PLAN

MOTIVATION

Ask: Why are streets sanded when they are icy? Why do snow tires have studs in them (or why do drivers use chains on their wheels)? *All of these are done in an effort to increase friction. Without the force of friction between our shoes and the street or between tires and the road, neither we nor our cars or bicycles can move.*

Too much friction is not good either. If possible, bring in a worn fan belt from a local garage. Explain that friction causes the wear on the belt. Wear on tires and shoes is caused by the same friction that allows us to move. Ask if they know the expression "the squeaky wheel gets the grease." Metal parts rub against each other in the squeaky wheel and cause a sound. Putting grease or oil on the axle makes the parts slide past each other easily, with no noise.

MATERIALS

shoe box, sand, sandpaper, wax paper, spring scale (force measurer)

Exceptional Student
IEP Chapter Goal

When shown pictures of various surfaces, the student will identify which surfaces produce the most friction. The visually impaired student must be allowed to feel the various surfaces.

EXTENSIONS

Application
Activity

This Activity will help students see how friction is reduced by a Hovercraft.

A. Gather these materials: a 10-cm square of cardboard, a straw, scissors, and a balloon.

B. Make a hole in the cardboard just large enough to accommodate the straw.

C. Cut the straw to a length of about 2 cm. Push it into the cardboard so that it is flush with the bottom of the board.

D. Blow up the balloon. Put a piece of tape or your finger on the bottom of the cardboard to cover the straw. Carefully put the balloon over the upper part of the straw.

E. Put the cardboard and the inflated balloon on a smooth table. Release the air. The expanding air escaping through the hole in the cardboard will lift the card so that a flick will shoot it across the table (because there is little friction).

☐ **A.** Explain how *friction* affects the force needed to move objects.

☐ **B.** Identify helpful and harmful effects of *friction*.

1 These children are going to play a game of tug-of-war. Do you think it will be a fair game? Do you think one group has an advantage?

If you said it would be unfair, you were correct. The children on the ice will be pulled easily. They will not be able to move the children standing on the ground. The reason for this is **friction** (**frik**-shun). *Friction* is a force that acts when two objects rub or slide over one another.

2 Friction keeps objects from moving. The friction between the ground and the children's shoes keeps them from slipping.

The friction is less between the shoes and the ice. Thus, the children on the ground will win easily.

Friction: A force caused when one object rubs against another object.

DEVELOPMENT

1 Teaching Tips—Ask: Why isn't this tug-of-war game fair? *Use this example to explain the force of friction. There is friction between the ground and the children's shoes. There is hardly any friction between the ice and the children's shoes.*

2 Skill Development—Students will explore the *cause and effect* relationships that explain how much friction there is between objects.

3 Smooth surfaces make less friction than rough surfaces. It takes more force to move an object over a rough surface than a smooth surface.

4 For example, suppose you want to push a heavy box across the ground. There is a lot of friction between the box and ground. This makes pushing the box very hard. Putting a blanket under the box reduces the friction. The blanket slides easily over the ground. Now mov-
5 ing the box is easier. The box would also slide more easily over a polished floor. Why?

Friction can be very helpful. One of the first uses of friction was to make a fire. Early humans found that rubbing two sticks together caused the sticks to become hot. The friction between the sticks could make them hot enough to cause a fire. In bicycle brakes, the metal of the brakes rubs against the rubber tire. The friction between these two surfaces causes the wheels to
6 slow. Can you think of some other helpful uses of friction?

EXTENSIONS

Enrichment

Science Skills—Inferring

When friction occurs in a system, heat is usually produced. Students can explore different systems to detect heat.

A. Have the students rub their hands together. Ask: What change in temperature do you detect?

B. Rub different surfaces together. Have students use their hands to detect any temperature changes. Suggested surfaces: sandpaper, wood, metal, fabric.

1. What is the effect of rubbing surfaces together?
2. What happens to the energy that is transferred from your muscles to the objects you rub together?

3 Teaching Tips—Obtain at least three grades of sandpaper and blocks of wood. Cut the sandpaper into smaller pieces so that pairs of students can have a piece of each grade. Have the students rub each piece across the block of wood. Ask them to explain why there is a difference when they rub the three pieces of sandpaper across the wood. The friction is greater with the coarse-grade sandpaper than with a fine-grade sandpaper. Give the students hand lenses to observe the surface of each sample of sandpaper.

4 Skill Development—Encourage the students to explore *cause and effect* relationships that explain how the smoothness or roughness of the surfaces of objects affects the friction between them.

5 Text Questions—The box would also slide more easily over a polished floor. Why? *A polished floor is very smooth; it is easier to slide an object over a smooth surface than over a rough surface.*

6 Text Questions—Can you think of some other helpful uses of friction? *Friction is what makes automobile brakes work; friction between tires and the road enables a car or bicycle to move.*

EXTENSIONS

Reinforcement

Science Skills—Observing

Have students bring in a variety of mechanical objects to examine. Their task is to locate parts of these objects that cause friction. Ask them if the friction is useful or if the friction should be reduced. Ask them to indicate how they would reduce the friction.

ACTIVITY

How is friction affected by different surfaces?

A. Gather these materials: shoe box, sand, sandpaper, wax paper, and spring scale.
B. Fill the box 1/2 full of sand. Attach the spring scale to the box.
C. Pull the box across a piece of wax paper.
  1. What force is needed to move the box?
D. Pull the box across a piece of sandpaper.
  2. What force is needed to move the box?
  3. Over which surface was it harder to pull the box?
  4. What effect does the type of surface have on friction?

Friction can cause problems, too. Too much friction makes heavy objects hard to move. When objects rub against each other, the surfaces are worn away. Look at your shoes. Fric-

ACTIVITY

Skill Development—*Measuring, Comparing and Contrasting*

Teaching Tips—Review with your students how to use the spring scale to measure force. You might want to tape the wax paper and sandpaper down to the table; otherwise, they might slide when the shoe box is pulled across them. The force registered on the spring scale is actually a measure of the frictional force that exists between the two surfaces. In order to move the box, you must overcome the frictional force between it and the surface it is on. Students might be interested in measuring the force of friction between other surfaces.

Answers to Questions—**1.** Answers should be in spring-scale units. **2.** The force should be greater than the force needed to move the box across wax paper. **3.** Sandpaper. **4.** Smooth surfaces have less friction.

tion with the ground causes the heels and soles to wear away. Friction also wears away the parts of machines. Belts connect the moving parts inside a car engine. They are worn away by friction. 7 What are some other problems caused by friction?

8 Too little friction is a big problem on icy roads. To solve this problem, we must increase the friction between the ice and the tires of cars. There are many ways to do this. Chains can be put on the tires. The chains make the surfaces of the tires rougher. Friction is increased. You can also throw sand on the ice. The sand grains make the icy surface rougher. Again, the friction is increased. 9 Can you think of other times when you would want to increase friction?

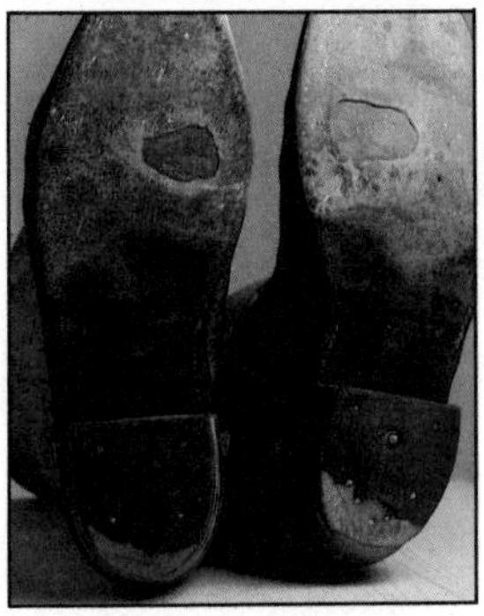

Section Review

Main Ideas: Friction is present when two surfaces rub or slide over one another. Brake systems are based on the force of friction. Too little friction can make it hard for us to move around.

Questions: Answer in complete sentences.

1. A girl rolls a ball across a field. The ball slows down and stops. Why does it do this?
2. Why do your hands get warm when you rub them together?
3. Why do we cut grooves in the cement on highways?
4. List three ways in which friction is helpful to us.

EXTENSIONS

Application

Research

Athletes need to have the right amount of friction between their feet and the ground so they can move properly. To help them, they use special shoes. Students can visit an athletic-shoe department and examine the different kinds of shoes used in different sports. They can make hypotheses about why different soles are used for different sports. They should compare and contrast shoes used for running, basketball, etc. For what kind of surface and what kind of movement is each shoe designed?

7 Text Questions—What are some other problems caused by friction? *Friction makes it more difficult to move objects.*

8 Teaching Tips—Present the students with this problem: How can you increase the friction on an icy surface? Have the students work in small groups to make their suggestions.

9 Text Questions—Can you think of other times when you would want to increase friction? *When running or walking across smooth floors (like gymnasiums); when trying to stop a moving vehicle (putting on the brakes increases friction).*

SECTION REVIEW

Answers to Questions

1. The friction between the ball and field slows the ball down.
2. Friction causes heat.
3. To increase the friction between the tires of cars and the road. The grooves make the road rougher.
4. It can prevent slipping on smooth surfaces; it can be used to brake a bike; it can be used to start a fire.

SECTION BACKGROUND

Wheels reduce friction because they roll past other surfaces rather than rub against them. Also, because they are round, only a small part of them touches the ground at one time. Ball bearings reduce friction for the same reasons.

The efficiency of a machine can be increased by reducing friction. Ball bearings are used to reduce friction in machines. They slide over one another easily, thus reducing friction between the moving parts in machines. For example, ball bearings are used in roller skates and skateboards to make the wheels turn more smoothly.

MATERIALS

shoe box, 4 books, 3 round pencils or dowels, string, spring scale

13-2. Friction and Wheels

The picture shows how some of the work of building the pyramids might have been done. Thousands of heavy stone blocks had to be moved into place. The builders probably put logs under the stones to reduce friction between the stones and the ground. When you finish this section, you should be able to:

- ☐ **A.** Explain how wheels and other round objects reduce friction.
- ☐ **B.** Explain how wheels make machines more *efficient*.

Can you picture a wheelbarrow with square wheels? It would be very hard to use to move a load of dirt. The round wheel was one of the earliest human inventions. People found that wheels make it easier to move things. A wheel reduces friction because only a small part of it touches the ground at one time.

BASIC TEACHING PLAN

MOTIVATION

Hold a "Science Toy-Car Race." Obtain a sheet of plywood large enough for at least five lanes of a racetrack. Paint lanes on the board. Have the students bring in some kind of toy car, racing car, or truck. Don't tell them what they are being used for. To begin this section, announce on the day the students have brought in their cars and trucks that they are going to be in a "Science Toy-Car Race." The most frictionless car in the class will be the winner. Run the races in heats. Put the board on a slant, and line the cars up behind a yardstick. To begin the race, lift the yardstick and let the cars roll. In that way, no car gets an unfair advantage. Let the winning car compete against the winning cars from all the other heats. When you have a winner, let all the students carefully examine that car. Why did it move faster than all the other cars? They should compare this car's wheels to the wheels on the other cars. The wheels of the winning car have less friction.

Wheels are not the only round objects that reduce friction. **Ball bearings** are also used to reduce friction in machines. A *ball bearing* is a smooth ball made of metal. Because the balls are smooth, they can roll next to each other easily. Ball bearings are used in roller skates and skateboards to make the wheels turn more smoothly. Look at the picture in the margin, which shows the inside of a wheel. The small metal balls are ball bearings. They reduce the friction. This allows the wheel to spin smoothly.

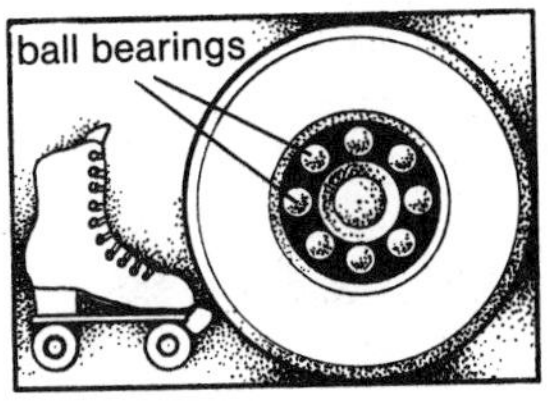

Ball bearings: Small metal balls used to reduce friction.

ACTIVITY

How do wheels reduce friction?

A. Gather these materials: shoe box, 4 books, 3 round pencils, string, and spring scale.
B. Put 4 books into the shoe box.
C. Fasten string to the box. Attach the string to the spring scale. Pull the box across the table a distance of 50 cm (20 in.).
  1. How much force was needed to pull the box?

D. Put 3 round pencils under the box.
E. Pull the box across the table a distance of 50 cm (20 in.).
  2. How much force was needed to pull the box this time?
  3. What effect did the rollers have on the friction? Explain your answer.

EXTENSIONS

Reinforcement
Activity

Here is another way to compare the force of friction of different objects.

A. Gather these materials: chalk, a book, a shoe, a sneaker, a piece of ice, a roller skate, and a board.

B. Set up the board as an inclined plane against the chalkboard.

C. Place any object, such as a shoe, at the chalkboard end of the board, and begin lifting that end. When the object first begins to slide, draw the level of the slant of the board on the chalkboard.

D. Try different objects, and compare the slant of the board required to make each of them slide.

E. If you have a force measurer, measure the force needed to pull each object across the board when it is flat. How does this measure of friction compare?

ACTIVITY

Skill Development—*Measuring, Comparing and Contrasting*

Teaching Tips—The students do not have to pull the box very far to obtain a reading on the force measurer. If they pull the box too far with the rollers under it, the box will eventually slide off the rollers. Their readings at this point will be inaccurate. Students could also measure the force needed to move the box when the box is placed on marbles or wheels. Make sure the students record their data on their charts. Use the data later to discuss the effects of rollers on friction.

Answers to Questions—1. Answers should be in spring-scale units. **2.** The force should be less than the force needed in the first trial. **3.** They reduced the friction, since there is less friction in rolling over a surface than in rubbing across a surface.

EXTENSIONS

Enrichment
Science Skills—
Comparing and Contrasting

Students can observe and compare the motion of objects with and without ball bearings.

A. Obtain a bicycle, roller skates, skateboards, and wheels that do not have ball bearings.

B. Have the students set each wheel in motion and see how long it spins before it stops. Have them compare the wheels with ball bearings to the wheels that do not contain ball bearings.

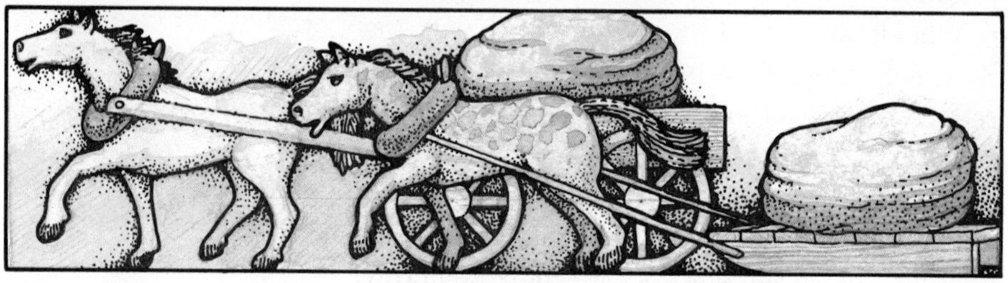

Efficiency: The amount of work done by a machine compared to the amount of work put into it.

1 Machines are more **efficient** (ee-**fish**-ent) if we can reduce friction. The *efficiency* of a machine depends upon how much work we get out of it. We never get out of a machine as much work as we put into it. Some of the work we put into the machine is lost to friction. Wheels and ball bearings can help reduce friction in a machine. They **2** increase the efficiency of the machine. Which of these two machines do you think is more efficient?

Section Review

Main Ideas: Friction in a machine can be reduced by using wheels and ball bearings. A machine is more efficient if friction is reduced.

Questions: Answer in complete sentences.

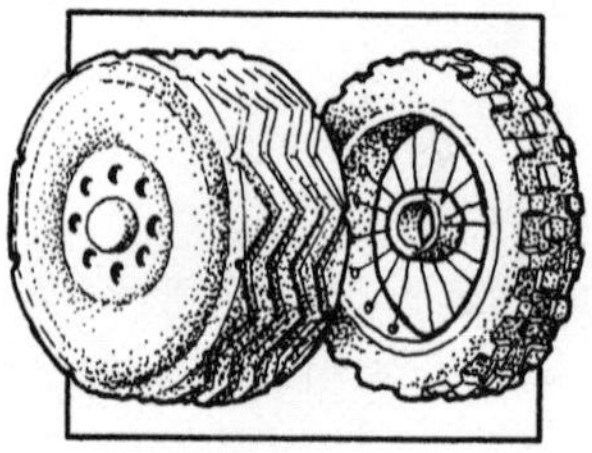

1. Which of these wheels would you use on a racing car? Explain your answer.
2. What effect does a ball bearing have on friction? Why?
3. How do ball bearings increase the efficiency of a machine?
4. How do you think people reduced friction before the invention of the wheel?

DEVELOPMENT

1 Teaching Tips—A perfect machine is 100 % efficient. All the energy put into a perfect machine is used to do work. Ask students if they think a perfect machine actually exists. It does not, since it is not possible to eliminate friction completely.
2 Text Questions—Which of these two machines do you think is more efficient? *The one on the left.*

SECTION REVIEW

Answers to Questions
1. The thin one, since it will have less friction than the wide one.
2. Ball bearings reduce friction. Objects can more easily roll over each other than rub against each other.
3. They reduce friction.
4. They probably made surfaces smoother.

13-3. Reducing Friction

The boat in the picture is called a **Hovercraft** (**huv**-er-kraft). Unlike other boats, a *Hovercraft* does not move through water. It rides on a layer of air just above the water. A Hovercraft can move very fast. Why do you think this is so? When you finish this section, you should be able to:

Hovercraft: A boat that rides on a cushion of air to reduce friction with the water.

☐ **A.** Explain how *lubrication* reduces friction.

☐ **B.** Explain the effect of lubricants on the efficiency of machines.

There is a great deal of friction between the bottom of a boat and the surface of the water. Speedboats with very large engines can move faster than some cars. But usually boats do not travel at high speeds. This is because friction is greater in the water than on land. The water touches the whole bottom surface of the boat. If

SECTION BACKGROUND

A lubricant is a substance that is used to create a smooth surface film between objects that come in contact. Lubricants increase the efficiency of machines because they reduce friction between their moving parts. Lubricated machine parts move more easily against one another. Therefore, they do not generate as much heat.

A variety of materials, such as petroleum jelly, oil, graphite, and wax, can be used as lubricants. All these materials make surfaces smoother and decrease friction.

MATERIALS

4 marbles, liquid soap, paper towels

BASIC TEACHING PLAN

MOTIVATION

You may want to build the Hovercraft described in the Extension on page T-212. Showing the students how it works would be a good motivation for this section.

Some students may have seen a Hovercraft, or they may even have ridden in one. Have them describe their experiences.

EXTENSIONS

Enrichment

Science Skills—Comparing and Contrasting

Students can compare and contrast the lubricating ability of various materials in the following Activity.

A. Gather these materials: petroleum jelly, wax, oil, graphite, and water.

B. Have the students make a chart listing the name of the lubricant, and its appearance, its feel, and its effect on materials.

C. Have them describe each material and record the information on the chart.

D. Have them put the material between two objects, such as their hands, bricks, wooden blocks.

1. What happens when the objects are rubbed together?
2. What effect does the material have on the friction between the objects?

you could reduce the amount of water touching the boat, it would go faster. A clever way to do this is to lift the boat. Lifting the boat just above **1** the water reduces friction. The Hovercraft blows air down. This cushion of air lifts the boat up. There is a slight space between the boat and the water. Thus, the Hovercraft is able to travel quite fast.

Lubrication: A way of reducing friction by using a liquid on the moving parts.

The problem of friction cannot always be solved by separating the two surfaces. In most machines, the parts must touch each other. We have to find other ways to reduce friction. **Lubrication** (loo-bri-**kay**-shun) is the method used in many machines.

Lubrication reduces friction by putting a material like oil between the parts of a machine. For example, rub your hand against your desk. You should feel the friction between your hand and the desk. Now wet your hand with a little **2** water. Your hand should slide easily across the desk. The water acts as a lubricant. A lubricant allows two surfaces to rub smoothly against one another. This reduces friction.

The efficiency of a machine is less if it has to do extra work against friction. But when lubrication helps make the friction less, the machine **3** becomes more efficient. In the following two examples, lubrication helps the machines run more efficiently.

The girl in the picture is putting some oil on the wheel of her bike. The oil will lubricate the moving parts of the wheel. Friction will be reduced. The bike will ride smoother.

220

DEVELOPMENT

1 Teaching Tips—Let the students infer how the Hovercraft works. List their inferences on the chalkboard. Make the Hovercraft described in the Extension on page T-212. Let them check their inferences by carefully observing the Hovercraft as it moves, or tell the students to continue reading their textbooks. They will find out if they are right as they read on in the text.

2 Skill Development—Have the students make *observations* and *inferences* about the effect of water on friction.

3 Teaching Tips—Bring in a machine that needs to be lubricated. Perhaps a student would like to bring in a bike that needs oiling. Run the machine without lubricating it first. Then add a lubricant, such as oil, and run the machine again.

Activity

How do lubricants reduce friction?

A. Gather these materials: 4 marbles, liquid soap, and a paper towel.

B. Rub your hands together. Do this for about 10 seconds.

1. What did you feel?

C. Put a small amount of liquid soap in your palm. Rub your hands together. Wipe your hands with a paper towel.

2. What happened when you rubbed your hands together this time?
3. Why was there a difference?

D. Hold the 4 marbles. Rub your hands together again.

4. How does this compare with rubbing your hands together without a lubricant?

E. Pour a small amount of lubricant (liquid soap) on the marbles. Rub your hands together while holding the lubricated marbles.

5. How did the lubricant affect the friction of the marbles?

EXTENSIONS

Application

Research

Scientists have tried for a long time to create perpetual-motion machines, but no one has ever succeeded. Students can research the history of these machines and report on them to the class. They should try to answer the following questions:

1. What was the purpose of attempting to create these machines? (Once they began to move, they would never stop.)
2. Why does none of them work? (You cannot totally eliminate friction, so eventually they will always slow down and stop.)

ACTIVITY

Skill Development—*Observing, Comparing and Contrasting*

Answers to Questions—1. Heat. **2.** There was less heat, and the hands felt slippery. **3.** The soap acted as a lubricant, reducing friction between the hands. **4.** There is less friction and less heat. **5.** The lubricant made the marbles slippery and reduced friction even more. The two together produced the least amount of heat.

EXTENSIONS

Enrichment

Science Skills—Measuring

Students can measure the effect of a lubricant by using a force measurer and comparing lubricated and unlubricated blocks.

A. Gather these materials: 1-m board, large wood block, petroleum jelly, force measurer.

B. Set up an inclined plane using the 1-m board.

C. Fasten the force measurer to the wood block. Slowly pull it up the incline.

1. What force is required to pull the block?

D. Smear petroleum jelly on the bottom of the wood block. Slowly pull the block up the board.

2. What force is required to pull the block?
3. What effect did the lubricant have on the friction between the board and the block?

4 A car engine also needs oil. The engine contains pistons that move up and down. When the pistons are oiled, they move up and down smoothly. Checking the oil level in a car is very important. Without the oil, the pistons will stop. The engine will not run efficiently.

5 Many kinds of materials are used as lubri-
6 cants. Look at the materials shown above. In what way could you use each as a lubricant?

Section Review

Main Ideas: Friction is caused when the moving parts in a machine rub against each other. A lubricant reduces friction. When the friction is reduced, the machine is more efficient.

Questions: Answer in complete sentences.

1. What effect does oil have on the moving parts of a toy wagon?
2. Why do people have the oil in their car engines checked?
3. How could you increase the friction between two moving parts?

4 Teaching Tips—Ask the students if they have ever seen how the oil is checked in a car. Ask the students why they think this is done. You might take the students outside to the parking lot and show them how to check the oil and explain why it is done.
5 Teaching Tips—Ask students if they have ever ridden a bicycle in the rain. What happened to the brakes? *The rainwater acts as a lubricant between the brakes and the wheels.*
6 Text Questions—In what way could you use each as a lubricant? *The grease and motor oil could be used in a car. The household oil could be used for sewing machines, roller skates, or any small machine around the home. Graphite can be used in locks to make them turn more easily.*

SECTION REVIEW

Answers to Questions
1. Oil lubricates the moving parts, thus reducing friction.
2. It is important to have enough oil in a car engine so that friction and heat are reduced as the parts move against one another.
3. By making the surfaces of the parts rougher

CHAPTER REVIEW

Science Words: Think of a word for each blank. List the letters **a** through **e** on paper. Write the word next to each letter.

The force caused when one object rubs against another is __a__. Small balls used to reduce friction are called __b__. To make a machine more __c__, we try to reduce the friction between its moving parts. Often, this is done by __d__. A liquid used to reduce friction is called a __e__.

Questions: Answer in complete sentences.

1. Why does a hockey puck slide across the ice easily?
2. Why can you use a nail file to change the shape of your nails?
3. Name one harmful example of friction.
4. Explain how friction acts in each of the following examples: (a) car brakes; and (b) an icy road.
5. When would it be helpful to increase friction?
6. Why does a flat tire increase friction with the road?
7. How do wheels help reduce friction in a machine?
8. Without pedaling faster, what is one way to make a bike go faster?
9. How does a lubricant reduce friction?
10. Why do you think highways and roads are slippery after it rains?

EXTENSIONS

Enrichment

Activity

Streamlining is a way of reducing friction. Students can observe this fact in the following Activity:

A. Gather these materials: string, a 2-in. × 4-in. board, clay, a water basin, and a force measurer.

B. Fill a sink or a rectangular basin with water.

C. Attach the force measurer to the board so that the board can be pulled through the water broadside. Add a mass of clay or some other mass to the board so that the board is just floating.

D. Using the force measurer, determine the amount of force needed to pull the board, broad side first, and then narrow side first, through the water.

1. Which side required less force, broad or narrow side? (Narrow)
2. Which shape required less force? (The more streamlined shape.)

E. Try sawing the end of the board to a point. Add the scraps of wood to the mass on top of the board. Measure the force needed to pull the board again.

3. Was there a difference in force needed? (Less force was needed.)

CHAPTER REVIEW

Science Words

a. Friction, **b.** ball bearings, **c.** efficient, **d.** lubricating, **e.** lubricant

Answers to Questions

1. The ice is smooth and slippery.
2. A nail file is rough. Rubbing it against your nails wears them down.
3. Friction wears down shoes.
4. **a.** The brakes rub against the car wheel, causing the wheel to slow down. **b.** An icy road has little friction, so objects slide over it.
5. On icy roads; on slippery floors
6. Because more of the wheel's surface is touching the road
7. Objects can roll rather than slide across a surface.
8. Reduce friction in the moving wheels
9. By making surfaces smoother
10. Rainwater acts as a lubricant, making the roads more slippery.

SUGGESTED WORKSHEET MASTERS
pp. T-171 q, r

SUGGESTED TEST MASTERS
pp. T-171 i, j

EXTENSIONS

Application
Science Skills—Predicting

Students should realize that machines do not lessen the amount of work needed to do a job; they just make it easier. This Activity will demonstrate this idea.

A. Using the material gathered for the Investigation, have the students first measure the force needed to lift the milk carton to the height of the top of the ramp.

B. Using the formula $W = F \times d$, find how much work was done lifting the carton straight up. Then, compare it with the force needed to move it up the ramp.

1. Which method needed more force? (Pulling straight up)
2. Which method needed more work? (They both needed the same amount of work.)

INVESTIGATING

How do scientists measure work?

A. Gather these materials: spring scale, string, meter stick, 3 pencils, milk carton, sand, 50-cm (20-in.) board, and 2 books.

B. Copy the chart shown here. Use it to record your results.

C. Fill the milk carton about 1/2 full of sand. Close the top. Fasten a piece of string to the carton.

D. Make an inclined plane by stacking the 2 books. Lay a board on them to form a ramp. Work is equal to the force times the distance. The formula for work is $W = F \times d$

E. Fasten the milk carton to the spring scale. Slowly pull the carton up the ramp. Record the force used and the distance up the ramp.

1. Using the formula, how much work was done moving the milk carton? Record.

F. Put more sand in the milk carton until the carton is about 3/4 full.

2. Do you think you will have to do more or less work now to pull the carton up the ramp?

G. Repeat step E.

3. How much work did you do? Record.

4. Was the amount of work different in the two trials? Why?

Load	Force	Distance	Work
1/2 full			
3/4 full			

INVESTIGATING

Skill Development—*Measuring*

Teaching Tips—You will need a good spring scale to measure force in this activity. To compute the work done, multiply the force times the distance the object was pulled. Work is expressed in terms of newton-meter. The formula for work is $W = F \times d$. The unit of force is the newton, and the unit of distance is the meter. Multiplying these units together gives us the unit newton-meter. If you do not want to introduce newton-m, use the numbers on the spring scale and measure the distance in cm. It takes more work to move the carton when it is three-quarters full of sand than when it is half full of sand. The distance is the same, but the force needed is greater. Therefore, more work is done.

Answers to Questions—1. Students should multiply force times distance. **2.** More work will be done. **3.** Again, students should multiply force times distance. **4.** Yes, more force was required to move the second carton. The second carton had more mass, and it required more work to move it the same distance.

CAREERS

Machinist ►

Machinists make the metal parts from which machines are made. They must be skilled in using machine tools to cut metal into exact sizes and shapes. All the parts must be made so that the finished machine will be as efficient as possible. People who want to be machinists must first study with a master machinist.

◄ Mechanic

What do you do when something goes wrong with your car or lawnmower or dishwasher? You may be good at do-it-yourself repairs. Or you may take it to a mechanic. Mechanics usually study machines at a technical school. They must know how machines work and how to fix them when they break down.

EXTENSIONS

Application

Research

Mechanical engineers design engines and machines that run on power. Almost all mechanical engineers work in manufacturing industries. A few work for the government, for example, in the Federal Power Commission or in the Environmental Protection Agency. Mechanical engineers must go to college for at least four years. For more information, contact: American Society of Mechanical Engineers, 345 East 47th Street, New York, N.Y. 10017.

Service-station attendants work at service stations pumping gas and checking the general running condition of automobiles and trucks. They check the belts and the oil and water levels in motor vehicles. They tell their customers when these items need to be replaced. A high school diploma is recommended. Most of the training required is on the job. To find out more about this job, students should visit a service station in their neighborhood and talk to the attendants.

CAREERS

Teaching Tips—For additional information, students should contact their high school vocation center. The counselor may be able to direct them to local businesses that hire people for these careers.

UNIT 5 ANIMAL AND PLANT

CHAPTER	SECTION	BASIC SCIENCE SKILLS	ACTIVITY MATERIALS STUDENT/GROUP	EXTENSIONS
CHAPTER 14 LIVING THINGS	**14-1** p.T-228 The Biosphere	*Finding the cause and effect* relationships in the biosphere p.T-230	plastic shoe box with lid, pebbles, soil, grass seeds, small plant, water	• Reinforcement pp.T-229, T-231 • Application p.T-230
	14-2 p.T-232 Is It Alive?	*Classifying* living things	piece of chalk, rock, cut flower, pencil, moss, ant	• Enrichment pp.T-234, T-235 • Application p.T-233
	14-3 p.T-236 Counting Living Things	*Recording data* on populations	42-cm lengths of insulated wire, metric ruler, meter stick, dried lima beans, 40 m of rope or string	• Enrichment pp.T-239, T-241 • Application pp.T-237, T-238, T-240
CHAPTER 15 THE CYCLES OF POPULATIONS	**15-1** p.T-242 Animal Life Cycles	*Comparing and contrasting* reproduction of brine shrimp, amebas, and hydras p.T-244	mealworms, jar with lid, bran, slice of potato or apple, ruler	• Enrichment pp.T-244, T-246 • Application pp.T-243, T-245
	15-2 p.T-247 Plant Life Cycles	*Comparing and contrasting* seeds from different plants p.T-248 *Observing* spores and *classifying* ferns p.T-250	radish or bean seeds, potting soil, styrofoam cups, water	• Reinforcement p.T-251 • Enrichment pp.T-249, T-250 • Application p.T-248
	15-3 p.T-252 Organisms on the Move	*Classifying* animals as migrators and nonmigrators p.T-253 *Comparing and contrasting* migration routes p.T-253, p.T-254	various seeds, plastic cup, water	• Reinforcement pp.T-253, T-255 • Enrichment pp.T-254, T-256
	15-4 p.T-257 Population Explosions	*Observing* a population explosion	3 different size jars, Daphnia, algae water, aged tap water, medicine dropper, small, flat dish	• Enrichment pp.T-258, T-259, T-260, T-261 • Application p.T-262
CHAPTER 16 SURVIVAL AND CHANGE	**16-1** p.T-263 Comparing Organisms	*Observing* differences in a population and *making conclusions* about variations p.T-264 *Comparing and contrasting* whales p.T-265, populations p.T-266	10 shells, metric ruler	• Reinforcement pp.T-264, T-266 • Enrichment pp.T-265, T-267
	16-2 p.T-268 Changing Populations	*Comparing and contrasting* changes in two populations p.T-269	100 red toothpicks, 100 green toothpicks, 40 m string, 4 stakes	• Reinforcement pp.T-270, T-271 • Enrichment p.T-269
	16-3 p.T-272 Disappearing Populations	*Predicting* and *inferring* effects of humans p.T-273 *Hypothesizing* possible causes of extinction of dinosaurs p.T-276		• Reinforcement pp.T-275, T-276 • Enrichment pp.T-273, T-274, T-277, T-278, T-279

POPULATIONS

EXTRA ACTIVITIES/ DEMONSTRATIONS	WORKSHEET MASTERS	EVALUATIONS
• Mini-field trip p.T-228 • Soil p.T-229 • Biosphere p.T-230		Section Review p.T-231
• Lichen p.T-232 • Watering p.T-234	Living Things (SK) p.T-225 j	Section Review p.T-235
• Counting p.T-236 • Cleared patch of ground p.T-237 • Counting animals p.T-238	Counting Living Things (AC) p.T-225 k Word Puzzle (SK) p.T-225 l	Section Review p.T-240 Chapter Review p.T-241 Test Masters pp.T-225 d, e
• Frogs eggs p.T-242 • Shrimp eggs p.T-243 • Moth eggs p.T-245	Animal Life Cycles (SK) p.T-225 m	Section Review p.T-246
• Fruit seeds p.T-249 • Germinating fruit seeds p.T-249	Parts of a Flower (SK) p.T-225 n	Section Review p.T-251
	Science Vocabulary (SK) p.T-225 o	Section Review p.T-256
• Population graph p.T-257	Variations (SK) p.T-225 p	Section Review p.T-261 Chapter Review p.T-262 Test Masters pp.T-225 f, g
• Differences in students p.T-263	Variations in a family (AH) p.T-225 q	Section Review p.T-267
• Finding paper moths p.T-268 • Chameleon p.T-269	Evolution of the horse (SK) p.T-225 r	Section Review p.T-271
• Investigating p.T-278	Extinct and Endangered Animals (SK) p.T-225 s	Section Review p.T-276 Chapter Review p.T-277 Test Masters pp.T-225 h, i

KEY (AC)—Activity (AH)—At Home (SK)—Skill

BOOKS FOR STUDENTS

Dallinger, Jane. *Grasshoppers*, Minneapolis: Lerner Pub., 1981
Dinneen, Betty. *The Family Howl*, illus. by Stephen Bernath, New York: Macmillan, 1981
Freedman, Russell. *Animal Superstars: Biggest, Strongest, Fastest, Smartest*, Englewood Cliffs, NJ: Prentice-Hall, 1981
Friedman, Judi. *Puffin, Come Back!*, illus. by Stephen Kress and others, New York: Dodd, 1981
Hartman, Jane E. *How Animals Care for Their Young*, New York: Holiday, 1980
Hunt, Patricia. *Koalas*, New York: Dodd, 1980
Jacobs, Francine. *Bermuda Petrel: The Bird that Would Not Die.* illus. by Ted Lewin, New York: Morrow, 1981
Lauber, Patricia. *Seeds: Pop, Stick, Glide*, illus. by Jerome Wester, New York: Crown Pub., 1981
——— *What's Hatching Out of the Egg?*, New York: Crown, 1981
McClung, Robert, M. *The Amazing Egg*, illus., New York: E.P. Dutton, 1980
Patent, Dorothy. *Sizes and Shapes in Nature; What They Mean*, New York: Holiday, 1979
Rahn, Joan. *Plants Up Close*, Boston: Houghton Mifflin, 1981
Welch, Martha, M. *Sunflower!*, New York: Dodd, 1981
Wise, William. *Animal Rescue: Saving Our Endangered Wildlife*, New York: Putnam, 1978

FILMS

Adaptations for Survival, 17 min, International
Baby Birds and Their Parents, 11 min, Centron
Elephants, Rhinos and Hippos, 5½ min, Coronet
Etosha: Place of Dry Water, 59 min, National Geographic
Flipper the Seal, 14 min, Coronet
Konrad Lorenz: Science of Animal Behavior, 14 min, National Geographic
Learning About Deer, 13 min, Britannica

COMPUTER AIDS

Insects, Tutorial, Apple, PET, BASIC, 16K + tape, Right On Programs

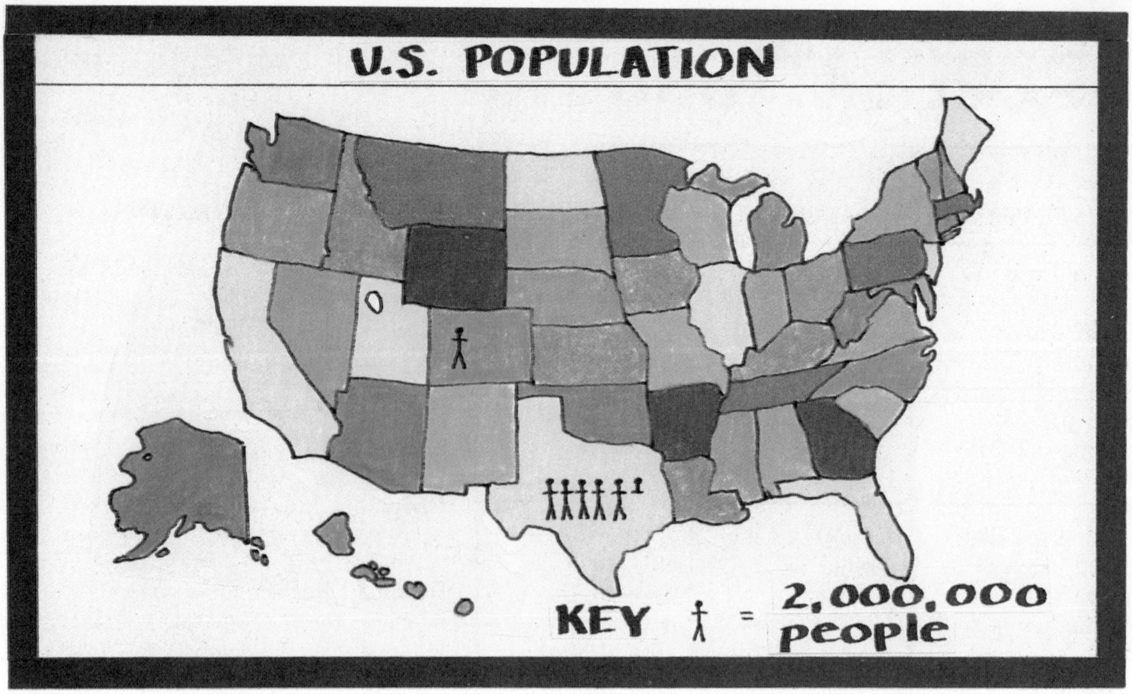

BULLETIN BOARD

Your class can develop a map of the United States which illustrates population density. Have some of the students draw a map of the United States with all the states outlined. Have other students look up the population of each state in an atlas. Use an outline figure of a person as a stencil to make several cutouts. Each cutout figure can be used to illustrate a specific number of people. Have the students calculate how many cutouts, or fractions of cutouts, are needed for each state, and paste them on the map.

FIELD TRIP IDEAS

To visit the zoo

Take your class to a zoo to look specifically for traits that have given the animals a better chance to survive. If possible, have a zookeeper speak to your students about unusual survival traits of some of the animals. You may wish to have the students choose an animal to draw. Have them label the particular characteristics of the animals they draw that enable them to survive.

To explore how population changes have affected your community

Have your students find out what the present population of your community is and what the population was ten years ago. If there has been a change in population, discuss the reasons for the change and how the difference in population size has affected the community. Take your class on a trip to observe changes that have occurred in the community due to an increase or decrease in population. Changes to look for include new or abandoned houses or apartment buildings, additions to schools or closed schools, new or closed businesses, new highways, and use of park areas for new buildings.

Name________________________________Date__________

Fold back answer key on line before copying.

LIVING THINGS

TEST CHAPTER 14

Read each question. Choose the best answer. Write the letter of your choice on the line at the right.

CHAPTER OBJECTIVES

1. The main forms of life in the biosphere are — 1. ______ — 1. d (1)
   a. animals. **c.** protists.
   b. plants. **d.** all of the above.
2. The sun provides living things with — 2. ______ — 2. a (1)
   a. energy. **c.** oxygen.
   b. minerals. **d.** carbon dioxide.
3. The biosphere is located — 3. ______ — 3. c (1)
   a. below the earth's crust.
   b. above the atmosphere.
   c. between the earth's crust and atmosphere.
   d. between the crust and the mantle.
4. The earth's crust provides plants with — 4. ______ — 4. a (2)
   a. nutrients. **c.** carbon dioxide.
   b. sunlight. **d.** oxygen.
5. Which statement is true? — 5. ______ — 5. c (2)
   a. Only animals need sunlight.
   b. Only humans need sunlight.
   c. Animals and plants need sunlight.
   d. Neither animals nor plants need sunlight.
6. What do green plants need from the atmosphere to make their own food? — 6. ______ — 6. d (2)
   a. sunlight and nutrients **c.** carbon dioxide and oxygen
   b. oxygen and sunlight **d.** carbon dioxide and sunlight
7. Which of the following is *not* a living thing? — 7. ______ — 7. a (3)
   a. a book **c.** a fungus
   b. algae **d.** a tree
8. Something that does not need food and water will *not* — 8. ______ — 8. d (3)
   a. reproduce. **c.** need energy.
   b. grow and change. **d.** do all of the above.

Name________________________________Date____________

9. b (3)

9. Simple, one-celled organisms reproduce by **9.** ____

a. becoming caterpillars. **c.** forming seeds.
b. splitting in half. **d.** becoming larger.

10. b (4)

10. So that they do not count the same animals twice, scientists **10.** ____

a. move with the animals.
b. mark them in some way.
c. do not let them out of their sight.
d. count only half of a population.

11. d (4)

11. To find out the approximate number of tomatoes in a field, a scientist would **11.** ____

a. count all the tomatoes.
b. look at the tomatoes and guess the number.
c. pick all the tomatoes and count them.
d. count the number of tomatoes in a small area.

12. d (4)

12. A population is **12.** ____

a. different kinds of organisms living in the same area.
b. different kinds of organisms living in different areas.
c. the same kind of organism living in different areas.
d. the same kind of organism living in the same area.

13. c (5)

13. Scientists count a population of sheep to find out **13.** ____

a. what the sheep eat.
b. how many hours the sheep sleep.
c. if the number of sheep is changing.
d. how fast the sheep can run.

14. d (5)

14. By counting a population of plants or animals, scientists can find out if either population **14.** ____

a. is getting smaller. **c.** is unchanged.
b. is getting larger. **d.** is doing all of the above.

15. a (5)

15. If a population of animals is growing too large, **15.** ____

a. they might run out of food.
b. scientists may not be able to count them.
c. they might need protection.
d. they have to be marked.

Name________________________________Date______________

THE CYCLES OF POPULATIONS

TEST CHAPTER **15**

Fold back answer key on line before copying.

CHAPTER OBJECTIVES

Read each question. Choose the best answer. Write the letter of your choice on the line at the right.

1. An organism that reproduces by budding is the **1.** ______ **1.** c (1)
- **a.** ameba. **c.** hydra.
- **b.** brine shrimp. **d.** butterfly.

2. The life cycle of every organism ends with **2.** ______ **2.** c (1)
- **a.** birth. **c.** death.
- **b.** growth. **d.** none of the above.

3. The order of growth in the life cycle of a butterfly is **3.** ______ **3.** b (1)
- **a.** larva, egg, pupa.
- **b.** egg, larva, pupa.
- **c.** pupa, larva, egg.
- **d.** egg, pupa, larva.

4. How do bees affect pollination? **4.** ______ **4.** a (2)
- **a.** They carry pollen from the anther to the stigma.
- **b.** They carry pollen from the stigma to the anther.
- **c.** They carry pollen to other insects.
- **d.** They do not touch the pollen.

5. The part of a flower that makes pollen is the **5.** ______ **5.** a (2)
- **a.** anther. **c.** spore.
- **b.** stigma. **d.** stem.

6. Which statement is true? **6.** ______ **6.** a (2)
- **a.** Pollen comes from male cones.
- **b.** Pollen comes from female cones.
- **c.** Pollen is made in male and female cones.
- **d.** Cones can reproduce without being pollinated.

7. Which of these plants does not reproduce from seeds? **7.** ______ **7.** d (3)
- **a.** a pine tree **c.** a fruit tree
- **b.** a rose **d.** a fern

8. Some plants can reproduce from **8.** ______ **8.** d (3)
- **a.** cuttings. **c.** buds.
- **b.** runners. **d.** all of the above.

Name________________________ Date__________

9. c (3) **9.** Ferns and mosses can reproduce by **9.** ______

a. pollination. **c.** dropping spores.
b. making seeds. **d.** dividing.

10. b (4) **10.** The first type of plants to grow in a new area during plant succession are **10.** ______

a. cone-bearing plants. **c.** oak trees.
b. grasses. **d.** maple trees.

11. d (4) **11.** Which of the following is *not* a reason that most animals migrate? **11.** ______

a. to find food
b. to reproduce
c. to get protection from the cold
d. to get away from insects

12. b (4) **12.** Animal migration is different from plant succession because **12.** ______

a. some animals migrate to raise their young.
b. plant succession is very slow.
c. animals migrate twice a year.
d. all of the above happen.

13. a (5) **13.** A population explosion can occur when there are **13.** ______

a. more births than deaths.
b. more deaths than births.
c. the same amount of births and deaths.
d. no births or deaths in the same year.

14. c (5) **14.** A population would *not* decrease because of **14.** ______

a. more members of a population moving out of an area.
b. lack of food.
c. good health.
d. crowded living space.

15. c (5) **15.** Foxes control the lemming population by **15.** ______

a. forcing them to migrate south.
b. taking all their food.
c. eating them.
d. chasing them into different areas.

Name________________________________Date______________

SURVIVAL AND CHANGE

TEST CHAPTER 16

Fold back answer key on line before copying.

Read each question. Choose the best answer. Write the letter of your choice on the line at the right.

CHAPTER OBJECTIVES

1. Populations can differ from each other in **1.** ______ **1.** d (1)
a. size. **c.** shape.
b. color. **d.** all of the above.

2. A population of thousands of viruses **2.** ______ **2.** c (1)
a. would fill a cup. **c.** is very small.
b. moves quickly. **d.** is none of the above.

3. The long necks of giraffes help them to survive because **3.** ______ **3.** c (1)
a. they can reach food other animals cannot.
b. they can spot their enemies quickly.
c. they can do both of the above.
d. they can do none of the above.

4. The differences between a large cat and a small cat are called **4.** ______ **4.** d (2)
a. populations. **c.** viruses.
b. migrations. **d.** variations.

5. A population of people can differ in **5.** ______ **5.** d (2)
a. age. **c.** weight.
b. height. **d.** all of the above.

6. Individuals in a population **6.** ______ **6.** d (2)
a. all look alike. **c.** are always the same size.
b. are all the same color. **d.** can have variations.

7. A variation among hares that makes it easier for them to survive the winter is their **7.** ______ **7.** c (3)
a. shape. **c.** color.
b. size. **d.** markings.

8. If tree trunks are dark, birds will eat **8.** ______ **8.** a (3)
a. more white moths. **c.** more moths.
b. more dark moths. **d.** fewer moths.

Name ______________________ Date __________

9. d (3)

9. Variations that help animals to survive are **9.** ______

a. not passed on to the young.
b. harmful to the young.
c. the same in all populations.
d. passed on to their young.

10. b (4)

10. An animal that is endangered is the **10.** ______

a. deer. **c.** dinosaur.
b. bald eagle. **d.** horse.

11. d (4)

11. Which of the following is *not* extinct? **11.** ______

a. dinosaurs **c.** labrador duck
b. passenger pigeon **d.** grizzly bear

12. b (4)

12. Which sentence is true? **12.** ______

a. There are more endangered animals than plants.
b. There are more endangered plants than animals.
c. There are the same number of endangered animals and plants.
d. There are no endangered animals or plants.

13. a (5)

13. Beavers almost became extinct because **13.** ______

a. humans killed so many of them.
b. the climate they lived in changed.
c. their populations had too many variations.
d. they were being eaten by bears.

14. d (5)

14. Animals can become extinct as a result of **14.** ______

a. a change in environment.
b. a change in the food supply.
c. human interference.
d. all of the above.

15. c (5)

15. One way to prevent whales from becoming extinct is **15.** ______

a. to increase their food supply.
b. to move them to fresh water.
c. to stop hunting them.
d. to do none of the above.

Name ______________________ Date ______________

Living Things

SKILL WORKSHEET

A. Identify the features of living things shown in the pictures below.

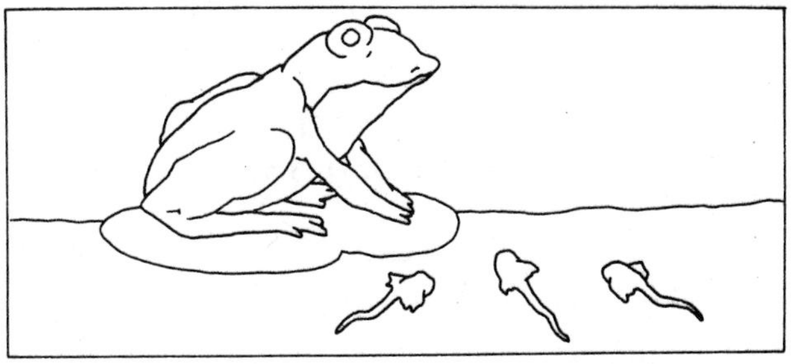

____

____

____

____

B. Draw a diagram that shows how the biosphere acts like a system.

Name ______________________ Date ______________

Counting Living Things

ACTIVITY WORKSHEET

You are studying how scientists count populations of living things. In this activity, you will count the population of pets owned by you and your classmates.

A. Have each person in your class fill in the questionnaire below. Tear it off along the dotted line.

B. Collect the questionnaires. Record the data on a master chart for your class.

C. Use the data to answer the following questions.

1. How many different pet populations are there?

   ____

2. What is the most common pet population?

   ____

3. What is the average age of the pets?

   ____

4. What is the average number of pets per person?

   ____

5. Are there more male or female pets?

   ____

Questionnaire	Pets			
Your Name	**Number**	**Type**	**Age**	**Sex**
Example: *John Smith*	*1*	*dog*	*2*	*female*

Name ______________________________ Date ______________

Living Things

SKILL WORKSHEET

Fill in the words defined below in the proper order to spell the title of a scientist who studies the world of living things.

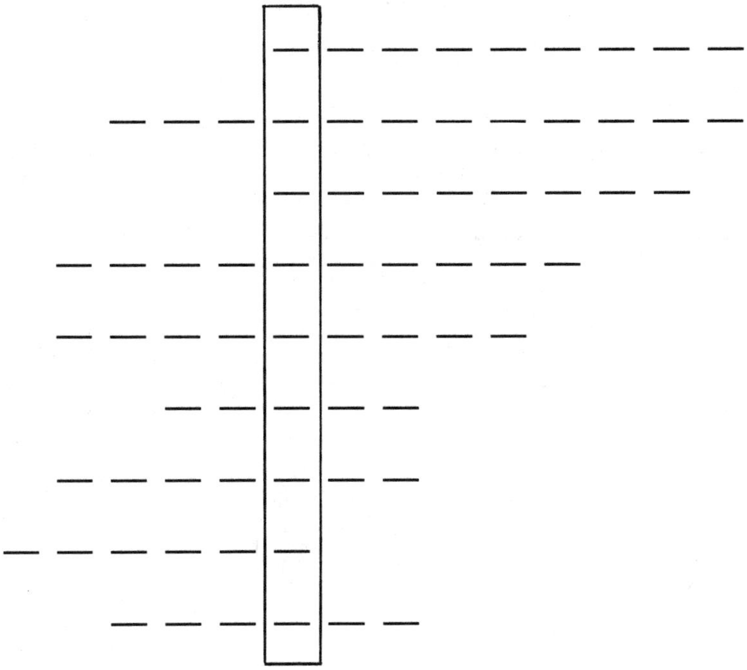

1. The layer of the earth that is made of living things
2. Reproduce, grow and change, need food, water and energy
3. An individual living thing
4. A group of the same kind of organisms that live in the same place
5. To make more of the same kind of organism
6. A very small plant, usually made of single cells
7. Very small, single-celled living things
8. Plants such as mushrooms and molds that have no leaves and stems
9. A set of things that work together to form a whole

Name ______________________________ Date ______________

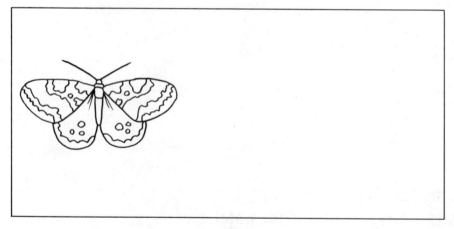

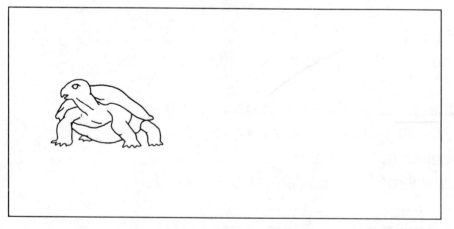

The Cycles of Population

SKILL WORKSHEET

Draw the life cycle of each animal shown below. Label each stage.

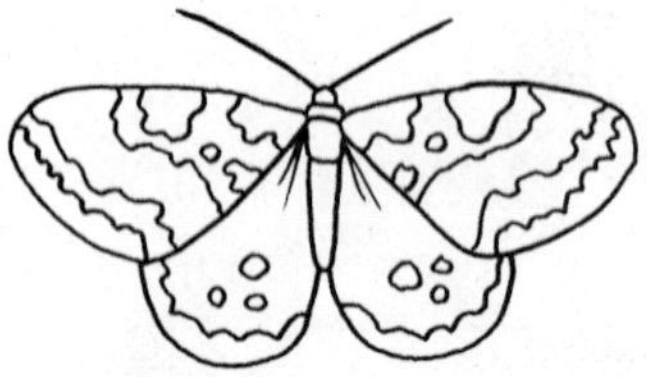

Name ____________________ Date ____________

The Cycles of Population

SKILL WORKSHEET

A. Connect the dots and label the parts of the flower.

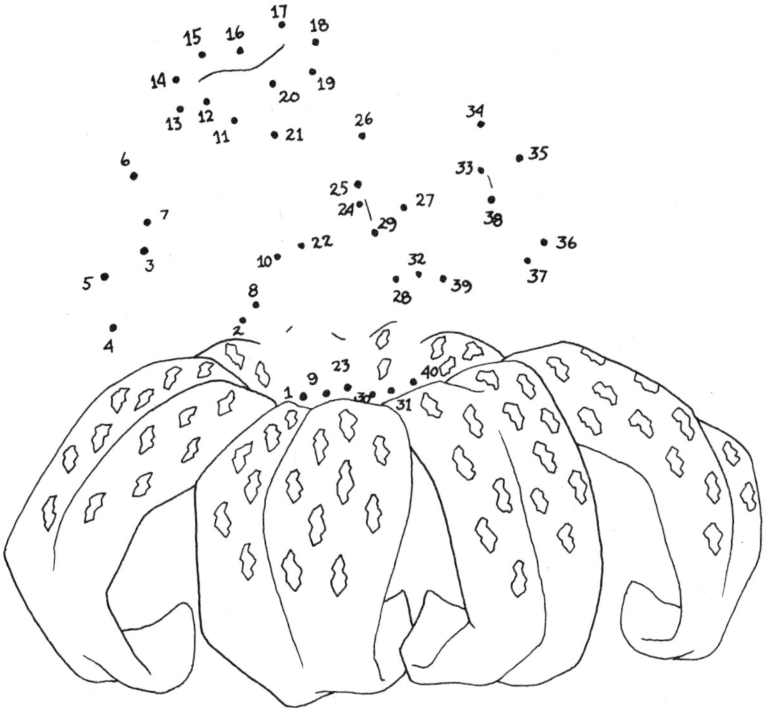

B. Use the correct words to complete the paragraph: seeds, pollen, insects, birds, anther, fruit, stigma.

Before a flower can make a new plant the yellow powder called __________ must travel from the __________, where it is made, to the __________. Wind, water, __________ and __________ can help carry this powder. After the flower is pollinated, __________ begin to grow. They are often contained in __________, such as apples or pears.

C. What method does each of these plants use to reproduce?

Strawberry ____________________

Potato ____________________

Name ______________________ Date ______________

The Cycles of Population

SKILL WORKSHEET

Fill in the blanks to identify the correct word. Use the circled letters to complete the sentence.

When we study the birth, growth and development, and death of plants and animals, we are studying their ________.

1. The young form of an organism (_) _ R _ A
2. A stage in the life cycle of an insect in which it is not active _ U _ A
3. The part of the flower that contains pollen A _ _ H (_) _
4. A yellow powder made by flowers P _ (_) L _ _
5. The part of a flower that receives pollen S _ (_) _ M A
6. Simple green, nonflowering plants (_) E _ _ S
7. Small, green plants that grow in velvety clusters on rocks _ O _ _ E (_)
8. Small, round objects that produce new fern plants _ P O _ (_) S
9. The movement of animals from place to place M _ _ R _ T I _ _
10. An insect that migrates _ O N _ R (_) H _ U _ T E _ _ L (_)
11. The movement of one plant after another into an area S _ C (_) E _ _ _ _ _ N

Name ____________________ Date ____________

Survival and Change

SKILL WORKSHEET

A. For each of the animals shown below name the trait that helps it survive.

____________________ ____________________

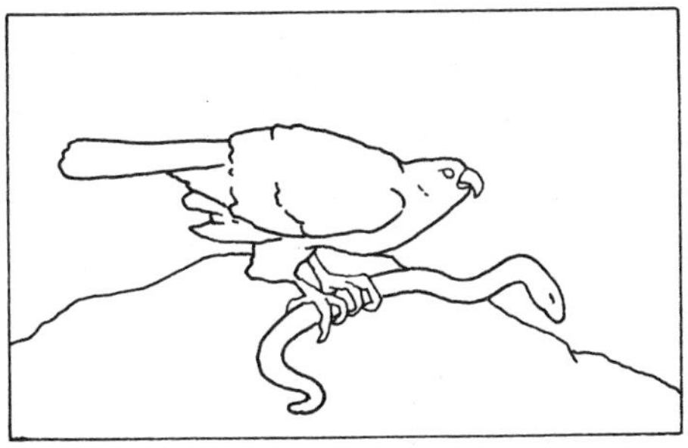

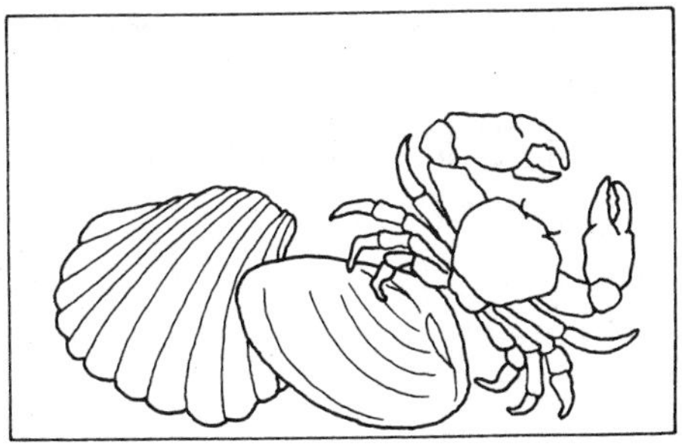

____________________ ____________________

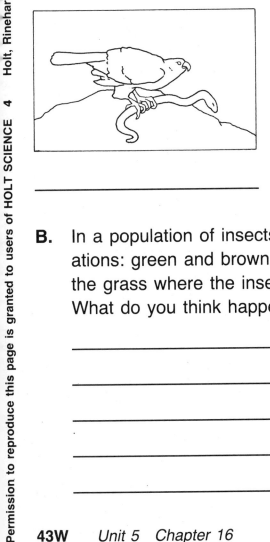

B. In a population of insects, there were two color variations: green and brown. One dry summer, all of the grass where the insects lived dried up and died. What do you think happened to the insects?

____

____

____

____

____

Name ______________________ Date ____________

Survival and Change

AT HOME WORKSHEET

Members of the same population can be very different from each other. Certain traits may vary a great deal. In this at home activity, you will compare some traits of each member of your family.

A. Gather these materials: tape measure and bathroom scale.

B. Fill in the chart below based on your measurements and observations of each member of your family.

Family Member	Height	Weight	Hair Color	Eye Color	Shoe Size	Hat Size
Example: Father	6′2″	175 lbs	black	brown	12	8

What are some differences and similarities you found among the members of your family?

Name ________________________ Date ____________

Survival and Change

SKILL WORKSHEET

Horses have not always looked the way they do now. They have changed over millions of years. The drawing below shows some of these changes.

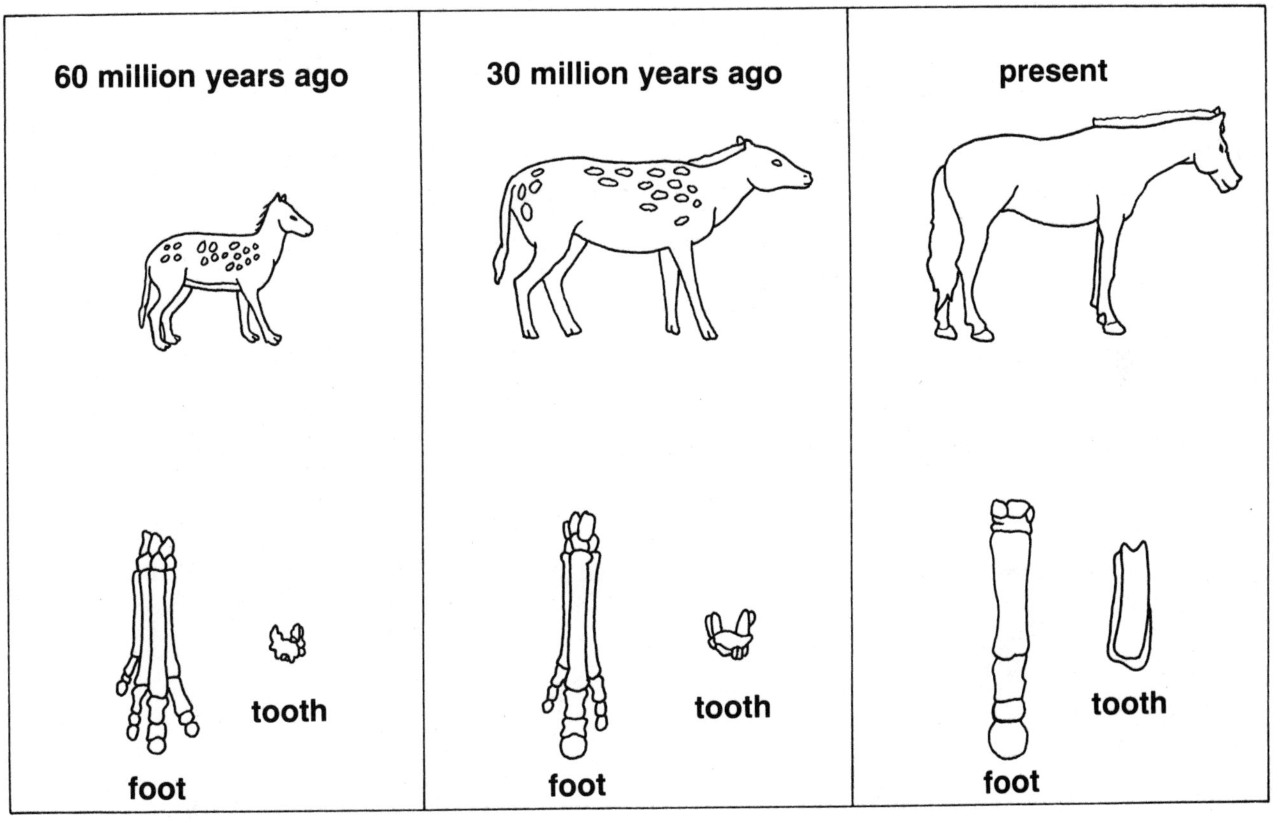

1. Which trait has changed the most? ____________
2. Name two other traits that have changed ____________

____

3. How do you think these changes helped horses to survive? ____________________

____

____

____

Name ______________________ Date ____________

Survival and Change

SKILL WORKSHEET

A. Label each of the animals shown below as endangered or extinct.

blue whale

____

dinosaur

____

eagle

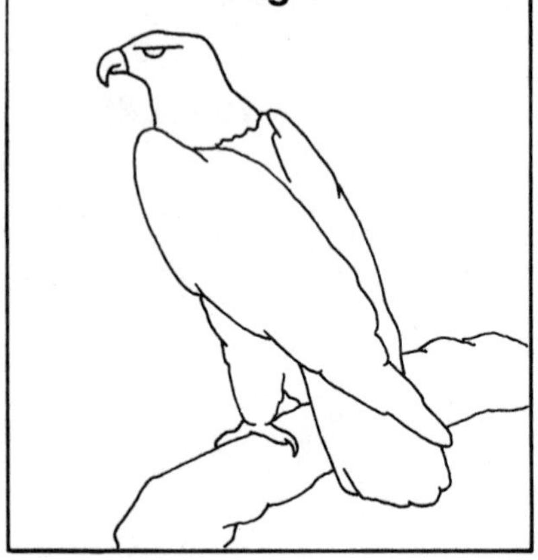

____

grizzly bear

____

Labrador duck

____

passenger pigeon

____

B. List some reasons why animals might become extinct.

____

____

____

Name________________________ Date______________

Living Things

CLASSIFYING, FINDING CAUSE AND EFFECT — SKILL WORKSHEET

A. Identify the features of living things shown in the pictures below.

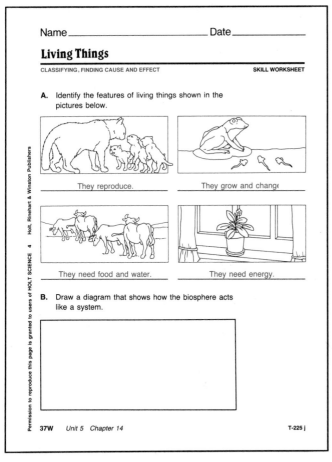

They reproduce.

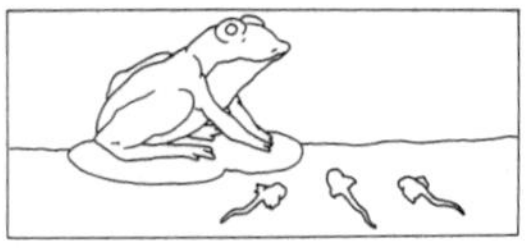
They grow and change

They need food and water.

They need energy.

B. Draw a diagram that shows how the biosphere acts like a system.

Name________________________ Date______________

Counting Living Things

ACTIVITY WORKSHEET

You are studying how scientists count populations of living things. In this activity, you will count the population of pets owned by you and your classmates.

A. Have each person in your class fill in the questionnaire below. Tear it off along the dotted line.
B. Collect the questionnaires. Record the data on a master chart for your class.
C. Use the data to answer the following questions.

1. How many different pet populations are there? ______
2. What is the most common pet population? ______
3. What is the average age of the pets? ______
4. What is the average number of pets per person? ______
5. Are there more male or female pets? ______

Questionnaire	Pets			
Your Name	Number	Type	Age	Sex
Example: John Smith	*1*	*dog*	*2*	*female*

Name________________________ Date______________

Living Things

BUILDING SCIENCE VOCABULARY — SKILL WORKSHEET

Fill in the words defined below in the proper order to spell the title of a scientist who studies the world of living things.

```
        (B)I O S P H E R E
   L I V (I)N G T H I N G S
        (O)R G A N I S M
  P O P U(L)A T I O N
  R E P R(O)D U C E
      A L(G)A E
  P R O T(I)S T
F U N G U(S)
    S Y S(T)E M
```

1. The layer of the earth that is made of living things
2. Reproduce, grow and change, need food, water and energy
3. An individual living thing
4. A group of the same kind of organisms that live in the same place
5. To make more of the same kind of organism
6. A very small plant, usually made of single cells
7. Very small, single-celled living things
8. Plants such as mushrooms and molds that have no leaves and stems
9. A set of things that work together to form a whole

Name________________________ Date______________

The Cycles of Population

SEQUENCING — SKILL WORKSHEET

Draw the life cycle of each animal shown below. Label each stage.

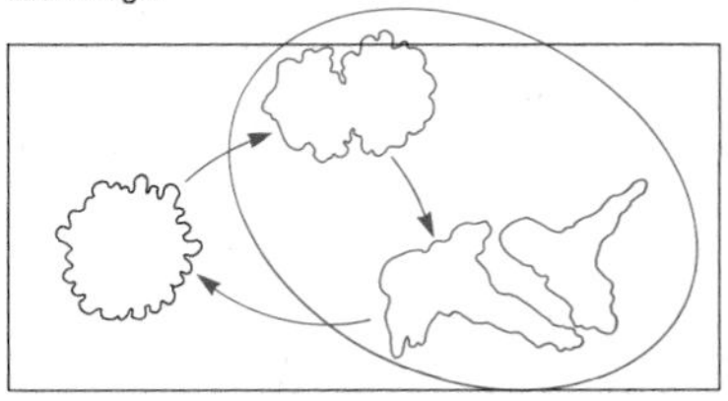

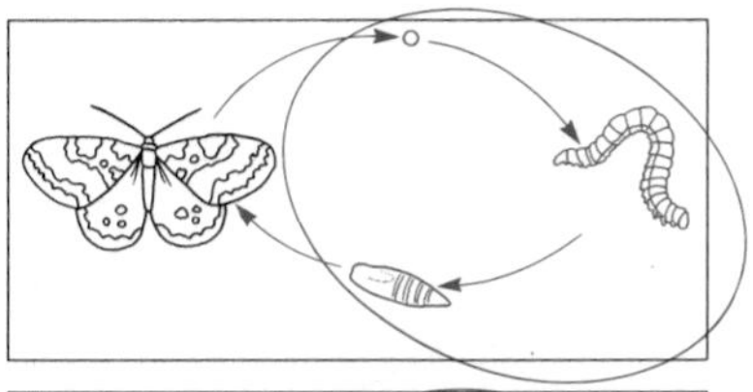

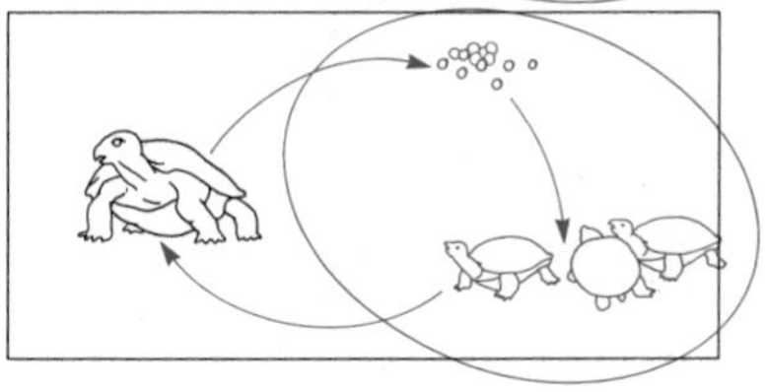

Name________________________ Date____________

The Cycles of Population

CLASSIFYING, BUILDING SCIENCE VOCABULARY — SKILL WORKSHEET

A. Connect the dots and label the parts of the flower.

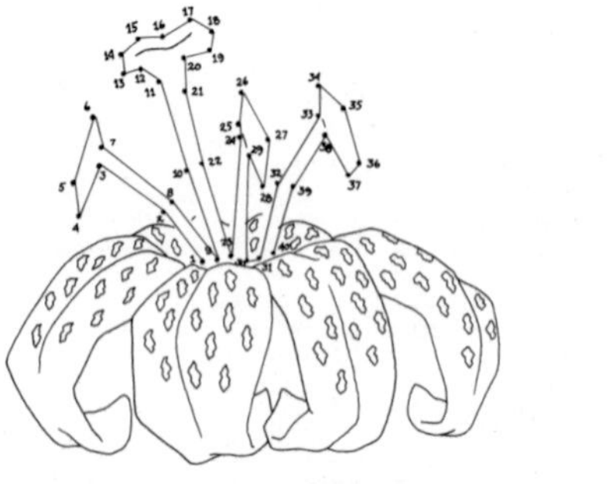

B. Use the correct words to complete the paragraph: seeds, pollen, insects, birds, anther, fruit, stigma.

Before a flower can make a new plant the yellow powder called pollen must travel from the anther, where it is made, to the stigma. Wind, water, insects and birds can help carry this powder. After the flower is pollinated, seeds begin to grow. They are often contained in fruit, such as apples or pears.

C. What method does each of these plants use to reproduce?
Strawberry Runners
Potato Buds (eyes)

Name________________________ Date____________

The Cycles of Population

BUILDING SCIENCE VOCABULARY — SKILL WORKSHEET

Fill in the blanks to identify the correct word. Use the circled letters to complete the sentence.

When we study the birth, growth and development, and death of plants and animals, we are studying their life cycles.

1. The young form of an organism (L) A R V A
2. A stage in the life cycle of an insect in which it is not active P U P A
3. The part of the flower that contains pollen A N T H (E) R
4. A yellow powder made by flowers P O (L) L E N
5. The part of a flower that receives pollen S T (I) G M A
6. Simple Green, nonflowering plants (F) E R N S
7. Small, green plants that grow in velvety clusters on rocks M O S S E (S)
8. Small, round objects that produce new fern plants S P O R (E) S
9. The movement of animals from place to place M I G R A T I O N
10. An insect that migrates M O N A R (C) H B U T T E R F L (Y)
11. The movement of one plant after another into an area S U C (C) E S S I O N

Name________________________ Date____________

Survival and Change

INFERRING, FINDING CAUSE AND EFFECT — SKILL WORKSHEET

A. For each of the animals shown below name the trait that helps it survive.

Long neck

Changing color

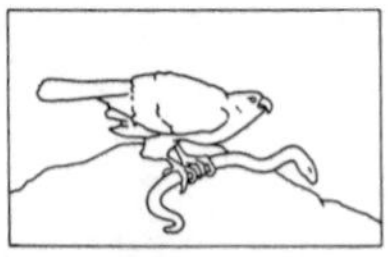

Good eyesight

Protective shell

B. In a population of insects, there were two color variations: green and brown. One dry summer, all of the grass where the insects lived dried up and died. What do you think happened to the insects?

The brown insects were better able to survive, since they blended in with the color of the soil. More green insects were eaten by birds. After a time, there were more brown insects than green insects.

Name________________________ Date____________

Survival and Change

AT HOME WORKSHEET

Members of the same population can be very different from each other. Certain traits may vary a great deal. In this at home activity, you will compare some traits of each member of your family.

A. Gather these materials: tape measure and bathroom scale.

B. Fill in the chart below based on your measurements and observations of each member of your family.

Family Member	Height	Weight	Hair Color	Eye Color	Shoe Size	Hat Size
Example: Father	6′2″	175 lbs	black	brown	12	8

What are some differences and similarities you found among the members of your family?

Name____________________ Date__________

Survival and Change

OBSERVING, FINDING CAUSE AND EFFECT — SKILL WORKSHEET

Horses have not always looked the way they do now. They have changed over millions of years. The drawing below shows some of these changes.

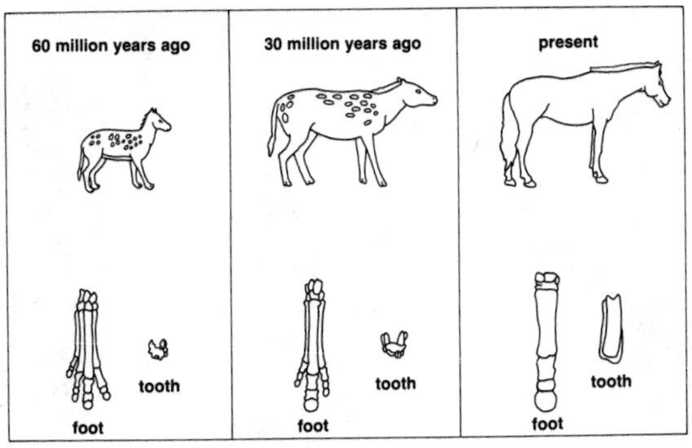

1. Which trait has changed the most? Height
2. Name two other traits that have changed Number of toes, shape of teeth
3. How do you think these changes helped horses to survive? Longer legs and a single hoof (instead of four toes) allowed horses to run faster and to escape from predators. Large, flat teeth allowed them to chew tough grasses.

Name____________________ Date__________

Survival and Change

CLASSIFYING, FINDING CAUSE AND EFFECT — SKILL WORKSHEET

A. Label each of the animals shown below as endangered or extinct.

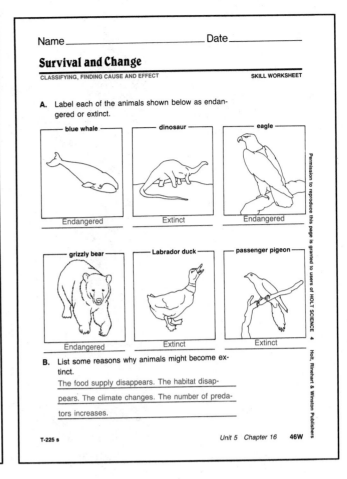

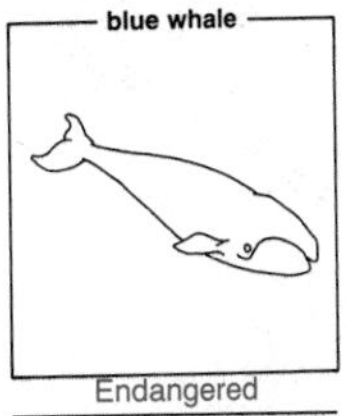

Endangered

Extinct

Endangered

Endangered

Extinct

Extinct

B. List some reasons why animals might become extinct.
The food supply disappears. The habitat disappears. The climate changes. The number of predators increases.

Unit Overview

This is a life science unit on plant and animal populations. Life on the earth is found in the biosphere, which includes the air, the upper surface of the earth's crust, and the oceans. Living things grow and change, consume food and water, use energy, and reproduce themselves. Plants and animals of one kind that live in one area are called populations. Biologists are interested in keeping track of numbers of individuals in populations. This information can tell a scientist if a certain plant or animal is in danger of becoming extinct.

Living things have life cycles, which biologists must study in order to understand how populations increase, decrease, and move from one area to another.

One-celled organisms can reproduce by simple cell division. An insect's life cycle may involve a complete change, from an egg to a wormlike stage, to a resting stage, to an adult insect. Other animals develop from an egg to a juvenile stage, to an adult. Plants, too, have varied life cycles. The largest group of plants are the flowering plants. Flowers are reproductive organs that produce seeds.

The size of a population depends on availability of food and living space and on competition from other populations. When animal populations move on a regular basis, they are said to migrate. Plant populations move, too, but their movements are slow and take place over a long period of time. Such movements are called plant succession.

Exceptional Student IEP Unit Goal

When shown a picture of a plant or an animal, the student will describe why we consider it a living thing and tell one way in which it is adapted to its environment.

Animal and Plant Populations

Unit Opener

This photograph shows five frogs clinging to a branch. Ask the students these questions: Where do you think these frogs are found? *In tropical rain forests.* Do you think they always cling together on the same branch? *No.* Why not? *If they did, it would be easier for other animals to find and eat them. They would also be competing for food.* How could you tell this kind of frog from others? *Size, shape, color, diet, habitat.* What characteristics of the frogs help them live where they do? *Their large, sticky feet.*

UNIT 5

LEARNING CENTER

A suggested title for a Learning Center for this unit is "Living, Growing, Changing." Photographs of a variety of animal and plant populations in their habitats can be used as a display. You may wish to keep a file of the worksheet masters from the Interunit material. You could also create a file of Extensions that are suitable for independent study projects. Materials for these Extensions should be available in the Learning Center. The following Extensions are especially suited for the Learning Center: plant and animal identification cards, p. T-229 (index cards); raising insects, p. T-239 (insects, terrarium, water, food); growing plants from cuttings, p. T-249 (cuttings, growing media, containers, water); factors affecting population growth and size, p. T-260 (bean plants, plant food, water); body mapping, p. T-264 (butcher paper, meter sticks, measuring tapes, crayons); observing birds, p. T-269 (bird feeder, bird seed). Another file could be created for suggested research topics using the following Extensions: organisms in aquariums and terrariums, p. T-239; mealworms, p. T-246; products from algae, fungi, and mosses, p. T-250; migration, p. T-253; environments, p. T-254; how sizes of animals have evolved, p. T-265; adaptations of humans to the environment, p. T-271; extinct and near-extinct animals, p. T-273; extinct plants, p. T-274; careers, p. T-279.

Chapter Objectives

1. Describe the components of the biosphere.
2. Explain how the biosphere is affected by the atmosphere and the crust of the earth.
3. Identify characteristics of living things.
4. Describe how populations are counted.
5. Explain the importance of counting populations.

SECTION BACKGROUND

The biosphere is the world of living things. It includes all living things—plants, animals, and protists—as well as water, air, and soil. We can think of the biosphere as the lower layers of the atmosphere and a thin layer of soil and water on the surface of the earth.

The biosphere is also a system of relationships among living things, nonliving matter, and energy. In this sense, the biosphere includes the sun, because the sun is the primary source of energy for the biosphere. Green plants are able to capture solar energy and convert it to a usable energy source—food. Animals, in turn, depend on plants for food either directly or indirectly. Animals eat plants and/or other animals. In this way, energy is passed from the sun throughout the biosphere in a series of energy chains called food chains.

MATERIALS

plastic shoe box with lid, or 1-l jar with screw top, pebbles, soil, grass seeds, small plant, water

Exceptional Student IEP Chapter Goal

At the end of this chapter, the student will verbally list the four features of living things.

CHAPTER 14

Living Things

14-1. The Biosphere

The earth is alive, from the bottom of the ocean to the tops of mountains. Living things are found on the edge of glaciers. Tiny creatures live in boiling hot springs. When you finish this section, you should be able to:

228

BASIC TEACHING PLAN

MOTIVATION

You might start the unit by taking the class on a mini-field trip outside the school building to observe living things. You can do this as a scavenger hunt. Give the students the following list of things to find: a thing that lives under a rock, a thing that lives in a log, a thing that flies, a blade of grass, a weed, a twig, a leaf, a thing that crawls on leaves, a thing that lives in the soil, and a thing that lives inside another living thing.

Tell the students that they should bring back only organisms that will not be harmed. They should describe those things they find but cannot bring back. After the field trip, discuss with the students each of the items on the list. Emphasize the variety of living things and the various places where they are found.

☐ **A.** Describe the parts that make up the *biosphere.*

☐ **B.** Explain the effect of the atmosphere and crust on the *biosphere.*

1 You can find forms of life in most places on the earth's surface. Forms of life are found (1) in soil, (2) in the ocean, (3) inside human beings, (4) on the land, (5) on plants, and (6) in the air.

2 Can you match the right picture with one of these forms of life?

EXTENSIONS

Reinforcement

Activity

Students could make a deck of animal and plant identification cards.

A. Tell the students to find pictures in magazines of all those organisms for which they would like to make a card.

B. The pictures should be cut out and mounted on index cards or cards cut from oaktag.

C. Each card should include the following:

1. a picture (or drawing) of the organism;
2. physical features of the organism;
3. the organism's habitat (ocean, lake, seacoast, desert, forest);
4. other important facts, such as where and how it gets its food.

This could be an ongoing project for this unit and the next unit. As you introduce new animals, plants, and protists, students working on this project can add to their identification cards. A space on the bulletin board might be reserved for the identification cards so that all students can benefit from the group research.

DEVELOPMENT

1 Teaching Tips—To help students think about where they might find life, put some rich loam in a brown paper bag. You might also put an earthworm in the soil. Show the bag to the students and ask them what is inside. Encourage them to guess and to ask questions. Tell them you will only give them yes or no answers. When they have identified what is in the bag, open it up and ask them if life exists in the soil. Let them examine the soil. Have them use magnifying glasses if they are available. Students should be able to find decaying bits of leaves, stems, and roots. They will not, however, be able to see the billions of protists that live in the soil. Tell the students that if the protists were not present, the plant and animal remains would not decay.

2 Text Questions—Can you match the right picture with one of these forms of life? *Earthworm in soil, sea horse in the ocean, insect on plants.*

EXTENSIONS

Application

Science Skills—Observing, Recording Data

Students could keep a nature notebook while studying this unit and the next unit. There will be many opportunities for them to make drawings, paste in pictures, and make observations of nature. The following suggestions will help the students organize their notebooks:

A. Students should be encouraged to make drawings or use pictures to help them describe what they see. Tell the students that they should put a photograph or drawing of a living thing on each left-hand page in their notebooks and write their descriptions and observations on the facing page.

B. Have a large variety of magazines available for the students to use as sources of pictures.

C. In addition, students could write stories, poems, and tales about their animals and plants.

D. From time to time, give the students an opportunity to go outside to observe and make drawings of trees, flowers, other plants, and small animals.

Biosphere: The layer of earth that is made up of living things.

All of the living things shown are part of the earth. This part of the earth is called the **biosphere** (by-ohs-sphere). Look at the picture below. The *biosphere* is in the middle of a "sandwich." The bottom of the sandwich is the outer **3** layer of the earth. This layer is called the crust. The crust contains rocks and soil. The top of the sandwich is the atmosphere. Living things need the gases in the atmosphere to continue living. Animals use oxygen. Most green plants use carbon dioxide. Animals and plants also need the sun. The sun is the source of energy for the biosphere. Plants need sunlight to make food. Animals eat plants and other animals.

System: A group of things that act together.

Protists: Organisms that are neither plants nor animals.

4 We might think of the biosphere as a **system**. The parts of a *system* work together. Look at the picture in the margin. It shows that the biosphere needs three things. They are sunlight, air, and the minerals in rocks and soil. The main forms of life are plants, animals, and **protists**. *Protists* are neither plants nor animals.

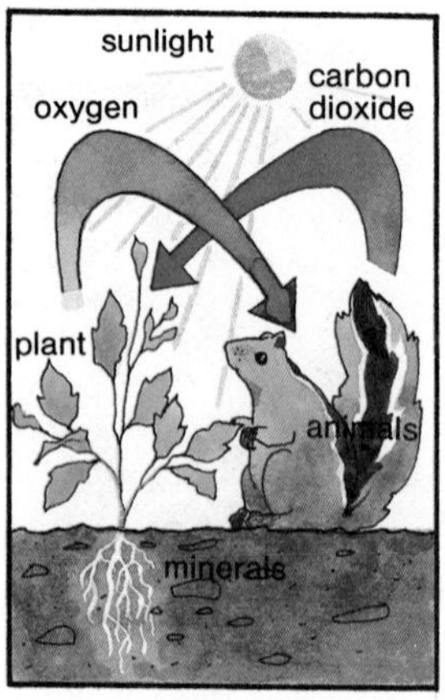

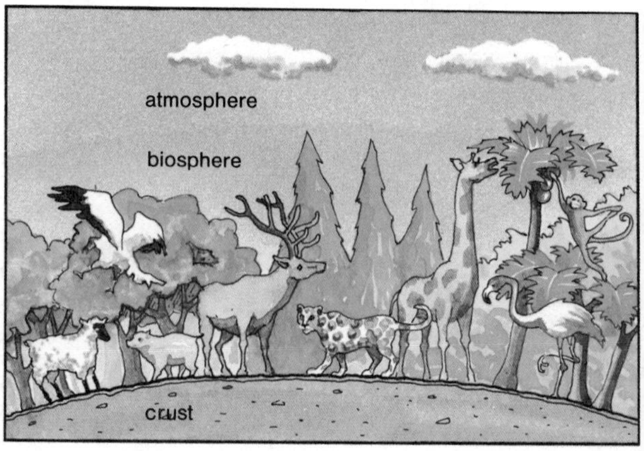

3 **Teaching Tips**—If you have followed the sequence of units in the book, the students will have already studied the crust and atmosphere of the earth. Review these two parts of the earth by making an overhead projection of the diagram on this page. Point out that living things need the minerals from the soil at the top of the earth's crust; the gases, such as carbon dioxide and oxygen, from the air; and water from both places. You should also discuss the importance of the sun.

4 **Skill Development**—Students are introduced to the *cause and effect* relationships that exist in a system like the biosphere.

ACTIVITY

What makes up the biosphere?

A. Gather these materials: plastic shoe box or 1-l (1.1 qt) jar, pebbles, soil, grass seeds, small plant, and water.

B. Place the pebbles on the bottom of the box. Add a layer of soil about 4 cm (1.6 in.) thick.

C. Add the plant. Sprinkle the grass seeds in the soil. Add a small amount of water. Slightly wet the soil.

1. What are the living things in the model?
2. What part does the soil play in the model?
3. What is the role of the air in the model? the role of the water?

Section Review

Main Ideas: The biosphere is made of animals, plants, and protists. Living things need the upper crust and the atmosphere.

Questions: Answer in complete sentences.

1. What is the biosphere?
2. How do the air and crust affect the biosphere?
3. What would happen to the biosphere if there were no sunlight?
4. Are the oceans part of the biosphere? Explain your answer.

EXTENSIONS

Reinforcement

Activity

In this Activity the students practice an American Indian technique called "still hunting." Take the students outdoors to the woods or a meadow and have them observe nature without making a sound. They must remain perfectly still and "hunt" for signs of activity.

A. Have the students take a pencil and a sketch pad or their notebook. Tell them they will be asked to observe what happens in a small area.

B. Tell the students they should just sit and observe all the things in their immediate environment. What animals do they see? What do the animals do? How long do the animals stay? What movements do the students detect? What causes these movements? Do animals and plants interact?

C. At the end of the time period, bring all the students together. Have them describe the things that they saw, heard, or smelled.

ACTIVITY

Skill Development—*Observing*

Teaching Tips—Terrariums are easy to build and maintain. See the back of this teacher's edition for instructions on keeping plants and animals in the classroom.

Answers to Questions—1. The plant and grass seeds. **2.** The soil provides minerals for the plants. It could also be a home for small animals. **3.** Air provides oxygen and carbon dioxide, and water is necessary for life.

SECTION REVIEW

Answers to Questions

1. A system including living things and sunlight, air, and minerals
2. Gases from the air are used by plants and animals; soil on the crust provides water and minerals.
3. It would no longer exist because no energy would be available.
4. Yes, many things live in the oceans.

Exceptional Student

Learning Disabled

Keeping plants and animals is a good way for the learning disabled to build self-esteem.

SECTION BACKGROUND

There are four major differences between living and nonliving things. These differences help us determine if something is living or nonliving. Living things have the following characteristics, which nonliving things lack:

1. Living things can reproduce organisms of their own kind.
2. Living things grow and change form.
3. Living things need food and water. They have the ability to respond to stimuli in the environment in order to obtain food and water.
4. Living things change food into energy needed to grow, move, and reproduce.

MATERIALS

piece of chalk, rock, cut flower, pencil, moss, ant

14-2. Is It Alive?

Pretend you are from another planet. You have a mission. It is to find out if there is life on the earth. How will you decide if something is alive? How are living things different from other things on earth? When you finish this section, you should be able to:

- **A.** Identify the four features of living things.
- **B.** Give examples of how *organisms* show these features.

Organism: A single living thing.

Algae: Very small plants, made up of one or more single cells.

Fungus: A protist, such as a mushroom or a mold, that has no leaves or stems.

The pictures you see below show two living things. Living things are called **organisms** (**or**-gan-i-zums). The green *organism* is made of single cells. It is called **algae** (**al**-jee). *Algae* are plants. They float on ponds. The mushrooms in the second picture are a **fungus** (**fun**-giss). A *fungus* is a type of protist. The mold on rotting fruit is also a fungus.

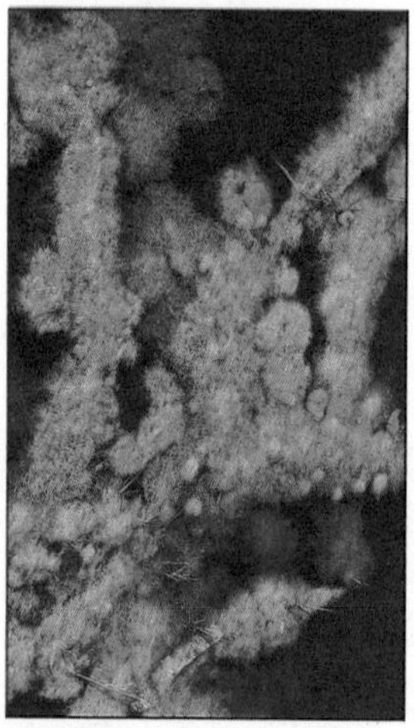

232

BASIC TEACHING PLAN

MOTIVATION

Bring to class a rock that has lichen growing on it. Lichens are the result of an association of two organisms, a fungus and an alga, living together symbiotically. One of the common lichens grows on bare rock or tree trunks. It is gray-green and has a flaky appearance. Ask students if the lichen has any evidence of life.

Text Questions—How will you decide if something is alive? How are living things different from other things on earth? Have the students make a list of the characteristics that determine whether or not something is alive.

Some features are common to all living things. **1** This is true for protists as well as for plants and animals. Four of these features are listed below and on page 234.

1. Living things **reproduce** (ree-pro-**doose**). All organisms come from organisms of the same kind. If living things could not *reproduce*, there would be no living things left on earth. Most single-celled organisms reproduce by splitting in half. Most plants reproduce by means of seeds.

Reproduce: To make more of the same kind of organism.

2. Living things grow and change. When the foal shown here was born, it was less than half the size of its mother. When it becomes an adult, it will be the same size as its mother. Small trees will grow to be as tall as many old trees in the forest. Some living things change form as they get older. When the caterpillar becomes an adult, it will be a butterfly.

EXTENSIONS

Application

Science Skills—Inferring

Students will be interested in knowing what causes water in ponds and aquariums to turn green. If you have had an aquarium set up for a month, green algae are probably growing in it. Use the presence of the algae in the aquarium to encourage the students' inquiry.

Ask the students to suggest what might have caused the color change in the aquarium. If a microscope is available, let them see some of the algae under the microscope.

DEVELOPMENT

1 Teaching Tips—All living things are classified into three kingdoms—plant, animal, and protist. The protists do not clearly have the characteristics of either plants or animals. Fungi, algae, and bacteria are protists. Algae contain chlorophyll; fungi and bacteria do not.

EXTENSIONS

Enrichment

Science Skills—Observing, Comparing and Contrasting

As a class demonstration, examine various seeds.

A. Gather these fruits: oranges, grapes, cucumbers, tomatoes, apples, avocados, pumpkins, and squash.

B. Cut open each of the fruits and let the students examine the seeds inside.

C. Have the students count the number of seeds in each fruit. How do the numbers compare?

D. Select one seed from each fruit and have the students examine the seeds with a hand lens. They should make a small drawing of each.

E. Save some of the seeds for planting. You will have to dry them first.

2 3. Living things need food and water. Most animals spend much of their time looking for food. Some animals eat only plants. Others eat
3 both plants and animals. Which of the animals shown here eats only plants? Which eats both plants and animals?

4 4. Living things need energy. An animal needs energy to run, swim, or fly. It gets the energy from the food it eats. Living things change food to energy inside their cells.

2 Teaching Tips—Food and water are essential for living things. Do a demonstration using two plants. Water one regularly; do not water the other. Ask students why plants need water. Relate this to students' own need for water. How do they feel when they are thirsty?
3 Text Questions—Which of the animals shown here eats only plants? *The antelope.* Which eats both plants and animals? *The bear.*
4 Teaching Tips—Except for green plants, which manufacture their own food, living things depend on other living things for food. For example, fungi live on dead organic matter. Animals eat plants and/or other animals.

ACTIVITY

How can you tell if it is alive?

A. Gather these materials: piece of chalk, a rock, a cut flower, pencil, moss, and an ant.

B. Use the chart in Main Ideas below to decide if each object is a living thing.

1. Which objects are living things?
2. How can you tell a living thing from an object that is not living?

Section Review

Main Ideas: Features of living things:

1. They reproduce.	Cells split in half to make more cells.
2. They grow and change.	Animals and plants grow in size. Caterpillars change to butterflies.
3. They need food and water.	Animals eat plants.
4. They need energy.	Body cells change food to energy.

Questions: Answer in complete sentences.

1. Is a crystal a living thing? Explain your answer.
2. A student blows up a balloon and says, "It grew bigger. It is alive." Is the student right?
3. How can you tell that something is not alive?
4. Is a seed alive? Explain.

EXTENSIONS

Enrichment

Activity

Mushrooms reproduce by means of spores. These are not seeds but special reproductive cells. Bring in some mushrooms you have purchased in a food store. *Do not* bring in wild mushrooms. The mushrooms should be very young and fresh. Cut off the stems so that you can set the caps bottom-side down on construction paper of different colors. Let the caps sit undisturbed over-night. Spores will be released and will form a pattern that reflects the pattern of the gills on the underside of the cap. Spores are microscopic. They can be examined under a microscope, if one is available.

ACTIVITY

Skill Development—*Observing, Classifying*

Teaching Tips—The living and nonliving things listed in the pupil text are only suggestions. Use whatever things you have available and include as much variety as you can.

Answers to Questions—1. Flower, moss, ant. **2.** Living things reproduce, grow and change, and need food, water, and energy.

SECTION REVIEW

Answers to Questions

1. No. It does not reproduce, and it does not need water, food, or energy.
2. No
3. It does not have all of the features of living things.
4. Yes. The seed will grow and change, and it needs food and water to do so.

SUGGESTED WORKSHEET MASTER
p. T-225 j

SECTION BACKGROUND

The number of organisms in a population can be estimated by counting random samples. Density is the number of organisms found in a certain area at a given time. If the density of a population is high, many organisms are living in an area at a given time. Knowing the size or density of populations is important for many reasons. Population counting is important when determining if a population is getting too large or if a population is endangered. Conservationists estimate the size of deer populations so that they can set quotas for hunters during annual deer-hunting seasons.

MATERIALS

42-cm lengths of insulated wire (1 for each student), metric ruler, meter stick, 1 or 2 bags of dried lima beans, 40 m of rope or string

14-3. Counting Living Things

Biologist: A scientist who studies the world of living things.

Population: A number of the same kind of organisms that live in the same place.

Suppose a disease is killing the trees in the picture. To keep track of the disease, you must count the trees. How will you count all the trees shown? When you finish this section, you should be able to:

- **A.** Describe a way to count a *population*.
- **B.** Explain why it is important to know the size of *populations*.

Biologists (bye-**oll**-oh-jists) study **populations** (pa-pew-**lay**-shuns) of living things. A *population*

BASIC TEACHING PLAN

MOTIVATION

Take the students outside to a grassy area. Challenge pairs of students to count the blades of grass in a square area 3 m (10 ft) on a side. Give them string to help them mark off their area. The students will quickly realize that counting the number of individual blades of grass is almost impossible. They could estimate the number of blades in the 3-m × 3-m area by counting the number of blades in a square area 30 cm (1 ft) on a side and multiplying by 100. If there is a forest nearby, relate counting the blades of grass to counting organisms in the forest.

Text Questions—How will you count all the trees shown? *Count the trees in several areas of a convenient size. Find the average number of trees in an area that size. Multiply by a factor that relates size of one sample area to the total area.*

is a number of the same kind of organism living in the same place. The picture in the margin shows a population of corn plants. What are some other populations?

Biologists can tell the size of a population by counting organisms. This helps them answer questions such as these:

1. Is the size of the population getting larger or smaller?
2. If the population is getting too small, should we try to protect the plants or animals?
3. If the population is getting too large, should we help make it smaller? Will there be enough food for all the living things?

Many people need to know the size of a population. Suppose you want to open a lumber company. You would want to know the number of trees in the area. A grocer would want to know the number of people in town. A teacher has to know how many students are in class. Can you think of any other examples?

EXTENSIONS

Application

Science Skills—Comparing and Contrasting

Have your students locate their city (or one near them) and other cities on a population-density map of the United States. They will realize that the human population is not evenly distributed. Discuss possible answers to the following questions:

1. Why are the greatest population densities found in cities?
2. What are the advantages and disadvantages of living in densely populated areas?
3. Do you think it is better to grow up with many neighbors or few neighbors? Why?

DEVELOPMENT

1 Text Questions—What are some other populations? *Ants, grasshoppers, humans, ferns, pine trees, deer, etc.*

2 Teaching Tips—Find several pictures that show populations of different plants and animals. Divide the class into groups and give each group a picture. Ask the students to find as many different kinds of organisms in the picture as they can and list them. Use the lists to introduce the concept of a population.

3 Teaching Tips—Have your students practice counting the organisms in a mini-environment. Mark off a square patch of ground 1 m on a side with string. Clear this patch down to the soil. At least once a week, have the students inspect the patch, count the organisms that have returned, and note how the patch has changed. If it is not possible to use a patch of ground, place pots of soil on the windowsill and have the students watch the changes that occur in them.

4 Text Questions—Can you think of any other examples? *Counting people living in a city to determine services needed; counting animals or plants to determine if they are endangered.*

EXTENSIONS

Application

Science Skills—Measuring, Recording Data

Your students can use the techniques of sampling and averaging to determine the population of students in your school. A discussion of how this might be done should result in the following procedure:

A. Find out how many classrooms there are in the school.

B. Determine the average number of students per classroom in a sample of several classrooms.

C. Multiply this average by the total number of classrooms in the school.

D. Compare your estimate with the actual number of students.

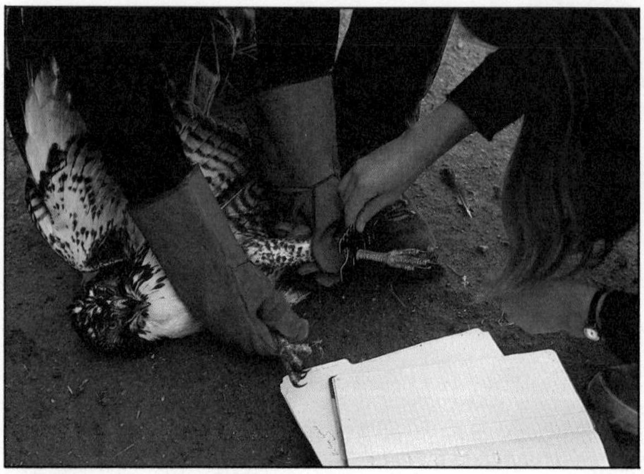

5 Animal and plant populations are counted in different ways. It may be hard to count animals. They move and are hard to find. They may be counted twice. They may live in places that are hard to get to.

Biologists have ways to mark the animals they count. Bands are put on the legs of some animals, such as birds. Other animals, such as rabbits, are marked on their ears. Radios are often put on animals like bears or deer. Biologists can follow the radio signals.

6

7 yellow flowers x 16 squares =
7 x 16 = 112 flowers in the field

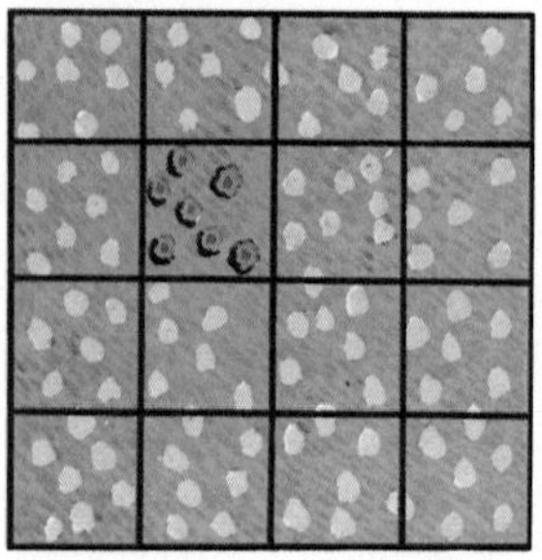

Plants do not move. So they are easier to count. Scientists do not count each plant in an area. They count the number of plants in a small plot of ground.

Suppose you wanted to count all the yellow flowers in a field. You would not have to count each flower. You could divide the field into squares. By counting the flowers in a square, you could get an idea of how many flowers are in the whole field.

5 Teaching Tips—Discuss with your students how they would go about counting birds or squirrels near their home or the school. How would they know they were not counting the same animal twice? Challenge them to go home and sit outside for a half hour and count one animal population. After they have done this, discuss why tagging techniques must be used to count animals. Because animals move, tagging is a way to make sure the same animal is not counted twice.

6 Teaching Tips—Have students count the number of squares and the number of flowers in one square. Multiply these two numbers to get the number of flowers in the entire picture.

ACTIVITY

How is a population counted?

A. Gather these materials: 42-cm length of wire and metric ruler.

B. Copy the chart shown here. Use it to record your data.

C. Go outside to the roped-off area. Two bags of beans have been spread out in this area.

D. Bend the piece of wire to make a square 10 cm (4 in.) on each side. You will count the number of beans in this square.

E. Close your eyes. Drop the square on the ground. Count the number of beans in the square.

F. Repeat step E 4 times in other places.

G. Add the numbers in the count column to get the total count. Divide the total by 5 to find the average count.

1. How could you find the total number of beans in the roped-off area?

Sample	Bean Count
1	
2	
3	
4	
5	
Total	
Average	

EXTENSIONS

Enrichment

Research—Library

Students could research the habitats, feeding habits, and life cycles of some of the organisms contained in aquariums or terrariums. If you have a class aquarium or terrarium, it would be especially interesting to use the organisms found there. Here are some suggested populations:

1. Algae—green, single-celled protists
2. Brine shrimp—small crustaceans that are related to lobsters and crabs
3. Daphnia—tiny freshwater crustaceans, also called water fleas, that are related to lobsters and crayfish
4. Snails—small shell animals
5. Aphids—tiny insects that live on plants

Students can find information about these populations in encyclopedias and other books. They should write a short report on each population.

ACTIVITY

Skill Development—*Recording Data*

Teaching Tips—You will need to purchase one or two bags of dried lima beans. Count the beans in the bags before beginning the Activity. To set up the Activity, use rope or string to mark off a square area 10 m on a side. Scatter the beans within this area. When you are ready to start, distribute 42-cm lengths of insulated wire. Insulated wire can be bent easily to form a square 10 cm on each side. The ends can be tied together, and the extra 2 cm of wire can be tied to form a handle. The students should drop their squares over their shoulders. This will ensure a random sample.

Answers to Questions—1. Multiply the average number of beans in a square area 10 cm on a side by 10,000.

Section Review

Main Ideas: Biologists use many methods to count populations of plants and animals.

Questions: Answer in complete sentences.

1. How can you find the size of a population without counting each organism?
2. Why is it important to know the size of a population of whales?
3. How could you find out if a population was getting bigger or smaller?
4. Why is it harder to count animals than plants?

People in Science

Kes Hillman

Dr. Hillman is a biologist in Kenya, a country in East Africa. She studies the population of elephants in that country. Dr. Hillman's father was a pilot. Because of this, she became interested in flying. When she went to Kenya, Dr. Hillman found that flying helped her to study elephants. In an airplane, she could cover a large area. She could take pictures and count elephants more easily from the air. She could spot sick or hurt elephants. Her work helps keep the elephant population strong and healthy.

Dr. Hillman can also tell if elephants are being killed illegally. Each year, poachers kill many elephants for their tusks alone, from which luxury items are made.

EXTENSIONS

Application

Activity

Have students, as a class, write to the U.S. Fish and Wildlife Service. They could ask if an animal population count is being carried on in their area, or if any animal species living in the area is endangered. The students could also request brochures about endangered species in the United States. The address for this agency is U.S. Fish and Wildlife Service, Department of the Interior, Washington, D.C. 20240.

SECTION REVIEW

Main Ideas—Computers are able to organize information about populations because computers can be programmed to provide information in many different forms. Computers can help people recognize trends in population density and make predictions so that steps may be taken to reverse harmful trends.

Answers to Questions

1. Take a sample and estimate total population based on the sample.
2. To find out if they are in danger of becoming extinct
3. By counting the population several times over a period of time
4. Because animals do not stay in one place

SUGGESTED WORKSHEET MASTER
p. T-225 k

CHAPTER REVIEW

Science Words: Match the terms in column A with the definitions in column B.

Column A	Column B
1. Biosphere	a. A group of the same kind of organism
2. System	b. The living layer of earth
3. Protists	c. A scientist who studies living things
4. Organism	d. Things that work together to form a whole
5. Algae	e. To make more of the same kind of organism
6. Fungus	f. Single-celled plants
7. Reproduce	g. A plant that has no leaves or stems
8. Biologist	h. Single-celled organisms
9. Population	i. A living thing

Questions: Answer in complete sentences.

1. In a drawing, show the biosphere, the atmosphere, and the crust.
2. How is the biosphere different from the other layers?
3. What might happen to the biosphere if the earth lost its atmosphere?
4. What are four features of all living things?
5. Why do living things need food?
6. Give one way in which living things reproduce.
7. Which would be easier: (a) counting birds in your yard, or (b) counting blue flowers in your yard?

EXTENSIONS

Enrichment

Science Skills— Finding Cause and Effect

Discuss the word *immigration* with your students. Have them look up the word in a dictionary. Point out the effect that the waves of immigration in the late 19th and early 20th centuries had on the population of this country. Discuss the reasons for immigration.

CHAPTER REVIEW

Science Words

1. b, **2.** d, **3.** h, **4.** i, **5.** f, **6.** g, **7.** e, **8.** c, **9.** a

Answers to Questions

1. The diagram should show the biosphere between the atmosphere and the earth's crust. See the diagram on page 230.
2. The biosphere is the living layer. No other layers contain life.
3. Plants and animals would die.
4. They reproduce, grow and change, and require food, water, and energy to live.
5. Food gives living things the energy they need to live.
6. Some reproduce from seeds; some divide in half; some produce eggs.
7. b. The flowers do not move, and it would be easier to estimate the total number.

SUGGESTED WORKSHEET MASTER
p. T-225 l

SUGGESTED TEST MASTERS
pp. T-225 d, e

Chapter Objectives

1. Describe the life cycles of animals and give several examples.
2. Describe the life cycles of plants that make seeds.
3. Describe some other ways in which plants can reproduce.
4. Describe and compare animal migration and plant succession.
5. Identify several factors that affect a population's size.

SECTION BACKGROUND

The life cycle of an organism is its life history from birth, through growth and development, to death. The creation of a new organism is the first step in a life cycle. Most animals reproduce sexually. Their life cycle begins when sperm produced by a male unites with an egg produced by a female.

In some animals, such as moths, beetles, and butterflies, the young are totally different from the adults. Insects such as moths, beetles, and butterflies have four distinct stages in their life cycles—egg, larva, pupa, and adult. This series of stages is called complete metamorphosis.

MATERIALS

2 or 3 mealworms, jar with a lid, bran, slice of potato or apple, ruler

Exceptional Student
IEP Chapter Goal

When asked by the teacher, the student will describe the life cycle of a plant that produces seeds and the life cycle of a human being.

CHAPTER 15

THE CYCLES OF POPULATIONS

15-1. Animal Life Cycles

The giant sea turtle is ready to lay her eggs. She comes out of the sea and onto the beach. She digs a hole in the sand and lays her eggs. What happens to the baby turtles? When you finish this section, you should be able to:

242

BASIC TEACHING PLAN

MOTIVATION

The giant sea turtle is a magnificent animal. Its habitat for laying and hatching eggs is decreasing in size because of increased development and use of beaches. When the baby turtles hatch, they leave the nest and crawl to the sea, where they mature into adults. Later the females return to a sandy beach to lay eggs.

Obtain fertilized frog eggs and place them in an aquarium. Have the students observe the eggs every day. Tadpoles will hatch from frog eggs in three to ten days. Ask the students if they know what will hatch from the eggs. *Tadpoles.* Ask what the tadpoles will become. *Frogs.*

Text Questions—What happens to the baby turtles? *They crawl into the sea, where those that survive grow to become adults. Many of the young do not survive.*

A. Describe and give examples of animal *life cycles.*

B. Explain how birth, growth and development, and death affect *life cycles* of living things.

Below is an enlarged picture of very small animals. They are about the size of a comma. These animals live in salt water. They are called **brine shrimp.** The dots next to them are *brine shrimp* 1 eggs. The eggs are very tiny. Brine shrimp reproduce by laying eggs. When the eggs hatch, the population changes size. New shrimp are added. The birth of animals helps populations 2 grow and survive. What would happen to the brine shrimp population if the shrimp stopped laying eggs?

Brine shrimp: A very small animal that lives in salt water.

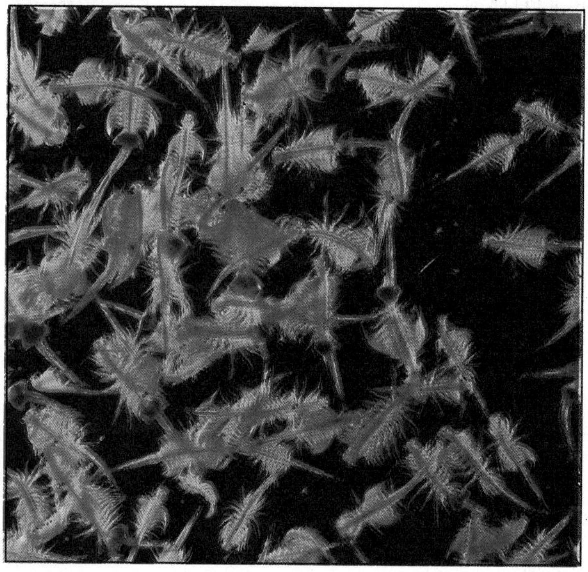

EXTENSIONS

Application

Activity

Have your students incubate fertilized chicken eggs. The eggs, incubators, and instructions can be obtained from a 4-H Club or a commercial hatchery.

The period of incubation is 21 days. A few days before the chicks hatch, let the students hold the eggs to their ears. They will be able to hear the chicks peeping inside. Because baby chicks need special care, you should send them to a hatchery as soon as they have hatched.

DEVELOPMENT

1 Teaching Tips—Brine-shrimp eggs can be purchased at a pet shop or ordered from a science supply house. You will also need synthetic sea salt, which can be purchased at a pet shop. Set up a saltwater aquarium by adding the sea salt to water according to package directions. Let the eggs hatch in the water. Keep a few eggs for students to examine with hand lenses.

2 Text Questions—What would happen to the brine-shrimp population if the shrimp stopped laying eggs? *The size of the population would decrease.*

EXTENSIONS

Enrichment
Activity

Have the class play a game called the "ameba game."

A. Have the students crowd into an open area in your classroom, the gym, or the playground.

B. Ask for volunteers to be the cell membrane, which surrounds the ameba and holds it together. Have these students form a circle around the other students, facing outward and locking arms.

C. Select one student inside the membrane to be the nucleus, or center, of the ameba. The other students inside the membrane represent the cytoplasm of the cell.

D. Ask the ameba to try walking around. The nucleus must give all the instructions. Computerlike instructions should be used (for example, left five paces; right four paces; left six paces, etc.).

E. Tell the ameba that it is going to reproduce. The membrane must split open and half the students who represent the cytoplasm must form a second ameba. A new nucleus should be chosen for the newly created ameba.

F. As a follow-up, have the students find out the meaning of these terms: cell membrane, nucleus, and cytoplasm.

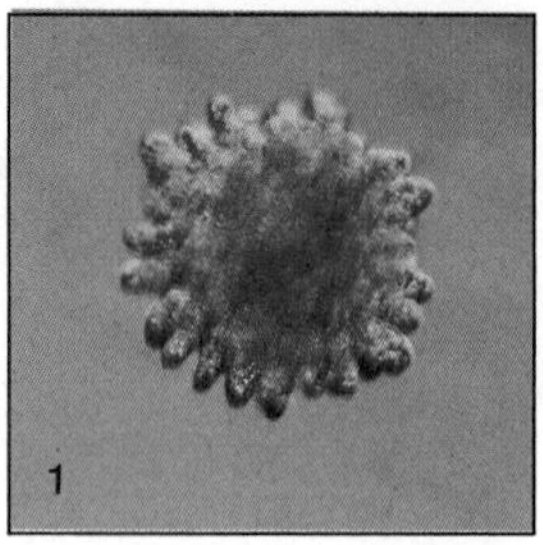
1

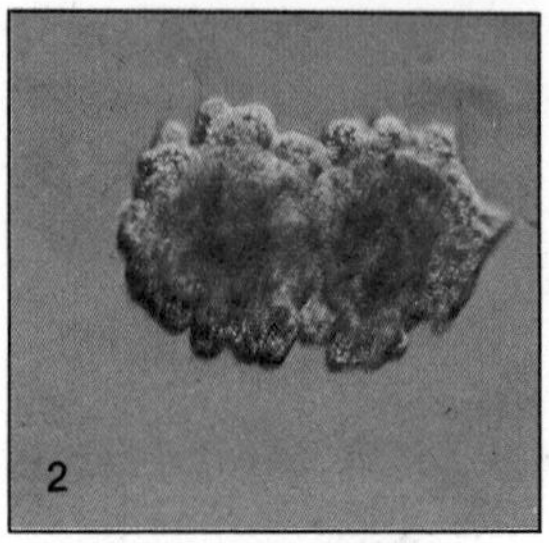
2

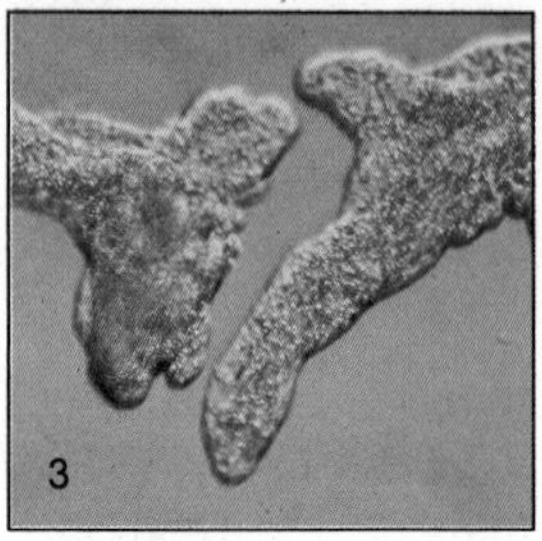
3

Ameba: A tiny animal found in pond water.

3 Look at the picture above. Picture 1 shows a very tiny animal found in pond water. It is called an **ameba** (ah-**mee**-bah). An *ameba* does not hatch from an egg. The ameba population grows in a different way. Each ameba reproduces by splitting in half. Pictures 2 and 3 show how an ameba does this. It takes an ameba about 1 hour to divide.

Hydra: A tiny animal found in lakes and ponds.

A tiny animal found in lakes and ponds is the **hydra** (**hi**-drah). *Hydras* live on the stems and leaves of water plants. They reproduce by budding. They form little buds on their bodies. Each bud grows into a new hydra. The picture in the margin shows how this happens.

Life cycle: The series of stages in the life of an organism.

4 Brine shrimp, amebas, and hydras are each born in different ways. Birth is the first step in the **life cycle**. All living things have *life cycles*.

There are three steps, or stages, in the life cycle of any living thing: (1) birth, (2) growth and development, and (3) death. They are shown on page 245. The length of a life cycle can be a few moments or a hundred years. Let's look at the life cycle of a butterfly.

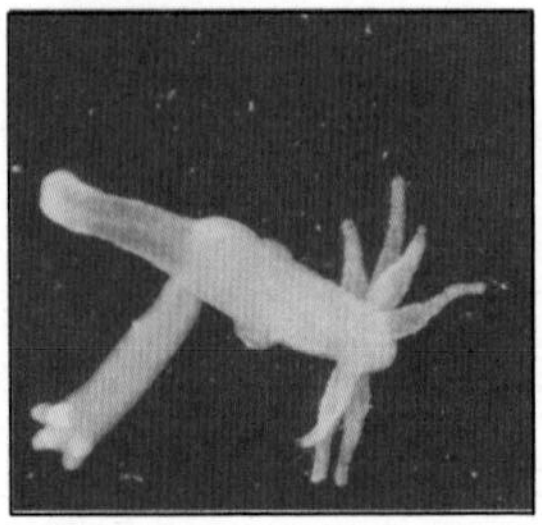

The butterfly's life begins as an egg. The egg is laid by a female butterfly. The egg hatches

3 **Skill Development**—Students can *compare and contrast* the reproduction of the ameba, the hydra, and the brine shrimp.
4 **Teaching Tips**—Review the reproductive processes of brine shrimp, amebas, and hydras. Have the students describe how these three organisms reproduce (laying eggs, dividing in half, budding). Have the students draw and label the life cycles of each of these organisms in their notebooks.
5 **Teaching Tips**—If you keep living organisms in the classroom, students will probably observe some of them dying. Death is part of the life cycle of all organisms.

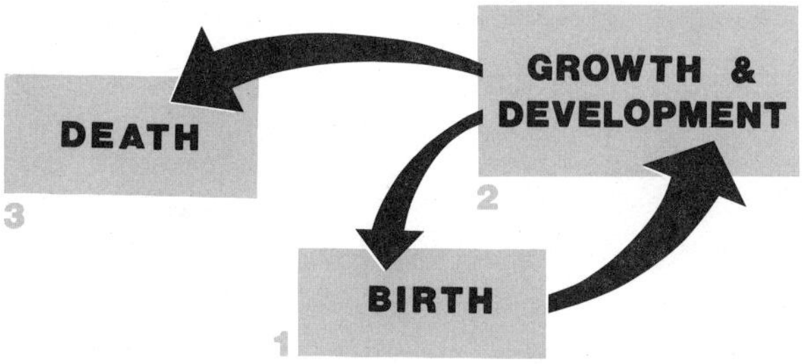

into a **larva** (**lar**-va). A *larva* is the young form of the organism. The larva of a butterfly is called a caterpillar. Caterpillars spend most of their lives looking for food. Many are eaten by birds. In time, the caterpillar stops growing. At this stage, it makes a cocoon. It becomes a **pupa** (**pyoo**-puh). During the *pupa* stage, it changes into an adult. Its wings, mouth, and legs grow. It becomes a butterfly. Adult butterflies lay eggs. The life cycle begins again. At some time, the
5 butterfly dies. Death is common to all living things. The organism might die of old age. Or it might be eaten by another organism. It might also die from disease. It might not be able to get enough food.

Larva: The young form in the life cycle of an organism.

Pupa: A stage in the life cycle of an insect in which the insect is not active.

6

6 **Teaching Tips**—On a transparency or on the chalkboard, make a drawing of the stages in the life cycle of a butterfly. Collect, or have the students collect, butterfly or moth eggs, or caterpillars. Put the eggs or caterpillars in several containers in the room. The containers should include a layer of sand as well as the leaves and twigs on which the caterpillars were found. Let the students observe the containers for several days and watch how they change.

EXTENSIONS

Application

Science Skills—Observing, Comparing and Contrasting

There are several organisms that can be raised easily in the classroom to allow the students to observe their life cycle first-hand. These organisms include: mealworms (larva stage of beetles), crickets, silkworms, and monarch butterflies. The eggs, larvae, or adults may be purchased from science supply houses, fish-bait stores, or pet shops.

Refer to the Activity on page T-246 for information about mealworms.

Crickets require a large, covered container with a soil layer, some water, and bran for food. The terrarium should be relatively dry. However, because crickets lay their eggs in moist soil, one area should be kept moist for this purpose.

Silkworms require a dry, sandy environment. They obtain moisture from the leaves of plants, such as mulberry leaves or lettuce. Put a few twigs in the terrarium to which the cocoons can be attached. The silkworm is the larva stage of the white silk moth.

EXTENSIONS

Enrichment

Research—Library

The life cycle of the mealworm is an example of complete metamorphosis. Ask the students to do research and find examples of incomplete metamorphosis. Some examples they will find are the life cycles of the dragonfly, the cricket, and the grasshopper. Explain that the eggs of these insects hatch, yielding young that more or less resemble the adult. The young molt, or shed their outer covering, several times to allow for growth. The process of development into an adult form does not involve total change of form, as it does when complete metamorphosis occurs.

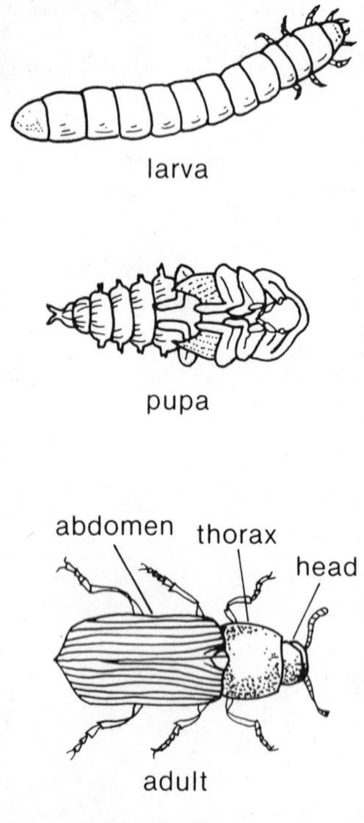

Fig. 15-1

SUGGESTED WORKSHEET MASTER
p. T-225 m

ACTIVITY

What is the life cycle of a beetle?

The beetle goes through the same stages of life as a butterfly.

A. Gather these materials: 2 or 3 mealworms, jar with a lid, bran, slice of potato or apple, and ruler.

B. Look at the mealworm. It is the larva stage of the beetle.

1. Does the mealworm have legs?
2. What does it eat?
3. When did the larva stage end?
4. What did it look like at this stage? What is this stage called?
5. What are the stages of a beetle's life cycle?

Section Review

Main Ideas: An animal goes through stages during its lifetime. These stages are birth, growth and development, and death.

Questions: Answer in complete sentences.

1. Describe the life cycle of a sea turtle.
2. What are three ways animals reproduce?
3. What are some reasons that living things die?
4. Draw the life cycle of a butterfly. Label the stages.
5. What is the life cycle of a human?

ACTIVITY

Skill Development—*Observing*

Answers to Questions—1. Yes. **2.** Bran. **3.** The larva stage ends when a pupa forms. The mealworms, depending on age, could enter the pupa stage soon. **4.** Its head is large, and its legs and wings are folded under its body. This is called the pupa stage. **5.** Egg, larva, pupa, and adult.

SECTION REVIEW

Answers to Questions

1. Eggs, young turtles, adult turtles
2. Dividing in half, budding, laying eggs, giving birth
3. Lack of food, old age, being eaten by other animals, disease
4. Diagram should show egg, larva, pupa, and adult stages.
5. Embryo, child, adult

15-2. Plant Life Cycles

Have you ever wondered what it would be like to be a tree? These are redwood trees. They are the largest and nearly the oldest living things on earth. Some redwoods are over 3,500 years old. They can be as high as 90 meters (300 feet). How are new redwood trees made? When you finish this section, you should be able to:

- **A.** Describe and give examples of plant life cycles.
- **B.** Compare life cycles of plants that make seeds with life cycles of plants that do not make seeds.

Like animals, plants have life cycles. Plant life cycles fall into two groups.

Group 1: Cycles of plants that make seeds
Group 2: Cycles of plants that do not make seeds

Some plants make their seeds in flowers. Other plants make their seeds in cones. The drawing shows the life cycle of a cone-bearing tree. What are the steps in the life cycle?

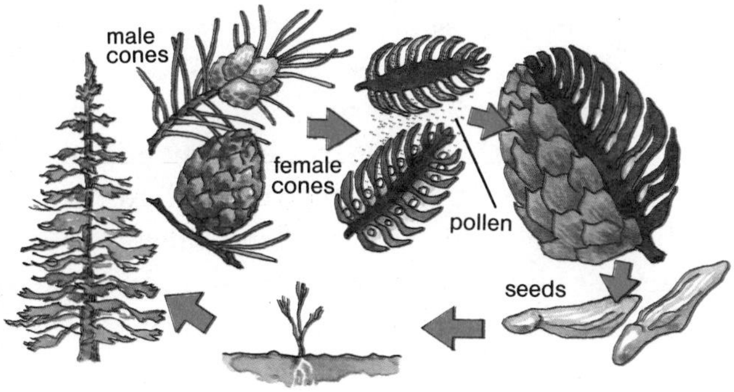

SECTION BACKGROUND

Plants that produce seeds comprise more than half of the plant kingdom. Evergreens, with needlelike leaves and seed-bearing cones, are a part of this group. They produce seeds but not flowers. Flowering plants make up the largest group of plants. Flowers contain the sexual reproductive organs of the plant. Pollination occurs when pollen from the male part of a flower (anther) lands on the female part of a flower (pistil). Pollen grains form tubes through which their nuclei make their way to the ovules where fertilization occurs. Seeds develop from the fertilized ovules.

Ferns and mosses have leaves, stems, and roots but no flowers. They reproduce by means of spores. Algae and fungi are protists. Algae contain chlorophyll and may be one-celled organisms or multicellular organisms such as kelp. Fungi include simple yeasts, molds, mildew, and mushrooms. They have no chlorophyll and obtain food from the surface on which they grow, which may be living matter or matter that was once alive.

Many plants can reproduce asexually by means of runners, which are slender, creeping stems that put out roots. Ferns and mosses can cover large areas in this way. Many flowering plants can reproduce from cuttings of roots, stems, or leaves.

BASIC TEACHING PLAN

MOTIVATION

If you have an aquarium in the classroom, there may be a green growth on the inside of the glass. This is probably algae. Point out that algae have things in common with redwood trees. They both contain chlorophyll, produce their own food, need sunlight and water, and have cells with cell walls. Bring in a fern and some moss as examples of plants that do not produce seeds.

Text Questions—How are new redwood trees made? *They develop from redwood seeds.*

DEVELOPMENT

1 **Text Questions**—What are the steps in the life cycle? *Pollen from male cones fertilizes eggs from female cones to produce seeds. Seeds germinate and grow into adult conifers.*

MATERIALS

radish or bean seeds, potting soil, Styrofoam cups, water

EXTENSIONS

Application

Activity

Students might enjoy bringing in flowers to examine. Not all flowers have both a stamen and a pistil. Many flowers are of one sex only. Students should bring in simple flowers such as day lilies, tulips, squash flowers, petunias, or roses. Flowers such as daisies and dandelions are too complex. The colored parts of the flowers will probably be the petals, although not always. The pistil has an enlarged base, the ovary. The stigma is sticky or covered with minute hairs to trap pollen. The anther resembles a little rectangular box and contains a yellow powder, pollen. Have the students answer these questions:

1. Does your flower have a stamen and a pistil?
2. How many anthers are there?
3. How many petals are there?

Have them make sketches of the stigma and anther.

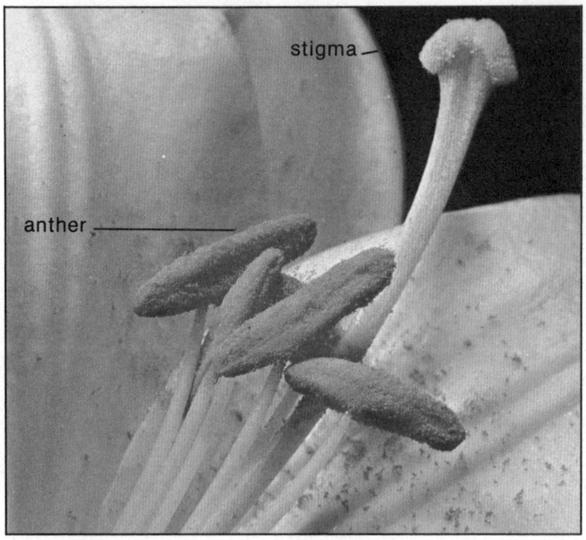

Anther: The part of a flower that contains pollen.

Pollen: A yellow powder made by the anthers of a flower.

Stigma: The part of a flower that receives pollen.

Let's look at the life cycle of plants that make [2] seeds from flowers. Many plants have flowers. Most flowers usually open in warm weather. Look at the flower shown above. One part of the flower is called the **anther** (**an**-thur). *Anthers* [3] make a yellow powder called **pollen** (**pahl**-len). Another part of the flower is called the **stigma** [4] (**stig**-mah). The *pollen* must move from the anther to the *stigma*. Then a seed can begin to form. Bees and other insects help move pollen. When insects walk on flowers, they catch pollen on their bodies. They carry the pollen from the anthers to the stigmas. Wind, water, birds, and other animals also carry pollen. Once pollen reaches a stigma, the flower is pollinated. Soon after, seeds begin to form. Most new plants grow from seeds.

2 Skill Development—*Compare* examples of seeds from different plants. You can *contrast* tiny grass seeds with acorns, for example.
3 Skill Development—Use a hand lens or microscope to *observe* pollen in a flower. The grains are very small. *Compare and contrast* pollen from different flowers.
4 Teaching Tips—Flowers growing on a plant may not all be the same. Some may have only the stamen, others only the pistil. The stamen is the male reproductive organ and includes the anther. The pistil is the female reproductive organ and includes the ovary and the stigma. Squash is an example of a plant with both male and female flowers. Other species have only male flowers on one plant and only female flowers on another. The two types of plants must be close together for seeds to form. Holly is an example of such a plant.

5 Fruit trees are flowering plants. The fruits grow around the seeds. When fruits fall to the 6 ground, their seeds stay in the soil. They can begin to grow into new fruit trees. In a few years, the new trees will flower. Seed formation starts all over again. The new trees add to the size of the fruit tree population. Plants must reproduce if a population is to survive.

Plants can also reproduce themselves in other ways. Some can make new plants if you put pieces of their roots, stems, or leaves in soil or water. Potatoes grow tiny buds called eyes. If you plant a piece of potato with the bud in it, a new potato plant will grow from the bud.

Strawberries reproduce by means of runners. A runner is a stem that grows on the ground. When the runner touches the ground, it takes root, and a new plant develops.

EXTENSIONS

Enrichment

Activity

Have the students grow plants from cuttings. Use a rooting medium such as soil or vermiculite. Try different plants such as begonias, coleuses, African violets, or snake plants. Take leaves with and without stems and insert them in the medium. Keep the medium damp. The time it takes for roots to develop will vary with the specimen. Plant the rooted cuttings in soil. Students should observe that the new plants are the same kind as the ones from which cuttings were taken.

5 Teaching Tips—Give pairs of students different fruits (apple, orange, peach, grape). Have the students cut the fruits open and remove all the seeds. Have them count the seeds in each fruit and compare their count with those of other groups. Point out that some fruits contain only one seed, while others contain many seeds.

6 Teaching Tips—Retain some of the seeds from the fruits the students cut up. Plant them in soil. Milk cartons with one side cut away and drainage holes punched in the bottom can be used as planters. Record how long it takes for each type of seed to germinate. If the seeds do not germinate, it may be because a condition necessary for that particular species of seed to sprout has not been met. (For example, some seeds must be kept at cold temperatures before they will germinate.) Grapefruit, orange, melon, and avocado seeds will sprout easily.

EXTENSIONS

Enrichment

Research—Library

Products made from algae, fungi, and mosses are important to people. Have the students do research on these products in encyclopedias and other sources. They will find information on such things as: peat, a fuel; penicillin, an antibiotic; agar, a culture medium for bacteria; diatomaceous earth, an ingredient in toothpaste, cleansers, and lightweight concrete. They will also find that red algae and brown algae are used as food for people and cattle in some countries.

Fern: A simple, green, non-flowering plant.

Moss: A small green plant that grows on rocks.

Spores: Small, round objects found on ferns, which can grow and form new fern plants.

Plants that do not produce seeds reproduce in many other ways. **Ferns** and **mosses** reproduce without seeds.

Ferns and *mosses* reproduce by means of
7 **spores**. These *spores* are much smaller than grains of salt. Look at the life cycle of the fern. Ferns are green plants with roots, stems, and leaves. Fern spores are produced in special
8 places on the underside of leaves. They can fall to the ground. If a spore falls on wet ground, it will grow into a thin, green, heart-shaped plant. The adult fern grows from this tiny plant. Most ferns have life cycles that last for years.

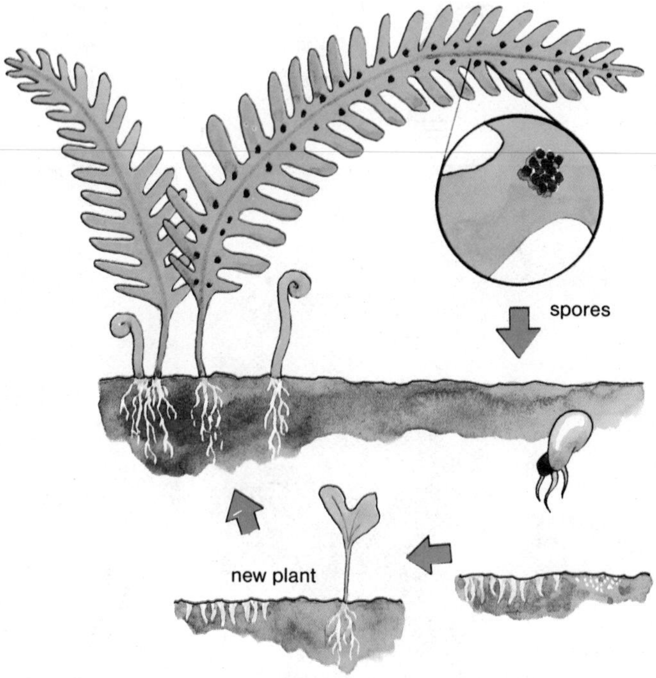

7 Skill Development—Have students *observe* the patterns that spore-producing bodies make on the undersides of fern leaves. If more than one variety of fern is available, students can *classify* the ferns according to these patterns. Bring several ferns to class.

8 Teaching Tips—Spores develop in special fruiting bodies, which in many ferns are located on the undersides of the leaves. The spores are very tiny. Use a hand lens to examine the spore-producing bodies. The location of these bodies varies, depending on the species of fern. Some line up along the midrib; others appear on the margin. The cinnamon fern has whole stalks that contain only the spore-producing structures.

ACTIVITY

How do plants grow from seeds?

A. Gather these materials: radish or bean seeds, potting soil, Styrofoam cup, and water.
B. Fill the cup 3/4 full of soil. Plant the seeds in the soil. Moisten the soil with the water.
C. Put the cup in a warm, sunny place.
D. Look at the cup each day for the next week. Be sure the soil is moist.
1. How long did it take for the seeds to sprout?
2. What do the seeds need in order to sprout?

Section Review

Main Ideas: Some plants make seeds and some do not make seeds. Plants can also reproduce if their stems, leaves, or roots are cut, and from runners.

Questions: Answer in complete sentences.

1. What are three ways in which plants can reproduce?
2. How does the plant shown in the margin reproduce?
3. Draw the life cycle of this plant.
4. In what way is a spore like a seed?

EXTENSIONS

Reinforcement
Activity

Let the students determine if the soil is necessary in the Activity on this page. Take some of the same type of seeds used for the Activity. Place them on a damp paper towel in a shallow dish. Keep the paper towel moist.

A. Ask the students if the seeds sprouted at all. Did they sprout faster with soil or without? (There should be little difference.)

B. Keep the seedlings in the same dish, supplied only with water. How long did they survive? (Not very long)

C. Students should conclude that soil is necessary once the seeds have germinated.

ACTIVITY

Skill Development—*Observing, Concluding and Generalizing*

Teaching Tips—Give different groups of students different kinds of seeds—bean, clover, grass. Make sure the students cover the seeds with soil. Explain that the soil should be moist but not soaking wet.

Answers to Questions— **1.** A few days. **2.** Water.

SECTION REVIEW

Main Ideas—Have the students make a diagram showing the life cycle of a flowering plant.

Answers to Questions
1. From seeds, spores, or runners
2. From seeds
3. Students should diagram the life cycle of a conifer.
4. Each spore can produce a new plant.

Exceptional Student
Learning Disabled

To reinforce the concept of what plants need in order to germinate and grow, draw a chart illustrating plant needs.

SUGGESTED WORKSHEET MASTER
p. T-225 n

SECTION BACKGROUND

Many birds and mammals migrate. Migration occurs when animals move from one region to another because of changes in their environment. Why populations respond to changing conditions in this way is not well understood. Some species move because of decreasing food supplies; others move in response to temperature changes. Still others move for reasons that are as yet unknown.

Plants also move from one place to another. Plant movement is called succession and takes place at a much slower rate than animal migration.

Succession is the series of changes that take place in a plant community as it gets older. There are two types of succession—primary and secondary. Primary succession begins on bare rock. Lichens grow and cause the rock to break down to form soil. Eventually other plants, such as mosses, grasses, and small flowering plants, are able to grow on the thin layer of soil. After thousands of years, succession may lead to a climax forest. Secondary succession begins on soil, not on bare rock. This kind of succession occurs when an event such as a fire clears the plant population from an area. Human intervention can also do this, as when a forest is cut to clear land for farming and the farm is later abandoned.

MATERIALS

seeds, such as cocklebur, burdock, sycamore, milkweed, dandelion, maple; plastic cup; water

15-3. Organisms on the Move

The animal shown in this picture is a harp seal. It lives near the Arctic Circle. In the summer, it may swim over 700 miles north of the Arctic Circle. When winter comes, herds of seals move south. Why do you think harp seals move south in winter? When you finish this section, you should be able to:

- ☐ **A.** Explain why animals *migrate* to new places.
- ☐ **B.** Identify the *migration* routes of populations of animals.
- ☐ **C.** Explain how plant populations move to new places.

BASIC TEACHING PLAN

MOTIVATION

Ask students to give examples of animals that migrate. Encourage the students to locate their animals' migration routes on a map of the world. Provide pictures of animals that migrate: harp seals (on this page), whales, warblers, monarch butterflies, bighorn sheep. Show these pictures to the students to give them an idea of the variety of animals that migrate.

Text Questions—Why do you think harp seals move south in winter? *They migrate because of the changing season and for breeding purposes.*

Most populations of animals live all their lives in the same place. Single organisms, like the black bear, might roam through a large forest looking for food. But most populations make their home in one place and stay there.

1 Populations of birds, insects, and mammals move each year. The movement of animals from place to place is called **migration** (my-**gray**-
2 shun). Why do animals *migrate*?

Scientists think that animals migrate for sev-
3 eral reasons. Many animals migrate in winter in order to reach warmer areas. Some animals migrate to find new sources of food. Others migrate to areas where they can raise their young under better conditions.

Migration: The movement of animals from place to place.

EXTENSIONS

Reinforcement

Research

Discuss the concept of migration with the students, or integrate this Activity with the discussion of migration on pages 253 and 254. Assign each of the animals listed below to a pair of students. Tell the students to find out if their animal migrates and, if it does, to show the migration route on a map.

1. Owls
2. Terns
3. Coyotes
4. Harp seals
5. Cardinals
6. Meadowlarks
7. Dolphins
8. Brown pelicans
9. Ring-necked pheasants
10. Antelope
11. Reindeer

DEVELOPMENT

1 **Teaching Tips**—Find a picture showing a flock of birds in flight. Have the students speculate about where the birds are going. Many species of mammals, birds, and insects migrate. Students may ask if humans migrate. Some humans do. The Lapps migrate with the reindeer, because they are dependent upon it for food.

2 **Skill Development**—Students can *classify* animals as migrators or nonmigrators. They can keep two separate lists, using research results from the Extension on this page.

3 **Skill Development**—Students can *compare and contrast* the migration routes and reasons for migration of bighorn sheep, monarch butterflies, and warblers. Have them make a chart listing the three animals. There should be a column for the routes and one for the reasons for migration. Have students research the answers in their textbooks.

EXTENSIONS

Enrichment

Research

Students should be aware of what the word *environment* means in regard to a living organism. Have students go through old magazines and cut out pictures of different environments. Environments your students should look for include: deserts, rocky seacoasts, beaches, underwater environments (fresh and salt), marshlands, farmlands, forests, grasslands, tropical jungles, Arctic tundra, mountaintops.

Bighorn sheep: An animal with curved horns that lives in the Rocky Mountains.

Monarch butterfly: A beautiful butterfly that migrates over long distances.

Harp seals migrate from north to south. Other animal populations migrate from east to west. This brings them to warmer places. Some populations migrate from high country to low country. For example, the **bighorn sheep** spends summers in the high meadows of the Rocky Mountains. In winter, the sheep move down to low country. They are moving away from the cold winters. **4**

Another animal that migrates is the whale. Scientists think whales migrate mainly to reproduce. They spend their summers in cold polar seas. During the winter they travel to warm seas. There they give birth and raise their pups. When spring comes, they return to the polar waters.

Some insects also migrate. The **monarch butterfly** (**moh**-nark) migrates over 1,600 kilometers (1,000 miles). At the end of each summer, it flies south from Canada. Some *monarch butterflies* go to the Gulf of Mexico. Others go as far as Mexico. In the spring, they begin their migration north.

5 You may have seen migrating birds in flight. One kind of migrating population is the warbler. Robins are warblers. Warblers leave South America early in March. Ten days later, they reach Florida. Warblers return to the places where they nested the year before. Warblers can fly 50–80 kilometers (30–50 miles) per hour. But they stop to rest and eat on migration. So the warblers do not travel north that fast.

Plant populations can move to new places, **6**

4 **Teaching Tips**—The bighorn sheep is an example of an animal that migrates to a different elevation. Point out how this is different from migrating to a different latitude. In both cases, the reason for migration is the seasonal shift in temperature.

5 **Teaching Tips**—Most migratory birds and mammals use established routes and travel on a more or less regular schedule. There are many species of warblers that migrate. They can be seen traveling north in the eastern part of the United States in late spring. If you live in this area, have students watch for them and report the return of one species.

6 **Skill Development**—*Compare and contrast* the responses of animals and plants to changes in environment. Animals are mobile; therefore they can migrate, or change their locations, often. Plants do not really migrate. Plant types change over a period of time because of the changes in the environment. This process is called succession, and it does not occur as often as animal migrations.

too. But plants move for other reasons. Plant migration is harder to see. It takes place slowly. When plants move into a place, it is called **succession** (suck-**seh**-shun).

Suppose a volcano erupts. It destroys all the plants and animals in an area. Only bare soil and rock are left. When the ground cools, *succession* starts. Wind or animals carry seeds into the area. The first seeds to come in and grow are grasses. Soon, seeds from other plants are carried in. A meadow of grasses and small plants forms. The next stage in succession is the arrival of cone-bearing plants. Pine trees start to grow. In the last stage, hardwood tree seeds arrive. Oak trees and maple trees start to grow. The movement of plants is very different from the movement of animals.

Succession: The movement of plant populations into an area.

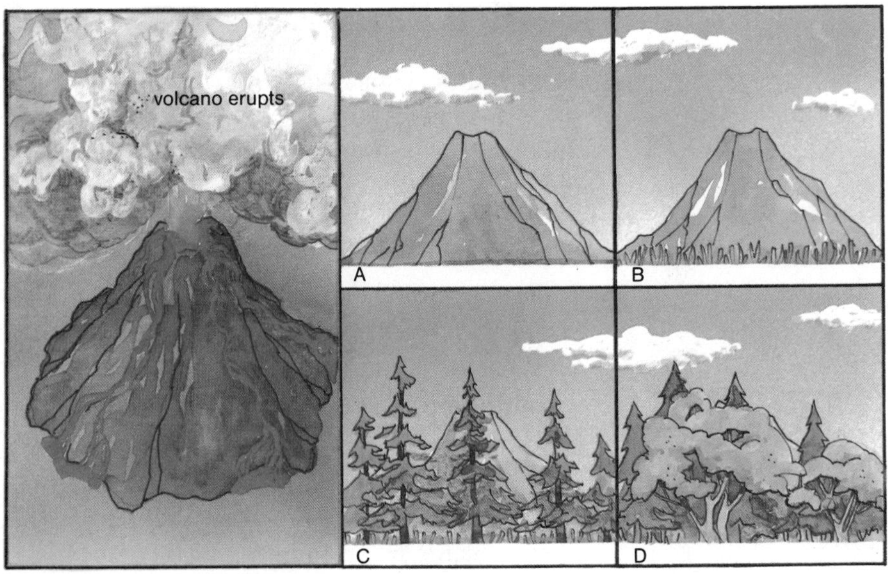

EXTENSIONS

Reinforcement

Science Skills—Observing, Inferring

Review primary and secondary succession with the students. Point out that the pioneer plants may be different in the two cases. Ask the students these questions:

1. After the glaciers receded, did mostly primary or secondary succession take place? (Mostly primary, since the glaciers stripped soil from the rock)
2. Have you ever seen examples of secondary succession? The students may have seen an abandoned field, a parking lot no longer used, or a building lot that had been swept by a fire. Ask if they noticed plants growing where there had been none before. How might the seeds of these plants have been carried to the new location?

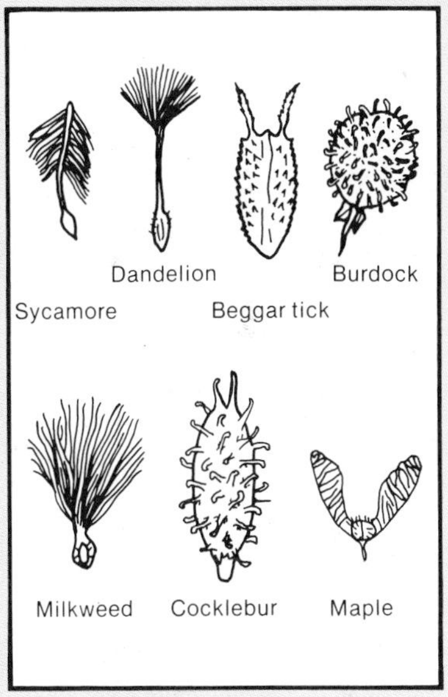

Fig. 15-2

Exceptional Student

Visually Impaired
Learning Disabled

Take the students on a seed-collecting trip. Feeling the seeds may increase understanding of how they are dispersed in nature.

ACTIVITY

Skill Development—*Classifying*

Teaching Tips—You will need to gather several types of seeds. The diagram shown here will help you to find some appropriate seeds. Cocklebur, beggarstick, and burdock have barbs or hooks that enable the seeds to fasten on animals that pass near the plant. The seeds are then rubbed off at a distance from the parent plant. The next four seeds in the diagram are equipped to float on air currents and be carried away. Some seeds, such as those of the jewel weed, are expelled with great force from the plant. This ensures that the seeds will fall far away from the parent plant.

Answers to Questions—1. The parachute-shaped seeds can float on air currents. Those with barbs cling to animals. **2.** Parts of the outer coat, such as down, wings, or barbs. **3.** Some are carried on the bodies of animals. Some are carried by the wind. Others can float in water. **4.** In order to make the population distribution more widespread and permit succession to take place.

EXTENSIONS

Enrichment

Activity

Start a seed display in your classroom by gluing seeds to brown paper. They could be categorized as follows: those used for food, those from trees, those from fruits and vegetables, those adapted for different kinds of dispersal, etc.

SUGGESTED WORKSHEET MASTER
p. T-225 o

7 ACTIVITY

What are some ways that seeds can travel?

A. Gather these materials: seeds, plastic cup, and water.

B. Look at each seed. Think of all the ways that a seed could travel. Drop it through the air. See if it floats in water. Try to stick it to your clothing.

1. How does the shape of the seed affect the way it might travel?
2. What parts of the seed help it travel?
3. What are some ways that seeds travel?
4. Why is it important for seeds to travel?

Section Review

Main Ideas: Plants and animals can move from place to place. Animal populations migrate to find food, to reproduce, or to reach a warmer place.

Questions: Answer in complete sentences.

1. Do bighorn sheep migrate for the same reason as whales? Explain your answer.
2. What is the migration route of the monarch butterfly?
3. How would a new population of plants reach a new place?
4. How does animal migration differ from the way plants move to new areas?

7 Teaching Tips—Activity commentary is on preceding page.

SECTION REVIEW

Main Ideas—Have the students explain the difference between migration and succession. Have them give examples of primary and secondary succession. They could refer to maps to emphasize the extent of animal migrations.

Answers to Questions

1. No. Bighorn sheep move because of food and climate. Whales apparently migrate to feed, and because of breeding habits.
2. The monarch butterfly migrates south from Canada to Mexico or the Gulf of Mexico, a journey of over 1,600 km.
3. Seeds are carried into the new surroundings. If the environment is suitable, the plants will grow.
4. Animals migrate in a yearly cycle; plant populations in an area change very slowly, not in a yearly cycle.

15-4.

Population Explosions

The plant shown here is Kudzu. About 40 years ago, people brought this plant from Japan. Soon, Kudzu was growing wild. What might have caused this to happen? When you finish this section, you should be able to:

- ☐ **A.** Identify the cause of population explosions.
- ☐ **B.** Identify four things that cause the size of a population to change.
- ☐ **C.** Predict what may happen if a population gets too large.

SECTION BACKGROUND

The number of organisms in a population can change over time. The size of the human population has exploded in recent years compared with its growth hundreds of years ago. In fact, the human population has nearly doubled in the last 30 years. In the past, it took the human population more than 1600 years to double its size. Populations of organisms increase if births increase and/or deaths decrease. Populations decrease if births decrease and/or deaths increase.

Populations cannot increase forever. Certain conditions in the environment limit the growth of populations.

MATERIALS

3 jars of different sizes; Daphnia; algae water; aged tap water; medicine dropper; small, flat dish

BASIC TEACHING PLAN

MOTIVATION

Show the students a graph representing human population growth from 6000 B.C. projected to A.D. 2000. What caused the population explosion? *Better disease control, medical advances, environmental control, increased food production.*

Text Questions—What might have caused this to happen? *The kudzu was able to compete very successfully for room to grow and for minerals from the soil. Evidently few, if any, insects or plant diseases in this country affected it.*

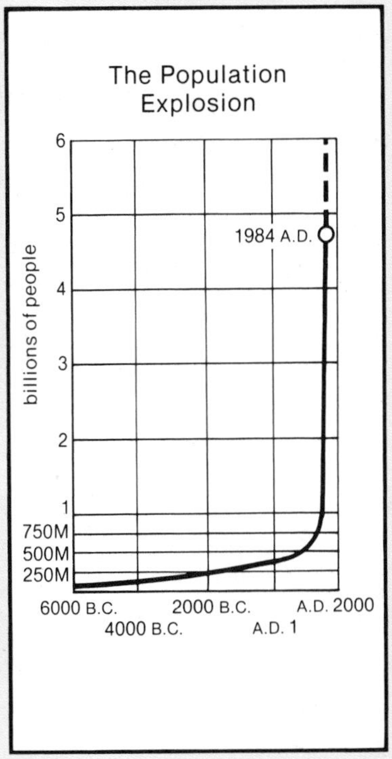

Fig. 15-3

EXTENSIONS

Enrichment

Activity

Many factors affect the size of a population. Space is one such factor. Overcrowding can have a negative effect on the size of a population. Discuss with the students how they might design an experiment to test this idea. Discussion may lead to the following experiment: Provide 20 containers, such as Styrofoam cups. Put the same amount of potting soil into each cup. Moisten the soil in each cup. Divide the cups into groups of five. In the first group, plant one radish seed in each cup. In the second, plant two seeds; in the third, plant five; and in the fourth, plant at least ten seeds. Observe the cups daily, and keep the soil moist. When the seeds start to sprout, make sure they are in sunny locations. Count the number of plants growing in each cup after one week. Record the number of plants in each cup daily for about two weeks. Did this experiment show that space has an effect on the size of populations?

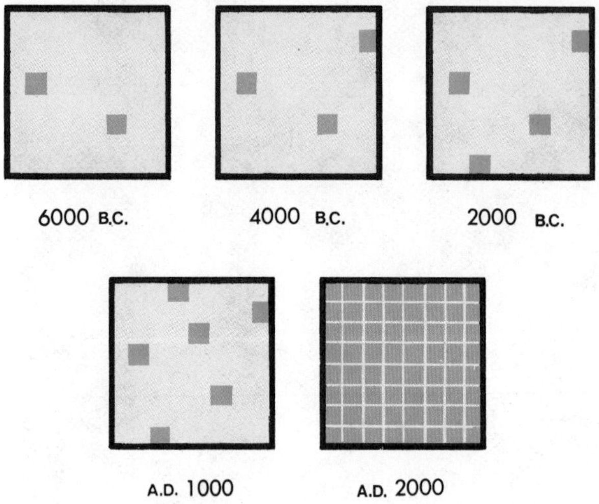

A population that grows very fast is said to be exploding. When this happens, there is not enough living space for the population. Look at
1 the diagram above. It shows the number of humans on each square mile of the earth. In 6,000 B.C., there were only two people for each square mile. For thousands of years, the population did not change much. But between A.D. 1,000 and the present, the human population exploded.
2 How many people are now living on a square mile?

3 The drawing shows some of the ways in which a population can change. Populations grow if there are more births than deaths. They also grow if more of their members move into the area. Populations decrease if more deaths occur than births. They also decrease if their members move out of the area.

DEVELOPMENT

1 Teaching Tips—For the first 2,000,000 years humans were on earth, they were hunter/gatherers and the earth's population did not exceed about 10 million. About 8000–7000 B.C. agriculture was discovered and the population started to grow. In the year A.D. 1800 the population reached 1 billion, and the rate of increase was less than 1 % per year. By 1960 the population had reached 3 billion, and the rate of increase was 2 % per year. In 1975 the population reached 4 billion, and the rate of increase dropped to 1.7 % per year. Current population estimates for the year 2000 range from 5.5 to 6 billion. These projections are below those common in the early 1970s because the rate of population growth is slowing.

2 Text Questions—How many people are now living on a square mile? *Sixty-four.*

3 Teaching Tips—You can illustrate population changes by studying the population of your classroom. Ask the students how the population of students in the class could increase. *A new student could join the class.* How could the size decrease? *Someone could move away.*

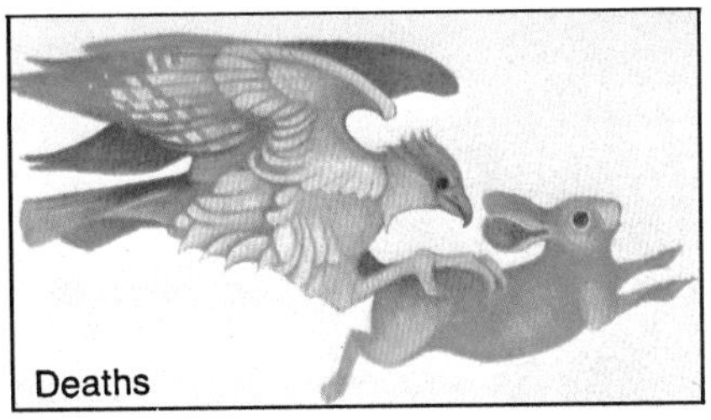

Let's look more closely at the changes in a population. Suppose you have a jar of flies like the one shown. You put food in the jar. Because there is food, the population of flies grows. You can see this in the second jar in the picture. What happens to the population of flies after a longer time? There is still plenty of food. But the population has decreased. Many of the flies have died because of the buildup of wastes in the jar.

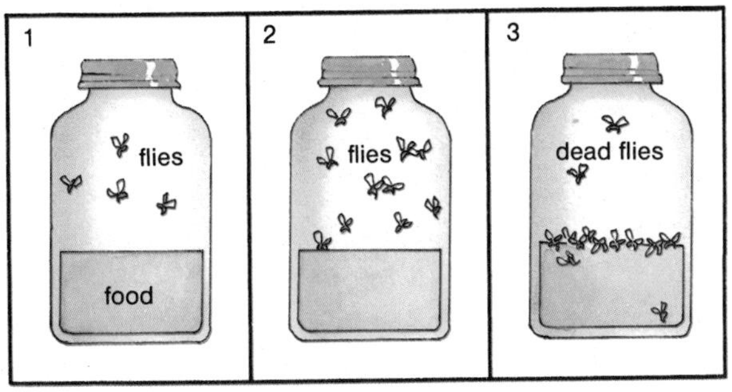

4 **Teaching Tips**—Ask the students how they could make the fruit-fly population continue to increase. They might suggest moving the flies to a larger jar and providing more food. They might also suggest a way to dispose of the waste materials produced.

EXTENSIONS

Enrichment

Science Skills—Observing

You can obtain fruit-fly cultures from science supply houses. Fruit flies are easy to care for, and students can learn much about population changes because the fruit flies reproduce quite rapidly. The fruit-fly cultures come in vials containing food and flies. Follow these procedures:

A. Have the students observe the cultures with a hand lens. Have them make a drawing of what they see. You may want to give the scientific name of the fly (*Drosophila melanogaster*) after the students have observed and made their drawing.

B. Have the students keep their cultures where they can observe them each day. After a few days the female flies should lay eggs. The eggs will hatch in a day, producing wormlike larvae. After about five days the larvae will enter the pupa stage. Within a week the adult fly should emerge from the pupa case. The life cycle of a fruit fly is about 14 days.

C. Students can observe the changes in the fruit-fly population by counting at first, then by estimating the total number as the population increases. Can the students conclude that limited space is a factor in population growth? The population of flies in the vial should decrease after a period of increase.

D. If you want to keep a classroom colony chamber, you will need a 4-l (1-gal) jar. A banana peel can serve as food, although the food contained in the vial from the science supply house is better because it inhibits mold growth.

EXTENSIONS

Enrichment

Activity

Students can determine the effects of various factors on population growth and size. Grow a number of bean plants as described in the Activity on page 251. Transfer plants to individual containers when they are large enough (when they have two to four leaves). Divide them into three groups, with at least two plants in each group. Place two groups in a sunny window. Water one of the two with plain water only. Use commercial plant food with water on the other. Place the third group in a dark corner of the room and continue to water. Have students observe the effects of these factors on the growth and size of the plants.

In this case, there was too little space for the flies. If the jar were bigger, more flies could live in it. But even that space would soon fill up.

In the next case, a lack of food limited the size of a deer population. Deer populations can grow very fast. Not long ago, the population of deer in the Florida Everglades exploded. The Everglades is a swamp. One year it flooded. The plants that the deer eat were covered by water. There was less food for the deer. Many of the deer became weak and sick. The sick deer died. The population started to decrease.

Some populations eat other populations. The fox shown here eats lemmings. If there are few foxes, the lemming population grows. Suppose **5** the foxes were killed by a disease. What do you think would happen to the lemming population? What do you think would happen to the lemming population if the foxes were healthy?

5 Text Questions—What do you think would happen to the lemming population? *The lemming population would increase because the fox population decreased.* What do you think would happen to the lemming population if the foxes were healthy? *There would be more foxes and therefore the lemming population would decrease.*

ACTIVITY

How does the amount of space affect the size of the population?

A. Gather these materials: 1 small, 1 medium, and 1 large jar; Daphnia; algae water; medicine dropper; and aged tap water.

B. Pour equal amounts of algae water into the 3 jars. Fill the jars with aged tap water.

C. Put the same number of Daphnia (about 10) in each jar. Put the jars in a place where there is plenty of light. It should not be too hot.

D. Each day for the next week, count the number of Daphnia in each jar.

1. How did the populations change?
2. What effect did the size of the jar have on the size of the population?

Section Review

Main Ideas: The size of a population depends on births, deaths, and the movement of members in and out of an area.

Questions: Answer in complete sentences.

1. What are two things that can cause a population to change size?
2. Do population explosions last forever? Why?
3. Is the human population getting bigger or smaller? What effect may this have?

EXTENSIONS

Enrichment

Activity

Introduce some of the Daphnia from the Activity on this page into an aquarium that has a lot of green algae growing in it.

A. Does the Daphnia population increase rapidly?

B. Does the green-algae population decrease rapidly?

C. Ask the students to predict whether the Daphnia population will continue to increase after most of the algae are gone.

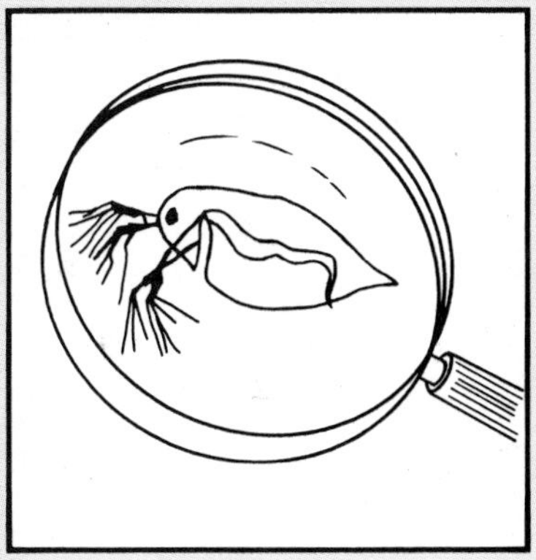

Fig. 15-4

ACTIVITY

Skill Development—*Finding Cause and Effect*

Teaching Tips—Daphnia are small aquatic animals about 2.5 mm long. You will need to order the Daphnia from a science supply house a few weeks before you do this Activity.

Answers to Questions—1. The most growth should be in the large jar, and the least growth in the small jar. **2.** The larger the jar, the greater the increase in population.

SECTION REVIEW

Answers to Questions

1. Birthrate and/or deathrate changes; food, living space, disease, other populations

2. No. Eventually the population will decrease due to lack of food or living space, disease, or an influx of other populations.

3. Bigger. This may lead to food shortages and excessive waste buildup.

Exceptional Student

Visually Impaired

Provide the students with magnifying glasses so that they can see the Daphnia.

EXTENSIONS

Application
Research/Library

The students can use books on natural history and botany to find out about the coconut-palm tree. These trees are found virtually everywhere that the climate is suitable for their growth. They are even found on tiny tropical islands that are thousands of miles away from any other land. These plants were able to spread out like this due to their seeds. The outer layer of a coconut is very hard and waterproof. The tree drops these seeds into the ocean, and they are carried away by the current. When they are thrown up on a beach, the seeds begin to grow into trees.

CHAPTER REVIEW

Science Words: Think of a word for each blank. List the letters **a** through **m** on paper. Write the word next to each letter.

__a__ are small animals that live in salt water. You can find __b__ in lakes and ponds.

The young form of an insect is called a __c__. The next stage in an insect life cycle is the __d__ stage.

The part of the flower that contains the pollen is the __e__. The yellow powder made by the anther is called __f__. The part of the flower that receives pollen is the __g__. A simple green plant is a __h__. A __i__ is a small round object found on ferns.

The movement of animals from place to place is called __j__. An animal with curved horns is the __k__. The name of a butterfly that migrates is the __l__. The movement of plants into an area is called __m__.

Questions: Answer in complete sentences.

1. What are some ways that animals reproduce? Give at least two ways.
2. What are two ways that plants can reproduce?
3. Do plants migrate? Explain your answer.
4. Describe two ways that population size can be controlled.
5. Describe the life cycle of a fern. Draw a diagram with labels to show your answer.

CHAPTER REVIEW

Science Words

a. Brine shrimp, **b.** hydras, Daphnia, **c.** larva, **d.** pupa, **e.** anther, **f.** pollen, **g.** stigma, **h.** moss, **i.** spore, **j.** migration, **k.** bighorn sheep, **l.** monarch, **m.** succession

Answers to Questions

1. Animals such as the ameba reproduce by simple division. Animals such as frogs reproduce by laying eggs. Insects also lay eggs.
2. Seeds, spores, cuttings (leaves, stems, or roots)
3. Plants do not migrate in the same way that animals do. Plants succeed one another as conditions in the environment change.
4. The food supply can be limited. The number of consumers (organisms that feed on the population) can be increased. Individuals can be moved out.
5. Refer to the diagram on page 250.

SUGGESTED WORKSHEET MASTER
p. T-225 p
SUGGESTED TEST MASTERS
pp. T-225 f, g

CHAPTER 16

SURVIVAL AND CHANGE

You should be able to tell the animals from the plants shown here. You can also see the difference between the two animal populations. But what about one population? When you finish this section, you should be able to:

16-1. Comparing Organisms

CHAPTER OBJECTIVES

1. Describe ways in which populations differ from each other.
2. Describe ways in which individuals in a population can vary.
3. Explain how differences in individuals in a population can affect their chances for survival.
4. Compare and contrast endangered and extinct populations.
5. Identify reasons why populations become endangered and extinct.

SECTION BACKGROUND

Living things on earth exist in many different sizes. The largest animal is the blue whale. It can be 30 m (100 ft) long and weigh 135,000 kg (150 t). The largest plant is the giant sequoia tree, which grows in California. It can grow to a height of more than 90 m (300 ft). Viruses are so small they can only be seen with an electron microscope. Living things differ in a variety of ways. These differences were brought about by changes that took place over a long period of time. Darwin's principle of natural selection helps explain why there are differences and how these differences play a part in the survival or extinction of animals and plants.

BASIC TEACHING PLAN

MOTIVATION

Bring in pictures of people from magazines or newspapers. Discuss differences in the appearance of these people with the class. Have five students from the class volunteer to stand in the front of the room. Ask the other students to make a list of the differences they see in those students. Discuss differences in animal populations. For instance, what differences in dogs of the same breed does a judge at a dog show look for?

MATERIALS

10 shells (of the same species), metric ruler

Exceptional Student
IEP Chapter Goal

At the end of this chapter, the student will cite two examples of how variations within a population can affect its survival.

EXTENSIONS

Reinforcement

Activity

You can use the idea of measuring body length to develop a body-mapping Activity. You will need sheets of butcher paper, measuring tapes, meter sticks, and crayons.

A. Have pairs of students trace outlines of each other's bodies on the butcher paper. Tell them to pay attention to such details as hands and fingers.

B. Then have your students make the following measurements and list them on the butcher paper: arm, leg, and finger lengths; thickness of arms and legs; waist size; head size; foot width.

C. Collect all the data systematically on one chart on the chalkboard or on chart paper. Have each student record his or her own data on the chart. Use a calculator to determine class averages.

D. Make a separate list showing the largest and smallest measurements.

A. Identify ways in which populations differ.

B. Compare organisms of the same population.

Look at these pictures of frogs. Each frog is from a different population. Their colors are different. They are also different sizes. What are some ways in which they are alike? **1**

2 Populations differ in many ways. List the ways in which you think animal populations can differ.

One way populations differ is in size.

264

DEVELOPMENT

1 Text Questions—What are some ways in which they are alike? *They have four legs, toes, two eyes, and similar body shapes.*

2 Skill Development—Students can *observe* differences in the population of the classroom. They should be encouraged to make *conclusions* about variations in populations.

A virus is very small. You need a very strong microscope to see it. It can show the virus enlarged 1,000 times. Four thousand viruses could fit on the period at the end of this sentence. Other populations are very large.

The largest animal is the blue whale. It is over 30 meters (100 feet) long. It weighs over 135,000 kilograms (150 tons). The largest plant is the Sequoia (seh-**kwoi**-ah) tree. It is over 90 meters (300 feet) tall.

Animals and plants are the sizes they are for a reason. Their size helps them survive. Giraffes can eat food that other animals cannot reach. They can also spot their enemies quickly. With their long necks, they can see over bushes and trees. Monkeys can move quickly because they are so small. Their speed helps them get food and avoid enemies. Tall trees can get extra sunlight. They tower over smaller trees.

EXTENSIONS

Enrichment

Research—Library

The average sizes of organisms in any animal populations have not remained the same through the centuries. Fossil remains show that the first horses were much smaller than modern horses. Beavers are thought to have been much larger in the past than they are now.

A. Ask the students to do research in encyclopedias and other books to find more examples of animal species that have changed size over time.

B. How long did it take for the animals to change to their present sizes?

3 Teaching Tips—Viruses are parasitic, disease-producing agents. They are capable of multiplying very rapidly inside the body of their host. They are the cause of smallpox, influenza, rabies, poliomyelitis, and foot and mouth disease in animals. Most viruses can only be seen with the aid of an electron microscope.

4 Skill Development—Ask the students to *compare and contrast* the size of the whale to their own size. They can do this by making drawings to scale of the whale and themselves.

5 Teaching Tips—Emphasize that animals and plants differ in ways other than size. Some animals are fast runners, others can climb trees, some have excellent eyesight. Even in a deer population, some deer are faster runners than others. If a pack of wolves is chasing the deer, the faster deer have a better chance for survival.

EXTENSIONS

Reinforcement

Activity

Students will enjoy playing this game. It can be used to emphasize differences in animal populations and among different species of animals.

A. Set up a racetrack at least 25 m long.

B. Arrange all the players in a straight line.

C. The player that you choose to direct the game calls out the name of an animal, such as "duck." Everyone must race to the end of the track, imitating the movement of a duck. The first one to reach the finish line is the Great Duck. Change the name of the animal for each race.

D. As a variation, give each student the name of a different animal. Which animal is able to move along the track the fastest?

Differences can occur within a population. 6 Look at the picture in the margin. It shows a population of land snails. Do you see any differ- 7 ences in size? Find the largest and the smallest snail. What are some other differences that you can see?

The pictures below show two different populations. What differences can you find among the living things in each population?

6 **Skill Development**—Students have the opportunity to *compare and contrast* individuals and populations.
7 **Text Questions**—Do you see any differences in size? *Yes.* What are some other differences that you can see? *Color, slight differences in shape.* What differences can you find among the living things in each population? *There are differences in the size, shape, and coloration.*

ACTIVITY

How do members of a population differ?

A. Gather these materials: 10 shells and a metric ruler.

B. Measure the length of each shell.

1. What is the length of the smallest shell?
2. What is the length of the largest shell?

C. List any other differences among your shells.

3. What are some ways in which living things differ?

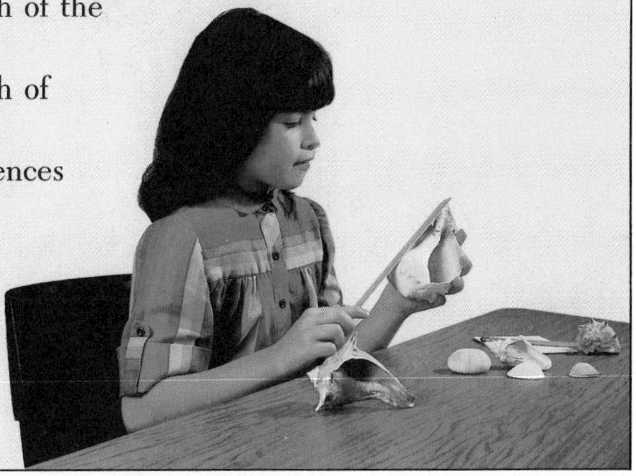

Section Review

Main Ideas: Members of different populations differ in size, shape, and color. Living things in the same population can also differ.

Questions: Answer in complete sentences.

1. List some ways that you differ from your mother and father.
2. What are three differences between a population of horses and a population of giraffes?
3. Find three differences in the population of leaves shown here.

EXTENSIONS

Enrichment

Science Skills—
Building Science Vocabulary

Ask the students to do some research on extreme differences in height among humans. Introduce the words *dwarfish*, *gigantism*, and *pituitary gland*, and ask the students to define these terms and see if they can find out what causes these extreme differences in height. They will find that if too much growth hormone is produced by the pituitary gland, a giant results, and if too little is produced, a midget results.

ACTIVITY

Skill Development—*Measuring, Recording Data*

Teaching Tips—Each group of students will need ten shells from the same population. You can use your own collections or purchase them from a shell shop. If you have difficulty obtaining enough shells for the class, you could use pine cones or leaves from the same tree (especially in the fall) or beans from the same bag.

Answers to Questions—1. Answers will vary. **2.** Answers will vary. **3.** Length, width, minor differences in color.

SECTION REVIEW

Answers to Questions

1. Answers should include height, weight, age, sex, hair color, eye color, etc.

2. Length of neck, overall height, coloration, presence of horns, etc.

3. Length, width, color

SUGGESTED WORKSHEET MASTER
p. T-225 q

SECTION BACKGROUND

A trait is a characteristic that is passed on from parent to offspring. An adaptation is an alteration or adjustment that enables one organism to survive in its environment better than similar organisms. Darwin called this process "survival of the fittest." Some giraffes were born with longer necks and were better able to survive because they could eat leaves from tall trees that other animals could not reach. The trait for longer necks was passed on to their offspring. This happened generation after generation, and eventually only giraffes with long necks survived. The long neck became an adaptation.

MATERIALS

100 red toothpicks, 100 green toothpicks, 40 m string, 4 stakes

16-2. Changing Populations

Once upon a time, there was a population of elephants that lived on an island. At first, there were both large and small elephants. After a long time, however, the population was made up only of small elephants. What caused this change? When you finish this section, you should be able to:

- **A.** Explain how a population can change over time.
- **B.** Explain how *variations* can affect an organism's chance for survival.

Variations: Differences among members of the same population.

You learned in the last section that there are differences among members of the same population. These differences are called **variations** (vare-ee-**ay**-shuns). *Variations* among organisms might include color, shape, or size.

Variations can affect the survival of a population. Animals that survive can reproduce. The variations that helped them survive are passed

BASIC TEACHING PLAN

MOTIVATION

Cut out six moths from construction paper (three black and three gray). Make them larger than life size. Tape together several sheets of black construction paper and put the paper on a table or on the floor in the center of the room. Place the moth cutouts on the paper. Pick one student. Have him or her quickly pick one moth from the black paper. Note the color of the moth. Put the moth back. Repeat this with five or six different students. Record the information on the chalkboard. Ask the students to explain the results. Because the background is black, the gray moths stand out and are more likely to be picked by the students than the black moths.

Text Questions—What caused this change? *The large elephants died out because there was not enough food to support them.*

on to their young. Let's look at the elephants on the island.

In this case, the island had too little food for all the elephants. The small elephants needed much less food than the large elephants. They were better able to live and reproduce. After a time, there were only small elephants living on the island.

Color can also affect survival. Suppose there are two colors of insects in a population. The two colors are green and red. The green insects are more likely to survive in a grassy place. They are not as easy to find as the red insects.

The picture on the left shows a hare. This hare can change its color. In the winter, its coat is white. In the summer, the color is brown. The second picture shows a hare from a different population. Its coat does not change. The color stays brown all year long. Which hare do you think would survive in the place shown in the two pictures?

DEVELOPMENT

1 Skill Development—*Compare and contrast* the elephant story with the insect story. Help the students identify the variation in each population that affected the survival of the organism. Students will be able to *infer* that protective coloration is a vital adaptation for many species.
2 Teaching Tips—Discuss other animals that change color. For example, ermines also are brown in summer and become white in winter. Chameleons and flounders change color with their environment.
3 Teaching Tips—Sometimes it is possible to obtain chameleons at pet shops or through science supply houses. If you can obtain one, demonstrate its ability to change color. Chameleons are able to turn brown or green, depending upon the background. Relate this to the story of the hare.
4 Text Questions—Which hare do you think would survive in the place shown in the two pictures? *The hare that can change color.*

EXTENSIONS

Enrichment

Activity

Ask your students to observe birds. This Activity can be facilitated by making a bird feeder and positioning it outside a classroom window. If you begin feeding the birds before the onset of the cold season, you must continue to provide food throughout the cold season.

A. Cut a hole about 10 cm in diameter in the side of a large plastic bleach container. (Be sure the container has been rinsed out thoroughly.)

B. Tie a string to the handle and suspend the feeder outside a classroom window from a tree branch. Fill the container with birdseed. Students could make similar bird feeders for use at home.

C. Use a bird-identification book to identify some of the visitors to the feeder.

Modification in a bird's beak is usually closely related to what the bird eats. The shape of the beak often indicates whether a bird is an insect eater, a seed eater, a flesh eater, a mud prober, or a wood borer. Short, heavy beaks are used for cracking seeds. Woodpeckers have long, slender, pointed beaks.

D. Ask these questions:

1. What kind of beak do most of the birds that visit the bird feeder have?
2. What kind of beak does a duck have? (It is flat, to enable the duck to probe in the mud.)

EXTENSIONS

Reinforcement

Science Skills—Finding Cause and Effect

A. Write the following animal traits on the chalkboard: dull coloration; great height; herd instinct; swimming speed; blubber under the skin; tail that can hang on to branches; ability to change color as background changes; superior eyesight; antlers or horns; hooked beak.

B. Have each student list as many animals as he or she can think of that possess each trait.

C. Have the students read their lists. Make a master list of animals that possess each trait on the chalkboard. Then have the students discuss why each trait is important to the animal's survival.

ACTIVITY

How does an organism's color affect its chance to survive?

A. Gather these materials: red and green toothpicks.

B. Copy the chart shown. Pretend the toothpicks are insects. You will be a bird that eats insects.

C. When your teacher says "Go," cover 1 eye with your hand. Pick up toothpicks with your other hand. After 20 sec, your teacher will tell you to stop.

D. Record the number of red and green toothpicks you picked up.

E. Repeat steps C and D twice.

1. How many red toothpicks did you pick up? how many green toothpicks?
2. Which color toothpick could you see more easily?
3. Which color "insect" has the better chance to survive?

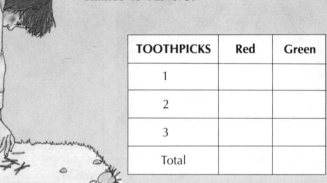

TOOTHPICKS	Red	Green
1		
2		
3		
Total		

ACTIVITY

Skill Development—*Comparing and Contrasting, Finding Cause and Effect*

Teaching Tips—Dye the toothpicks with food coloring the day before the Activity. Make sure you have the same amount of each color toothpick (at least 100 green and 100 red). Before class, stake off a square area 10 m on a side in the grass and run a string around the stakes. Scatter the toothpicks as randomly as you can. Tell the students that the toothpicks represent insects and that the students are going to pretend to be birds. They will have 20 seconds to "fly" into the staked-off area and find as many "insects" as they can. Repeat the process twice and record the number of each color toothpick they pick up. To make the hunt more challenging, tell the students to cover one eye with a hand while picking up the toothpicks.

Answers to Questions—**1.** Answers will vary. **2.** Red. **3.** Green.

Now let's look at what happened to the peppered moths in England. Peppered moths rest on tree trunks during the day. Birds feed on the peppered moths. Before factories were built in the 1850's, most tree trunks were light in color. Birds could see the dark-colored moths more easily than the light-colored moths. More of the dark moths were eaten. So more light-colored moths survived and reproduced. But what if the tree trunks changed color? The factories put black soot into the air. The soot settled on the bark of the trees. Many of the tree trunks became black. Soon, the number of dark moths increased. The birds did not see them. They blended in with the dark tree trunks. The birds ate more light-colored moths. The dark moths survived.

Section Review

Main Ideas: Populations can change over time. The change is due to variations among the members of the population. Changes in the environment can affect which members of a population survive.

Questions: Answer in complete sentences.

1. How can variations affect the chance that a living thing will survive? Give two examples.
2. Are all changes in the environment helpful to a population? Explain.
3. Look at the picture of the moths on this page. Explain how this population of moths changed over time.

EXTENSIONS

Reinforcement
Research

Human survival has depended in part on the ability of humans to adapt to changing and varied environments. Have your students do research to determine how human beings have used their intelligence and physical characteristics to survive. They can begin by learning how primitive humans created and used tools (the thumb was an advantage here), made weapons to kill game, used fire to help them withstand cold climates, made garments and shelters to protect themselves from the weather, and planted crops.

5 Teaching Tips—Students have already discussed the value of protective coloration. Tell the students that dull colors that blend into the surroundings are not always an advantage in survival. Male birds, for example, have bright plumage. Female birds seem to be more attracted to the individuals with the brightest colors. This means that the most brilliantly colored males are more likely to mate and produce offspring.

SECTION REVIEW

Answers to Questions

1. A variation may give an individual an advantage in his or her environment. Examples of variations are the giraffes with longer necks and the moths whose color blended with the color of the tree trunks.
2. No. If the climate becomes colder, for example, only those individuals who are better able to withstand the cold will live to reproduce.
3. As the bark of the trees got darker, more of the light-colored moths were eaten by birds. More of the dark-colored moths survived.

SUGGESTED WORKSHEET MASTER
p. T-225 r

SECTION BACKGROUND

An organism that no longer exists on earth is said to be extinct. Since colonial days, more than 60 species of animals have become extinct in the United States. These animals include the passenger pigeon, heath hen, great auk, Carolina parakeet, and Labrador duck. An organism that is in danger of becoming extinct is called endangered. There are about 1,700 plant species and 170 animal species that are now considered seriously endangered. The animals include the whooping crane, the American bald eagle, the American crocodile, the California condor, the grizzly bear, the blue whale, the bison, the musk ox, and the trumpeter swan.

Endangered species are now protected by law. With this protection, the number of individuals in some species has increased and chances for the survival of the species have improved.

MATERIALS

none

16-3. Disappearing Populations

A long time ago, dinosaurs roamed the land. There were many populations of dinosaurs. Dinosaurs lived on earth for over 160 million years. Then they were gone. Why did they die? When you finish this section, you should be able to:

- **A.** Identify populations that are *extinct* or in danger of becoming *extinct*.
- **B.** Explain what might cause the *extinction* of populations.

Extinct: Describes a population that no longer exists.

Organisms that no longer live on the earth are called **extinct** (ek-**stinkt**). Dinosaurs became *extinct* millions of years ago. On page 273 are pictures of two other extinct animals. Picture 1 shows a Labrador (**lab**-bra-dore) duck. Picture 2 shows a passenger pigeon. Both of these birds became extinct within the last 100 years.

BASIC TEACHING PLAN

MOTIVATION

Find some pictures of dinosaurs or several books about dinosaurs. Read some information about the dinosaurs to your students and show them pictures of these incredible animals. Some of your students may know quite a bit about the dinosaurs. Let these students share what they know with the rest of the class.

Text Questions—Why did they die? *Scientists are not sure what caused the populations of dinosaurs to become extinct.* It would be interesting to write down the students' answers and refer to them later.

2

1 More than 170 kinds of animals and 1,700 kinds of plants are now rare. Their numbers are decreasing. Someday, all of them may be gone. They are all in danger of becoming extinct. They are called **endangered** (en-**dane**-jurd) organisms. 2 Can you name an organism that is in danger of becoming extinct?

The animals shown on page 274 are *endangered*. They are the bald eagle and grizzly bear. 3 There are many reasons why living things become endangered. A change in the weather over a long time is one reason. Suppose warm temperatures caused the ice around the North and South Poles to melt. Some of the land would be flooded. Many plants and animals would not be

Endangered: Describes a population in danger of being extinct.

EXTENSIONS

Enrichment

Research—Library

Humans are responsible for the extinction or near extinction of many species of animals. Two of the ways by which humans bring about extinction are overkill, either for food or for furs, and elimination of habitat. Assign specific animals to groups of students and ask them to answer the following questions by doing library research.

A. How was the animal brought to extinction or near extinction?

B. Is it too late for this animal to be rescued from extinction?

C. If not, what has been done, if anything, to reverse the trend?

D. If something is being done, are the efforts effective?

Some of the animals the students might study are: the California condor, the blue whale, the whooping crane, the Siberian tiger, the white rhinoceros, the passenger pigeon, and the American bison.

DEVELOPMENT

1 Skill Development—Have the students *predict* what will happen to many animal and plant species if steps are not taken to stop overkill and habitat destruction. Ask them to *infer* what will happen to the total number of animal and plant species if humans do not alter their ways.

2 Text Questions—Can you name an organism that is in danger of becoming extinct? See the chart on page 275.

3 Teaching Tips—Passenger pigeons became extinct because of the direct intervention of humans. In the 19th century there were millions of passenger pigeons. Toward the end of that century tens of millions of passenger pigeons were slaughtered by professional hunters. The last passenger pigeon died in a zoo in 1914. The American bison narrowly escaped extinction at the hands of hunters who moved west with the railroads. A few scattered herds were left when laws were passed to protect the bison. Because the animal does well in captivity, it will probably not be lost.

EXTENSIONS

Enrichment
Research—Library

Emphasis thus far has been on endangered and extinct animal species. Many plant species have become extinct, too. Ask the students to do some research to find out what kinds of plants were alive when the dinosaurs existed.

A. Do any of these plants still exist? (Species of ferns and horsetails do, for example.)

B. Are plants that lived so long ago useful to us today? (Review the fact that the remains of these plants have formed the oil, coal, and gas reserves we use today.)

able to live. They would slowly die until none were left.

4 Human beings can endanger plants and animals. Many buffalo, beavers, and otters were killed. Their skins were used for clothes. As the human population grows, there is less room for animal and plant populations.

Endangered organisms are now protected. It is a crime to hunt them. Is it important to protect animals and plants? What difference does it make to other living things if an animal or plant becomes extinct? You will learn the answers to these questions in the next unit.

DON'T
SHOOT
HAWKS
ALL HAWKS
ARE PROTECTED
BY STATE LAWS

A change in the environment can also endanger organisms. The ivory-billed woodpecker feeds only on insects in dead trees. The forests where they lived were cut down. The old trees were replaced with new trees. This destroyed their food supply. The birds became extinct. Biologists asked that some old trees be allowed to remain. How would this help the ivory-billed woodpecker to survive?

4 **Teaching Tips**—Species have always died out, and new species have arisen to take their places. This is the basis of the evolutionary process. Since humans have become such a dominant species, however, the rate of extinction of other species has increased. Since the year 1600, 120 mammal and 162 bird species have become extinct. Ask the students to consider what natural events might lead to extinction. They should mention fires, hurricanes, droughts, volcanic eruptions, and ice ages. Humans contribute by destroying habitats—for example, by building shopping malls and highways, or by farming in tropical rain forests. Humans have also introduced alien plants and animals into environments. One example of this is the introduction of the rabbit into Australia. The rabbit had no natural predators there, and its population exploded. Another way humans intervene is to overkill a species for food, skins, or some other product (oil from whales, for example).

The chart below lists some of the extinct and endangered animals in North America.

Some Extinct North American Animals	
Passenger pigeon	Ivory-billed woodpecker
Heath hen	Carolina parakeet
Great auk	Labrador duck
Some Endangered North American Animals	
Whooping crane	Puma
American bald eagle	Musk ox
American crocodile	Trumpeter swan
California condor	Key deer
Grizzly bear	Blue whale

Some whales are almost extinct. Too many of them have been killed. Laws have been passed to limit the number of whales that can be killed. But a few countries like Russia and Japan still hunt whales.

EXTENSIONS

Reinforcement

Activity

Tell the students that they are going to design animals. Give them a description of a habitat, including its available food and its climate, and ask them to put together an animal that they think would survive under the given conditions. One example might be a mountain habitat with grasses and other plants. The natural enemies are eagles and mountain lions. The climate is very cold. The animal is a mammal.

The traits the students give their animal might include:

1. long fur to survive the cold;
2. gray color to blend in with the rocks, especially when young;
3. hooves that will not slip on rock;
4. horns to defend itself against the mountain lion;
5. big, flat teeth to chew grass and other plants.

5 **Teaching Tips**—This is an example of how a change in an organism's environment can cause it to become extinct. Some animals have very specific environmental requirements. The slightest change in the environment will result in a change in the organism or extinction.

6 **Text Questions**—How would this help the ivory-billed woodpecker to survive? *By leaving some old trees, the woodpecker would still have its source of food.*

EXTENSIONS

Reinforcement

Science Skills—Predicting, Finding Cause and Effect

Your students may have "designed" an animal (Extension, page T-275). If they have not, ask them to choose an animal. Using either their own animal or a real animal, have them list ways in which their animal might become extinct. The animal suggested on page T-275, for example, might become extinct if the eagle population suddenly increased and all the young were eaten.

SUGGESTED WORKSHEET MASTER
p. T-225 s

7 Why did the dinosaurs become extinct? Some scientists think that too many dinosaur eggs might have been eaten. Others think that the climate became cooler. The dinosaurs were used to a warm climate and died. Dinosaur eggs with very thin shells have been found. This may mean that some disease was killing the animals. Or a giant asteroid may have hit the earth. This may have caused a giant dust cloud. The cloud would have blocked light from the sun. Plants need sunlight. If the plants they ate died, many dinosaurs also would have died. Scientists have tried to explain why the dinosaurs became extinct. No one knows for sure why they died. What do you think happened?

Section Review

Main Ideas: Many populations have become extinct. Others are in danger of becoming extinct. Endangered populations are protected by law.

Questions: Answer in complete sentences.

1. What is the difference between an extinct and an endangered population?
2. Name an endangered population. Why is it endangered?
3. What might have happened to the dinosaurs?
4. Why should we stop living things from becoming extinct?

7 **Skill Development**—This is a good place to point out to students that scientists *hypothesize* about events such as the extinction of dinosaurs but may never be able to prove their theories.

SECTION REVIEW

Answers to Questions

1. An extinct population no longer exists on the earth; an endangered population is one whose numbers are decreasing and which is in danger of becoming extinct.
2. Blue whale. Too many have been killed by hunters.
3. A drastic change in environment or food supply, too many predators, disease
4. Any species contributes to a web of life in its environment. Removing one leaves a space in this web.

CHAPTER REVIEW

Science Words: Match the terms in column A with the definitions in column B.

Column A	Column B
1. Variations	a. A population that might become extinct
2. Extinct	b. Differences among members of the same population
3. Endangered	c. A population that does not exist anymore

Questions: Answer in complete sentences.

1. What are some differences in the populations shown on page 263?
2. What are some differences you might see in a population of trees?
3. The peppered moths in England changed from light to dark. How did this happen?
4. Giraffes eat leaves. Which type of giraffe shown in the picture would have a better chance of surviving if the trees were tall? Explain.
5. Squirrels are very fast. How does a squirrel's speed help it survive?
6. Each of these living things is endangered: bald eagle, humpback whale, California condor, grizzly bear. Choose one. Tell why it is endangered.
7. What are some things that you could do to help stop the extinction of plants or animals?

EXTENSIONS

Enrichment

Science Skills—Building Science Vocabulary

Ask the students to find the meaning of these words in a dictionary: camouflage, adaptation, mutation, species.

CHAPTER REVIEW

Science Words

1. b, **2.** c, **3.** a

Answers to Questions

1. Size, shape, and color

2. Size, appearance of the bark, size of leaves, number of leaves, resistance to diseases

3. The environment changed. The tree trunks were covered with soot and dust, making the trunks darker. The dark moths blended in more easily than the light moths, so more light moths were eaten.

4. The taller giraffes would have a better chance of getting food. Their chance of survival is better than that of the giraffes with short necks.

5. A squirrel can run away quickly from other animals, such as dogs and cats.

6. Change in the environment, overkilling, disease

7. Obey laws that are passed to protect them

SUGGESTED TEST MASTERS
pp. T-225 h, i

EXTENSIONS

Enrichment

Science Skills— Building Science Vocabulary

Have students look up the word *hibernation*. Hibernation is a method some animals use to escape extremes of temperature or other unfavorable conditions. Point out that very few animals—woodchucks and brown bats are examples—are true hibernators. Other animals, such as bears, become dormant during the winter.

INVESTIGATING

What populations are near your school?

A. Gather these materials: magnifying glass and a stick to dig with.

B. Copy the chart shown below.

C. When you see a living thing, make a mark for that population.

D. You will search in an area 10 m × 10 m. Your teacher will take you to the spot.

E. Look for living things that are shown on the chart. Use the stick to dig around rocks and roots. Be careful not to destroy the area.

1. What is the largest population?
2. What is the smallest population?
3. Are there more animal populations or plant populations?
4. Do you think the populations will be the same next month? in 6 months? Why?

ORGANISM

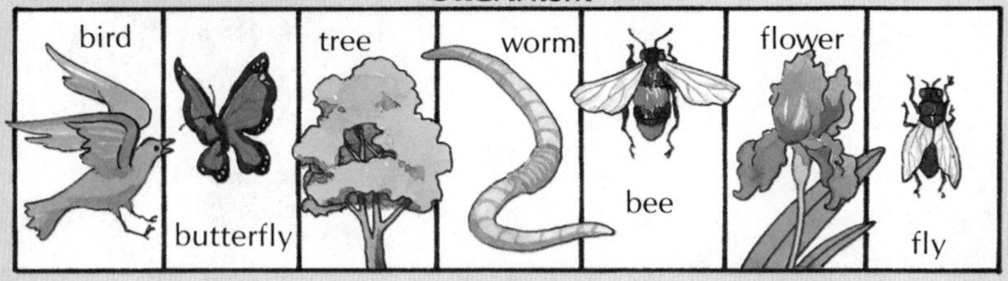

NUMBER

278

INVESTIGATING

Skill Development—*Recording Data*

Safety Tips—Caution students to be careful with the sticks.

Teaching Tips—Choose a grassy area if possible. Paved areas can be included if necessary. Mark off the area with a stout rope anchored at the corners before taking the class out. Caution students to disturb the soil as little as possible. The object is not to dig up or alter plants but to move the very top layer of soil to see if any organisms are living among the plant roots. Use the magnifying glasses even on the paved area.

Answers to Questions—**1.** Answer depends upon what is found. **2.** Answer depends upon what is found. **3.** Answer depends upon what is found. **4.** Probably not. After one month there may be changes in environment, such as lack of rain or abundant rain. After six months the seasons will have changed and the environment will certainly have changed.

CAREERS

Horticulturist ▶

Horticulturists (hore-ti-**kull**-chur-ists) are people who work with plants. They work in greenhouses and gardens. They try to improve the plants they grow.

A visit to a greenhouse will help you understand what horticulturists do. They must know about soils and fertilizers.

A horticulturist needs to go to school after high school.

◀ Entomologist

Entomologists (en-toe-**moll**-eh-jists) study insect populations. They may study termites, cockroaches, bees, ants, or butterflies.

Some entomologists try to find ways to control harmful insects. Others do research. They work in universities. Entomologists need a college degree in biology. Many people study and collect insects as a hobby.

EXTENSIONS

Enrichment

Research—Library

Wildlife-management specialists make field studies of animals. They band birds and animals to help keep track of population movements. They also keep counts of plant and animal populations. Since many wildlife refuges are also used for hunting, fishing, boating, hiking, camping, and logging, the wildlife managers have to be very aware of everything happening in their areas so that they can control activities wisely.

Game wardens and game-management officers enforce hunting and fishing regulations. They also have a public-relations function and explain the laws in speaking before various organizations.

CAREERS

Teaching Tips—For more information on these careers, write American Society for Horticultural Science, 70 North Saint Asaph Street, Alexandria, VA 22314; or Entomological Society of Washington, Director of Insects, U.S. National Museum, Washington, D.C. 20560.

UNIT 6 ANIMAL AND PLANT

CHAPTER	SECTION	BASIC SCIENCE SKILLS	ACTIVITY MATERIALS STUDENT/GROUP	EXTENSIONS
CHAPTER 17 ENERGY FOR LIVING	**17-1** p.T-282 Communities	*Observing* communities	glass jar, lid, potting soil, seeds, sprinkler, water	• Reinforcement p.T-285 • Enrichment pp.T-283, T-284, T-286 • Application p.T-286
	17-2 p.T-287 Green Plants	*Hypothesizing* about photosynthesis	celery stalks and leaves, 2 small jars, water, food coloring, knife, plastic bag, rubber band	• Reinforcement p.T-289 • Enrichment p.T-290, T-291 • Application p.T-288
	17-3 p.T-292 Using Oxygen	*Comparing and contrasting* interdependence p.T-293 and CO_2-O_2 cycle p.T-295	2 small bottles with caps, aged tap water, straw, bromothymol blue (BTB)	• Enrichment pp.T-293, T-294, T-295, T-296, T-297
CHAPTER 18 THE FOOD CYCLE	**18-1** p.T-298 Food Makers	*Comparing and contrasting* producers p.T-300 and foods containing sugar and starch p.T-301	iodine solution, dropper, cornstarch, rice, carrots, cereal, potato, paper towel or newspaper, knife	• Reinforcement p.T-300 • Enrichment pp. T-299, T-302 • Application pp.T-299, T-301
	18-2 p.T-303 Food Takers	*Classifying* consumers p.T-304 and producers, herbivores, and carnivores p.T-307	construction paper, small cards with the names of organisms, glue	• Reinforcement p.T-306 • Enrichment p.T-308 • Application pp.T-304, T-305, T-307
	18-3 p.T-309 The Decomposers	*Comparing and contrasting* decomposers, producers, and consumers p.T-309 *Sequencing* relationships of producers, consumers, and decomposers p.T-312	banana slices, plastic sandwich bags, yeast	• Reinforcement p.T-312 • Enrichment pp.T-311, T-313 • Application p.T-310
CHAPTER 19 THE WEB OF LIFE	**19-1** p.T-314 Food Chains	*Sequencing* path of food in a food chain p.T-316	terrarium, mustard seeds, crickets, frog	• Enrichment pp.T-315, T-317 • Application pp.T-316, T-317
	19-2 p.T-318 Connected Food Chains	*Sequencing* events in a food chain p.T-318 *Comparing and contrasting* predators and prey p.T-321	board, paper, small nails, hammer, scissors, yarn	• Reinforcement pp. T-319, T-320 • Enrichment p.T-321
	19-3 p.T-322 The Balance of Nature	*Recording data* on a graph	graph paper, crayons	• Enrichment pp.T-323, T-324, T-325
	19-4 p.T-326 People Affect Communities	*Finding the cause and effect* relationships between humans and the environment p.T-328	motor oil, mineral oil, bird feather, water, brush, paper towels, newspaper	• Reinforcement pp.T-328, T-329 • Enrichment pp.T-327, T-331, T-332 • Application pp.T-330, T-333

COMMUNITIES

EXTRA ACTIVITIES/ DEMONSTRATIONS	WORKSHEET MASTERS	EVALUATIONS
• Animals p.T-282 • Community p.T-283 • Habitats p.T-283	• Communities (SK) p.T-279 j	Section Review p.T-286
• Factory p.T-287 • Roots, stems p.T-289		Section Review p.T-291
• Stomata p.T-293 • O_2 from elodea p.T-293	• Oxygen-carbon dioxide cycle (SK) p.T-279 k • Photosynthesis (AC) p.T-279 l	Section Review p.T-296 Chapter Review p.T-297 Test Masters pp.T-279 d, e
• Pictures of food makers p.T-298 • Examining different foods p.T-299 • Producers p.T-301		Section Review p.T-302
• Pond sketch p.T-305	• Communities (AC) p.T-279 m • Chart (SK) p.T-279 n	Section Review p.T-308
• Bread mold p.T-309	• Decomposers (AH) p.T-279 o • Maze (SK) p.T-279 p	Section Review p.T-312 Chapter Review p.T-313 Test Masters pp.T-279 f, g
• Pictures of animals eating p.T-314 • Food chains p.T-315		Section Review p.T-317
• Community chart p.T-319 • Food web p.T-319	• Food web (SK) p.T-279 q	Section Review p.T-321
• Food web p.T-322 • Human effects p.T-324	Pollution (AH) p.T-279 r	Section Review p.T-325
• Investigating p.T-332	Science word puzzle (SK) p.T-279 s	Section Review p.T-330 Chapter Review p.T-331 Test Masters pp.T-279 h, i

KEY (AC)—Activity (AH)—At Home (SK)—Skill

BOOKS FOR STUDENTS

Hartman, Jane E. *Animals That Live in Groups*, New York: Holiday, 1979

John, Naomi. *Roadrunner*, illus. by Peter and Virginia Parnall, New York: Unicorn/Dutton, 1980

McDearman, Kay. *Foxes*, New York: Dodd, 1981

Newton, James R. *Forest Log*, illus. by Irene Brady, New York: Crowell, 1980

Prince, J. H. *How Animals Hunt*. New York: Elsevier/Nelson, 1980

Pringle, Laurence. *Natural Fire: Its Ecology in Forests*, New York: Morrow, 1979

Rabinowich, Ellen. *Seals, Sea Lions and Walruses*, New York: Watts, 1980

FILMS

Animal Behavior, 11 min, International

Animal Communities and Groups, 11 min, Coronet

Animals and Their Homes, 11 min, Coronet

Conserving Our Environment, 14 1/2 min, Coronet

Food Cycle and Food Chains, 10 1/2 min, Coronet

Introducing Ecology: Dependence and Sharing, 10 1/2 min, Coronet

Plants and Animals Depend on Each Other, 12 min, Coronet

Pond Life Web, 10 min, National Geographic

Why Animals Live Where They Do, 11 min, Coronet

FILMSTRIPS

Animals That Build Their Homes, a series, National Geographic, *Beavers, Wasps*

Exploring Ecology, 5 sound filmstrips, 14 min, National Geographic

Living Things Adapt to Their Environment, 10 min, Society for Visual Education

The Forest: A Stable Community, 55 frames, Britannica

The Pond: How Living Things Change Their Community, 55 frames, Britannica

COMPUTER AIDS

Odell Lake, Simulation, Apple, BASIC, 32K + DOS 3.2, Creative Computing

Odell Lake, Educational game, Atari, BASIC, 16K + D; BASIC crtdg, Atari Prog Exchng

Odell Woods, Simulation, Atari, BASIC, 16K + D; BASIC crtdg, Atari Prog Exchng

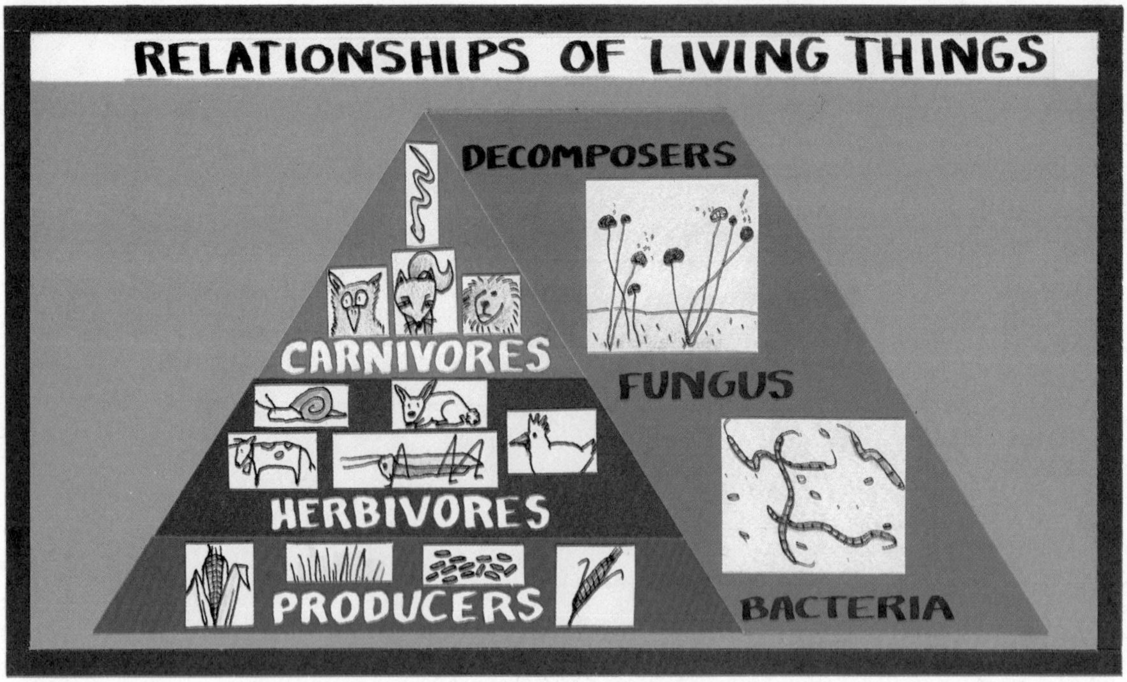

BULLETIN BOARD

This bulletin board is designed to illustrate the interdependence of living things. Have your students draw pictures of producers, consumers, and decomposers. Then suggest using these pictures to make a pyramid collage to show how living things are related. The pyramid should follow the design of a community chart. Your students should place a collage of producers at the base of the pyramid, a collage of plant eaters (herbivores) in the middle of the pyramid, and a collage of meat eaters (carnivores) at the top of the pyramid. Decomposers should be placed along the sides of the pyramid. You may wish to divide the class into four groups, making each group responsible for a different category.

FIELD TRIP IDEAS

To visit a farm

Arrange for the students to visit a farm. Have them make a list of the living things kept on the farm and classify them as producers, herbivores, carnivores, or omnivores. Discuss with the students the relationship between the things produced on the farm and the food consumed at home.

To identify how people change their environment

Suggest taking a walk through the neighborhood to see how people have changed the environment to satisfy their needs. Prior to the trip, locate an area that shows a variety of changes (i.e., parks, buildings, roads, drainage ditches, housing developments, and farms). During the trip, stop at several places and let your students discuss what they think the area might have looked like before the changes were made. Also allow them to speculate about why certain changes were made and what effects these changes may have had on the natural community.

Name________________________Date____________

Fold back answer key on line before copying.

ENERGY FOR LIVING

TEST CHAPTER 17

CHAPTER OBJECTIVES

Read each question. Choose the best answer. Write the letter of your choice on the line at the right.

1. A community is made of **1.** ______ **1.** a (1)

a. plants and animals that live in the same area.
b. plants and animals that live in different areas.
c. only plants that live in the same area.
d. only animals that live in the same area.

2. Which of the following is *not* a member of the ocean community? **2.** ______ **2.** c (1)

a. seaweed **c.** frogs
b. whales **d.** fish

3. Each member of a community lives in **3.** ______ **3.** a (1)

a. a special habitat. **c.** a parasite.
b. a dead log. **d.** the same habitat.

4. Organisms in a community **4.** ______ **4.** b (2)

a. live independently of each other.
b. always interact with others.
c. are all parasites.
d. are all the same.

5. The way in which protists and termites work with each other is an example of **5.** ______ **5.** a (2)

a. mutualism. **c.** photosynthesis.
b. habitat. **d.** parasitism.

6. A relationship that includes a parasite is **6.** ______ **6.** c (2)

a. two earthworms living under the same rock.
b. a bird and a cow that help each other.
c. a mosquito sucking the blood of a human.
d. all of the above.

7. When green plants make food, all of the following are combined except **7.** ______ **7.** b (3)

a. air. **c.** water.
b. sugar. **d.** minerals.

Name________________________________Date____________

8. d (3) **8.** The green material inside a plant cell that makes it possible for green plants to make food is called **8.** _____

a. photosynthesis. **c.** the nucleus.
b. carbon dioxide. **d.** chlorophyll.

9. d (3) **9.** The energy that plants need to make sugar comes from **9.** _____

a. chlorophyll. **c.** low temperatures.
b. oxygen. **d.** sunlight.

10. c (4) **10.** Water and minerals enter a plant through its **10.** _____

a. trunk. **c.** roots.
b. leaves. **d.** stem.

11. c (4) **11.** Photosynthesis occurs in **11.** _____

a. the root cells. **c.** the leaf cells.
b. the stem cells. **d.** the root hair cells.

12. d (4) **12.** Carbon dioxide enters a plant through **12.** _____

a. its roots. **c.** thin tubes.
b. its stems. **d.** tiny holes in the leaf.

13. a (5) **13.** Oxygen is given off into the atmosphere by **13.** _____

a. plants. **c.** plants and animals.
b. animals. **d.** only human beings.

14. d (5) **14.** Which of the following does *not* happen during the oxygen–carbon dioxide cycle? **14.** _____

a. Plants use the carbon dioxide given off by animals.
b. Animals use the oxygen given off by plants.
c. Carbon dioxide and oxygen move through the biosphere.
d. Animals use the carbon dioxide given off by plants.

15. b (5) **15.** In the oxygen–carbon dioxide cycle, **15.** _____

a. only the atmosphere takes part.
b. both atmosphere and biosphere take part.
c. animals give off oxygen.
d. none of the above takes place.

Name________________________Date__________

Fold back answer key on line before copying.

THE FOOD CYCLE

TEST CHAPTER 18

CHAPTER OBJECTIVES

Read each question. Choose the best answer. Write the letter of your choice on the line at the right.

1. When you eat carrots you eat food that is stored **1.** ______ **1.** c (1)

a. in the leaves. **c.** in the roots.
b. in the seed. **d.** in the stem.

2. Food is stored in different parts of plants in the form of **2.** ______ **2.** b (1)

a. fat and sugar. **c.** starch and salt.
b. sugar and starch. **d.** none of the above.

3. Living things that are able to make their own food are called **3.** ______ **3.** a (1)

a. producers. **c.** decomposers.
b. consumers. **d.** composers.

4. Consumers are living things that **4.** ______ **4.** a (2)

a. eat plants or animals.
b. produce their own food.
c. do not eat plants or animals.
d. feed on wastes and dead animals.

5. Human beings are **5.** ______ **5.** c (2)

a. herbivores. **c.** omnivores.
b. carnivores. **d.** none of the above.

6. An animal that is an herbivore is **6.** ______ **6.** c (2)

a. the lion. **c.** the rabbit.
b. the seal. **d.** the wolf.

7. Which of the following is *not* a producer of food in a water community? **7.** ______ **7.** d (3)

a. cattails **c.** algae
b. water lilies **d.** fish

8. A crane in a pond community is **8.** ______ **8.** a (3)

a. a consumer. **c.** a decomposer.
b. a producer. **d.** an herbivore.

Name_______________________________Date____________

9. c (3) **9.** The squirrels in a forest community **9.** ______
a. are producers.
b. are animal eaters.
c. are plant eaters.
d. are plant and animal eaters.

10. b (4) **10.** When decomposers feed on dead organisms, **10.** ______
a. they give off oxygen.
b. they break them down.
c. they make them grow.
d. nothing happens.

11. a (4) **11.** Which of these is *not* usually a decomposer? **11.** ______
a. algae
b. molds
c. yeast
d. bacteria

12. c (4) **12.** Bacteria are **12.** ______
a. never harmful.
b. found only in water.
c. tiny decomposers.
d. large plants.

13. a (5) **13.** As an organism decays, it gives off materials **13.** ______
a. that go back into the community.
b. that are useless to the members of the community.
c. that are poisonous to the members of the community.
d. that can be used only by animals.

14. b (5) **14.** Plants that make food from materials that have been returned to the soil are **14.** ______
a. decomposers.
b. producers.
c. consumers.
d. all of the above.

15. d (5) **15.** Molds help green plants to make food by giving off **15.** ______
a. chlorophyll.
b. bacteria.
c. oxygen.
d. carbon dioxide.

Name________________________________Date____________

Fold back answer key on line before copying.

THE WEB OF LIFE

TEST 19 CHAPTER

CHAPTER OBJECTIVES

Read each question. Choose the best answer from those listed. Write the letter of your choice on the line at the right.

1. The organism that is last in a food chain **1.** ______ **1.** b (1)
a. cannot be decomposed.
b. becomes food for decomposers.
c. is food for other consumers.
d. never dies.

2. A food chain in which a rabbit eats grass could end with **2.** ______ **2.** a (1)
a. a fox. **c.** a flower.
b. a fly. **d.** a tree.

3. A food chain describes **3.** ______ **3.** b (1)
a. how animals travel in a community.
b. how energy travels in a community.
c. which foods are healthy.
d. all of the above.

4. The broken-down materials at the end of a food chain **4.** ______ **4.** c (1)
a. are used only by animals. **c.** are used by producers.
b. are unhealthy. **d.** are never used again.

5. A predator is an animal that **5.** ______ **5.** b (2)
a. is killed and eaten by another animal.
b. kills another animal and eats it.
c. only eats plants.
d. is at the bottom of a food chain.

6. In a food web, **6.** ______ **6.** a (2)
a. there are overlapping food chains.
b. all the animals eat the same food.
c. no animals eat the same food.
d. there are only two food chains.

7. Food chains and food webs *cannot* exist without **7.** ______ **7.** d (2)
a. producers. **c.** decomposers.
b. consumers. **d.** all of the above.

Name ______________________ Date ____________

8. b (2)

8. A dragonfly would prey on **8.** ______

a. a frog. **c.** a snake.

b. a mosquito. **d.** a hawk.

9. d (3)

9. The *balance of nature* means that there are **9.** ______

a. the same number of plants as animals.

b. too many prey animals.

c. too many predators.

d. predators to control prey population.

10. b (3)

10. What would happen to the number of trees if the number of harmful beetles increased? **10.** ______

a. It would increase. **c.** Nothing would happen.

b. It would decrease. **d.** Trees would become consumers.

11. c (3)

11. Which statement is true? **11.** ______

a. Plants do not depend on animals.

b. Animals do not depend on plants.

c. Plants and animals depend on each other.

d. Plants do not need air.

12. b (3)

12. As a population of consumers increases, its food supply **12.** ______

a. may increase. **c.** stays the same.

b. may decrease. **d.** tastes better.

13. d (4)

13. Scientists who study the environment are **13.** ______

a. predators. **c.** doctors.

b. teachers. **d.** ecologists.

14. b (4)

14. Human beings **14.** ______

a. leave most areas unchanged.

b. change an area to meet their own needs.

c. do not affect other living things.

d. do not cause harm to an area.

15. d (4)

15. Water that has been polluted can **15.** ______

a. kill animal life. **c.** be harmful to drink.

b. kill plant life. **d.** all the above.

16. d (4)

16. Which of the following may *not* be an effect of spraying insect poisons on crops? **16.** ______

a. harming large animals. **c.** harming humans.

b. killing insects. **d.** cleaning the air.

Name ______________________ Date ______________

Communities

SKILL WORKSHEET

Identify the following organisms as belonging to either a forest community or a pond community.

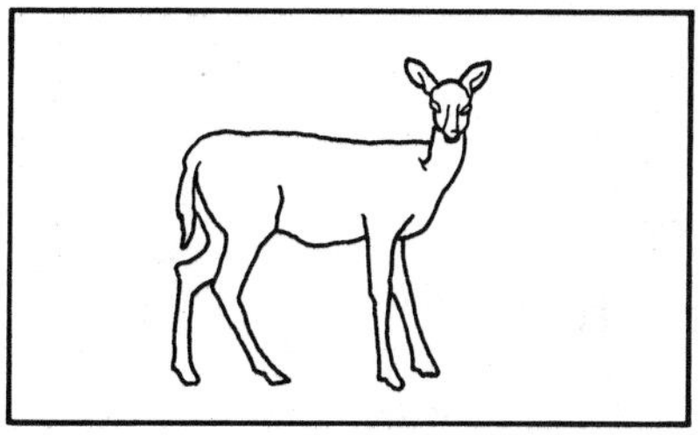

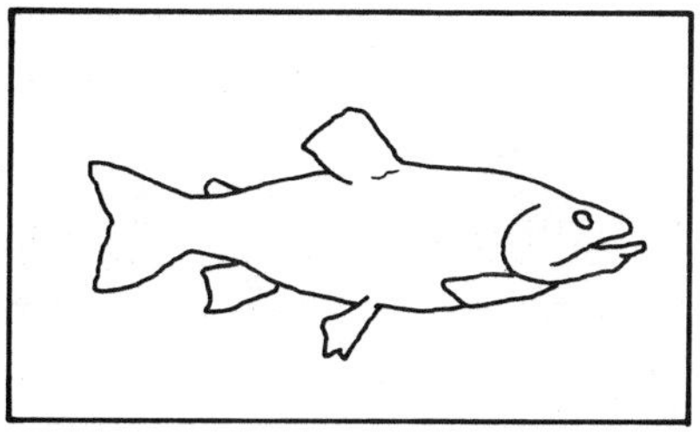

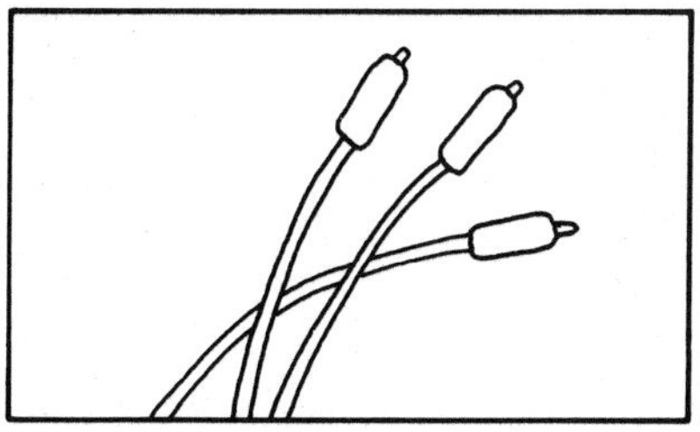

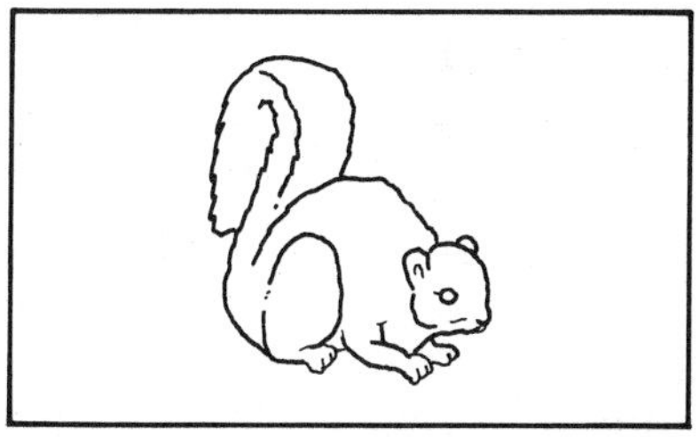

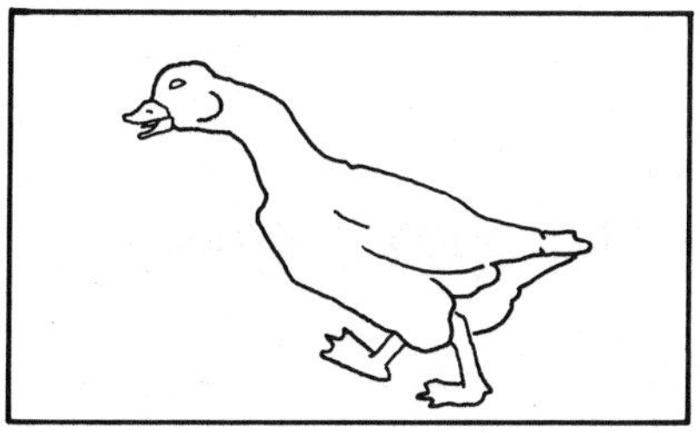

Name ________________________________ Date ____________

Green Plants and Using Oxygen

SKILL WORKSHEET

A. Complete the diagram of the oxygen–carbon dioxide cycle by placing the following words in their correct postions in the diagram.

photosynthesis	water	energy
carbon dioxide	minerals	oxygen
respiration	light	chlorophyll

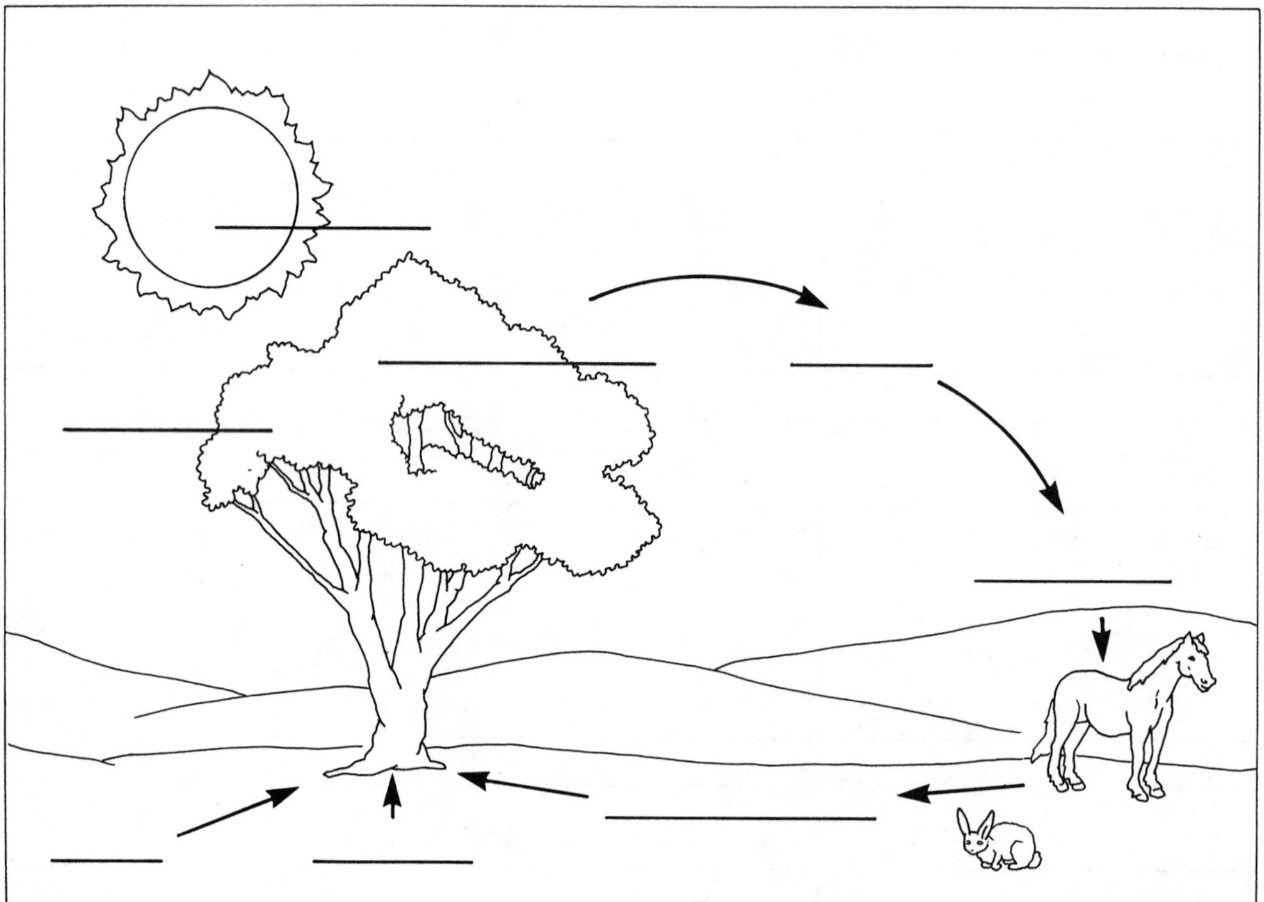

B. Write a simple equation for photosynthesis.

____

____

Name ______________________________ Date ______________

Green Plants and Using Oxygen

ACTIVITY WORKSHEET

In this activity, you will observe photosynthesis taking place.

A. Gather these materials: elodea, funnel, large glass jar with water.
B. Fill the jar with water, Place the elodea at the bottom of the jar and cover it with the funnel.
C. Fill the test tube with water. Hold your thumb over the opening of the test tube. Turn the test tube over and lower it into the water. Remove your thumb and place the test tube over the funnel as shown. Make sure the test tube remains full of water.
D. Place the jar in a sunny place for a few days. Observe the test tube each day and record your observations below.

QUESTIONS

1. What happened in the test tube? ______________

____

2. What replaced the water in the test tube? ________
3. What gas do you think is in the test tube? ________

____

____

Name ____________________ Date ____________

The Food Cycle

ACTIVITY WORKSHEET

Forest Community

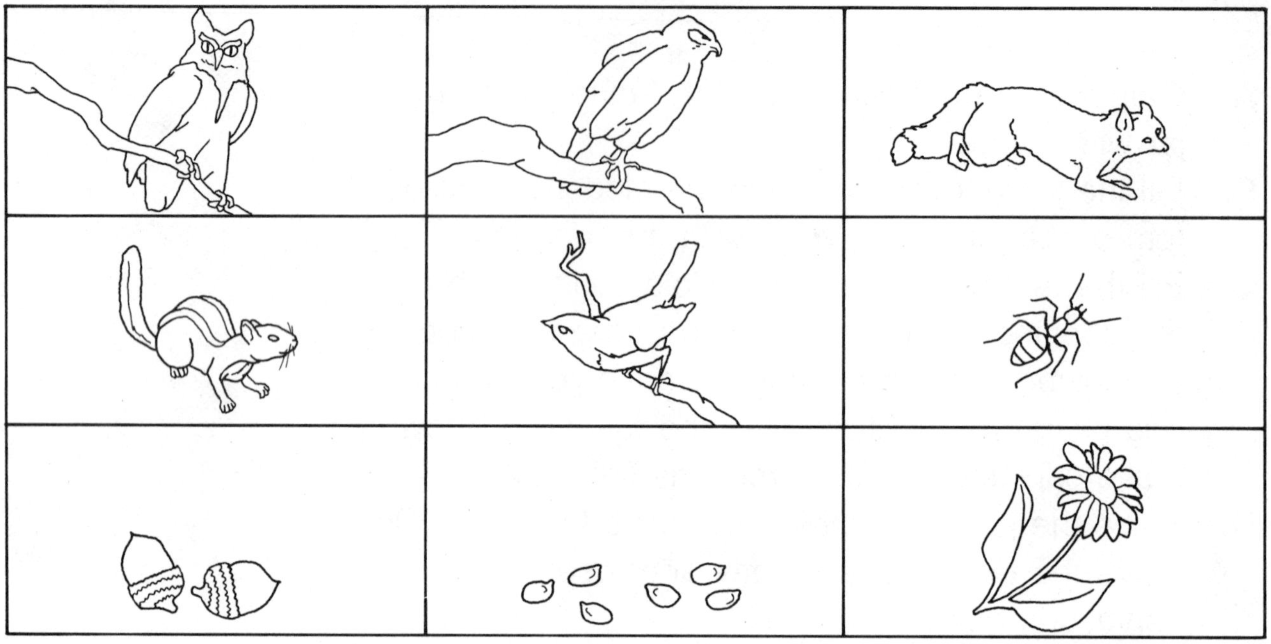

Water Community

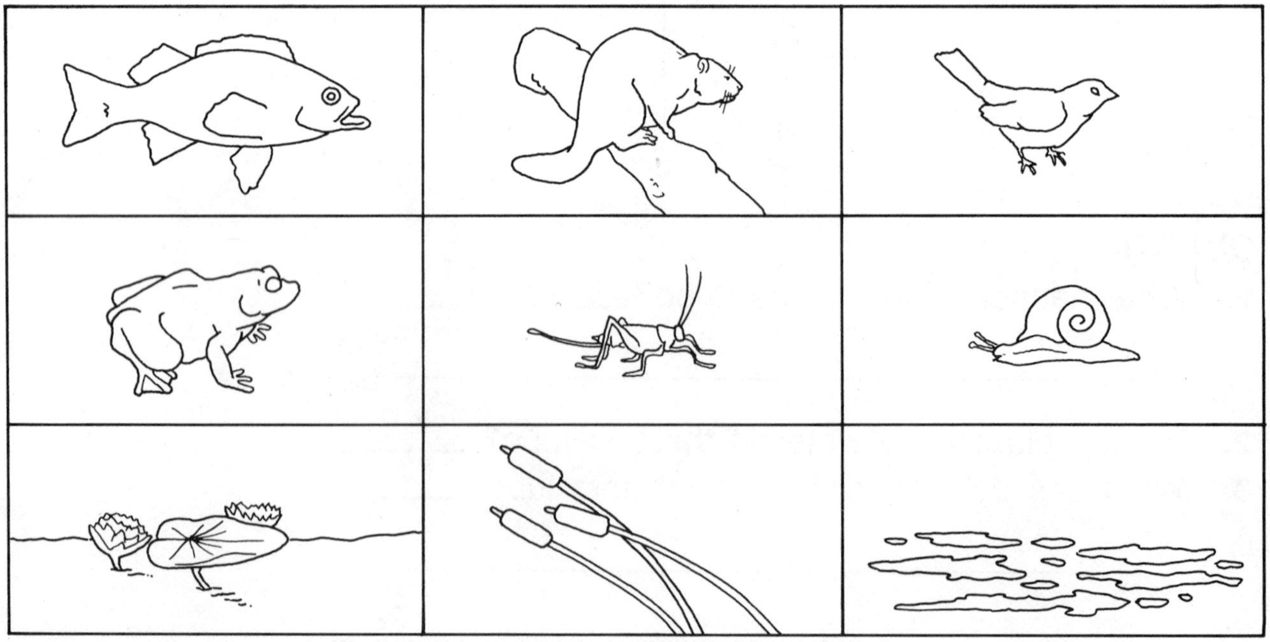

Refer to activity on p. 306

Name ______________________________ Date ________________

The Food Cycle

SKILL WORKSHEET

Identify each of the organisms listed below as a producer (p), an herbivore (h), a carnivore (c), an omnivore (o), or a decomposer (d).

Wheat	___	Fox	___
Hawk	___	Cricket	___
Turtle	___	Mold	___
Cow	___	Frog	___
Human	___	Squirrel	___
Lettuce	___	Yeast	___

Draw a community chart including these organisms.

Name ______________________________ Date ________________

The Food Cycle

AT HOME WORKSHEET

You are learning about decomposers. Yeast is a decomposer. Yeast can digest the sugar and starch in decaying material. When this happens, the gas, carbon dioxide, is formed. You will see carbon dioxide gas being formed in this activity.

A. Gather these materials: yeast, sugar, water, 2 glasses.
B. Dissolve 2 tablespoons of sugar in ½ glass of warm water.
C. Add ½ package of yeast to the mixture and stir.
D. Observe the mixture and record your observations below.
E. Repeat steps B to D using cold water.

QUESTIONS

1. Were bubbles of carbon dioxide formed? ____________
2. Did the bubbles form more quickly in warm water or cold water? ______________________
3. Does decomposition take place faster in a warm place or a cold place? ________________

Name ______________________ Date ____________

The Food Cycle

SKILL WORKSHEET

Identify the words defined below. If you identify them in the correct order they will guide you through the maze.

1. Makes own food

____

2. Tall water plants

____

3. Floating water plant

____

4. Foods made by green plants

____

5. Eats plants or animals

____

6. Eats only plants

____

7. Eats only animals

____

8. Eats both plants and animals

____

9. To become rotten

____

10. Feeds on wastes

____

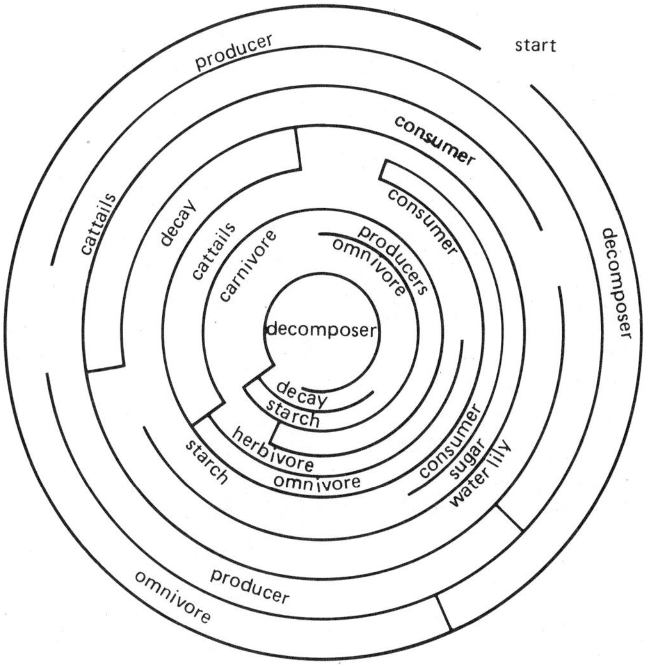

Name ______________________ Date ______________

The Web of Life

SKILL WORKSHEET

A. Draw a food web that includes green plants, grass-hoppers, frogs, snakes, owls, rabbits, wolves, moose, bacteria, and flies.

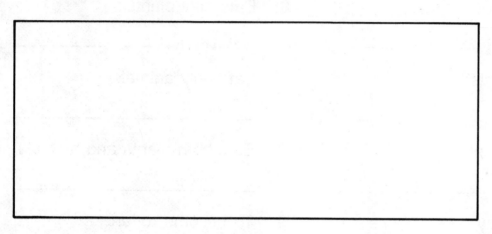

B. List the predators and prey in your food web.

Predators | Prey

C. What would happen to the food web if the number of rabbits suddenly increased?

____

____

____

____

Name ______________________ Date ______________

The Web of Life

AT HOME WORKSHEET

You are learning about pollution and how it affects the environment. In this activity, you will see how pollution affects you and your neighborhood.

Take a pollution survey of your neighborhood. Use the chart below to record your observations. One example has been filled in for you.

Type of Pollution	Description	Source	Cause
Air	Black smoke	Power plant	Burning fuel
Water			
Noise			
Visual			
Litter			

Suggest some ways that the pollution you observed could be controlled.

____

____

Name ______________________ Date ______________

The Web of Life

SKILL WORKSHEET

Find the correct science terms in the puzzle and use them to complete the sentences.

1. The path that food travels in a community is called a ______________________.
2. Food chains that overlap are called ______________.
3. An animal that kills and eats other animals is called a ______________________.
4. An animal that is eaten by another animal is called a ______________________.
5. ______________ study living things and their environments.

P	R	E	Y	Z	B	Y	L	A	T
R	O	A	L	F	R	W	A	D	D
E	C	O	L	O	G	I	S	T	S
D	B	O	W	O	A	R	I	K	U
A	F	O	O	D	C	H	A	I	N
T	W	E	L	W	D	N	M	M	R
O	K	A	R	E	L	C	B	S	T
R	T	E	L	B	A	V	E	A	B
U	V	O	A	S	S	R	O	L	M

Name ____________________ Date ____________

Communities

CLASSIFYING — SKILL WORKSHEET

Identify the following organisms as belonging to either a forest community or a pond community.

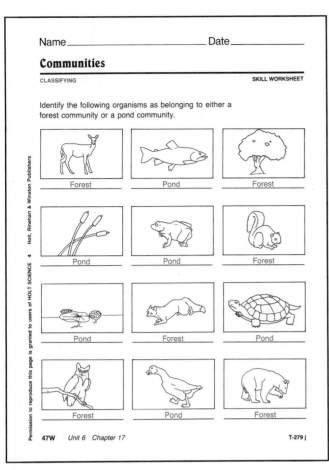

	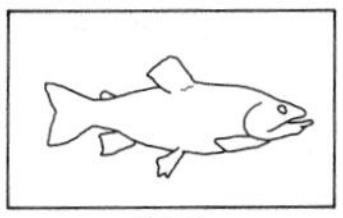	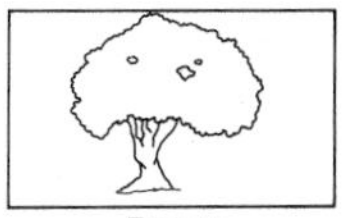
Forest	Pond	Forest
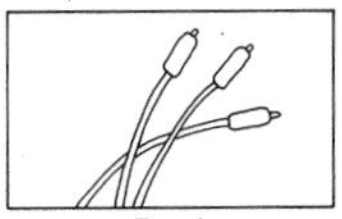		
Pond	Pond	Forest

Pond	Forest	Pond

Forest	Pond	Forest

Name ____________________ Date ____________

Green Plants and Using Oxygen

SEQUENCING, FINDING CAUSE AND EFFECT — SKILL WORKSHEET

A. Complete the diagram of the oxygen–carbon dioxide cycle by placing the following words in their correct postions in the diagram.

photosynthesis,	water	energy
carbon dioxide	minerals	oxygen
respiration	light	chlorophyll

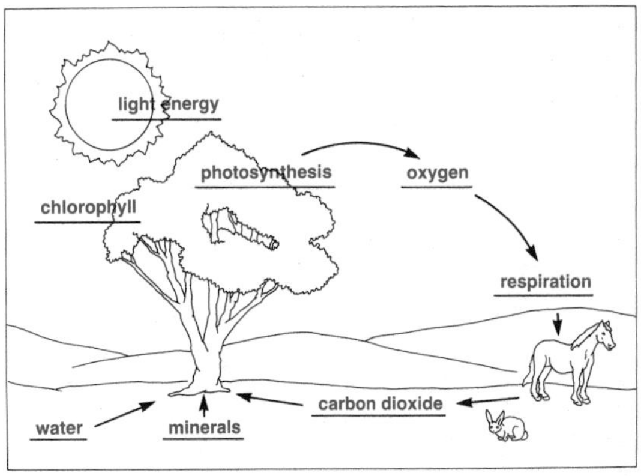

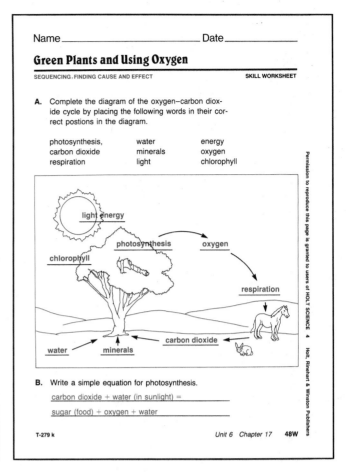

B. Write a simple equation for photosynthesis.

carbon dioxide + water (in sunlight) =

sugar (food) + oxygen + water

Name ____________________ Date ____________

Green Plants and Using Oxygen

ACTIVITY WORKSHEET

In this activity, you will observe photosynthesis taking place.

A. Gather these materials: elodea, funnel, large glass jar with water.

B. Fill the jar with water, Place the elodea at the bottom of the jar and cover it with the funnel.

C. Fill the test tube with water. Hold your thumb over the opening of the test tube. Turn the test tube over and lower it into the water. Remove your thumb and place the test tube over the funnel as shown. Make sure the test tube remains full of water.

D. Place the jar in a sunny place for a few days. Observe the test tube each day and record your observations below.

QUESTIONS

1. What happened in the test tube? The water disappeared.
2. What replaced the water in the test tube? A gas
3. What gas do you think is in the test tube? Oxygen. Since the plant was in sunlight, photosynthesis was taking place.

Name ____________________ Date ____________

The Food Cycle

ACTIVITY WORKSHEET

Forest Community

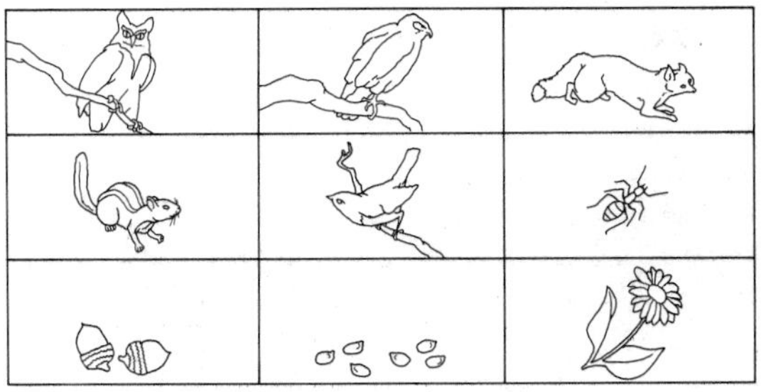

Water Community

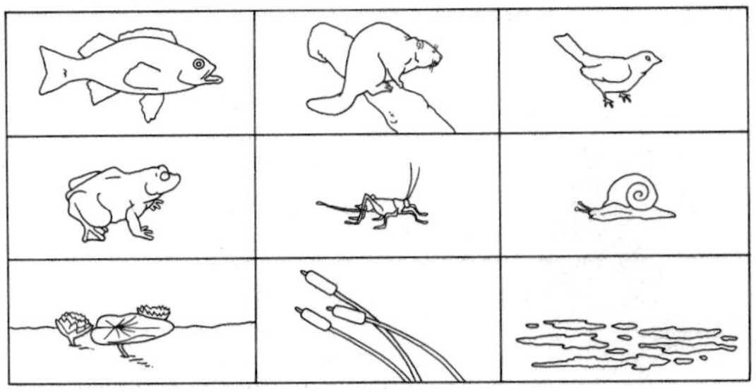

Refer to activity on p. 299

Name____________________ Date__________

The Food Cycle

CLASSIFYING, SEQUENCING — SKILL WORKSHEET

Identify each of the organisms listed below as a producer (p), an herbivore (h), a carnivore (c), an omnivore (o), or a decomposer (d).

Wheat	p	Fox	c
Hawk	c	Cricket	h
Turtle	o	Mold	d
Cow	h	Frog	c
Human	o	Squirrel	h
Lettuce	p	Yeast	d

Draw a community chart including these organisms.

Name____________________ Date__________

The Food Cycle

AT HOME WORKSHEET

You are learning about decomposers. Yeast is a decomposer. Yeast can digest the sugar and starch in decaying material. When this happens, the gas, carbon dioxide, is formed. You will see carbon dioxide gas being formed in this activity.

A. Gather these materials: yeast, sugar, water, 2 glasses.
B. Dissolve 2 tablespoons of sugar in ½ glass of warm water.
C. Add ½ package of yeast to the mixture and stir.
D. Observe the mixture and record your observations below.
E. Repeat steps B to D using cold water.

QUESTIONS

1. Were bubbles of carbon dioxide formed? Yes
2. Did the bubbles form more quickly in warm water or cold water? Warm
3. Does decomposition take place faster in a warm place or a cold place? Warm

Name____________________ Date__________

The Food Cycle

BUILDING SCIENCE VOCABULARY — SKILL WORKSHEET

Identify the words defined below. If you identify them in the correct order they will guide you through the maze.

1. Makes own food — Producer
2. Tall water plants — Cattails
3. Floating water plant — Water lily
4. Foods made by green plants — Starch and sugar
5. Eats plants or animals — Consumer
6. Eats only plants — Herbivore
7. Eats only animals — Carnivore
8. Eats both plants and animals — Omnivore
9. To become rotten — Decay
10. Feeds on wastes — Decomposer

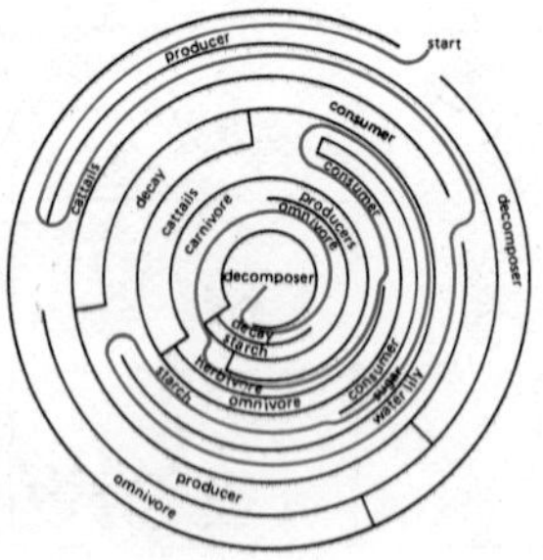

Name____________________ Date__________

The Web of Life

CLASSIFYING, FINDING CAUSE AND EFFECT, SEQUENCING — SKILL WORKSHEET

A. Draw a food web that includes green plants, grasshoppers, frogs, snakes, owls, rabbits, wolves, mosses, bacteria, and flies.

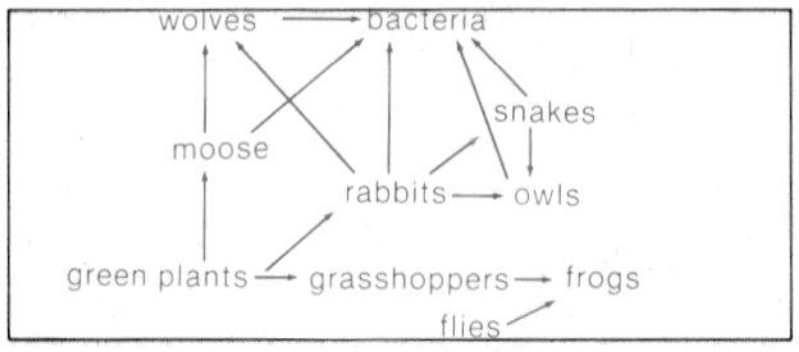

B. List the predators and prey in your food web.

Predators	Prey
Wolves	Grasshoppers
Owls	Frogs
Snakes	Snakes
Frogs	Rabbits
	Moose
	Flies

C. What would happen to the food web if the number of rabbits suddenly increased?

At first, the number of green plants would decrease while the number of predators (wolves, owls, snakes) would increase. Eventually, the number of rabbits would begin to decrease until a balance was reached.

Name____________________ Date__________

The Web of Life

AT HOME WORKSHEET

You are learning about pollution and how it affects the environment. In this activity, you will see how pollution affects you and your neighborhood.

Take a pollution survey of your neighborhood. Use the chart below to record your observations. One example has been filled in for you.

Type of Pollution	Description	Source	Cause
Air	Black smoke	Power plant	Burning fuel
Water			
Noise			
Visual			
Litter			

Suggest some ways that the pollution you observed could be controlled.

Students may suggest better laws, improved technology, more public awareness, etc.

Name____________________ Date__________

The Web of Life

BUILDING SCIENCE VOCABULARY SKILL WORKSHEET

Find the correct science terms in the puzzle and use them to complete the sentences.

1. The path that food travels in a community is called a food chain.
2. Food chains that overlap are called food webs.
3. An animal that kills and eats other animals is called a predator.
4. An animal that is eaten by another animal is called a prey.
5. Ecologists study living things and their environments.

P	R	E	Y	Z	B	Y	L	A	T
R	O	A	L	F	R	W	A	D	D
E	C	O	L	O	G	I	S	T	S
D	B	O	W	O	A	R	I	K	U
A	F	O	O	D	C	H	A	I	N
T	W	E	L	W	D	N	M	M	R
O	K	A	R	E	L	C	B	S	T
R	T	E	L	B	A	V	E	A	B
U	V	O	A	S	S	R	O	L	M

Unit Overview

This is a life science unit on ecology, the study of organisms and how they relate to their environment. Individuals combine to form populations, which interact to form communities. Every organism in a community has its own habitat, and within a given habitat, organisms can be interdependent (mutualism). Through the process of photosynthesis, green plants capture the energy of the sun to combine carbon dioxide and water to make sugar (food) and oxygen. This is a starting point on the oxygen–carbon dioxide cycle, which involves the production of oxygen by the green plants and the consumption of oxygen by animals. Animals in turn give off carbon dioxide, which is used by the plants.

As producers of food (sugar and starch), green plants feed consumers in various communities. Consumers may be herbivores (plant eaters), carnivores (meat eaters), or omnivores (both). Nutrients and carbon dioxide are returned to the community when such decomposers as molds, bacteria, and yeasts react with dead organisms.

Food chains are used to describe the path of food in a community. The sequence usually includes a producer, a herbivore, and one or more carnivores. Communities are complex, and food webs are used to describe overlapping food chains. Because the interdependence among organisms is so important, the balance of nature is often affected by the disruption of one member of a chain or web.

Exceptional Student IEP Unit Goal

When asked by the teacher, the student will describe these aspects of a community: food chain, producer, consumer, and habitat.

Animal and Plant Communities

Unit Opener

This is a photograph of an owl catching a fish. There are over 130 species of owls. They belong to the order *Strigiformes*. Owls are nocturnal birds of prey. Their bills and claws are similar to those of hawks. Special adaptations to nocturnal activity include soft plumage and highly developed sense organs. The soft, fluffy plumage makes noiseless flight possible. Owls generally approach their prey noiselessly, grasp the prey with both feet, and carry it to a perch where it is usually swallowed whole. Only a few species of owls feed on fish. Most owls prey on snails, insects, mice, birds, rabbits, and even larger animals. One species even eats crabs! None of the owls are plant eaters. Owls have been objects of superstition since ancient times, probably because of their nocturnal habits and eerie cries. They were once regarded as an omen of death. However, they were also the symbol of the goddess Athena, the goddess of wisdom.

UNIT 6

LEARNING CENTER

A suggested title for a Learning Center for this unit is "The Web of Life." Photographs showing scenes of groups of animals, different habitats and foods, and pollution can be used as a display. You may wish to keep a file for the worksheet masters and Extensions that the students can work on independently.

The following Extensions are especially suitable for the Learning Center. The materials for these Extensions should be available in the Learning Center: plant cell structure, p. T-290 (microscope, onion, knife, glass slide, cover slip, iodine solution, drawing paper); plant respiration, p. T-293 (limewater, pan, small plant, wooden block, wide-mouth jar); seltzer tablet, p. T-294 (seltzer tablet, water, vial with cap, plastic tube, glass jar, BTB); plant seeds, p. T-299 (lima bean seeds, bush bean seeds, paper towels); community chart, p. T-312 (community chart, pencil); predator graph, p. T-325 (graph paper, colored pencils).

In addition, an index file of suggested research topics could be set up in the Learning Center, as follows: symbiosis, p. T-285; parasites, p. T-286; chemosynthesis, p. T-295; anaerobes, p. T-296; chemical cycles, p. T-297; nutrition, p. T-299; carnivorous plants, p. T-304; diets in other lands, p. T-304; nurse interview, p. T-310; microcommunities, p. T-313; food chains, p. T-315; sharing food, p. T-317; predator-prey, p. T-321; ocean food web, p. T-321; community changes, p. T-327; environment questions, p. T-329; careers, p. T-331; careers, p. T-333.

Chapter Objectives

1. Explain what a community is and give examples.
2. Describe how populations in a community interact; include examples of mutualism and parasitism.
3. Identify conditions that green plants need to grow.
4. Explain how green plants carry on photosynthesis.
5. Describe the carbon dioxide–oxygen cycle.

SECTION BACKGROUND

In the biosphere, most populations share their environments with other populations of living things. A group of populations that live together in the same area is called a community. The myriad relationships that exist in any community are of major importance. These relationships are referred to as ecological relationships. Simply naming all the populations in a community does not tell us much about the community. The ecologist needs to know how each organism gets its food and how it affects other organisms. Furthermore, all organisms need energy to exist. In the study of communities, we need to know how energy is transferred through the community. This idea is developed in the last chapter.

MATERIALS

2-gallon glass jar or plastic container with lid, potting soil, seeds (grass, radish, wheat), water sprinkler

Exceptional Student IEP Chapter Goal

At the end of this chapter, the student will give one reason for each of the following: why plants need animals, why animals need plants, and why all things need to live in a community.

CHAPTER 17

ENERGY FOR LIVING

17-1. Communities

Can populations live alone? Scientists know of no living population that exists apart from other living things. How do different populations get along with each other? When you finish this section, you should be able to:

BASIC TEACHING PLAN

MOTIVATION

Put a small animal, such as a grasshopper, worm, spider, or mealworm, in a large glass jar. Make sure air can get into the jar. Place the jar in the center of the room for the students to look at. Ask the students if this animal, or even a group of these animals, could live in the jar without anything else. Ask them why they think so. Most students will say no. List their reasons on the board. Their reasons should be a natural introduction to the study of communities.

Text Questions—Can populations live alone? *No. All populations require interaction with other populations.* How do different populations get along with each other? *Sometimes living things interact for the benefit of both organisms and sometimes for the benefit of one population.*

☐ **A.** Identify how populations relate to each other in a *community.*

☐ **B.** Describe the features of a *community.*

☐ **C.** Describe life in different *habitats.*

There are very few places on earth where living things cannot be found. Most living things live near other living things. All the plants and animals that live in the same area are called a **community** (kuh-**mew**-nit-tee). There are many kinds of *communities*. Communities of clams, crabs, snails, and algae live in the ocean. Grass and prairie dogs (**prayr**-rhee) are community members of the grasslands, or prairie.

Community: All the plants and animals that live in the same area.

Camels and cacti are community members of a desert. Communities of frogs, turtles, pond lilies, and fish live in ponds.

Each member of a community lives in a certain place. That place is called a **habitat** (**ha**-bi-tat). There are many *habitats* within a com-

Habitat: The place where a thing lives within a community.

EXTENSIONS

Enrichment

Science Skills—Classifying

Conduct a community scavenger hunt using magazine pictures of organisms.

A. Cut out pictures of organisms that are found in desert, woodland, or pond areas.

B. Divide the class into three groups, one for each community.

C. Without the class's knowledge, scatter the pictures around the playground.

D. Stage a scavenger hunt by having all groups simultaneously try to gather all the pictures of organisms that would normally be found in "their" community.

DEVELOPMENT

1 Teaching Tips—Take the students outside for about 10 min. Locate an area at the edge of the woods that has a variety of plants and either evidence of animals or actual animals. When looking for animals, look for insects. There are on the average over 4 billion insects per square mile. Have the students either point to or identify as many different plant and animal populations as they can within 50 m of where they are. Make a list of these on large chart paper. Use this list of populations to introduce the concept of community. While outside, use the site to introduce the concept of habitat.

2 Teaching Tips—A habitat is a natural home or dwelling place for an organism. While you are outside, have the students look for these natural homes. A dead log is an excellent example. It is a home for many different insects. Have the students look for nests in the trees. Carefully turn over small rocks. The soil is the habitat for many animals.

EXTENSIONS

Enrichment
Activity

A biome is a major community or life zone characterized by distinct life forms. In this Extension, students are to find pictures that represent various biomes.

A. Gather magazines, scissors, glue, and large sheets of construction paper.

B. Give students the following list of biomes:

TERRESTRIAL	AQUATIC
Tundra	Lakes
Taiga	Ponds
Deciduous forest	Streams
Rain forest	Rivers
Grassland	Ocean
Desert	Shoreline
	Coral reefs
	Tide pools
	Estuaries

C. Discuss the various biomes listed. Students may have to do some research on what characterizes each of the biomes listed.

D. Assign several biomes to each group of students. Their task is to find at least two pictures for each biome they are assigned. They should make a list of the populations that are shown in the picture.

E. Let the students use the bulletin board or a full-length wall to show their findings. Divide the bulletin board into sections for each of the biomes listed above.

Exceptional Student
Learning Disabled

To reinforce the concept of community, instruct the student to illustrate a community. Have the student discuss how the organisms interact.

munity. In a forest, the soil is the habitat of earthworms and small insects. A salamander's habitat may be an old log. Deer and birds live among the trees and shrubs.

In a pond, cattails grow in the moist soil and mud at the water's edge. Pond lilies are found floating on top of the water. The habitat of frogs, tadpoles, small fish, and insects may be under **3** rocks, under plants, or in the mud. Can you think of any other habitats?

Populations need each other in order to sur- **4** vive. In any community, plants, animals, and protists work with each other. There are a number of ways in which living things work with each other. Let's look at a few.

5 A dead log is a habitat. A population of termites lives in the log. The termites eat the wood. However, they cannot digest the wood. Protists live inside the termites. The protists

3 Text Questions—Can you think of any other habitats? *The ocean, extremely cold climates.*

4 Teaching Tips—Ask the students how they interact with other organisms in their community. Point out that interactions can be helpful to both those involved, harmful to one and helpful to another, or neither helpful nor harmful.

5 Teaching Tips—Make a diagram on the board in which you show and label a dead log, a termite, and a protist. Draw arrows showing how each of the three organisms has an *effect* on the other—a dead log is a home for termites; a termite is a home for protists; protists help termites digest food; a log is food for termites.

digest the wood for the termites. This is an example of how organisms work with each other. The dead log is a home for the termites. The termites eat the wood. The protists have a "home" inside the termites. The protists help the termites. They digest their food. The way these organisms depend on each other is called **mutualism** (**mew**-chew-uhl-ism). *Mutualism* is a relationship in which two or more organisms help each other. What are some other examples of mutualism?

Mutualism: A relationship in which two or more organisms live together and help each other.

ACTIVITY

What are the features of a habitat?

A. Gather these materials: 2-gallon glass or plastic container with lid, potting soil, seeds (grass, radish, wheat), and water sprinkler.
B. Put soil in the container until it is about 1/3 full.
C. Spread all the seeds in the container.
D. Water the seeds and soil.
E. Put your habitat in a sunny, warm place.
F. Make a drawing of your habitat each day. Show the changes that are taking place.

1. What would happen to the seeds if there were no soil?
2. Which seeds do you think will grow first?
3. Do you think all the seeds will grow? Explain.

EXTENSIONS

Reinforcement
Research

Within communities, organisms interact with each other. "Symbiosis" means living together in close association. Symbiotic relationships may provide food, shelter, support, or transportation for one or both of the organisms involved. Introduce three types of symbiosis: mutualism—two or more organisms living together in a relationship that is helpful to both; commensalism—two or more organisms living together in a relationship in which one is helped and the other is neither helped nor harmed; parasitism—a relationship in which one organism benefits, but the other is harmed. Have students do research and identify two examples of each type of symbiosis.

6 Text Questions—What are some other examples of mutualism? *Algae and fungi that live together as lichens; bacteria living inside the digestive tracts of humans or other animals.*

ACTIVITY

Skill Development—*Observing, Recording Data*

Teaching Tips—Divide the students into small groups, making each group responsible for creating a habitat. The habitats should be cared for throughout the unit. Many spontaneous learning experiences will emerge from observing these habitats. Make sure the students follow the instructions carefully. Keep the habitats in a well-lighted area away from drafts.

Answers to Questions—**1.** They would not grow. **2.** Have the students check their predictions as the plants start to grow. **3.** Some will not grow because not all seeds are viable.

Exceptional Student
Visually Impaired

The student will need a partner for this Activity.

EXTENSIONS

Enrichment

Research—Library

Interested students can do research on parasitic relationships. They could compare and contrast the way parasites live, reproduce, and affect their host organisms. They should identify the characteristics a successful parasite needs to survive. They can pick a particular parasite and describe its life cycle to the class. They should answer these questions:

1. Is it an internal or external parasite?
2. How does it attach itself to its host?
3. How many hosts does it normally have?
4. Does it eventually kill its host?

Application

Activity

Instead of beginning your habitat from purchased seeds, have your students use wild seeds. Have them leave their habitats uncovered for a few days in front of an open window. It is important that they keep the soil loose and moist. They should examine their habitats every day for signs of growth.

Parasite: An organism that feeds off another living organism.

Sometimes, only one organism is helped. The other is not. One organism takes something from the other or harms it. Suppose you are bitten by a mosquito. The mosquito is a blood sucker. It uses your blood as food. The mosquito is helped. But you may be harmed. The mosquito gets food. You may get a disease caused by protists the mosquito carries. Biologists call the mosquito a **parasite** (**pare**-uh-sight). A *parasite* is a living thing that feeds off other living things.

There are many other ways in which organisms in a community interact. You will learn about these ways in other sections of this unit. The thing to keep in mind is this: Organisms in communities depend on each other. No organism lives alone.

Section Review

Main Ideas: Plants, animals, and protists live together in communities. Each member of a community has its own habitat. The organisms in a community work with each other.

Questions: Answer in complete sentences.

1. Describe three different communities.
2. How do the habitats of a tadpole and an earthworm differ?
3. Give an example of the way organisms work together in a community. Explain.
4. What do you think would happen to the organisms in a pond if the pond dried up?

7 **Teaching Tips**—Most students will have been bitten by an insect of some kind. Use this experience to discuss the concept of a parasite.

SECTION REVIEW

Answers to Questions

1. Communities of clams, crabs, and snails live in the ocean. Communities of grass and prairie dogs live in grasslands. Communities of camels and cacti live in the desert.
2. The tadpole lives in a water environment; the earthworm lives in the soil.
3. Termites using a log for a home and for food. The relationship of termites and protists is an example of mutualism.
4. Many would die; those that were able to would move to a new environment.

SUGGESTED WORKSHEET MASTER
p. T-279 j

When you see a green plant, you really are looking at a factory. Factories make things. Some factories make cars, airplanes, clothes, or chairs. If green plants are like factories, what do they make? When you finish this section, you should be able to:

- ☐ **A.** Identify the things green plants need to make food.
- ☐ **B.** Explain what is meant by *photosynthesis*.

17-2. Green Plants

Green plants are very different from animals. When your hand is in sunshine, it gets warm. Nothing else happens. A plant does not have hands. But it does have leaves. Leaves that are in sunshine can make food. Green plants are the only living things on earth that can make food.

SECTION BACKGROUND

Green plants are the only organisms able to manufacture their own food. The energy source for food production is sunlight. During photosynthesis, carbon dioxide and water are united in the presence of chlorophyll to form sugar and oxygen. Some of the food produced by a green plant is used by the plant as it carries out its life processes. The remaining food is converted to starch and stored in the plant.

Chlorophyll is the green pigment in plants. It acts as an energy trap. Photosynthesis cannot take place without this green pigment. Even plants that are brown and red, such as certain seaweeds, have chlorophyll in their cells. Chlorophyll makes photosynthesis possible.

MATERIALS

celery stalks and leaves, 2 small jars, water, food coloring, knife, plastic bag, rubber band

BASIC TEACHING PLAN

MOTIVATION

Make an overhead projection of a factory and a green plant. Ask: What are some of the characteristics of a factory? *A product is made; parts are put together to make something; factories use energy to make their products; different parts of the factory make different parts of the product.* Have the students compare a factory to a green plant.

Text Questions—If green plants are like factories, what do they make? *Food.*

DEVELOPMENT

1 Teaching Tips—Two days before you begin this section, put a plant in a closet. On the day this section is covered, take the plant out and *compare* it with a plant left in sunlight. The plant kept in the closet will have turned a pale yellow. Have the students *hypothesize* about what might have caused this.

EXTENSIONS

Application

Activity

Plants are responsive to gravity, water, light, and touch. These responses are called tropisms. In this Extension, students investigate phototropism.

A. Gather these materials: shoe box, soil, radish seeds, milk carton, razor blade, light source.

B. Plant the radish seeds in a milk carton that you have cut in half. Water the soil and put the box in normal light. In a few days, small plants should be growing. See Fig. 17-1.

C. Cut a narrow slot the length of the shoe box. Place the shoe box over the young plants. Direct a light source at the slot. Leave the setup in this arrangement for two days.

D. Have the students predict how they think this apparatus will affect the growth of the plant. In about two days, there should be a noticeable effect. The plants should grow toward the light.

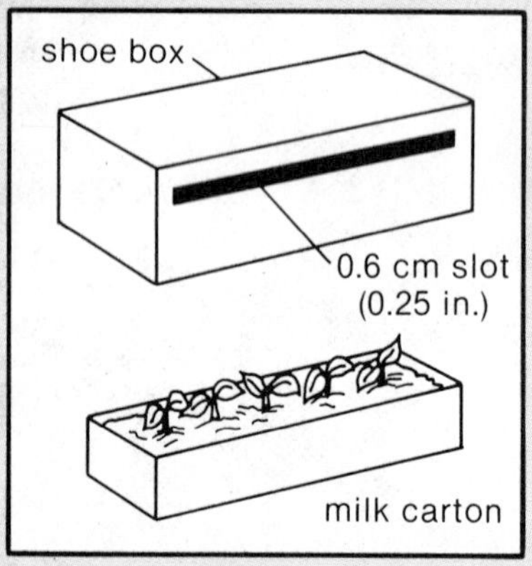

Fig. 17-1

2 Look at these leaves from different plants. Plants make their food in the leaves.

The picture below shows what a green leaf looks like under a microscope. The tiny box-like **3** objects are **cells**. Food for the plant is made in the *cells*. If you look closely, you can see tiny green parts inside each cell. This material is called **chlorophyll** (**klore**-oh-fill). The *chlorophyll* gives the plant its green color. Chlorophyll makes it possible for green plants to make food.

The way green plants make food is called **4** **photosynthesis** (fo-to-**sin**-thuh-sis). *Photo-* means "light," and *-synthesis* means "to put together." In *photosynthesis*, a plant uses sunlight. The

Cell: The smallest unit of which all organisms are made.

Chlorophyll: The green material inside a green plant cell.

Photosynthesis: The way green plants make food.

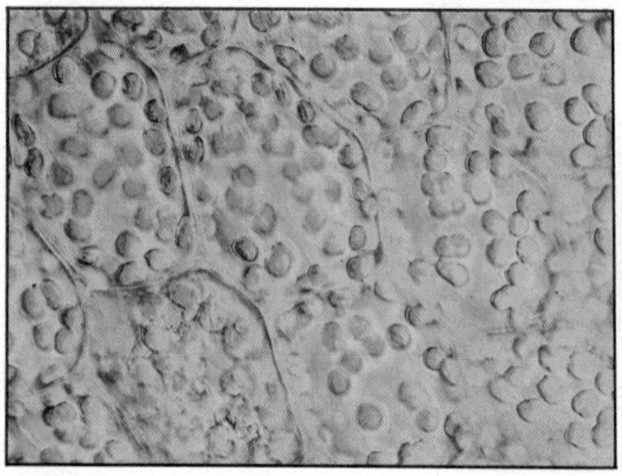

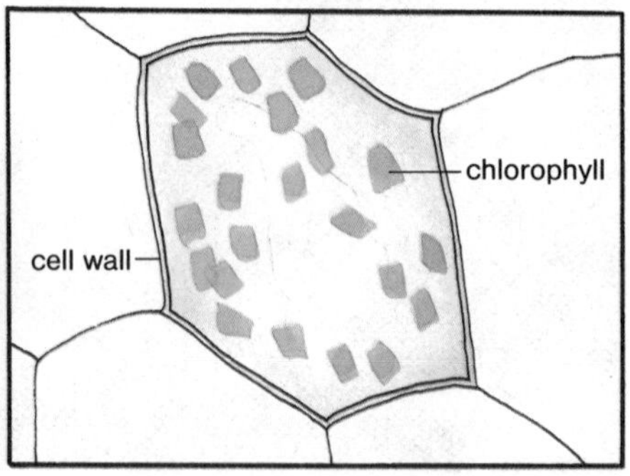

2 Teaching Tips—Bring in samples of leaves from different plants. Have the students *observe* the different sizes and shapes of the leaves.
3 Teaching Tips—Set up several microscopes. On each, put a leaf from a green plant. Have the students *observe* the cells of the green plant. Tell them to make a drawing of one of the cells. Have them locate the cell wall and the chloroplasts. If you can't do this, make an overhead transparency of both the microscopic photograph of a plant cell and the drawing of a cell on this page. Use these to discuss the parts of the cell and, in particular, a plant cell.

sunlight helps it put together air, water, and minerals to make food. The food that plants make is sugar. Let's look more closely at how green plants combine these things to make food.

The picture below shows the parts of a green plant. The materials for photosynthesis must get to the leaf cells. Water and minerals come from the soil. They enter the plant through its roots. Tiny root hairs let water and minerals come into the root. The water and minerals travel from the roots to the stems or trunk of the plant. Inside the stems are thin tubes. The water is carried up the tubes to the branches. Then it is carried to the leaves.

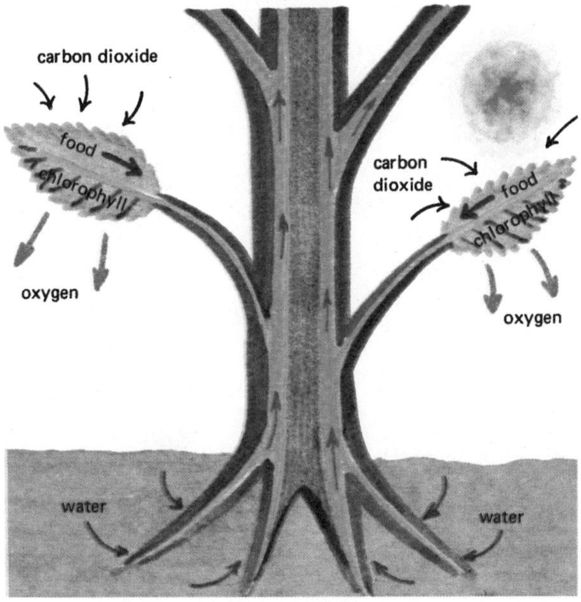

EXTENSIONS

Reinforcement

Science Skills—Observing

In this Extension the students will observe the cell structure of a plant leaf. Have the students do the following:

A. Gather these materials: leaf from an elodea plant, microscope, glass slide, cover slip, tweezers, drawing paper.

B. Put a drop of water in the center of the slide. Carefully pull a leaf off the elodea plant and put it in the drop of water.

C. Cover the leaf with a cover slip.

D. Observe the elodea leaf under the microscope. Look carefully at the cells of the leaf.

E. Make a drawing of an elodea cell. Identify the cell wall, nucleus, and chloroplasts. (The nucleus may be hard to see because of the large number of chloroplasts.)

4 **Teaching Tips**—Draw a diagram of a plant on the chalkboard. Show the students that photosynthesis is the process by which plants take sunlight and make food. This is a simple and understandable way to explain the process.

5 **Teaching Tips**—Have a plant available. Carefully remove the plant from the soil so that the students can compare the roots, stem, and leaves. Ask the students to describe how they think water from the soil gets to the leaves of the plant. If you do the Activity in this section, you can let their responses be predictions. If you don't, you might want to put celery stalks in colored water. In an hour or two, there should be visual evidence that water travels up the stem by capillary action.

Exceptional Student

Visually Impaired

To help the student visualize photosynthesis, the teacher could make a three-dimensional model that illustrates the parts of the plant involved in this process. Have the student feel the model.

EXTENSIONS

Enrichment
Activity

In this Activity, the students will examine the structure of a plant cell. Have the students follow these steps:

A. Gather these materials: microscope, onion, knife, glass slide, cover slip, iodine solution, drawing paper.

B. Cut a piece of onion. Peel off a small piece of the thin skin you find between the layers.

C. Put this piece of skin on the glass slide. Put a drop of iodine solution on the onion skin. Carefully put the cover slip over the onion skin. The iodine will make it easier to see the parts of the cells.

D. Look at the cells of the onion under a microscope. The cells should be rectangular or box shaped. Each cell should be outlined by the iodine solution. The dark spot in each cell is the nucleus.

E. Make a drawing of the onion cells.

Carbon dioxide: A gas that is needed by green plants to make food.

Oxygen: A gas that is given off by the leaves of green plants.

6 The picture on page 289 also shows that green plants need light and a gas called **carbon dioxide** (**kar**-bon die-**ox**-ide). The *carbon dioxide* enters the plant through holes on the bottom of the leaves. The sunlight provides energy. The plant uses the energy to combine carbon dioxide and water to make sugar. During photosynthesis, the leaves give off a gas. This gas is called **oxygen** (**ox**-i-jen).

ACTIVITY

How do water and minerals get to the leaves of a green plant?

A. Gather these materials: celery stalks and leaves, 2 small jars, water, food coloring, knife, plastic bag, and rubber band.
B. Fill the 2 jars with water. Add a small amount of food coloring.
C. Cover the stem of 1 piece of celery with a plastic bag. Fasten it with a rubber band.
D. Put the covered stalk and uncovered stalk of celery in separate jars. Leave them in the jars for at least 1 hour.
E. Look at the 2 celery stalks.
1. What do you see?

F. Cut the 2 stalks in half.
2. How do you know that water moves up the stalk?
3. How do you think the water gets to the leaves of a plant? Draw a picture to show how this happens.

6 Teaching Tips—Students could act out the process of photosynthesis. Use construction paper to make the following signs: carbon dioxide, light, green plant, leaf, root, stem, chlorophyll, water, oxygen, and sugar. Select students to act as these parts of the process. The plant should have roots and several green leaves.

ACTIVITY

Skill Development—*Comparing and Contrasting, Inferring*

Teaching Tips—Each group of students will need two celery stalks. Food coloring of any color will do. The celery stalk wrapped in plastic is a control for the experiment. The movement of water up the stem of the celery should take about an hour.

Answers to Questions—1. The uncovered celery will show evidence that water has moved up the stalk. **2.** The uncovered stalk will show the food coloring in cross-section. **3.** It travels up the narrow tubes in the celery stalk. See the diagram on page 289.

Section Review

Main Ideas: The equation below shows how plants make their own food.

carbon dioxide + water (in light) =
sugar (food) + oxygen + water

Questions: Answer in complete sentences.

1. How is the cell of a green plant like a factory?
2. A plant needs water. What other things does it need to make its food?
3. Where do the things green plants need to make food come from?
4. How does a green plant make food?

People in Science

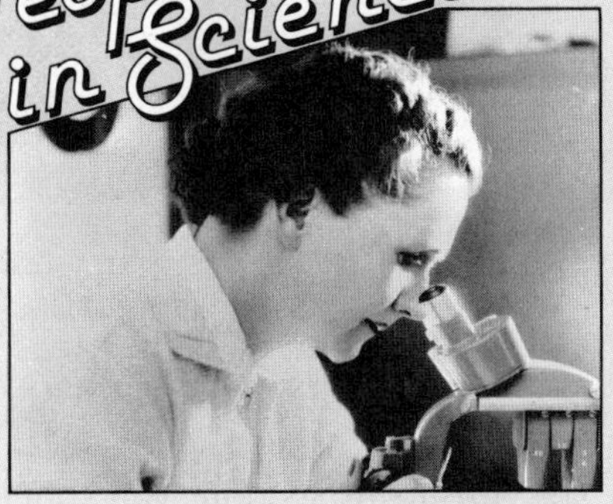

Rachel Carson

Rachel Carson was an ecologist. This means she studied the way plants and animals live together in their environments. In 1962, she wrote a book called *Silent Spring*. In her book, Carson said that people were poisoning the earth. We were using dangerous chemicals to kill insects that harm plants. These chemicals could also cause many plants to die. Soon there would be less food for animals. There would be no spring season on earth. Because of her book and others like it, laws were passed to protect the earth. But still more needs to be done to save plants and animals.

EXTENSIONS

Enrichment

Activity

In this Activity, the students will observe that plants absorb carbon dioxide. Have the students follow these steps:

A. Gather these materials: 2 vials with caps, water, a water plant (anacharis), and BTB.

B. Put green BTB into two vials. (To make green BTB solution, blow into a jar containing water and blue BTB.) Add a sprig of anacharis to one vial and cap it. The other vial is the control.

1. What color change do you predict?
2. What was the color change?
3. What do you conclude about plants and carbon dioxide?

SECTION REVIEW

Answers to Questions

1. The cell is like a factory because it combines various materials and energy to make a product. The product is food.
2. Carbon dioxide, sunlight, chlorophyll
3. Sunlight comes from the sun; carbon dioxide comes from the air; water comes from the soil.
4. A green plant combines carbon dioxide and water in the presence of sunlight and chlorophyll and converts these materials to sugar and oxygen.

SECTION BACKGROUND

Organisms interact in a community on many levels. In this section, the oxygen–carbon dioxide cycle is introduced and explained as an important connection between plants and animals.

In the presence of light, green plants take in carbon dioxide and give off oxygen. The carbon dioxide is used in the food-making process of photosynthesis. Photosynthesis provides the major source of oxygen in the atmosphere. Animals use oxygen in respiration and give off carbon dioxide. This cycle establishes an interdependent relationship between animals and plants.

MATERIALS

2 small bottles, aged tap water, straw, bottle of bromothymol blue (BTB)

17-3.

Using Oxygen

The deer shown here is eating food that was made by plants. But it is also breathing air. The deer needs the oxygen in the air. What part of the biosphere makes the oxygen that animals need? When you finish this section, you should be able to:

☐ **A.** Identify the ways in which plants and animals depend upon each other for their food and energy.

☐ **B.** Explain what is meant by the *oxygen-carbon dioxide cycle.*

BASIC TEACHING PLAN

MOTIVATION

Compare our human "machine" to a furnace. Discuss the role of fuel (food) and air (oxygen) in keeping the fire going.

Text Questions—What part of the biosphere makes the oxygen that animals need? *Green plants in the biosphere make oxygen.*

You learned in the last section that plants need light, water, minerals, and carbon dioxide.
1 This is one way living things need non-living things. In the biosphere, living things also need each other. Animals need plants. Plants need animals. Let's find out why.

Plants need carbon dioxide for photosynthesis to take place. Carbon dioxide is a gas found in
2 the air. It enters the plant through tiny holes in the bottom of the leaf. The picture below shows
3 these tiny holes.

You learned that during photosynthesis, plants make sugar. Sugar is a source of energy. It is used by the leaves and the rest of the plant to grow. During photosynthesis, the plant also
4 makes oxygen. This oxygen is given off by the plant. It goes into the air. Most of the oxygen in the air is made by green plants.

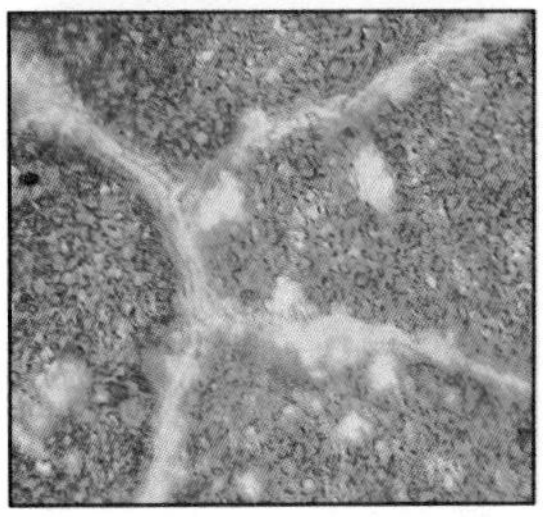

EXTENSIONS

Enrichment

Activity

The students can observe how respiration occurs in plants by completing this Activity. Have them follow these steps:

A. Gather these materials: limewater, a pan, a small plant, a wooden block, and a wide-mouth jar.

B. Fill the pan with limewater. Place the wooden block in the center of the pan.

C. Place the plant on top of the block and cover it with the jar. The mouth of the jar should touch the bottom of the pan.

D. Put the pan in a dark place overnight. Observe any changes in the limewater. The limewater will turn milky, indicating that carbon dioxide was produced. The water level will rise, indicating that oxygen was taken up by the plant.

DEVELOPMENT

1 Skill Development—Encourage students to *compare and contrast* how living things need nonliving things and how living things need each other. The concept of interdependence is introduced here, although the term is not used in the student text.

2 Skill Development—Emphasize the *process* by which carbon dioxide enters the leaf. Draw a diagram on the chalkboard showing the tiny holes through which the gas enters the plant.

3 Teaching Tips—Bring in the leaves from some houseplants. Strip off a bit of the skin from one of the leaves. Place it on a slide with a drop of water and a cover slip. Let the students observe the cells under a microscope. If you can obtain a plant such as plantain, peel off a thin layer from the bottom of a leaf. You may be able to observe the air openings (stomata).

4 Teaching Tips—The release of oxygen can be observed by placing a few tips of elodea, tips down, in a jar of water. Set the jar in sunlight and observe the oxygen bubbles. Place a piece of cardboard in front of the jar to block off the light. Notice that the flow of bubbles stops.

EXTENSIONS

Enrichment

Science Skill—Hypothesizing

Students can use their knowledge of the bromothymol blue reaction to test their hypothesis about what gas is released from a seltzer tablet.

A. Gather these materials: seltzer tablet, water, vial with cap, plastic tube, glass jar, and BTB.

B. Fill both the vial and the jar half full with water.

C. Push the plastic tube through a hole in the cap of the plastic vial. See Fig. 17-2.

D. Drop a piece of seltzer tablet into the vial. Cap the vial and run the tube into the glass jar. Gas will start bubbling out of the water and flow into the glass jar.

E. Put a few drops of BTB into the water in the jar. The BTB will turn green and then yellow. Ask the students if they can determine what gas was released (carbon dioxide).

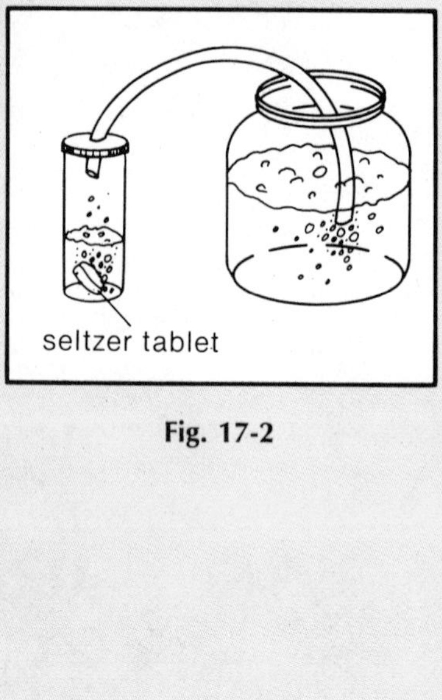

Fig. 17-2

The two animals shown here need oxygen to live. They get the oxygen from the air by breathing. Oxygen helps animals get energy from the food they eat. Animals give off carbon dioxide when they exhale. The carbon dioxide goes into the atmosphere.

5 The diagram below shows how these gases move through the biosphere. They move back and forth between green plants and animals.

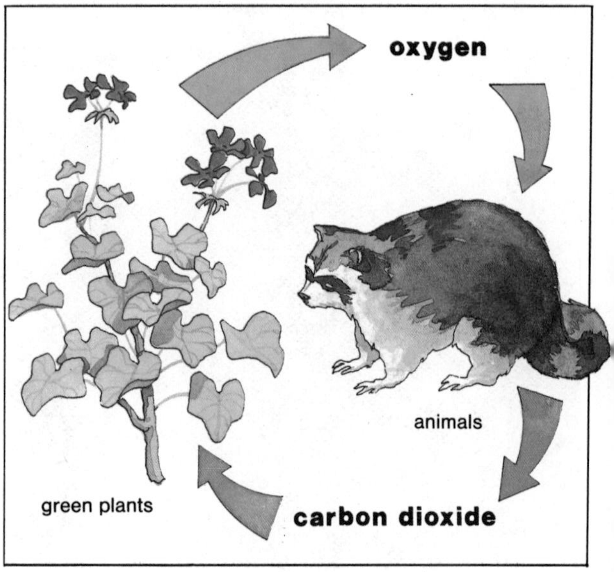

5 Teaching Tips—Discuss with the students the gases that animals and plants use. The following list might help:

Plants produce oxygen.
Animals use oxygen.
Animals produce carbon dioxide.
Plants use carbon dioxide.

6 The chart on the bottom of page 294 looks like a circle. It shows a cycle. It is called the **oxygen-carbon dioxide cycle**. In this cycle, plants, animals, and the two gases interact. Oxygen and carbon dioxide are cycled through plants , animals, and the air. The biosphere and the atmosphere take part in the *oxygen-carbon dioxide cycle*.

Oxygen–carbon dioxide cycle: The way in which these gases interact with plants, animals, and the air.

8 This cycle also takes place in ponds and in the oceans. The picture below shows a pond community. Green plants and animals live together in the pond. The oxygen the animals need is in the water. The animals take the water into their bodies. They remove the oxygen and use it. Plants use the carbon dioxide in the water. The gases are cycled through the water just as they are cycled through the air.

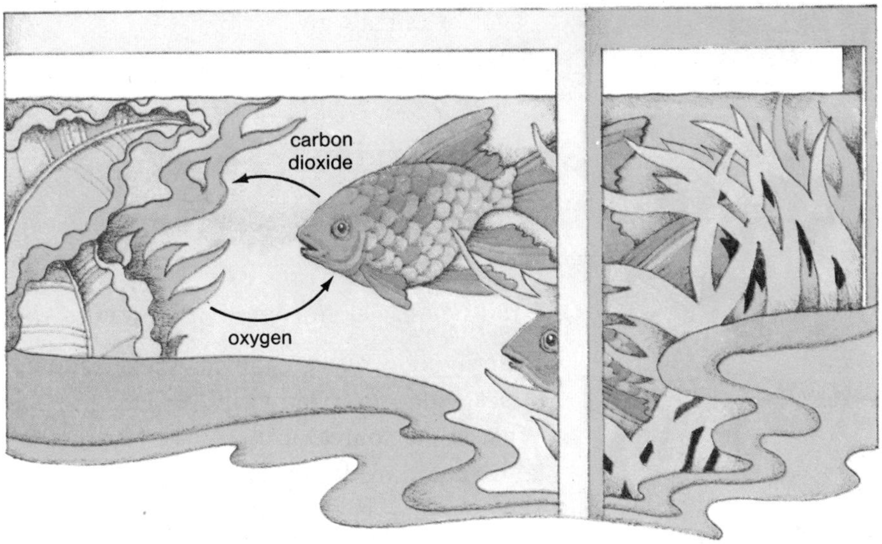

EXTENSIONS

Enrichment

Research—Library

Students can use magazines and biology textbooks to do research on chemosynthetic organisms. These are organisms that use chemical energy instead of light energy to make food. The students should research what chemicals are used, where the organisms are found, and what kind of food they make.

6 Teaching Tips—Use the statements above to introduce the carbon dioxide–oxygen cycle. Draw a diagram on the chalkboard to show the relationships.

7 Skill Development—Encourage the students to discuss the *cause and effect* relationships between the gases (oxygen and carbon dioxide) and the plants and animals. Help them see how plants and animals are interdependent.

8 Skill Development—Help the students *compare and contrast* the carbon dioxide–oxygen cycle in water with the cycle in the air. Oxygen and carbon dioxide dissolve in water and are therefore available to the plants and animals that live in aquatic environments.

EXTENSIONS

Enrichment

Research—Library

Students can use biology textbooks to do research on animals that do not need oxygen to live. They are called anaerobic organisms. The students should research what chemicals they use in place of oxygen, where they live, and what kind of food they use.

ACTIVITY

What gas do animals give off?

A. Gather these materials: 2 small bottles with day-old tap water, a straw, and a bottle of blue BTB.

B. Fill both bottles 3/4 full of day-old tap water. Add blue BTB until the bottles are full. Blue BTB turns yellow if carbon dioxide is in the water.

C. Put a straw into 1 of the bottles. Exhale through the straw.

1. What is the color of the water in each bottle?
2. What do you think happened in each bottle?
3. What gas do humans and other animals give off?

Section Review

Main Ideas: The chart below shows the oxygen-carbon dioxide cycle.

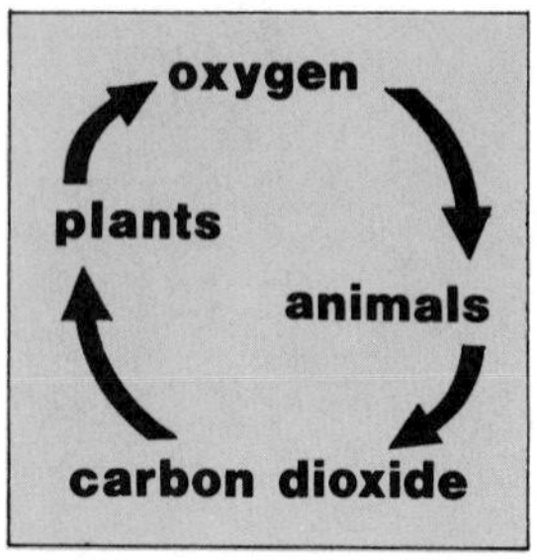

Questions: Answer in complete sentences.

1. Describe how oxygen and carbon dioxide interact with a frog and a lily pad.
2. What is the source of these gases in the air: (a) carbon dioxide, (b) oxygen?
3. What would happen to animals if all the green plants died?

ACTIVITY

Skill Development—*Observing, Inferring*

Teaching Tips—One of the bottles in the experiment is a control. BTB is an indicator that changes from blue to green to yellow in the presence of carbon dioxide.

Answers to Questions—1. The one into which you exhaled turned green and then yellow. The other one stayed the same. **2.** Nothing happened in the control bottle. Carbon dioxide was released when you exhaled into the other bottle. **3.** Carbon dioxide

SECTION REVIEW

Answers to Questions

1. The lily pad produces oxygen, which the frog inhales. The frog exhales carbon dioxide, which the lily pad uses.
2. a. animals, b. plants
3. They would not have a source of oxygen and would die.

Exceptional Student

Visually Impaired

The student will need a partner for this Activity.

SUGGESTED WORKSHEET MASTERS
p. T-279 l; for Sections 17-2 and 17-3, p. T-279 k

CHAPTER REVIEW

Science Words: Think of a word for each blank. List the letters **a** through **j** on paper. Write the word next to each letter.

Plants and animals live together in a __a__. Each organism lives in a home called a __b__.

Two organisms of a different kind may live together and help each other. This is called __c__. An organism that feeds on other organisms is called a __d__.

The process by which green plants make food is called __e__. Light is used by the green material found in the __f__ of the plant's leaves. The green material is called __g__.

The gas needed by plants to make food is called __h__. The gas given off by green plants is called __i__. Plants and animals pass these two gases back and forth in the __j__.

Questions: Answer in complete sentences.

1. How do a habitat and a community differ? Name one of each.
2. What is one example of mutualism?
3. Look at the picture on page 282. Name the two organisms shown. What is the habitat of each?
4. What is the makeup of the community you live in? Describe your habitat.
5. In a drawing, show how green plants make food. Label light, chlorophyll, carbon dioxide, oxygen, and sugar.

EXTENSIONS

Enrichment

Research—Library

Using biology and ecology textbooks, students can do research on other important chemical cycles found in nature, such as the nitrogen cycle. They should research why this chemical is important to living things, whether other chemicals are involved in the nitrogen cycle, and what kinds of living things are involved in this cycle.

CHAPTER REVIEW

Science Words

a. Community, **b.** habitat, **c.** mutualism, **d.** parasite, **e.** photosynthesis, **f.** cells, **g.** chlorophyll, **h.** carbon dioxide, **i.** oxygen, **j.** oxygen–carbon dioxide cycle

Answers to Questions

1. A community includes all the plants and animals that live in the same place (forest); a habitat is a home or place where an organism lives (soil).
2. Dead tree, termite, and protist
3. The seals and the birds both occupy the same rocky habitat.
4. Answers will vary.
5. See Fig. 17-3.

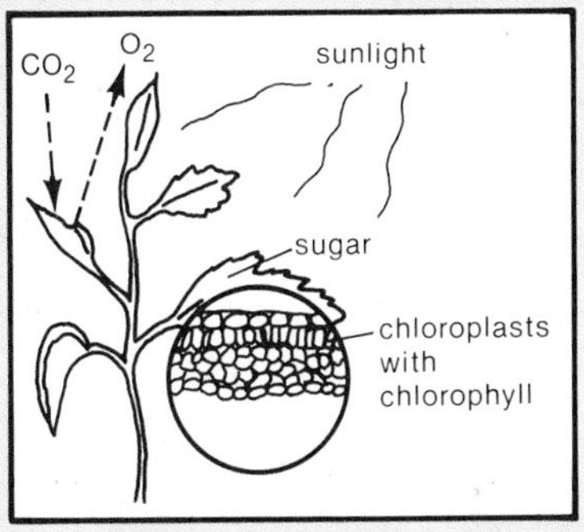

Fig. 17-3

SUGGESTED TEST MASTERS
pp. T-279 d, e

Chapter Objectives

1. Identify producers and describe how they store food.
2. Describe consumers and identify the types of consumers.
3. Identify producers and consumers in water and land communities.
4. Explain the role of decomposers.
5. Describe the interaction of producers, consumers, and decomposers.

SECTION BACKGROUND

This chapter introduces the students to three types of organisms that exist in any community: producers, consumers, and decomposers. Each of the following three sections introduces one of these organisms.

Green plants are the producers in a community. They are able to produce their own food (sugar and starch) by photosynthesis. Plants store their food in the seeds, roots, or stems. All communities have green plants as their essential and ultimate source of food and energy. Because the study of food relationships in a community is relatively complex, scientists use community charts to study the types of producers and other living things found in an area.

MATERIALS

iodine solution, dropper, foods (corn starch, rice, carrots, cereal, potato), paper towel or newspaper, knife

Exceptional Student IEP Chapter Goal

When shown ten pictures of a variety of plants and animals, the student will identify which are food producers and which are food consumers. When different plants and animals are mentioned to the visually impaired students, they will tell which are food producers and which are food consumers.

CHAPTER 18

THE FOOD CYCLE

18-1. Food Makers

Every living thing in a community needs food to live. There must be a source of this food. There are many different sources of food. In every community, there are food makers. When you finish this section, you should be able to:

BASIC TEACHING PLAN

MOTIVATION

Find a variety of pictures showing different communities: forests, ponds, lakes, tidal zones, rivers, deserts, and so on. Ask the students to identify the food makers in each of the pictures. Emphasize those plants whose roots, seeds, or stems are edible. Your class could also make a list of the common fruits and vegetables they eat. If possible, obtain pictures of the plant or tree for each fruit or vegetable they select.

☐ **A.** Identify the *producers* of food in a community.

☐ **B.** Identify where food is stored in plants.

Some of the food made by a plant is used to keep the plant alive. The rest is stored in different parts of the plant. **1** The stems, roots, and leaves are all places where food can be stored. **2** When you eat carrots, you are eating the roots of a plant. Broccoli is mostly the stem of a plant. Spinach and lettuce are leaves of plants. Peanuts are seeds. A fruit is food that has seeds.

EXTENSIONS

Enrichment
Research

Have your students research the nutritional value of various fruits and vegetables. They should discover such facts as the following: carrots contain vitamin A, which helps prevent night blindness; oranges contain vitamin C, which helps prevent scurvy; and bananas provide us with our potassium requirement.

Application
Science Skills—Observing

Students can observe the structure of a plant seed.

A. Gather these materials: lima bean seeds, bush bean seeds, and paper towels.

B. Before beginning the Activity, soak the seeds for about 24 hours.

C. Give each group of students two of each kind of seed.

D. Ask the students what they think the inside of each seed looks like. Have them make a drawing showing their predictions.

E. Now have the students open the seeds and make a drawing of each half of the seed.

F. Have them identify the cotyledons and the embryo.

DEVELOPMENT

1 Teaching Tips—Obtain the following foods: broccoli, carrots, spinach, lettuce, peanuts, and strawberries. Give each group of students a few of the foods. Have them identify which of the foods are roots, stems, or leaves. What do all the foods have in common? *They are all sources of food. They also all come from plants.*
2 Teaching Tips—Generalize about the foods in the previous teaching tip and identify them as producers.

EXTENSIONS

Reinforcement

Science Skills—Recording Data

In the first chapter of this unit, the students made environments in which they planted several varieties of seeds. This Extension is designed to help students structure their investigation of the growth of the plants in the environments.

A. Students should record in a chart what happens to the (bean) plants during each of these time periods:

1. during the first two weeks of growth;
2. during the third and fourth weeks of growth;
3. during the fifth and sixth weeks of growth;
4. during the seventh and eighth weeks of growth.

B. Students should answer the following questions as they observe plant growth:

1. When do the leaves first appear?
2. How fast does the plant grow?
3. Do leaves ever fall off the plant? Why?
4. Will the plants live forever?
5. When do flowers appear?
6. When do seeds appear?

Because green plants can make, or produce, their own food, they are called **producers** (pro-**doo**-sirs).

Producers: Living things that are able to make their own food.

3 Let's compare *producers* found in a water community with those in a forest community. The producers in a water community are green **4** plants. There are four types of plants in this community: (1) Some plants have roots such as the **cattails** (**kat**-tails) shown in the picture below. (2) There are plants that live on the surface of the water. One of these is the **water lily**. (3) There are many plants that live under the water. (4) There are also tiny floating plants, such as algae. In water communities, algae are very important producers of food.

Cattails: A tall plant that lives in the water.

Water lily: A plant with large, flat, floating leaves with a flower in the center.

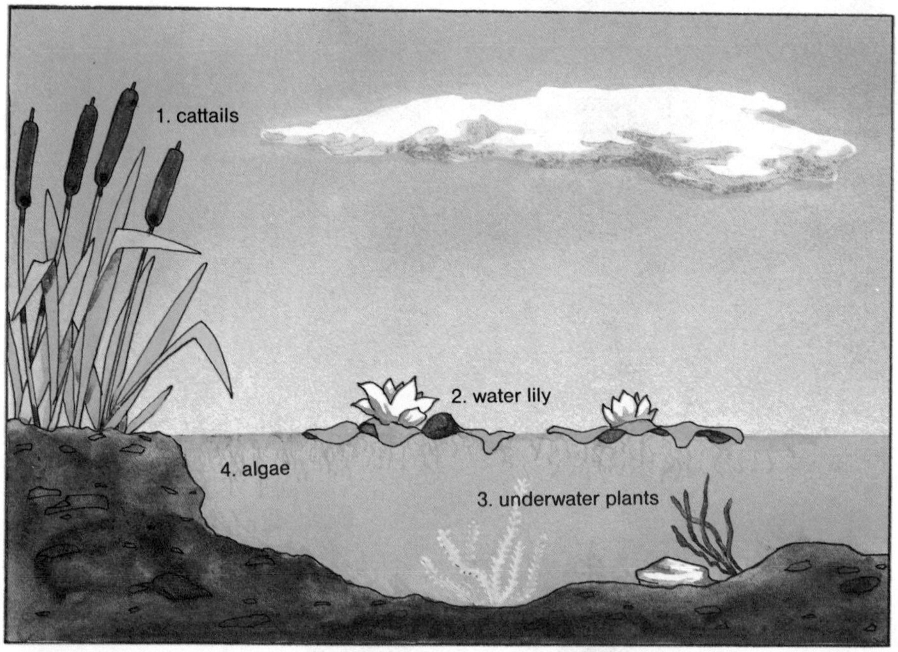

3 **Skill Development**—Students can *compare* the types of producers found in this aquatic community. You might want to set up an aquarium in the classroom so that students can *observe* an aquatic environment directly.

4 **Teaching Tips**—Obtain samples of the four types of producers found in the water community: cattails, water lilies, underwater plants (elodea), and algae. Stress the fact that although they may look different, they are producers because they make sugar and starches.

5 In a forest community, the food makers are also the green plants. Look at the picture above. The food makers are shown in different places. 6 There are three types of food makers in the forest. They are found in layers. (1) The bottom, or ground, layer contains mosses, wildflowers, and ferns. (2) The next layer is made of bushes and other low-growing plants. (3) The last layer is the trees. The trees and plants have roots, which grow into the ground.

7 The food made is in the form of sugar and **starch**. It is stored in different parts of the plants. It becomes a source of energy for living things that eat the plants. When you eat a plant food, you are eating sugar and *starch*. Foods that contain starch include bread, spaghetti, potatoes, rice, and cereals. Sugars are found in fruit, corn, and nuts.

Starch: A type of food made by green plants.

EXTENSIONS

Application

Activity

Students can have a firsthand experience with an aquatic community by building an aquarium using simple materials. Have the students follow these steps:

A. Gather these materials: 1-gal containers, tap water, anacharis plants, guppies, snails, Daphnia, and algae.

B. Age the tap water for 24 hours in the containers that will be used as the aquariums.

C. Each aquarium should receive several of each of the organisms. Students should put the plants in first, then add the animals.

D. They should observe the aquarium and record the following data in a chart:

1. the name of each plant or animal;
2. a drawing or description of it;
3. the number of each plant or animal;
4. what the animals do;
5. what the animals eat.

5 **Skill Development**—Have the students *compare* the forest community producers with the producers in a water community.
6 **Teaching Tips**—Take the students outside to a forest area. Help them identify the three types of producers that exist in the forest. Find examples of mosses and small plants as the first layer. Identify examples of bushes or other low-growing plants as the second layer. The trees are the third layer. If you cannot go outside, display pictures or samples of the plants in the classroom.
7 **Skill Development**—*Compare and contrast* foods that contain sugar and starch. Have samples of foods that represent each type. Discuss the fact that foods with starch need to be digested more thoroughly before they can be used by our bodies.

Exceptional Student

Visually Impaired

Using shoe boxes, make dioramas that illustrate water and forest communities. Have the student feel the plants and animals in each community.

EXTENSIONS

Enrichment
Activity

Students can observe what happens to stored starch in plants when we eat by completing this Activity. Have the students follow these steps:

A. Gather these materials: iodine, dropper, paper towel, and carrot.

B. Cut the carrot into small pieces and chew one piece without swallowing it.

C. Place the chewed carrot on the paper towel.

D. Put one drop of iodine solution on the carrot and observe what happens.

1. What happens to the color of the iodine solution?
2. Does this differ from what happened when the iodine was placed on the raw carrot in the text Activity?
3. How would you explain the difference?

Exceptional Student
Visually Impaired

Assign a partner to the student for this Activity.

ACTIVITY

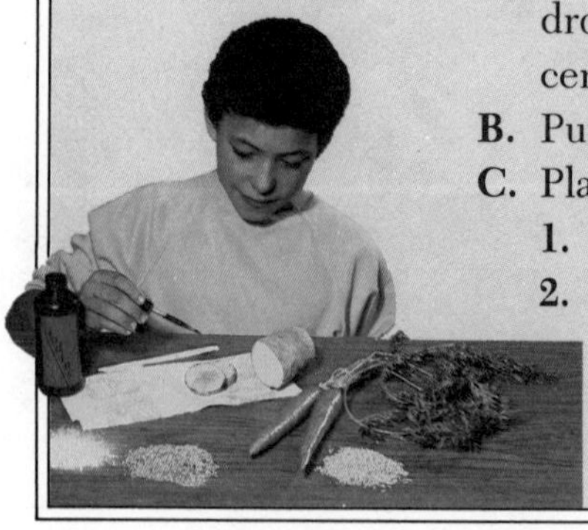

How can you test plants to see if food is stored in them?

A. Gather these materials: iodine solution, eye dropper, foods (cornstarch, rice, carrots, cereal, potato), paper towel, and a knife.
B. Put a small piece of potato on a paper towel.
C. Place 1 drop of iodine solution on the potato.
1. What happens to the color of the iodine?
2. Does this food contain stored starch?
3. Which foods contain stored starch?
4. What other foods do you think contain stored starch?

Section Review

Main Ideas: Green plants are called producers. They make their own food. Some food is used to keep the plant alive. Extra food is stored as starch or sugar in the stems, roots, and seeds.

Questions: Answer in complete sentences.

1. Which of the following are food makers: (a) corn, (b) horse, (c) lettuce, (d) turnip, or (e) sheep?
2. Where does a plant store food?
3. What are three types of producers in a water community?
4. What are some foods that you eat that contain starch?

ACTIVITY

Skill Development—*Finding Cause and Effect, Recording Data*

Teaching Tips—In this Activity, students use a simple test for starch: iodine turns black in the presence of starch. Starch is a basic food produced by plants. Several foods are suggested for the test. Expand the list as you wish. Students will need only a very small sample of each food they test. One drop of iodine on each food item will be sufficient.

Answers to Questions—**1.** It turns black. **2.** Yes. **3.** Cornstarch, rice, carrots, cereal. **4.** Beans, breads, cakes, cookies.

SECTION REVIEW

Answers to Questions
1. Corn, lettuce, turnip
2. Stems, roots, leaves
3. Cattails, water lilies, algae
4. Potatoes, bread

Both of the animals shown here eat plants. The blue whale eats tiny organisms that float in seawater. It swims with its mouth open. It drinks gallons of water filled with the small organisms. The grasshopper eats plants that grow on the land. Neither the whale nor the grasshopper makes its own food. Each has to get its food by eating other organisms. In what ways are you like the whale and the grasshopper? When you finish this section, you should be able to:

☐ **A.** Identify organisms in a community that are *consumers*.

☐ **B.** Compare *consumers* based on the type of food they eat.

☐ **C.** Identify examples of *consumers* in a water and a land community.

18-2.

Food Takers

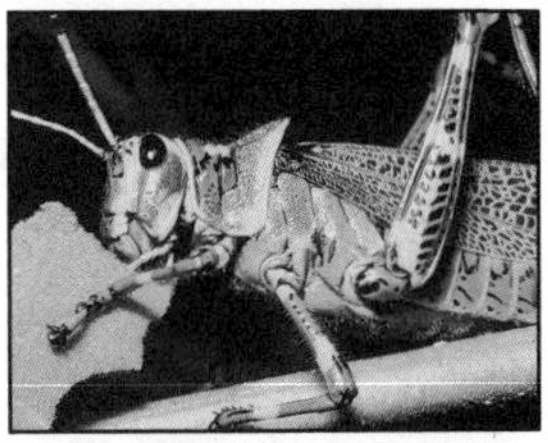

SECTION BACKGROUND

A living thing that eats plants or animals is called a consumer. Human beings, cats, dogs, birds, alligators, beetles, worms, fish, and snails are all examples of consumers. Consumers that eat only plants are called herbivores. Grasshoppers, chipmunks, and the giant blue whale are examples of herbivores. The sugar and starch present in the plants provides them with the energy and raw materials needed for their life processes. Consumers that feed only on other animals are called carnivores or meat eaters. Some consumers eat both plants and animals. They are called omnivores.

MATERIALS

2 sheets of construction paper, small cards with the names of an organism, glue

BASIC TEACHING PLAN

MOTIVATION

Many of your students will be surprised that the giant blue whale eats microscopic organisms. You might make a list of animals and ask the students to guess what kind of food they eat (plants, animals, or both). These examples can help you get started: hawk (animals), pelican (animals), seagull (both), giraffe (plants), lion (animals), turkey (plants), owl (animals), chipmunk (plants), worm (both), shark (animals), ant (both).

Text Questions—In what ways are you like the whale and the grasshopper? *Humans do not make their own food. They must eat plants and animals to get the energy they need to live.*

EXTENSIONS

Application

Research

Students may be interested in learning about carnivorous plants, that is, plants that eat animals. Plants such as the Venus flytrap and the pitcher plant have special structures to capture and digest animals, usually insects. Students can do research to discover how the plants do this and why. They should investigate where these plants are found and if they can still be considered producers.

Research—Library

Since humans are omnivores, we eat all kinds of food. Students can use almanacs and atlases to learn about the diets of people in other countries. They should select one country and research what kind of plants and animals people eat there and how they prepare them. They can give a report to the class of their findings.

Human beings and other animals are not producers. They are not green plants, which can make their own food. They get their food by eating plants and animals. The lettuce, sandwich bread, orange juice, and pear that the boy is eating come from producers. Lettuce is the leaf of a lettuce plant. Pears are fruit from pear trees. Orange juice comes from oranges, which are also fruit. Bread is made from wheat. 1

The ham on his sandwich does not come from a producer. Ham is meat. Meat comes from animals.

Consumer: A living thing that eats plants and/or animals.

Herbivore: A consumer that eats only plants.

Carnivore: A consumer that eats only animals.

Omnivore: A consumer that eats both plants and animals.

A living thing that eats plants and/or animals is 2 called a **consumer** (kon-**sue**-mer). Human beings and all other animals are *consumers.* Some consumers eat only plants. These animals are called 3 **herbivores** (**err**-bih-vors), or plant eaters. *Herb-* comes from a Latin word that means "grass." The suffix *-vore* comes from a Latin word that means "to eat." Cattle, deer, squirrels, mice, rabbits, grasshoppers, and butterflies are *herbivores.*

Some consumers feed only on other animals. 4 These consumers are called **carnivores** (**kar**-nih-vors), or meat eaters. *Carni-* comes from a Latin word that means "meat." Foxes, coyotes, wolves, lions, seals, and frogs are *carnivores.*

Human beings eat both plants and animals. We are called **omnivores** (**om**-nih-vors). *Omni-* means "all." Bears, chickens, and some turtles are also *omnivores.* 5

Herbivores, carnivores, and omnivores are found in both water and forest communities.

DEVELOPMENT

1 **Skill Development**—Point out to the students that some organisms do not make their own food. These types of organisms are *classified* as consumers. Ask the students to name a number of organisms that are consumers.

2 **Skill Development**—Students could *compare and contrast* the following consumers: deer, fox, and bear. After writing their names on the board, ask the students to list under each animal the kinds of foods that make up its daily diet.

3 **Teaching Tips**—Introduce the word "herbivore" by writing the names of animals that eat only plants (cattle, deer, squirrels, mice, and rabbits) on the chalkboard.

4 **Teaching Tips**—Introduce the word "carnivore." These are meat eaters. List some animals that are carnivores (foxes, coyotes, wolves, lions, seals, frogs).

5 **Teaching Tips**—Introduce the word "omnivore." Omnivores eat both plants and animals. List some examples (humans, bears, chickens, turtles).

Exceptional Student

Learning Disabled

Using magazine pictures, have the student make three separate collages to illustrate each of the following: herbivores, carnivores, and omnivores.

6 A pond is a good place to find out about consumers in a water community. Look at the picture below. This is the same water community you saw on page 300. Let's compare the consumers in the pond. You cannot see the smallest consumers. The photo in the margin shows the tiny consumers magnified. These are tiny floating animals. They eat tiny floating plants. Since they eat plants, they are herbivores. You can also see other herbivores. Insects, snails, and
7 tadpoles are pond herbivores. Where are they found in the pond?

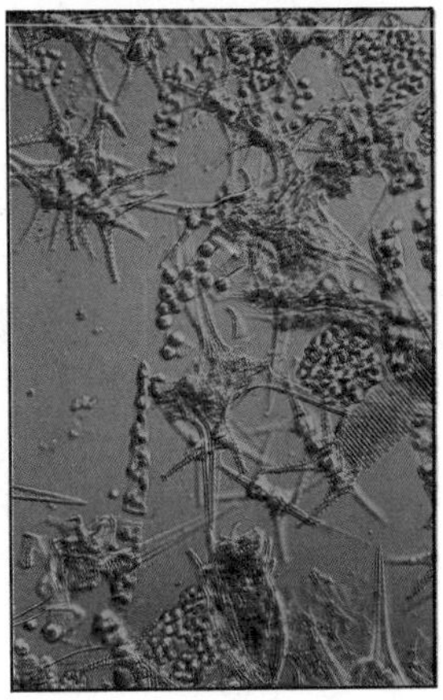

There are also many carnivores in the pond community. The crane is a water bird that eats
8 fish. Can you find other carnivores?

EXTENSIONS

Application

Activity

Students can observe how consumers behave in a habitat.

A. Have the students gather these materials: terrariums that were started earlier in the unit, crickets, and seeds.

B. Introduce about four crickets into the terrarium. Have the students also put into the terrarium a variety of seeds and other food items—roots and stems of plants, opened seeds, bean leaves, mustard and grass seeds, dead insects.

C. Have the students observe what the crickets do when they are put into the terrarium.

D. Students should record their data on a chart that lists the types of food in the terrarium. They should then look for evidence that indicates the type of food being eaten.

6 Skill Development—To classify the types of consumers in a pond community, give small groups of students an unmarked sheet of transparent paper or tracing paper. Have them make a general sketch of the pond area. Then have them identify all the animals that they think eat only plants. Have them trace all the plant-eating animals using one color pencil. Now have them identify the carnivores in the pond community. They should trace them using another color pencil. Also have them find an omnivore.

7 Text Questions—Where are they found in the pond? *Some are in the water, others are along the edge among the vegetation.*

8 Text Questions—Can you find other carnivores? *No. The turtle is an omnivore.*

EXTENSIONS

Reinforcement

Science Skills—Classifying

In this Activity, students can classify organisms in a community as either producers or consumers.

A. Gather these materials: copies of the "community chart" found in the interunit material, magazines that contain pictures of a variety of animals and plants, glue, scissors.

B. Have your students create their own pictorial community charts. Identify the type of community you want each pair or group of students to work on. Choose from ocean, tundra, tropical area, or arctic region.

C. Give groups of students magazines and instruct them to locate and cut out pictures of producers and consumers for the type of community they are investigating. They should separate consumers into plant eaters and animal eaters.

D. They should glue the plants and animals on the "community chart" at the appropriate level.

E. Have each group report to the class by showing their charts and explaining how they arranged the organisms on the chart.

ACTIVITY

How do producers and consumers interact in a community?

A. Gather these materials: 2 sheets of construction paper, small cards with the name of an organism, and glue.

B. Make a community chart on each sheet of construction paper. Label 1 chart "Forest Community." Label the other "Water Community."

C. Start with the cards labeled "forest community." Divide the cards into producers and consumers.

1. What are some producers in the forest?
2. What are some of the consumers?

D. Glue the cards on the community chart to show how the organisms interact.

3. How do the consumers at the top of the chart get food from the producers at the bottom?

E. Repeat steps C and D with the cards labeled "water community."

4. How is the water community like the forest community?

Look at the drawing of a forest community. This is the same forest that you saw on page 301. **9** You can see many herbivores. The insects and small rodents, such as squirrels and chipmunks, are herbivores. Some of the larger animals are

ACTIVITY

Skill Development—*Classifying*

Teaching Tips—The students will use small cards containing the names of organisms in two different communities. They will use the cards to classify the organisms. Make copies of the organism cards shown in the interunit material. The students should place the producers in the bottom section of the chart. The animals should be divided between the two upper sections (herbivores and carnivores).

Answers to Questions—**1.** Nuts, seeds, and flowers. **2.** Chipmunk, robin, ant, owl, hawk, and fox. **3.** They eat animals that eat plants. **4.** It has producers and consumers.

10 also herbivores. Which of these are shown in the forest scene?

There are many carnivores. The owl eats insects. It also eats chipmunks and other small animals. Some of the birds eat worms and small
11 insects. They also eat seeds. What kind of consumer is this type of bird?

12 The diagram on page 308 shows the three groups in a community. The plants are on the bottom. They produce the food for the groups above them. Next, we find the plant eaters. They become food for the animal eaters. This is a community chart. A community chart shows how energy moves through a community. The plants produce food by photosynthesis. This food energy is then used by the consumers.

EXTENSIONS

Application
Activity

Students can observe the behavior of carnivores in their terrariums. Have the students follow these steps:

A. Gather these materials: terrarium with crickets, frogs.

B. Put a carnivore into the terrarium and observe its behavior. Frogs are easy to obtain and can be returned to their natural environment. Frogs can be purchased at pet stores, or they can be found in their natural environment.

C. Put one frog into each terrarium. Let the students observe the frog in the terrarium. Have them make a list of the things the frog does.

D. Ask the students what they think frogs eat. They will soon observe the frogs eating crickets or other plant eaters that are in the terrariums.

9 **Skill Development**—To *classify* the kinds of consumers that live in the forest community, you can use the same techniques as described in the Basic Teaching Plan on page T-298.
10 **Text Questions**—Which of these are shown in the forest scene? *Deer.*
11 **Text Questions**—What kind of consumer is this type of bird? *Omnivore.*
12 **Skill Development**—Make copies of the chart shown on page 308, but do not include any written information on it. Include only the words *plants, plant eaters,* and *animal eaters* in their appropriate places. Write the names of the following organisms on the chalkboard: trees, grasses, seeds, chipmunks, butterflies, owls, foxes, lions. Using the chart, ask the students to classify these animals according to the type of organism they think each one is. Ask the students to write the words *producer, herbivore,* and *carnivore* on the chart.

EXTENSIONS

Enrichment

Science Skills—Hypothesizing

One way to distinguish what kind of food an animal eats is by its teeth. The teeth of a herbivore are shaped differently from those of a carnivore or omnivore. Have your students hypothesize what the teeth of each type of animal would look like and then look at pictures of various animals to check their hypotheses.

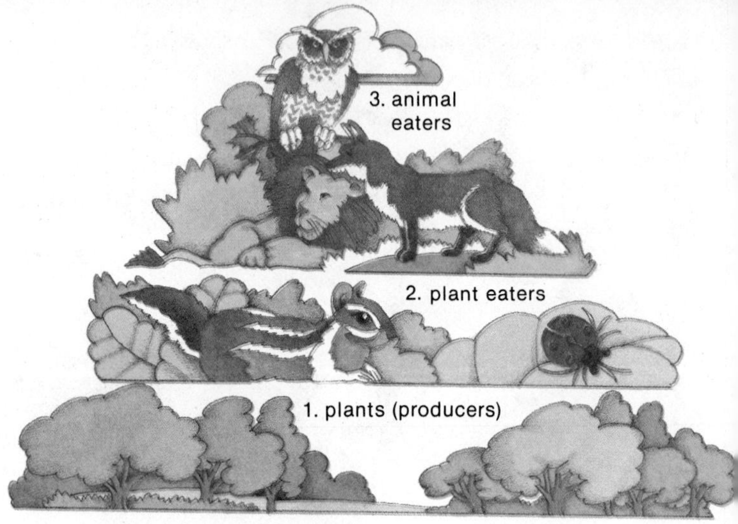

Community Chart

Section Review

Main Ideas: Living things are either producers or consumers. Consumers can be either herbivores, carnivores, or omnivores.

Questions: Answer in complete sentences.

1. How is a producer different from a consumer? Name one of each.
2. What is the difference between a herbivore and a carnivore? Name one of each.
3. List the foods you ate for dinner last night. Which foods came from producers? Which came from consumers?
4. Draw a community chart for the pond shown on page 305. Identify one producer, one herbivore, and one carnivore. List them on the chart.

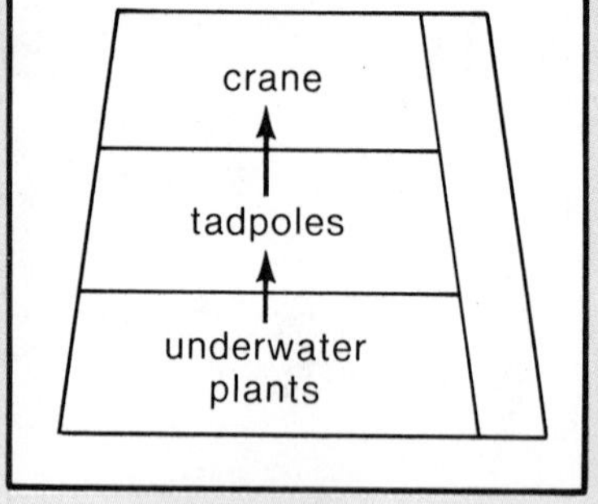

Fig. 18-1

SUGGESTED WORKSHEET MASTER
pp. T-279 m, n

SECTION REVIEW

Main Ideas—Have the students make up a community chart using organisms of their own choice.

Answers to Questions

1. Producers (plants) are able to make their own food by photosynthesis. Consumers (animals) must depend on plants or other animals for their food.
2. Herbivores are animals that eat only plants; carnivores are animals that eat other animals. Herbivores—cattle, deer, squirrels, mice, rabbits. Carnivores—foxes, coyotes, wolves, lions, seals, frogs.
3. After the students have listed their foods and classifications, ask them to determine if they ate any herbivores, carnivores, or omnivores.
4. See Fig. 18-1.

Would you make a sandwich with this bread? The bread was once fresh. It was left out in the air. Now there is a black mold growing on it. What caused this to happen? When you finish this section, you should be able to:

18-3. The Decomposers

- ☐ **A.** Explain what happens to organisms that die in a community.
- ☐ **B.** Identify organisms that feed on dead animals and plants.
- ☐ **C.** Explain how *decomposers* interact with producers and consumers.

Producers and consumers do not live forever. When they die, they begin to change. They begin to rot. We say that they **decay** (de-**kay**). Tiny organisms in every community make things *decay*. These living things get their food from wastes and dead organisms. They are called **decomposers** (de-kom-**poz**-ers). The prefix *de-*

Decay: To become rotten.

Decomposer: A living thing that feeds on wastes and dead organisms.

SECTION BACKGROUND

In each community, there are organisms that are neither producers nor consumers. These organisms are decomposers. Decomposers are nongreen plants able to break down food materials that remain in the cells of dead animals and plants. Bacteria, molds, and yeasts are decomposers. As a result of the action of decomposers on wastes and dead organisms, water, carbon dioxide, and minerals are given off or released into the soil. Producers reuse these raw materials to produce more food.

MATERIALS

12 banana slices, 2 plastic sandwich bags, yeast

BASIC TEACHING PLAN

MOTIVATION

Before beginning this section, prepare some bread mold. Use bread with no preservatives to speed up the process. Put pieces of bread in plastic bags. Place the bags in a moist, warm, dark place. Mold should start to grow within two days.

Text Questions—What caused this to happen? *The bread was left in a moist, warm, dark place for several days.* You could discuss the purpose of preservatives in breads and other foods.

DEVELOPMENT

1 **Skill Development**—Introduce the idea that there are some organisms that get their food from wastes and dead organisms. *Compare and contrast* these decomposers with producers and consumers.

EXTENSIONS

Application
Research

Have your students interview the school nurse or doctor to find out about the effects of harmful bacteria on the human body. The following questions could be asked:

1. How are bacteria-related illnesses treated?
2. What measures are taken to prevent the spread of bacteria in the school?
3. Are some people more susceptible to bacteria-related illnesses than others?

means "to undo." *Compose* means "to put together." So *decompose* means "to undo what is put together," or to break down. When decomposers feed on dead organisms, they make them decay by breaking them down.

Molds, yeasts, and bacteria (bak-**tear**-rhee-ah) are decomposers. They are very tiny non-green plants. They have no chlorophyll. They cannot carry on photosynthesis to make their own food.

2 Picture 1 is an enlarged photograph of mold growing on a slice of bread. Molds grow best where it is moist, warm, and dark. The bread shown on page 309 is decaying. A mold is living and growing on it.

3 Picture 2 shows bacteria. It would take 25,000 bacteria to fit on a line 2.5 centimeters (1 inch) long. Over 2,000 kinds of bacteria are known today. Some are harmful. Some are not. They are found in the air, on our skin, and inside our bodies. Certain bacteria grow only on plants. Others feed on animals. Still others grow only on humans. They all need food to survive.

Yeasts are shown in picture 3. Yeasts need sugar to live. They can live on the sugar in fresh fruit.

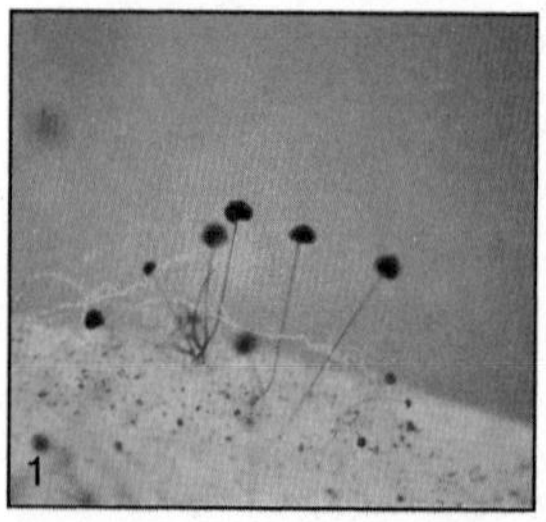
1

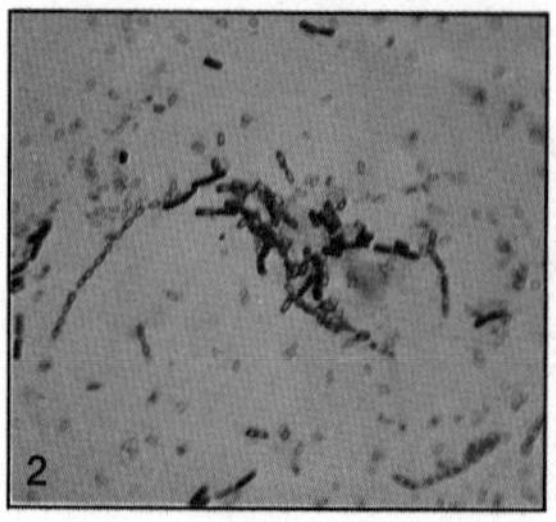
2

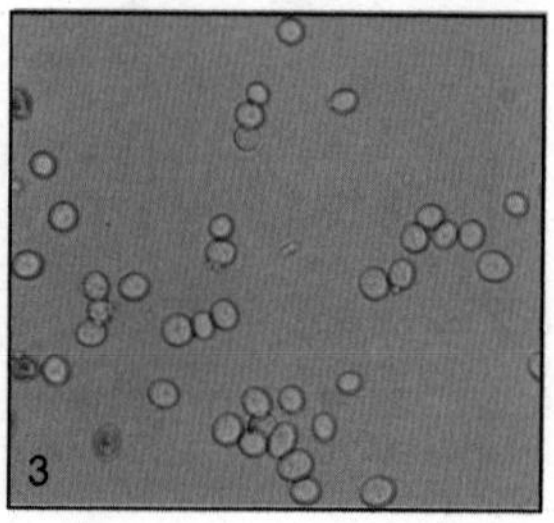
3

2 **Teaching Tips**—A mold is one example of a larger group of decomposers known as fungi. Other examples of fungi include mushrooms, mildew, rust, and smut. Fungi have no vascular tissue. They reproduce by means of spores, and they lack chlorophyll. Have samples of some of these fungi for the students to look at.

3 **Teaching Tips**—Bacteria are microscopic organisms. They belong to the phylum protista. We have grouped the bacteria with decomposers. However, some bacteria are actually consumers. In this section, we refer to bacteria as organisms that feed on dead or decaying organisms.

ACTIVITY

How do decomposers decay organisms?

A. Gather these materials: 2 banana slices, 2 plastic sandwich bags, and yeast.

B. Put a slice of banana inside each of the 2 plastic bags. Sprinkle some yeast on 1 slice.

C. Close both bags. Write "yeast" on the bag with the yeast.

D. Look at both bags each day for 5 days.

1. What difference do you see between the banana with yeast and the one without yeast?
2. How is the banana with yeast changing?
3. What is causing this change?

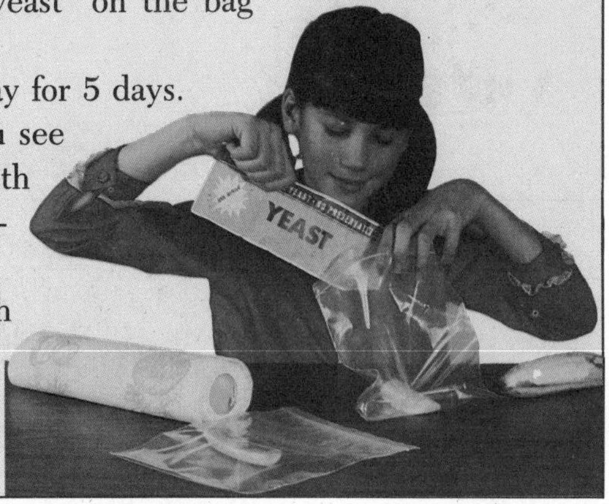

Decomposers in a community are important. They break down and decay dead organisms. As they decay, these organisms give off materials. These materials go back into the community. Yeast, molds, and bacteria give off carbon dioxide as they feed on wastes and dead organisms. The carbon dioxide is then used by green plants to make food.

The diagram on page 312 shows decomposers, producers, and consumers in a community. This is another example of a cycle. (1) The green plants make food for animals. (2) The animals

EXTENSIONS

Enrichment

Science Skills—Comparing and Contrasting

This Activity will demonstrate the effect of temperature and light on the growth of mold. Have the students follow these steps:

A. Gather these materials: bread, sandwich bags, and a shoe box.

B. To test the effect of light on the growth of mold, follow these procedures. Put two pieces of bread into separate sandwich bags. Put one bag in a shoe box. Put the other on top of the box. Leave the box in a place where there is light, but do not put it in direct sunlight. Leave the bread alone for a week to ten days. Check the pieces each day, however.

1. Which piece of bread had mold growing on it first?
2. How does light affect the growth of mold?

C. To test the effect of temperature on the growth of mold, follow these procedures. Put three pieces of bread into separate sandwich bags. Place one bag under a lamp, leave another at room temperature, and put the third in the refrigerator. Leave them alone for a week to ten days, being sure to check them each day.

3. Which piece of bread had mold growing on it first?
4. How does temperature affect the growth of mold?

ACTIVITY

Skill Development—*Comparing and Contrasting, Finding Cause and Effect*

Teaching Tips—The results of this Activity will not be known for several days. Put all the bags on a table so that you control all the factors except the presence of yeast on one of the banana slices.

Answers to Questions—1. The banana with yeast is turning dark and getting smaller. **2.** It is being broken down by the action of yeast on the sugar in the banana. **3.** The yeast.

EXTENSIONS

Reinforcement
Science Skills—Classifying

Now that the students have been introduced to decomposers, they can complete the community chart they made in the last section so that it includes producers, consumers, and decomposers.

A. Gather these materials: the community chart, and pencil.

B. To the list of organisms that was already used, add decomposers such as bacteria, molds, and yeast.

C. Have the students classify the organisms by listing them in the appropriate section on the community chart.

D. Have the students discuss their finished charts.

4

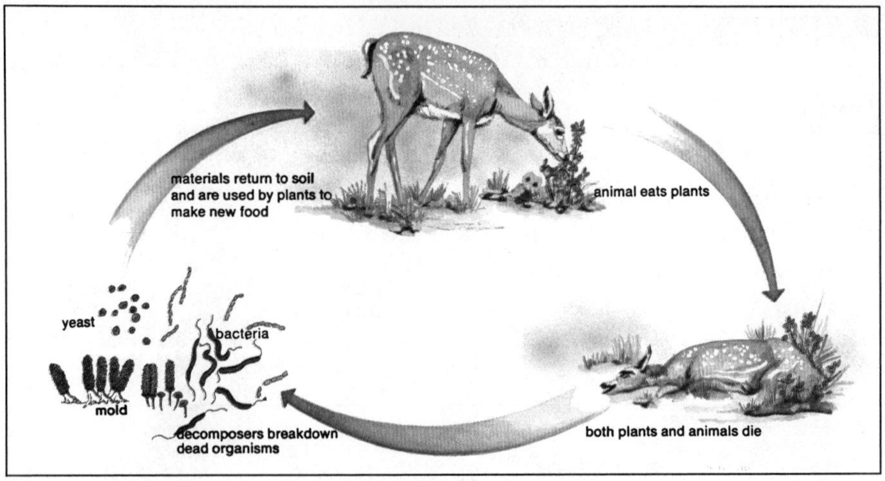

and plants die. (3) The decomposers "eat" the dead organisms. The dead organisms are broken down. (4) The decomposers put materials back into the air and soil. These materials are used by green plants to make food.

Section Review

Main Ideas: Decomposers get their food from wastes and dead organisms. When organisms decay, the soil, air, and water get the materials needed to help keep other living things alive.

Questions: Answer in complete sentences.

1. What are three organisms that feed on dead organisms?
2. Suppose a squirrel dies in the forest. What will happen to its body after a few days?
3. Show in a diagram how trees, a squirrel, and bacteria are related in a community.

4 Skill Development—Have your class follow the *sequence* of the diagram that illustrates how producers, consumers, and decomposers are related.

SECTION REVIEW

Answers to Questions

1. Molds, bacteria, and yeast
2. It will decay. Decomposers break down the organism.
3. Trees provide food and oxygen for the squirrels. The squirrels exhale carbon dioxide for the trees. Trees and squirrels die, and bacteria feed on the dead trees and squirrels. The bacteria give off carbon dioxide as they feed on the wastes.

CHAPTER REVIEW

Science Words: Match the terms in column A with the definitions in column B.

Column A	Column B
1. Producer	a. A living thing that feeds on wastes
2. Cattails	b. Living things that make their own food
3. Water lily	c. To become rotten
4. Starch	d. A tall plant that lives in the water
5. Consumer	e. A consumer that eats plants and animals
6. Herbivore	f. A consumer that eats only plants
7. Carnivore	g. A plant with flat, floating leaves
8. Omnivore	h. A food made by green plants
9. Decay	i. A consumer that eats only animals
10. Decomposer	j. A living thing that eats plants or animals

Questions: Answer in complete sentences.

1. Make a list of the foods you ate today. Label the foods that are producers "P." Label the consumers "C."
2. Name three producers in a forest community.
3. Where do plants store food?
4. What kinds of consumers are these animals: (a) deer, (b) owl, (c) grasshopper, and (d) human?

EXTENSIONS

Enrichment

Research—Library

Students may be interested in learning about microcommunities. These are tiny, self-contained worlds. Examples are the organisms found in the leaves of the pineapplelike plants called bromeliads. The leaves of these plants form a central cup that holds water. In this water, a variety of insects and amphibians live. Another interesting fact about these plants is that they can grow high above the ground by anchoring themselves to trees. Students can use ecology and botany books to learn what kind of organisms live in these microcosms and what kind of communities they form.

CHAPTER REVIEW

Science Words

1. b, **2.** d, **3.** g, **4.** h, **5.** j, **6.** f, **7.** i, **8.** e, **9.** c, **10.** a

Answers to Questions

1. Answers will vary.
2. Mosses, small plants, wildflowers, lichens, trees, bushes
3. Roots, stems, and leaves
4. (a) herbivore, (b) carnivore, (c) herbivore, and (d) omnivore

SUGGESTED WORKSHEET MASTERS
pp. T-279 o, p

SUGGESTED TEST MASTERS
pp. T-279 f, g

Chapter Objectives

1. Explain what a food chain is and give examples.
2. Explain food webs, including predators and prey.
3. Describe the balance of nature and explain how communities affect food webs.
4. Identify ways in which humans affect other communities.

SECTION BACKGROUND

The path that food travels in a community is called a food chain. Food chains describe how producers, consumers, and decomposers depend on one another for food. Most food chains include a producer, a herbivore, and one or more carnivores. Food chains are represented on community charts by listing the producers and consumers and drawing arrows to connect them. The arrows show the path the food takes.

Food chains are also energy chains. Energy travels through the community along these food chains. For high-level consumers to obtain energy, they eat animals that eat plants. The original energy in the community is derived from the conversion of sunlight to food by green plants.

MATERIALS

terrarium (which was made in Chapter 17, Section 1), mustard seeds, crickets, frog

Exceptional Student
IEP Chapter Goal

When given a list of the following organisms—leaves, chipmunks, nuts, birds, caterpillars, and foxes—the student will illustrate the food web. The visually impaired student will verbally describe the food web.

CHAPTER 19

The Web of Life

19-1. Food Chains

Hawks have very good eyes. They can see small animals from great heights. Hawks eat mice, snakes, and small birds. How are these consumers related? When you finish this section, you should be able to:

BASIC TEACHING PLAN

MOTIVATION

The day before you begin this section, give the students this assignment: Find one picture in a magazine that shows an animal eating. Encourage them to find pictures of animals eating in their natural habitats rather than pictures of house pets eating prepared pet food. Have the students look at their pictures. They should name the animal and the food it is eating. Have them draw an arrow from the food to the animal. The arrow represents a food chain, and it is always drawn from the food to the animal that eats the food. Use the pictures to introduce the concept of the "food chain."

Text Questions—How are these consumers related? *They are part of a food chain.*

☐ **A.** Explain what a *food chain* in a community is.

☐ **B.** Describe a *food chain* in a community.

The path that food travels in a community is called a **food chain**. A *food chain* describes how living things depend on each other for food. Most food chains include a green plant, a plant eater, and one or more animal eaters.

Food chain: The path that food travels through a community.

Each food chain leads to an animal that is not eaten by other animals. But this is not where a food chain ends. Members of food chains die. Then they become food for decomposers. The decomposers break down wastes and dead organisms all along the chain. The broken-down materials go back into the soil and water. They are used by producers to make more food.

To show a food chain, list each organism. Then draw an arrow to the organism it eats. Look at the picture. It shows a food chain for a bird, a grasshopper, and grass.

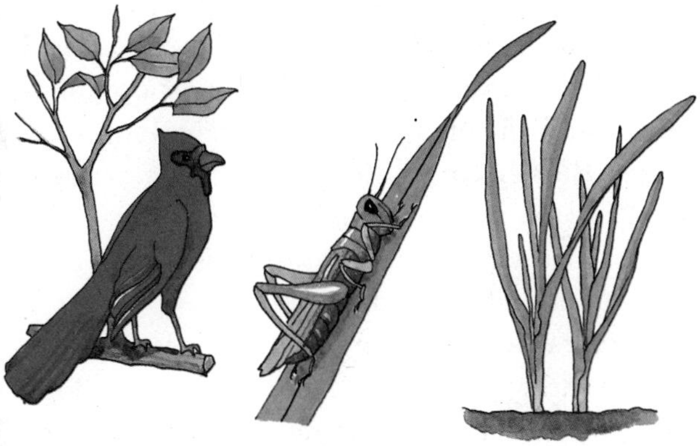

EXTENSIONS

Enrichment

Research—Library

Students can use magazines and other reference materials to do research on food chains that do not start with green plants. A good example is the food chain that exists along the midocean ridge. It is too dark for plants to grow there, but the heat and chemicals coming from the earth allow bacteria to grow. Students will learn that these bacteria are the producers in a food chain that does not depend on the sun for energy.

DEVELOPMENT

1 Teaching Tips—Give each student a food item, such as a carrot, a piece of fruit, or a nut. Tell them they are going to eat the food item. Write the name of the food and the word *human* on the chalkboard. Draw an arrow from the food item to the word *human*. Use this to define the idea of the food chain. Let the students eat their food. Ask for other examples of food chains.

2 Teaching Tips—Stress the importance of decomposers in completing the cycle and in returning carbon dioxide to the community.

3 Teaching Tips—Make an overhead projection of the three organisms—grass, grasshopper, bird. Ask the students to draw arrows to show the food chain for these three organisms.

EXTENSIONS

Application
Activity

This Extension is a suggestion for a short field trip to a place where the students can observe food chains. Take the students to a site such as a pond, meadow, or forest. Have them locate one animal, insect, bird, or fish and observe it. Have them first guess the kind of food the organism eats. Then have them observe the organism to find out what it does eat.

This Activity might be suitable as a homework assignment. Many students have bird feeders or live in areas where birds, squirrels, chipmunks, and other animals can be observed.

ACTIVITY

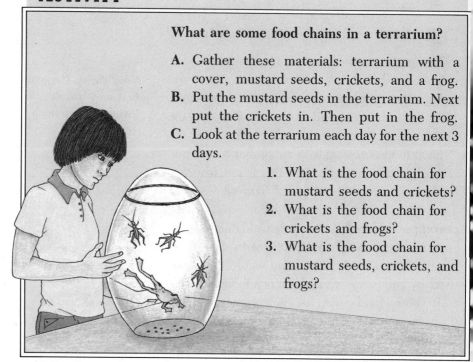

What are some food chains in a terrarium?

A. Gather these materials: terrarium with a cover, mustard seeds, crickets, and a frog.
B. Put the mustard seeds in the terrarium. Next put the crickets in. Then put in the frog.
C. Look at the terrarium each day for the next 3 days.

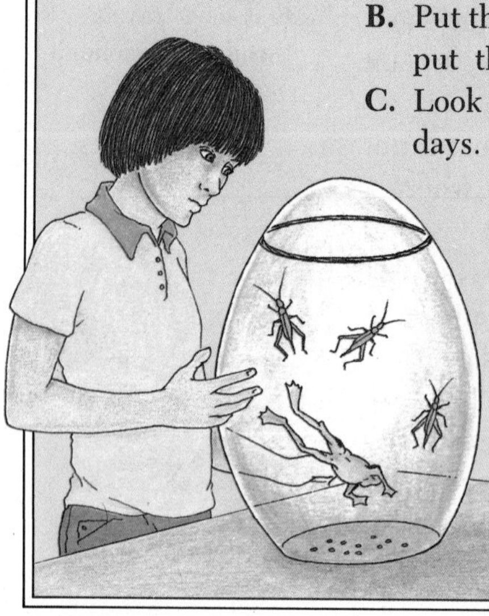

1. What is the food chain for mustard seeds and crickets?
2. What is the food chain for crickets and frogs?
3. What is the food chain for mustard seeds, crickets, and frogs?

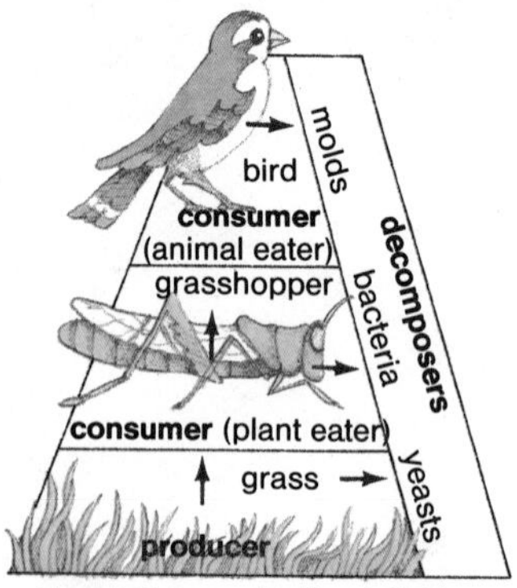

Forest Community Food Chains

Organisms exchange energy through a food chain. We can show this food chain on a community chart. The energy starts at the bottom of the chart. Energy comes from food. Plants produce food for the grasshopper. The grasshopper becomes food for the birds. As organisms die, they become food for the decomposers. 4

The drawing shows organisms in a forest. The arrows drawn from each organism show food chains. What are some of the food chains in the forest? 5

316

ACTIVITY

Skill Development—*Observing*

Teaching Tips—You may want to set up only a few terrariums with animals. This will make management easier. However, if the students are responsible and will take care of their terrariums, you might want to set up a terrarium for each group of three students. The Activity is designed to give students the opportunity to observe firsthand how animals and plants interact in a community. Make sure the terrariums are not too moist. This could be harmful to the crickets. Put 40 or more mustard seeds, 5 or more crickets, and 1 frog in each terrarium.

Answers to Questions—**1.** Mustard seeds→crickets. **2.** Crickets→frog. **3.** Mustard seeds→crickets→frog.

4 **Skill Development**—The students should be able to put in *sequence* the path that food travels in a food chain.
5 **Text Questions**—What are some of the food chains in the forest? *Worm→bird, acorn→squirrel.*

Section Review

Main Ideas: A food chain describes how energy travels in a community. Most food chains include a green plant, a plant eater, and one or more animal eaters. Decomposers are also part of a food chain.

Questions: Answer in complete sentences.

1. Draw a food chain for a leaf, a caterpillar, and a bird.
2. Draw a community chart. Describe a food chain in the community chart for the leaf, the caterpillar, and the bird.
3. What other organisms should be added to the community chart in question 2?
4. List one food you ate today. Draw a food chain that includes you, the food you ate, and the source of food for the food you ate.

EXTENSIONS

Application
Activity

If the students have not as yet started an aquarium, now would be a good time to do so. They should be sure to use aged water and to include producers, consumers, and decomposers. They should draw the food chains they observe in the aquarium. If they cannot set up an aquarium of their own, they may be able to visit a local pet store and observe one there. They could ask the store owner about the food eaten by the different organisms in the aquarium.

Enrichment
Research

If two animals in a community eat the same food, they are in competition with each other. For both animals to survive, they must share the food source. One way of doing this is for each of them to use it in a different way. Students can research how similar animals share a food source. For example, finches are small seed eating birds. If two types of finches lived near each other, they would have to share the seeds. Both types can survive, however, because they have different size beaks. One type eats only large seeds, and the other only small seeds.

SECTION REVIEW

Answers to Questions

1. Leaf→caterpillar→bird
2. See Fig. 19-1.
3. Decomposers such as bacteria
4. Answers will vary.

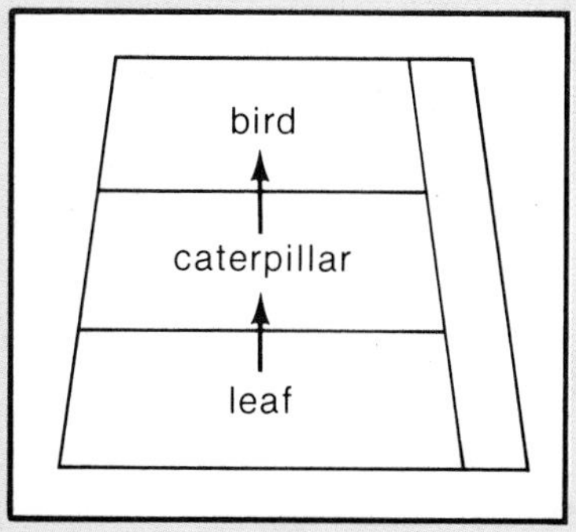

Fig. 19-1

SECTION BACKGROUND

Any given community has many individual food chains. It is rare for these chains to exist in isolation. Energy pathways are more complex and are known as food webs. Most food webs have several kinds of producers that are eaten by first-order consumers (plant eaters). Not every kind of plant is eaten by every herbivore. Mice probably eat more fruits and seeds, grasshoppers eat juicy leaves, and rabbits eat coarser stems of plants. Second-order consumers (animal eaters) also exercise preference when it comes to selecting food. They will choose animals that are easily captured, suitable to taste, and a convenient size.

MATERIALS

1 in. (2.5 cm) thick board at least 12 in. × 12 in. (30 cm × 30 cm), sheet of paper, 9 small nails, hammer, scissors, yarn

19-2. Connected Food Chains

The picture shows what scientists think life was like when the dinosaurs were alive. Some dinosaurs were herbivores. Others were carnivores. What are some food chains that might have existed at that time? Did the food chains connect with each other? When you finish this section, you should be able to:

- ☐ **A.** Trace a *food web* through a community.
- ☐ **B.** Tell the difference between a *predator* and a *prey*.

1 Suppose you are bitten by a mosquito. A friend says, "You are now a source of food for a hawk." Would you believe your friend?

Suppose the mosquito is eaten by a dragonfly. Then a frog eats the dragonfly. The frog is eaten by a snake. A hawk swoops down and eats the snake. The food the mosquito took from you **2** ends up as food for the hawk! Can you write the chain of events from the mosquito to the hawk?

BASIC TEACHING PLAN

MOTIVATION

Students may not realize that some dinosaurs were herbivores and others were carnivores. Brontosaurus and Stegasaurus were herbivores, while Allosaurus and Tyrannosaurus rex were carnivores.

Text Questions—What are some food chains that might have existed at that time? *Plants→Brontosaurus→Allosaurus.* Did the food chains connect with each other? *They connected to form food webs.*

DEVELOPMENT

1 Skill Development—Students should put into *sequence* the events in a food chain.

2 Text Questions—Can you write the chain of events from the mosquito to the hawk? See the previous note on this page. Here is the list of events for the food chain: your blood→mosquito→dragonfly→snake→hawk.

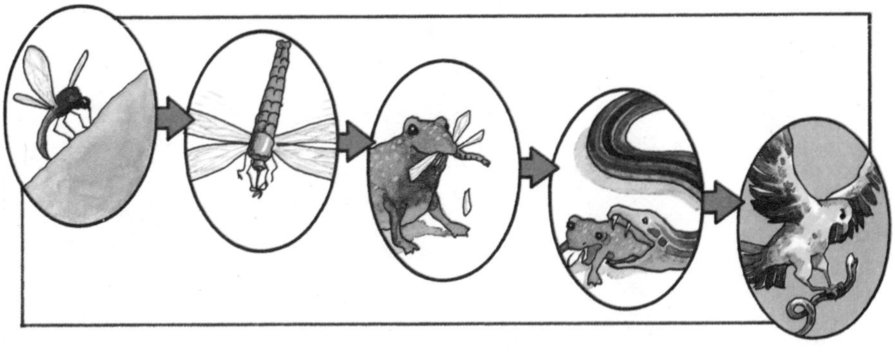

Most communities have many food chains. Most animals in a food chain eat more than one kind of food. Because of this, food chains often connect or overlap. Picture the food chains for seeds, a mouse, a snake, and a hawk. The food chains would look like the drawing. The mouse is food for both the hawk and the snake. The snake is food for the hawk. Food chains that overlap are called **food webs**. Sometimes, just two food chains overlap to form a *food web*. A food web may also have many overlapping food chains.

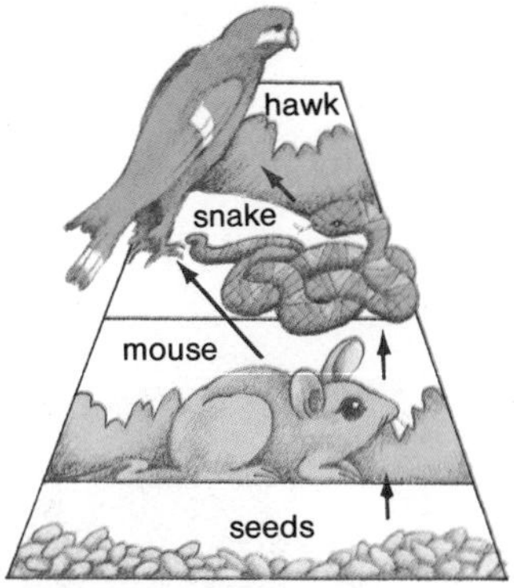

Food web: Food chains that connect or overlap.

Here is a food web that you might find in many communities. There are many food chains that overlap. One food chain is tree→beetle→bird→cat. Another food chain that overlaps the first one is tree→grasshopper→bird→cat. What is a third food chain in the web shown?

The food web on page 321 shows that squirrels eat nuts from the tree. Grasshoppers and beetles eat the tree's leaves. Bats and birds eat beetles and grasshoppers. Cats eat squirrels and birds. Five different food chains are involved.

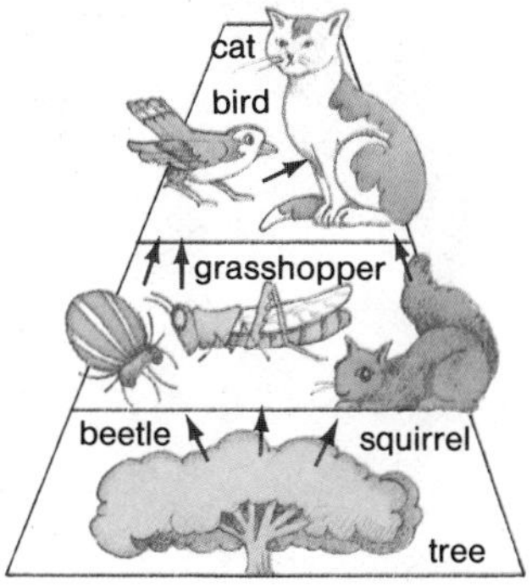

EXTENSIONS

Reinforcement

Science Skills—Recording Data

Students can find out what the food relationships are in different communities. Producers, consumers, and decomposers for two different communities are listed below. The students may have to do some research to learn exactly what the food relationships are. They should draw a diagram of the entire food web of the community.

A. Desert Community
1. Producers: cactus, sage
2. Plant eaters: rabbits, grasshoppers, desert rats
3. Animal eaters: owls, lizards, scorpions
4. Decomposers: molds, bacteria, yeast

B. Prairie Community
1. Producers: corn, wheat, grass
2. Plant eaters: locusts, quail, prairie dogs
3. Animal eaters: humans, rattlesnakes, hawks
4. Decomposers: molds, bacteria, yeast

3 Teaching Tips—Make an overhead transparency of a community chart. List the following organisms on the chart: seeds, mouse, snake, hawk. Do not connect the arrows yet. Ask the students what animal might eat seeds. Draw a food chain from the seeds to the mouse. Ask what might eat the mouse. The students should say both the hawk and the snake. Draw two arrows from the mouse. Ask what might eat the snake. *The hawk will.* Draw an arrow from the snake to the hawk. Tell the students that they have made a food web.
4 Teaching Tips—Display the completed food web by making a copy on a transparency or putting it on the chalkboard. Have the students identify at least three different food chains that overlap. They should start with the tree.
5 Text Questions—What is a third food chain in the web shown? *Tree→squirrel.*
6 Teaching Tips—Challenge the students to find all five food chains in the food web. This is a good place to begin to discuss the interdependence among organisms and to show how an upset or disturbance in one part of a food chain can have multiple effects.

EXTENSIONS

Reinforcement
Activity

The students can use the materials from the Activity in the text to create a food web for an ocean community.

A. Next to the nails they should write the names of these organisms: plankton, shrimp, herring, tuna, shark, whale, bacteria.

B. Tie the end of the yarn around the nail labeled *shark* and decide what organisms the shark would eat for food. Continue stringing the yarn as was done in the Activity.

1. Which organisms in the web are the producers?
2. Which are the consumers?
3. Which are the decomposers?
4. Which organisms would lose their food source if the shrimp were removed?

Activity

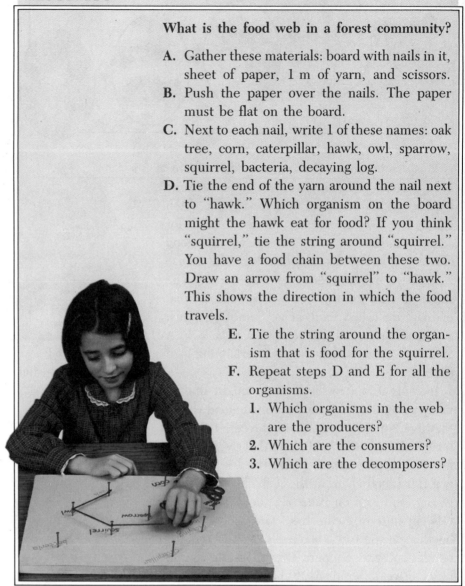

What is the food web in a forest community?

A. Gather these materials: board with nails in it, sheet of paper, 1 m of yarn, and scissors.

B. Push the paper over the nails. The paper must be flat on the board.

C. Next to each nail, write 1 of these names: oak tree, corn, caterpillar, hawk, owl, sparrow, squirrel, bacteria, decaying log.

D. Tie the end of the yarn around the nail next to "hawk." Which organism on the board might the hawk eat for food? If you think "squirrel," tie the string around "squirrel." You have a food chain between these two. Draw an arrow from "squirrel" to "hawk." This shows the direction in which the food travels.

E. Tie the string around the organism that is food for the squirrel.

F. Repeat steps D and E for all the organisms.

1. Which organisms in the web are the producers?
2. Which are the consumers?
3. Which are the decomposers?

ACTIVITY

Skill Development—*Classifying, Sequencing*

Teaching Tips—Use wood that is relatively soft. The board should be at least 12 in. × 12 in. If you want to save time, hammer 9 nails into the board near the edge in the shape of a circle. The nails should not have heads. To use the board, push a piece of paper onto the board over the nails. The names of the organisms can be written on the paper to allow you to use the board again. Students are to make a food web by connecting pairs of organisms one pair at a time. Each connection is actually a food chain. Be sure the students indicate the direction in which the food moves with an arrow. The arrow should be drawn from the source of the food to the consumer. Students will realize that some organisms can be food for more than one animal.

Answers to Questions—**1.** Oak tree, corn, decaying log. **2.** Caterpillar, hawk, owl, sparrow, squirrel. **3.** Bacteria.

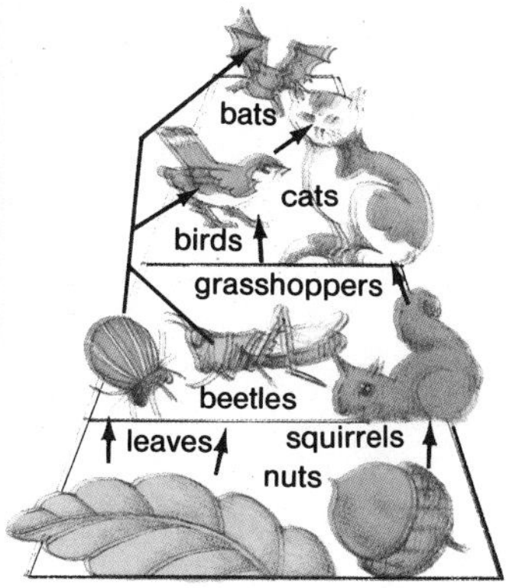

The leaves are the producers in four of the food chains shown here. The beetles, grasshoppers, birds, and bats each are members of two food chains. Cats are part of three chains. The nuts and squirrels belong to just one chain.

Food chains and food webs show us that life really depends on death. One animal eats another, and so on. An animal that kills another animal and then eats it is called a **predator** (**pred**-ah-tore). The animal that is eaten is called the **prey** (**pray**).

Predator: An animal that kills other animals for food.

Prey: An animal that is eaten by other animals.

Section Review

Main Ideas: Food chains that connect or overlap are called food webs. An animal is either a predator or the prey.

Questions: Answer in complete sentences.

1. Draw a food web for these organisms: hawk, snake, caterpillar, beetle, and seeds.
2. Which organisms in the above food web are predators? Which are prey?
3. What is the difference between a food chain and a food web?

EXTENSIONS

Enrichment

Research—Library

Have your students do research to develop food webs for the following ocean organisms: starfish, barnacles, algae, snails, and mussels. They will find that the starfish consume mussels; mussels, snails, and barnacles all consume algae. Algae are the producers in this community.

Science Skills—Comparing and Contrasting

Students can do research to *compare and contrast* the different ways predators hunt their prey. They should pick two predators and investigate the type of prey they hunt. Do they hunt in groups or alone? Which sex does most of the hunting? At what time of day do they hunt? How is the prey divided among the group, if there is a group? Where do these predators and their prey fit in the food web of their community? The students can report their findings to the class.

7 **Skill Development**—*Compare and contrast* animals that are predators and those that are prey. Predators are animal eaters. Prey are animals eaten by other animals.

SECTION REVIEW

Answers to Questions

1. See Fig. 19-2.
2. The hawk and snake are predators. The caterpillar and beetle are prey.
3. Food chains link two or more organisms. Food webs are overlapping food chains.

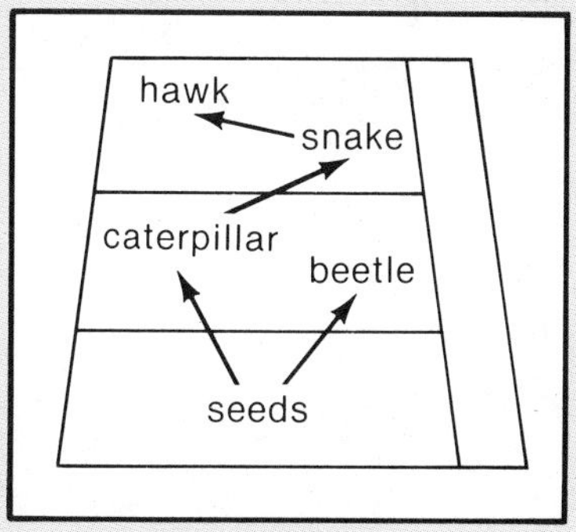

Fig. 19-2

SUGGESTED WORKSHEET MASTER
p. T-279 q

SECTION BACKGROUND

Everywhere you look, there is evidence of change in nature. Yet, even though there are short- and long-term changes occurring, nature tends to move toward a balance. Biologists agree that this balance is unstable. It is often too responsive to the effects of short- and long-term change. However, the overall condition is called a steady state by biologists. The process of adjustment is known as homeostasis.

It is helpful to focus on population fluctuations to understand the balance of nature. As stated above, populations tend to change, but they are conditioned by the process of homeostasis. For example, when a new population is introduced into a favorable environment, there is a rapid population growth at first. In a closed system, the population will then characteristically diminish. In an open system, such as in a natural environment, the population will fluctuate. However, the population seems to fluctuate around some average density or steady state. The population will increase for a while; then a period of population decline will follow. It is important to note that populations can decline to zero. When this happens, the population becomes extinct.

MATERIALS

graph paper, crayons

19-3. The Balance of Nature

Nature has ways of balancing itself. This farm cat is one way. She is a living mouse trap. She affects the number of mice that live in her community. What do you think will happen to the number of mice if the cat leaves or dies? When you finish this section, you should be able to:

- ☐ **A.** Explain the effect on a community food web if one part of it changes.
- ☐ **B.** Give examples of how nature balances itself.

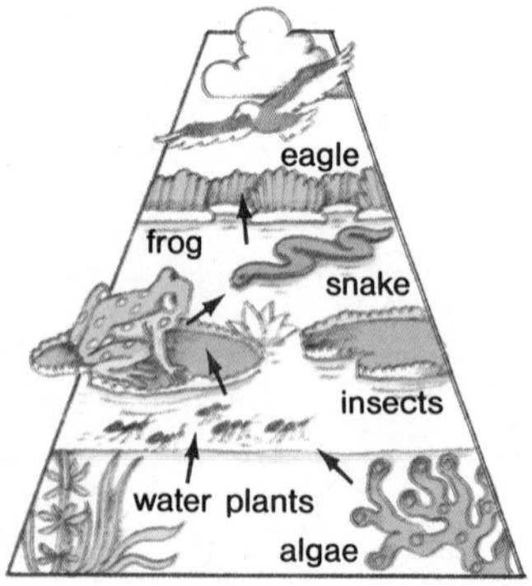

Look at the food web shown here. It is a simple one. It involves water plants, algae, insects, frogs, snakes, and an eagle. The pond food web is the way all the organisms get energy to live. The eagle gets its energy by eating snakes. The snakes eat frogs. The frogs eat insects. The insects eat plants. What do you think would happen to the snake population if the eagles died? How would an increase in the snake population affect the frog population? Answers to these questions will help you understand how nature balances itself. Let's find out.

BASIC TEACHING PLAN

MOTIVATION

Have pictures of other predator–prey relationships available and discuss the interrelationships.

Text Questions—What do you think will happen to the number of mice if the cat leaves or dies? *The number of mice will increase.*

DEVELOPMENT

1 **Text Questions**—What do you think would happen to the snake population if the eagles died? *The snake population would probably increase at first.* How would an increase in the snake population affect the frog population? *Since the snakes eat frogs, there would be a rapid decrease in the frog population. If the frogs were the only source of food for the snakes, there would eventually be a decrease in the snake population.*

2 At one time, scientists believed that deer in Arizona were in danger of being killed off. Their predators were the puma, the wolf, and the coyote. Scientists tried to solve this problem by killing the predators. In less than 20 years, the deer population got much larger. They ate all the green plants around them. They even ate tiny, young trees. This destroyed the forest. The deer could not find enough food. They began to
3 starve to death. Was killing the deer's predators a good idea?

4 This story shows that all plants and animals in a community depend upon each other to survive. If something happens to one member of a food chain or food web, other members are affected. Look what happened when the deer's predators disappeared from the food chain. The number of deer increased. But the number of green plants did not. The deer began to die because the forest was no longer able to feed so many of them.

2 Teaching Tips—Draw a food web on the chalkboard that shows the following relationships: green plants→deer; deer→wolf; deer→puma; deer→coyote. The students should see that when the wolves, pumas, and coyotes are eliminated, the deer population will increase. But because there are many more deer, the vegetation in the forest will soon be destroyed by the overpopulation of deer.

3 Text Questions—Was killing the deer's predators a good idea? *No.*

4 Teaching Tips—This is a good example of homeostasis as discussed in the Section Background.

EXTENSIONS

Enrichment

Science Skills—Inferring

Students can participate in a game in which they make food chains for a specific community. They will "eliminate" one population from the community and infer the effects of the change.

A. Gather these materials: index cards, and yarn.

B. Write the names of the following organisms on separate cards: berries, hickory nuts, acorns, roots, deer, rabbits, squirrels, beetles, foxes, bobcats, hawks.

C. Select ten students to participate in the community game. Give each student a different card. Tape the card to the student so that others can see it. Have the students form a circle.

D. Ask each student to tell the name of the organism he or she represents and indicate if it is a producer or a consumer.

E. Give one student a ball of yarn. Tell that student to connect with another organism following the rules of food chains. Each time a student gets the yarn, he or she is to make a new food chain. The yarn should not be cut at this time because you will eventually have a food web linking together all the organisms.

F. Using a pair of scissors, cut the yarn that links any one organism with the others. Ask what other organisms are affected by the elimination of this organism from the food web. You might cut another organism out and repeat the question.

EXTENSIONS

Enrichment

Research

Have the students research at least one group of organisms that would decrease if these organisms in a community increased:

Spiders (flies and small insects)
Owls (mice)
Frogs (flies)
Coyotes (rabbits)
Starfish (clams)

Research—Library

Microscopic plants called algae sometimes undergo enormous growth spurts called blooms. Students can research why these blooms occur. They should answer the following questions to guide their research: What kinds of animals feed on this algae? How does a bloom affect other populations? How is the balance of nature restored after the bloom?

What do you think will happen if the number of frogs in a pond increases? The frogs will eat more insects. The number of insects will decrease. Then the frogs may begin to die. There will not be enough food for them.

5 The story of the deer shows that nature has a way of checking, or balancing, itself. The natural predators of the deer could have controlled the number of deer in the community. This is what **6** is meant by the "balance of nature." Predators do not often kill more prey than they need to survive. There was no danger of the deer being killed off as the scientists thought. Without these natural enemies, however, the growing number of deer did not have enough food to survive. So nature stopped the rapid growth of deer by itself. Because of the lack of food, many deer died.

5 **Teaching Tips**—Write the term "balance of nature" on the chalkboard. Ask the students to explain what this means in terms of the "deer story" and the "frog story."

6 **Teaching Tips**—On the chalkboard, make three columns. Label the first, "human change"; the second, "plant or animal affected"; and the third, "effect on the balance of nature." Have each student copy the chart. Go outside to find examples of how humans have affected the balance of nature. Cutting down trees for a building, for example, affects the trees, birds, and insects and may cause a decline in the bird and insect populations.

ACTIVITY

How does nature balance populations?

A. Gather these materials: graph paper and crayons.

B. Make a bar graph. Use the data shown in the chart.

1. During which year were many plants being eaten by the rabbits?
2. What happened to the plants during that year?
3. What effect did this have on the rabbit population?
4. How did nature balance the rabbit population?

RABBITS LIVING IN CANADA

Year	Population Size (in thousands)
1920	20
1921	60
1922	65
1923	75
1924	60
1925	20

Section Review

Main Ideas: Animals and plants in a community depend upon each other to survive. If something happens to one member of a food chain or web, other members are affected.

Questions: Answer in complete sentences.

1. What would happen to the number of insects in a pond if the number of turtles increased?
2. What would happen to the number of green plants if the number of insects increased?
3. Draw a food web showing green plants, seeds, deer, and wolves. What would happen to the deer if the plants and seeds died?

EXTENSIONS

Enrichment

Science Skills—Finding Cause and Effect

Students can add to their understanding of how nature balances populations by adding the following information to the bar graph they made in the Activity. It will show how the predator–prey relationship affects the lynx and rabbit populations. Have the students draw a bar graph for the lynx population using a different color so that they can distinguish the lynx and rabbit populations.

Year	Lynx Population Size (in thousands)
1920	5
1921	15
1922	20
1923	35
1924	45
1925	50

1. What happened to the rabbit population as the lynx population increased?
2. What happened to the lynx population as the rabbit population decreased?
3. How do these two populations balance each other?

ACTIVITY

Skill Development—*Recording Data, Concluding and Generalizing*

Teaching Tips—Explain that the number 20 on the data chart means 20,000. The data are based on rabbit skins sold at Hudson's Bay Company posts.

Answers to Questions—1. During the year when the rabbit population was highest (1923). **2.** The plant population decreased. **3.** The rabbit population decreased. **4.** The competition for food seems to regulate the rabbit population.

SECTION REVIEW

Answers to Questions

1. The insect population would decrease.
2. There might be a decrease.
3. See Fig. 19-3. The deer population would decrease because of lack of food.

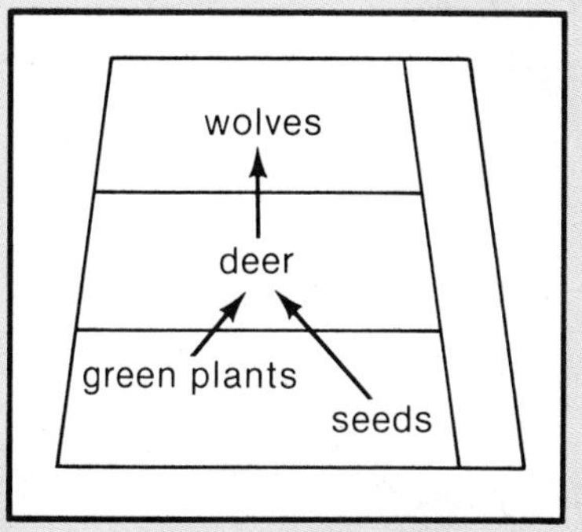

Fig. 19-3

SUGGESTED WORKSHEET MASTER
p. T-279 r

SECTION BACKGROUND

Human beings, like all other animals, need food to survive. Humans are as much a part of the food web as algae. An increase in the human population will naturally have an impact on food sources. Humans, like other organisms, also affect the environment in which they settle. All organisms require energy and resources to survive. Humans have requirements that include food, power (coal, oil, natural gas, hydroelectric, solar, nuclear), soil, forests, and land for settlement. Because of these requirements, humans have affected the quality of the environment. Wastes, gases vented into the atmosphere by automobiles and factories, and increased development of the land contribute to the problems associated with environmental pollution.

MATERIALS

motor oil, mineral oil, bird feather, water, brush, paper towels or newspaper

19-4. People Affect Communities

As human beings, we are part of food webs and communities. We can affect communities like any other animals or plants. This lake was once clean. It had many fish and other forms of life. People could swim in the lake. Now look what has happened. How did people affect this lake community? When you finish this section, you should be able to:

☐ **A.** Identify the kinds of things *ecologists* do.

☐ **B.** Describe ways that human beings affect communities.

326

BASIC TEACHING PLAN

MOTIVATION

Have the students look through magazines for pictures showing ways, both positive and negative, that humans have affected the environment. The picture in the students' text shows one of the harmful effects. Find magazines that have pictures that show a variety of effects. Have each student find one picture. Set aside a place on the bulletin board for the pictures. Have each student briefly tell about the picture and the nature of the effect. Then have the student put the picture on the bulletin board.

Text Questions—How did people affect this lake community? *They dumped solid waste materials. Not only is it an ugly sight, but the decomposition of these materials could have a harmful effect on the wildlife of the lake.*

Over the past 20 years, people have become concerned about the environment. They realize that living things need a clean environment in order to live. Scientists who study living things
1 and their environments are called **ecologists** (ee-**kol**-lo-jists). *Ecologists* study the air, water, and soil. They try to learn all they can about the needs of organisms. They know that human beings are also part of food chains.

Ecologist: A scientist who studies living things and their environments.

The word *ecology* comes from the Greek word *oikos*. This word means "household, home, or place to live." So ecology deals with organisms and their environments. Ecologists study how living things within a population affect each other. They also study how different populations affect each other.

EXTENSIONS

Enrichment

Research

Have your students research how their neighborhood has changed over the years. They can visit municipal offices and libraries, and interview people to find answers to the following questions:

1. When was their town established?
2. What was the land like before the town was built?
3. How have traffic, people, and natural occurrences affected their community?
4. What parts of their town have shown the greatest changes in number of people over the last 5 to 10 years?

DEVELOPMENT

1 Teaching Tips—Ecologists are especially interested in studying the relationships of living things to their surroundings and to one another. They study how living things are affected by physical factors such as temperature, weather, altitude, water, and light. They also study how living things are affected by one another.

EXTENSIONS

Reinforcement

Science Skills—Concluding and Generalizing

In this Extension, students make a food web in which humans are an integral part.

A. Write the following organisms on the chalkboard: grass, corn, wheat, radishes, beans, chickens, cattle, rabbits, foxes, humans, and hawks.

B. Have the students make a food web using all the organisms listed. The foxes, humans, and hawks are animal eaters. Encourage the students to show as many food chains as possible. See Fig. 19-4. As you can see, humans are connected to most of the organisms directly.

C. At this point, ask the students what is missing from the food web. They should suggest decomposers. Add the decomposers (bacteria, fungi, yeasts). Have students draw food chains to include the decomposers.

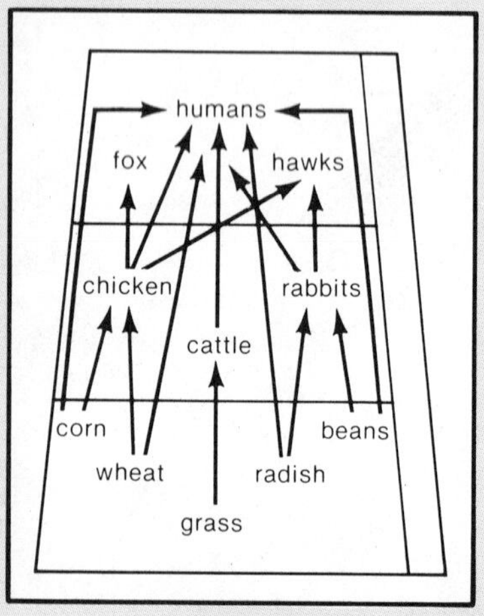

Fig. 19-4

All living things in the biosphere are connected. Living things also need non-living things like soil, water, and air. If something happens to soil, water, or air, living things will be
2 affected. Let's see how humans can cause some of these changes.

3 Human beings make use of the environment in which they live. Unlike other animals, humans can change an area to meet their own needs. When they do this, it affects other living things in the community. Sometimes the effects are not good ones. The picture below shows how wastes from homes and factories may enter a
4 river. What are some other ways a stream may become polluted?

2 Teaching Tips—Ask the students to make a list of the ways humans affect their communities. Write the list on the chalkboard. Encourage the students to include both positive and negative effects.
3 Skill Development—Students should be able to explain the *cause and effect* relationships between humans and the environment.
4 Text Questions—What are some other ways a stream may become polluted? *Nuclear reactor waste water, trash or garbage dumping, chemical seepage through the soil.*

5 Adding harmful things to air and water causes what is known as pollution. The water in polluted streams is unfit to drink. It also kills plant and animal life. Suppose the polluted stream 6 water reaches a pond. What do you think would happen to its community members? What would happen to the food chains and food webs?

7 Air pollution is also a problem. Factories and cars give off harmful gases into the air. Insect poisons that farmers spray on their crops also pollute the air. Some of these poisons kill harmless animals as well as insects. They may also harm people.

5 Teaching Tips—Discuss air and water pollution with the students. Ask them what things might pollute the air and the water. Also discuss what is being done to reduce pollution of the air and water. Help the students understand the conflict between our needs and the health of the environment.

6 Text Questions—What do you think would happen to its community members? *If the pollutants were toxic, they could kill some of the organisms.* What would happen to the food chains and food webs? *If organisms that are food for other organisms were reduced, the consumer population would decrease.*

7 Teaching Tips—Ask the students how humans have tried to reduce air pollution. Focus on the improvements made in the exhaust systems of automobiles and factories.

EXTENSIONS

Reinforcement

Research

Have your students learn more about their environments by researching answers to the following questions:

1. What living things share your neighborhood with you?
2. Are any of the other living things harmful to people? Which ones?
3. Are any of the other living things helpful to people? Which ones?
4. What is the source of food for people in your community? Where does the food come from?
5. Where does the garbage from your community go?
6. Where does bathroom waste water from houses in your community go?

EXTENSIONS

Application
Activity

Detergents are often used to help clean up oil spills. Students can observe the effect a detergent has on a drop of oil in the following Activity. Have the students follow these steps:

A. Gather these materials: motor or lubricating oil, water, a small plastic cup or bowl, and liquid detergent.

B. Fill the bowl with water and place one drop of oil in the center of the water.

C. Drop by drop, add detergent to the center of the spot of oil and observe any changes. Count the number of drops of detergent added before any observable change occurs.

D. Repeat step **C** using different detergents to see if the results vary.

E. Try to clean the feather used in the Activity on this page using the most effective detergent.

1. What happened to the spot of oil when the detergent dropped on it?
2. How many drops of detergent did it take for there to be an observable change in the oil?
3. Why would people have to be careful when using detergents to clean birds?

ACTIVITY

How do oil spills affect the environment?

A. Gather these materials: motor oil, mineral oil, feather, water, brush, and newspaper.

B. Spread the newspaper over your desk.

C. Look at the bird feather. Notice its appearance and weight. Coat the feather with motor oil.

1. What effect did the motor oil have on the bird feather?
2. How would this affect a live bird?

D. Using water, mineral oil, and a brush, try to clean the motor oil off the feather.

3. What effect did your cleaning have on the bird feather?

Section Review

Main Ideas: Human beings often affect the environments and communities of other living things. Humans are connected to all living things through the web of life.

Questions: Answer in complete sentences.

1. What is ecology?
2. What are two things that ecologists do?
3. What would happen to the food chains in a pond if the water became polluted?
4. What is an example of pollution?
5. How could wastes harm the environment?

ACTIVITY

Skill Development—*Finding Cause and Effect, Inferring*

Answers to Questions—1. It made the feather heavy and dirty. **2.** Since the oil will not come off easily, a live bird covered with oil would die. **3.** It is difficult to clean the feather.

SECTION REVIEW

Answers to Questions

1. The study of organisms and their environment.
2. They study how living things within a population affect each other and how different populations affect each other.
3. Polluted water could kill the plants. This would reduce the insect population, which would affect the frog and fish populations. A decrease in frogs and fish would mean less food for the hawks.
4. Putting gases into the air, exhaust from cars, insect spray, wastes from homes going into the water.
5. If they are not treated, they could pollute the water.

CHAPTER REVIEW

Science Words: Unscramble the letters to find the correct terms. Match them with the definitions.

1. EDOOWBF (two words)
2. YREP
3. TERROPDA
4. CHIDOFANO (two words)
5. GELOCITSO

a. The path food travels in a community
b. Food chains that overlap
c. An animal that eats other animals
d. An animal that is eaten by other animals
e. A scientist who studies living things

Questions: Answer in complete sentences.

1. How is a food chain different from a food web?
2. Use arrows to show the food chain for a deer, a wolf, and leaves.
3. Draw a food web on a community chart for leaves, chipmunks, nuts, birds, worms, and a fox.
4. Which of the above organisms is a predator? Which are its prey?
5. Suppose the wolf population in a forest got very large. What would be the effect on the deer in the forest?
6. How would plants be affected by the change in the wolf population?
7. Would the population of wolves keep getting larger? Explain your answer.
8. How does pollution affect living things in a stream?

EXTENSIONS

Enrichment

Research

Have your students research the following careers related to human communities:
- sociologist
- zoning officer
- water treatment plant technician

Tell them to find out such things as the nature of each job, training requirements, and working conditions.

CHAPTER REVIEW

Science Words

1. Food web—b, **2.** prey—d, **3.** predator—c, **4.** food chain—a, **5.** ecologist—e

Answers to Questions

1. A food web is the result of several food chains overlapping.
2. Leaves→deer→wolf
3. See Fig. 19-5.
4. The fox is a predator. Its prey could be birds and chipmunks.
5. The deer population would decrease.
6. Since there would be fewer deer, the plant population would increase.
7. Probably not. If they killed too many deer, their food supply would decrease.
8. If the pollutants are toxic, some of the organisms in a stream could die.

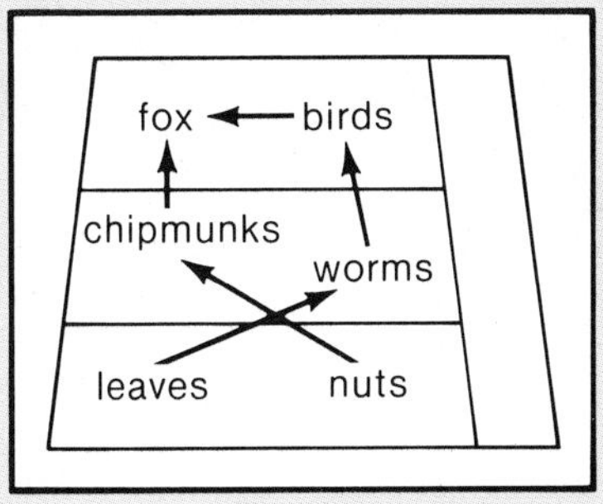

Fig. 19-5

SUGGESTED WORKSHEET MASTER
p. T-279 s

SUGGESTED TEST MASTERS
pp. T-279 h, i

EXTENSIONS

Enrichment
Activity

To continue their investigation into how much consumers eat, the students can observe how variations in the food supply may affect the eating habits of a consumer. Have the students follow these steps:

A. After observing the crickets for five days and discovering their average consumption per day, increase the food supply and observe for another five days to see if there is any change in their eating habits.

B. Decrease the food ration and observe for five days to see if there is any change.

C. After completing steps **A** and **B**, return the food supply to its original level and again observe the crickets' eating habits.

1. Was there any change when the food supply was increased? If so, what was it?
2. Was there any change when the food supply decreased?
3. Was there any change when the food supply returned to its original level?
4. What can you conclude from this Activity?

INVESTIGATING

How much do consumers eat?

A. Gather these materials: 2 crickets, wide-mouth jar with cap, mustard seeds, water, and cotton balls.

B. Make a cricket home. Put a wet cotton ball in the jar. Put about 40 mustard seeds in the jar.

C. Put 2 crickets in your cricket home. Cover the top of the home. Put holes in the cap so that air can get in the jar.

D. Each day for the next 5 days, count the number of seeds left in the cricket home. At the end of 5 days, put the crickets back in a terrarium, or keep feeding them in the cricket home.

1. About how many seeds do the crickets eat each day?
2. Do you think 40 seeds are enough food for 4 crickets for 5 days? Explain your answer.
3. Frogs eat crickets. How many crickets do you think a frog needs to eat in a day to survive?

INVESTIGATING

Skill Development—*Observing, Recording Data, Concluding and Generalization*

Teaching Tips—You can obtain crickets at a local pet shop, or they can be ordered from a science supply house. The purpose of the wet cotton is to provide the moisture that the crickets will need. Mustard seeds are very small and are difficult to count. To aid in the counting, put the seeds on pieces of masking tape or moistened label paper. One or two pieces will hold all the seeds.

Answers to Questions—1. Answers will vary. **2.** If there are seeds left at the end of five days, the answer is yes. If all the seeds are gone before five days pass, the answer is no. **3.** Use the question as motivation. Some of the students may want to investigate to find out.

CAREERS

Forest Ranger ►

Forest rangers are people who protect the plants and animals that live in forests. Some forest rangers help animals that are hurt or sick. Others take people on nature walks. They teach people about the kinds of living things around them.

Forest rangers also look for fires. Sometimes fires are started by careless people.

◄ Conservationist

Conservation means protecting or guarding. Conservationists try to protect endangered plants and animals. They work outdoors in fields, forests, or mountains. Some conservationists study how air pollution harms plants and animals. Others may go out in boats to test for water pollution. Conservationists also study how humans affect animals and plants.

EXTENSIONS

Application

Research

Students may be interested in doing research on these additional careers. Environmental protection engineers apply engineering principles to the prevention, control, and management of environmental problems. They tend to specialize in one form of pollution control. An advanced degree is required. Additional information may be obtained from the American Institute of Industrial Engineers, Inc., 23 Technology Park Atlanta, Norcross, GA 30092.

Recreation specialists work with many organizations, especially the National Park Service. They help park rangers with preservation and restoration work through campground operations and lectures. Some college education is helpful. Additional information can be obtained through the National Recreations and Park Association, 1601 North Kent Street, Arlington, VA 22209.

CAREERS

Teaching Tips—For additional information about forest rangers, students should contact the Forest Service, U.S. Department of Agriculture, Washington, DC 20250. For additional information about conservationists, students should contact the Soil Conservation Service, U.S. Department of Agriculture, Washington, DC 20250.

GLOSSARY/INDEX

In this Glossary/Index, the definitions are printed in *italics*.

Absorb: *to take in and hold light,* 106
Air, carbon dioxide in, 115; molecules in, 115–116, 129; oxygen in, 115; pollution of, 329; temperature of, 117; water vapor in, 142
Air mass: *a large volume of air that takes on the temperature and moisture of the area over which it forms,* 137–138
Air pollution (pol-**oo**-shun): *the presence of dirt, dust, and chemicals in the air,* 165–167
Air pressure: *the weight of the atmosphere caused by molecules pushing down on the earth's surface,* 130; and predicting weather, 131–132
Algae (**al**-jee): *very small plants made up of one or more single cells,* 232
Ameba (ah-**mee**-bah): *a tiny animal found in pond water,* 244
Angle: *the direction at which light bounces off something,* 82
Animals, carnivores, 305–307; endangered, 273–276; extinct, 272; herbivores, 304–307; life cycles of, 242–245; migration of, 253–254; omnivores, 304; population explosion of, 258–260; predators, 321; prey, 321; survival of, 268–271; variations in, 268–271. *See also* Living things.
Anther (**an**-thur): *the part of a flower that contains pollen,* 248
Appalachian Mountains, 35, 41–42
Asteroid (**ass**-ter-oyd): *an object made of rock and metal from outer space,* 168
Atmosphere (**at**-muh-sfeer): *the air that surrounds the earth,* 115; changes of in the past, 167–168; ionosphere of, 117; mesosphere of, 116; stratosphere of, 116; troposphere of, 115. *See also* Air.

Bacteria, 310
"Balance of nature," 322–324
Bald eagle, 273
Ball bearings: *small metal balls used to reduce friction,* 217
Balloons, 128–130
Barometer (buh-**rahm**-uh-ter): *an instrument used to measure the air pressure,* 130
Bicycle, 202–204
Bighorn sheep: *an animal with curved horns that lives in the Rocky Mountains,* 254
Biologist (bye-**oll**-oh-jist): *a scientist who studies the world of living things,* 236–237
Biosphere (**by**-ohs-sphere): *the layer of earth that is made up of living things,* 230
Bird, food chain for, 315; migration of, 254
Bjerknes, Vilhelm (**byerk**-nes), 126
Blizzard (**bliz**-erd): *a storm that brings cold winds and blowing snow,* 158–159
Boats, 219–220
Brine shrimp: *a very small animal that lives in salt water,* 243
"Butter gun," 71
Butterfly, life cycle of, 244–245

Carbon dioxide (**kar**-bon die-**ox**-ide): *a gas in the air that mixes with rain*

to weather rocks; a gas that is needed by green plants to make food; in air, 115; in photosynthesis, 290; weathering by, 43
Carnivore (**kar**-nih-vor): *a consumer that eats only animals,* 304–305, 307
Carson, Rachel, 291
Cattails (**kat**-tails): *a tall plant that lives in the water,* 300
Cell: *the smallest unit of which all organisms are made,* 288
Chemical weathering (**kem**-eh-kohl): *a change in the minerals of a rock as it breaks down,* 43
Chlorophyll (**klore**-oh-fill): *the green material inside a green plant cell,* 288
Cirrus clouds (**seer**-us): *clouds found high in the sky that look like feathers or curls,* 120
Clouds, cirrus, 120; cumulus, 121; formation of, 115; stratus, 121
Colorado River, 47
Colors, 101–104, 105–108
Community (kuh-**mew**-nit-tee): *all the plants and animals that live in the same area,* 283–285; food web in, 319–321, 322–324; human effect on, 326–329
Community chart, 307, 316
Compound machine: *a machine made of two or more simple machines,* 307–309
Computers, and weather forecasts, 124
Concave mirror: *a mirror that bends in,* 89
Condensation (kahn-den-**say**-shun): *the change of a gas into a liquid,* 142
Cone-bearing tree, 247
Conservationist, 333
Consumer: *a living thing that eats plants or animals,* 304–307, 311–312
Continental drift: *the idea that the continents are moving,* 28, 29–30
Convex mirror: *a mirror that bends out,* 89
Core: *the center of the earth; it is made of nickel and iron,* 13
Crust: *the thin, solid, outer layer of the earth,* 11–12
Cumulus clouds (**kyoom**-yoo-lus): *patches of puffy, white clouds,* 121
Curved mirrors, 87–90

Data: *facts, or pieces of information,* 2
Dead log habitat, 284–285
Decay (de-**kay**): *to become rotten,* 309
Decomposer (de-kom-**poz**-er): *a living thing that feeds on wastes and dead organisms,* 309–310, 311–312
Deer, in food web, 323; population explosion of, 260
Dew point: *the air temperature at which water condenses,* 142
Dinosaur (**dine**-uh-sor): *an animal that lived on the earth a long time ago,* 168, 272, 276
Dome-shaped mountains: *mountains formed when magma pushes up part of the crust without breaking the surface,* 37
Doorknob, 198–199
Drizzle (**driz**-ul): *very small drops of slowly falling rain,* 148

Earth, core of, 13; crust of, 11–12; mantle of, 12–13
Earthquake: *a sudden movement of part of the earth's crust,* 16–17; measuring of, 18–19
Ecologist (ee-**kol**-lo-jist): *a scientist who studies living things,* 327
Edgerton, Harold E., 69
Efficiency: *the amount of work done by a machine compared to the amount of work put into it,* 218
Egg beater, 203
Einstein, Albert (**ine**-stein), 66
Elephant population, changes in, 268–269

Endangered (en-**dane**-jurd): *describes a population in danger of being extinct,* 273–276
Entomologist, 279
Environment, human use of, 328–329; pollution of, 328–329
Erosion: *the carrying away of rocks and soil by wind and water,* 45–46; by glaciers, 50–51; by rivers, 46–47
Evaporation (ee-vap-uh-**ray**-shun): *the change of a liquid into a gas,* 142
Extinct (ek-**stinkt**): *describes a population that no longer exists,* 272

Fault: *a crack in the earth's crust where rocks can move,* 17–18, 31
Fault-block mountains: *mountains formed by the pushing up of rocks along a fault,* 36
Fern: *a simple, green, non-flowering plant,* 250
Fixed pulley: *a pulley that stays in place as the load moves,* 194–195
Flashlight, 90
Flower, 248
Focal point (**foe**-kul): *the point at which a lens brings light beams together,* 97
Focus (**foh**-kus): *to bring light beams together at a spot,* 87
Folded mountains: *mountains formed by folding and squeezing the earth's crust,* 35
Food chain: *the path that food travels through a community,* 315–316, 318–321, 322–324; humans in, 326–329
Food web: *food chains that connect or overlap,* 319–320, 322–324
Force: *a push or pull on something,* 175–176
Forest community, consumers in, 306–307; producers in, 301
Forest habitat, 284
Forest ranger, 333
Fossils (**foss**-sills): *traces of plants and animals in rocks,* 29
Friction (**frik**-shun): *a force caused when one object rubs against another object,* 212–215; in machines, 216–218; reduction of, 217–218, 219–222; and wheels, 216–218
Fronts: *the places where cold and warm air masses meet,* 147–148, 149–152
Fruit trees, 249
Fulcrum (**ful**-crum): *the turning point of a lever,* 189–191
Fungus (**fun**-giss): *a protist, such as a mushroom or a mold, that has no leaves or stems,* 232

Gear wheel: *a simple machine that is a wheel with teeth,* 203–205
Geologist (jee-**ahl**-oh-jist): *a scientist who studies rocks and other features of the earth's layers,* 11, 29
Glacier (**glay**-shur): *a large body of moving snow and ice,* 50; erosion by, 50–51
Grand Canyon, 47
Grass, food chain for, 315
Grasshopper, 303; food chain for, 315
Grizzly bear, 273
Groundhog Day, 123

Habitat (**ha**-bi-tat): *the place where a thing lives within a community,* 283–284
Hammer, 191
Hare, 269
Harp seal, 252; migration of, 254
Herbivore (**err**-bih-vor): *a consumer that eats only plants,* 304–305, 306–307
Hillman, Dr. Kes, 240
Horticulturist, 279

Hovercraft (**huv**-er-kraft): *a boat that rides on a cushion of air to reduce friction with the water,* 219–220
Humans, as changers of the land, 53–55; effect on communities, 326–329; population explosion of, 258
Humidity (hyoo-**mid**-ih-tee): *the amount of water vapor in the air,* 161–163
Hurricane (**her**-uh-kayn): *a storm that forms over warm oceans near the equator,* 156
Hydra (**hi**-drah): *a tiny animal found in lakes and ponds,* 244
Hygrometer (hy-**grahm**-uh-ter): *an instrument used to measure the humidity in the air,* 162–163

Ice Age, 50–51
Inclined plane: *a slanted surface, which is sometimes called a ramp,* 179–180, 184
Ionosphere (eye-**ahn**-oh-sfeer): *the layer of air farthest from the earth (up to 1,000 kilometers),* 117
Ivory-billed woodpecker, 274

Jet stream: *fast-moving winds high in the troposphere,* 146

Kudzu, 257

Lake community, 326
Land, conservation of, 54; human changes in, 53–55; natural changes in. *See* Erosion; Weathering.
Larva (**lar**-va): *the young form in the life cycle of an organism,* 245
Lava (**lah**-vah): *red-hot melted rock coming out of the earth's crust,* 21
Lens: *a piece of curved glass that bends light,* 97–100
Lever: *a bar resting on a turning point,* 189–191
Life cycle: *the series of stages in the life of an organism,* 244–245; of plants, 247–250
Light, bending of, 92–95, 96–100; and colors, 101–108; focusing of, 87–90; and opaque objects, 75; reflection of, 64, 78–79, 81, 83–85; sources, 63; speed of, 66–67; spreading of, 70–71; and translucent objects, 75
Light sources: *objects that produce light,* 63
Light wave, 73
Living things, counting of, 236–238; features common to, 233–234; survival of, 268–271
Lubrication (loo-bri-**kay**-shun): *a way of reducing friction by using a liquid on the moving parts,* 220–222

Machine: *anything that makes work easier,* 179–180; compound, 206–209; efficiency of, 218; friction in, 216–218; lubrication of, 220–222; simple, 179–191, 193–196, 198–205; with wheels, 193–196
Machinist, 225
Magma (**mag**-ma): *red-hot melted rock under the earth's crust,* 21–22
Mantle: *a thick, hot layer found under the crust of the earth,* 12–13
Matterhorn, 50
Mauna Loa (Ma-oo-na **Lo**-a), 23
Measurements: *observations that are made by counting something,* 3
Mechanic, 225
Mercalli Earthquake Scale, 18
Mesosaurus (me-zo-**sor**-us), 29
Mesosphere (**mez**-uh-sfeer): *the layer of air from 50 to 80 kilometers above the earth,* 116
Meteorologist (mee-tee-or-**ahl**-uh-jist): *a scientist who studies the weather,* 120

Microscope (my-kruh-skope): *an instrument that makes small things look large,* 99
Migration (my-**gray**-shun): *the movement of animals from place to place,* 253–255
Minerals (**min**-err-als): *materials of which rocks are made,* 43
Mirage (muh-**razh**): *something we see that really isn't there,* 94–95
Mirror, concave, 89; convex, 89; curved, 87–90; reflection of light by, 81, 83–85
Mohole, 14
Mohorovičic, Andrija (Ahn-**dree**-ha Mo-ho-**ro**-veh-chick), 14
Mold, 309–310
Molecule (mahl-uh-kewl): *the smallest particle of a substance,* 115; in air, 129
Monarch butterfly (moh-nark): *a beautiful butterfly that migrates over long distances, 254*
Mosquito, as parasite, 286
Moss: *a small green plant that grows on rocks,* 250
Mt. St. Helens volcano, 20, 22
Mountains, Alps, 35; Appalachian, 35, 41–42; dome-shaped, 37; fault-block, 36; folded, 35; Himalaya, 35; Matterhorn, 50; Sierra Nevadas, 36; Stone Mountain, 36
Movable pulley: *a pulley that moves with the load,* 194–195
Movie projector, 209
Mutualism (**mew**-chew-uhl-ism): *a relationship in which two or more organisms live together and help each other,* 285–286

National Oceanic and Atmospheric Administration (NOAA), 171
National parks, 54
Nature, balance of, 322–324
Newton, Isaac, 104
Nitrogen, in air, 115
Norris Dam, 53

Observations: *anything that we can learn by using our senses, such as sight or hearing,* 1
Observe: *to notice something by seeing or using any of your senses, such as hearing,* 1
Omnivore (om-nih-vor): *a consumer that eats both plants and animals,* 304
Opaque material (oh-payk): *a material that blocks light,* 75
Optician, 111
Organism (or-gan-i-zum): *a single living thing,* 232. *See also* Living things.
Oxygen (ox-i-jen): *a gas that is given off by the leaves of green plants;* in air, 115; in photosynthesis, 290, 293
Oxygen-carbon dioxide cycle: *the way in which these gases interact with plants, animals, and the air,* 295

Pangaea (Pan-gee-a): 28
Parasite (**pare**-uh-sight): *an organism that feeds off another living organism,* 286
Particle (par-tih-kul): *a very small piece of matter,* 71
Peppered moth, 271
Periscope (**pehr**-ih-skope): *an instrument that uses two mirrors to see around corners,* 84–85
Photographer, 111
Photosynthesis (fo-to-**sin**-thuh-sis): *the way green plants make food,* 288–290
Physical weathering (**fizz**-eh-kahl): *the changing of a rock's size and shape as it breaks down,* 43
Plants, endangered, 274; food production by, 287–290; forest

community, 301; life cycle of, 247–250; migration of, 254–255; parts of, 289; as producers, 300–301; water community, 300
Plates: *large sections of the earth's crust,* 32–34
Pollen (**pahl**-len): *a yellow powder made by the anthers of a flower,* 248
Pollution (pol-**oo**-shun), 328–329; air, 165–167
Pond community, consumers in, 305
Pond habitat, 284
Population (pa-pew-**lay**-shun): *a number of the same kind of organisms that live in the same place,* 236–237; changes in, 268–271; differences in, 264–266
Population explosion, 258–260
Potatoes, reproduction of, 249
Prairie dogs (**prayr**-rhee), 283
Precipitation (prih-sip-uh-**tay**-shun): *moisture that falls from the sky,* 121, 143
Predator (**pred**-ah-tore): *an animal that kills other animals for food,* 321
Predict: *to forecast on the basis of observations or past experience,* 2
Prey (**pray**): *an animal that is eaten by other animals,* 321
Primary colors, 108
Prism (**priz**-um): *a piece of glass that bends light and separates it into colors,* 101–104
Producers (pro-**doo**-sirs): *living things that are able to make their own food,* 300–301, 307, 311–312
Protists (**pro**-tists): *organisms that are neither plants nor animals,* 230
Pulley: *a simple machine that is a wheel with a rope moving around it,* 194–195
Pupa (**pyoo**-puh): *a stage in the life cycle of an insect in which the insect is not active,* 245
Pyramids, 216
Rain, and erosion, 45–46; formation of, 143, 147–148
Rainbow, 101, 103
Ramp, 182
Record: *to put down in writing,* 2
Redwood trees, 247
Reflection: *the bouncing back of light,* 64, 78–79, 81, 83–85
Reproduce (ree-pro-**doose**): *to make more of the same kind of organism,* 233
"Ring of fire," 23
Rivers, Colorado, 47; and erosion, 46–47; Russian, 47
Russian River, 47
Rusting of iron, 43

San Andreas fault (Sahn Ahn-**dray**-us), 31
Scissors, 209
Screw: *an inclined plane that winds around in a spiral,* 184
Screwdriver, 200
Sea turtle, 242
Sediment (**sed**-i-ment): *broken-up rock carried in a river,* 47
Seeds, 247–249; migration of, 255
Seismograph (**size**-mo-graf), 19
Seismologist, 59
Sequoia tree, 265
Shadow: *the dark area caused when an object blocks light,* 67
Sierra Nevada Mountains, 36
Spectrum (**spek**-trum): *the group of seven colors that make up white light,* 101
Spores: *small, round objects found on ferns, which can grow and form new fern plants,* 250
Spring scale, 176
Starch: *a type of food made by green plants,* 301

Stigma (stig-moh): *the part of a flower that receives pollen,* 248
Stone Mountain, 37
Storms, blizzards, 158–159; hurricanes, 156; thunderstorms, 157; tornadoes, 157
Stratosphere (**strat**-uh-sfeer): *the layer of air from 16 to 48 kilometers above the earth,* 116
Stratus clouds (**strat**-us): *low, flat sheets of gray clouds that spread out over the sky,* 121
Strawberries, reproduction of, 249
Succession (suck-**seh**-shun): *the movement of plant populations into an area,* 255
Sugars, production by plants, 290, 301
Surveyor, 59
System: *a group of things that act together,* 230

Taik, Seol Man, 187
Telescope (**tell**-uh-skope): *an instrument that makes faraway things look closer,* 99–100
Television weather forecaster, 171
Temperature (**tem**-per-a-chure): *the degree of hotness or coldness of the air,* 117; and air pressure, 129–132
Temperature-humidity index (THI), 161
Termite population, 284–285
Thunderstorm (**thun**-der-storm): *a storm that brings thunder, lightning, heavy rains, and strong winds,* 157
Tornado (tore-**nay**-doh): *a storm that produces a spinning, funnel-shaped cloud,* 157–158
Translucent material (tranz-**loo**-sent): *a material that blurs light as it passes through,* 75
Transparent material (tranz-**pair**-ent): *a material through which light can pass,* 75
Troposphere (**trope**-uh-sfeer): *the layer of air closest to the earth (from 8 to 16 kilometers),* 115

Variations (vare-ee-**ay**-shuns): *differences among members of the same population,* 268–271
Virus, 265
Volcano (vohl-**kay**-no): *an opening in the earth's crust through which lava escapes,* 20; formation of, 22–23

Watch, 205
Water community, consumers in, 305; producers in, 300
Water cycle (**sy**-kul): *the evaporation and condensation of water over and over again,* 143
Water lily: *a plant with large, flat, floating leaves with a flower in the center,* 300
Water vapor: *water in the form of a gas,* 142; in air, 115, 142
Wave: *a movement like a swell of water,* 73; light, 73
Weather, 120; forecasting of, 123–125; fronts and, 147–148, 149–152; movement across United States, 149–151
Weather forecasters, 151, 153, 171
Weather forecasts, 124–125
Weather map, 149–152
Weather report, 120
Weathering (**weather**-ing): *the breaking of rock into smaller pieces,* 42–43

Wedge (wej): *two inclined planes joined together to form a sharp edge,* 185
Wegener, Alfred, 25
Weight, measuring of, 176
Whales, 265, 275, 303
Wheel and axle: *a simple machine that is a wheel that turns on a rod,* 199–200
Wheels, and friction, 216–218
Wind, formation of, 133–135
Winding staircase, 183–184
Work, 175–176, 178–180

X rays, 63

Yeasts, 310

PHOTO CREDITS

HRW Photos by Russell Dian appear on pages 2, 11, 12 left, 24, 33, 38, 44, 48, 51 bottom, 52, 58, 64, 65, 66, 67 both, 68, 71, 73, 75, 79, 81, 84, 89 both, 93, 97 bottom, 103, 106, 107, 111 top right, 124, 125, 133, 134, 142, 144, 146, 149, 152, 161, 162, 163 left, 166, 167 top left, 171 top right, 175 bottom left, 176 top, 179 both, 183, 184, 185 both, 189, 190, 191, 194 bottom, 195, 199 both, 201 bottom, 203, 207, 209 top, 220 top, 239, 249 left, 251 top, 267 both, 285 bottom, 290, 302, 306, 311, 320, 333 right.

HRW Photos by Louis Fernandez appear on pages 180 top, 186 right, 194 top, 198, 200 top, 222 left, 287, 299, 304 top, 309, 322, 327, 333 left.

HRW Photos by Jim Foote appear on pages 178 right, 201 top left and right, 209 bottom, 213 top.

HRW Photos by Richard Hutchings appear on pages 202, 205 both, 213 bottom, 220 bottom, 288 top.

HRW Photos by Ken Karpappear on pages 177, 231, 246, 261, 330.

HRW Photos by Ken Lax appear on pages 176 bottom, 177, 181, 186 left, 194, 200 bottom, 214, 215, 217, 221, 222 right.

HRW Photos by Yoav Levy/Phototake appear on pages 180 bottom, 293 top and bottom right, 296.

p. iv—NASA; p. v—Bell Telephone Labs; Focus on Sports; p. vi—Werner H. Muller/Peter Arnold, Inc.; Kojo Tanaka/Animals Animals; p. vii—W. E. Harvey/Photo Researchers, Inc.; p. viii—Daniel Brody/Stock Boston; p. 1—Pat Lanza Field/Bruce Coleman, Inc.; p. 3—Keith Gunnar/Bruce Coleman, Inc.; p. 5—NOAA.

Unit 1: p. 8-9—Gianni Tortoli/Photo Researchers, Inc.; p. 10—American International Pictures Inc.; p. 12 right—NASA; p. 15—U.P.I.; p. 17—The Granger Collection; p. 19—U.S. Geological Department; p. 20—Photo Researchers, Inc.; p. 21—Franz Lazi/F.P.G.; p. 23—Marvin E. Newman/Woodfin Camp & Assoc.; p. 25—The Granger Collection; p. 27—NASA; p. 31—George Hall/Woodfin Camp & Assoc.; p. 35 top right—Louise K. Broman/Photo Researchers; bottom—Stock/Boston; p. 36—Alexander Lamont/Bruce Coleman Inc.; p. 37—Photo Researchers, Inc.; p. 41—Diane M. Lowe/Stock Boston; p. 42—Photo Researchers, Inc.; p. 43—Leonard Lee Rue III/Bruce Coleman; p. 45—Herman Kokojan/Black Star; p. 46 top—Grant Heilman; bottom—Richard Frear/National Park Service; p. 47—John S. Shelton; p. 49—Phyllis Greenberg/Photo Researchers, Inc.; p. 50—W. Muller/Peter Arnold, Inc.; p. 51 top—Larry Nielsen/Peter Arnold, Inc.; p. 53—Bob McNerling/Taurus Photos; p. 54 top—Eric Calonius/E.P.A. Documercia; bottom—Jack Rattien/National Park Service; p. 55—Bob W. Smith/E.P.A. Documerica; p. 59 right—Vance Sterano/Bruce Coleman Inc.; left—Photo Researchers, Inc.

Unit 2: p. 60-61—Howard Millard; p. 62—Ira Block; p. 63 top—Runk/Schoenberger/Grant Heilman; bottom—Courtesy Hand Surgery Assocs.; p. 64—NASA; p. 69—The Granger Collection; p. 70—Bill Apton/The Image Bank; p. 74—Jean Gaumy/Magnum; p. 78—Peter Arnold/Peter Arnold; p. 82—HRW Collection; p. 86—Photo Researchers, Inc.; p. 87—Ken Kay/Time Life Books—Light & Vision Series; p. 92—Bell Telephone Labs; p. 95—Richard Weymouth Brooks/Photo Researchers, Inc.; p. 96—Ken Kay/Time Life Books—Light & Vision Series; p. 97 top left—Richard Megna/Fundamental Photos; top right—Fundamental Photos; p. 99 both—Al Satterwhite/The Image Bank; p. 100 right—Frank Whiting/The Image Bank; left—Ted Baker/NASA; p. 101—Jim Harrison/Stock Boston; p. 102—B. Ruth/Bruce Coleman, Inc.; p. 106—A. Boccaccio/The Image Bank; p. 111 bottom left—Steve Goodman/SUNY College of Optometry.

Unit 3: p. 112-113—Ray Atkeson; p. 114—NASA; p. 119—Keith Gunnar/Bruce Coleman, Inc.; p. 120—Karen Collidge/Taurus Photos; p. 121 left—John Colwell/Grant Heilman; right—Vance Henry/Taurus Photos; p. 123—Leonard Lee Rue III/Animals Animals; p. 126—Dept. of Atmospheric Science, Univ. of California at Los Angeles; p. 128—Grafton Smith/The Image Bank; p. 136 left—Ira Block/The Image Bank; right—Robert Azzi/Woodfin Camp & Assoc.; p. 138—Erik Simonsen/The Image Bank; p. 141—Focus on Sports; p. 145—Franklin Boden/Stock Boston; p. 153 all—NOAA; p. 155—Cliff Feulner/The Image Bank; p. 156—Flip Schulke/Black Star; p. 157—NCAR; p. 158—Shostal Assoc.; p. 159—Alex Webb/Magnum; p. 160—Allen Rokach; p. 163 right—Gene Moore/Phototake; p. 164 bottom—W. K. Almond/Stock Boston; top—Marc Solomon/The Image Bank; p. 165 top right—John Colwell/Grant Heilman; bottom right—George Hall/Woodfin Camp & Assoc.; bottom left—Garry McMichael/Picture Group; p. 167 top right—John Vachon/The Image Bank; bottom right—Roger Werth/Woodfin Camp & Assoc.; p. 171 left—NOAA.

Unit 4: p. 172-173—HRW Photo by David Spindel; p. 174—Karl Hentz/The Image Bank; p. 175 bottom right—Joe DiMaggio/Peter Arnold; p. 178 left—E. R. Degginger/Bruce Coleman, Inc.; p. 187—John McGrail/Discover Magazine; p. 193—Werner H. Muller/Peter Arnold; p. 206—Richard Hutchings; p. 211—Frank Siteman/Stock Boston; p. 219—George Young/Colour Library International; p. 225 right—John Coletti/Stock Boston; left—Louis Fernandez.

Unit 5: p. 226-227—Z. Leszczynski/Animals Animals; p. 228—Kojo Tanaka/Animals Animals; p. 229 top—Breck Kent/Animals Animals; bottom right—Animals Animals; bottom left—Oxford Scientific Films/Animals Animals; p. 232 left—E. R. Degginger/Animals Animals; right—Manuel Rodriguez; p. 233—Fritz Prenze Brace/Bruce Coleman, Inc.; p. 234 both—David C. Fritts/Animals Animals; p. 236—Manuel Rodriguez; p. 237 top—D.P.I.; bottom—Harvey Lloyd/Peter Arnold, Inc.; p. 238—Charles Palek/Animals Animals; p. 240—Doug Hart; p. 242—Ron & Valerie Taylor/Bruce Coleman, Inc.; p. 243—Runk/Schoenberger/Grant Heilman; p. 244 all—Carolina Biological Supply; p. 245 left and right—Breck Kent/Animals Animals; center right—Ann Hagen Griffith/D.P.I.; center left—Edmond R. Taylor/D.P.I.; p. 247—Breck Kent/Earth Scenes; p. 248—Runk/Schoenberger/Grant Heilman; p. 249 right—Grant Heilman; p. 251 bottom—Edmund R. Taylor/D.P.I.; p. 252—Carolins Kroeger/Animals Animals; p. 253—Brian Milne/Animals Animals; p. 254 top—C. A. Morgan/Peter Arnold, Inc.; bottom—E. R. Degginger/Animals Animals; p. 257—J. C. Stevenson/Earth Scenes; p. 260 left—Tom McHugh/Photo Researchers, Inc.; right—Leonard Lee Rue III/D.P.I.; p. 263—C. Haagner/Bruce Coleman, Inc.; p. 264 left—David Overcast/Bruce Coleman; right—Zig Leszczynski/Animals Animals; p. 265—Courtesy of the American Museum of Natural History; p. 266 top left—Runk/Schoenberger/Grant Heilman; center—Barry Runk/Grant Heilman; bottom—Inger McCabe; p. 269 top right—Manuel Rodriguez; bottom left—John S. Flanner/Bruce Coleman, Inc.; bottom right—Phil Dotson/D.P.I.; p. 271—M.W. F. Tweedie/Bruce Coleman, Inc.; p. 272—Jane Burton/Bruce Coleman; p. 273 left—Bruce Coleman, Inc.; right—Runk/Schoenberger/Grant Heilman; p. 274 left—Jeff Foote/Bruce Coleman, Inc.; right—Clyde H. Smith/Peter Arnold, Inc.; p. 275—Ray Gilbert/Photo Researchers, Inc.; p. 279 right—Richard Choy/Peter Arnold, Inc.; left—Manuel Rodriquez.

Unit 6: p. 280-281—T. N. Liversedge/Photo Researchers; p. 282—E. R. Degginger/Bruce Coleman, Inc.; p. 283 left—Runk/Schoenberger/Grant Heilman; right—Phil Dotson/D.P.I.; p. 285 top—William E. Ferguson; p. 286—H. Pleischinger/Peter Arnold, Inc.; p. 288—Manfred Kage/Peter Arnold, Inc.; p. 291—Bettmann Archives; p. 292—Jim Zipp/Photo Researchers, Inc.; p. 293 left—Peter Arnold, Inc.; p. 294 left—E. R. Degginger/Animals Animals; right—Timothy Egan/Woodfin Camp & Assoc.; p. 298—Lowell Georgia/Photo Researchers, Inc.; p. 303 top—Animals Animals; bottom—R. Ellis/Photo Researchers, Inc.; p. 304 bottom—Runk/Schoenberger/Grant Heilman; p. 305—Manfred Kage/Peter Arnold, Inc.; p. 310 all—Runk/Schoenberger/Grant Heilman; p. 314—W. E. Harvey/Photo Researchers, Inc.; p. 321—Grant Heilman; p. 323—Paul Dotson/D.P.I.; p. 326—Dan Budnik/Woodfin Camp & Assoc.; p. 328—James Karales/Peter Arnold, Inc.; p. 329—USDA Photo.

ART CREDITS

Anthony Accardo, pages 72, 76, 80, 83, 88, 93, 104, 135, 188, 208, 212, 216, 270, 277, 316, 332

Gary Allen, pages 19, 25, 26, 28, 29, 32, 51, 81, 84, 85, 140, 145, 150, 197, 210, 217, 218, 258

Ebet Dudley, pages 7, 12, 22, 29, 32, 34, 35, 37, 73, 77, 87, 90, 102, 116, 147, 148, 158, 182, 192, 196, 204, 209, 230, 238, 245, 247, 250, 255, 259, 278, 286, 294, 300, 301, 305, 307, 315, 317, 319

Jan Pyk, pages 308, 316, 318, 319, 321, 322

Pat Stewart, pages 13, 71, 75, 82, 94, 98, 118, 123, 130, 131, 139, 140, 141

Vantage, pages 4, 5, 7, 79, 85, 89, 90, 91, 95, 96, 105, 108, 109, 115, 124, 154, 187, 189, 191

SAFETY IN THE

The Activities in *Holt Science* have been designed with safety in mind. Nonetheless, wherever children work with materials of any sort, the potential for unsafe practices exists. The following suggestions are offered with the intent of reducing that potential.[1]

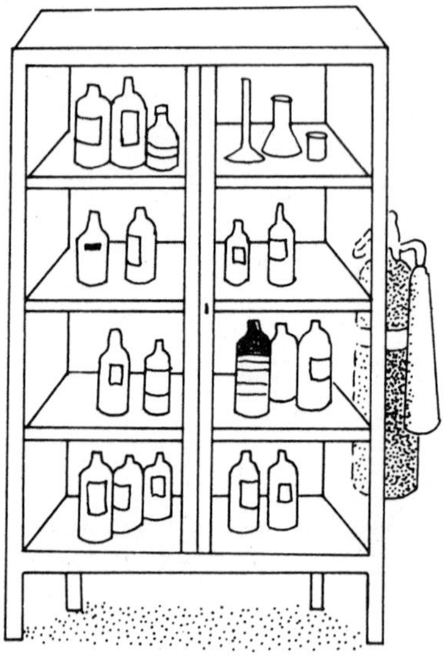

SAFETY CHECKLIST

1. Check your classroom on a regular basis to insure that all possible safety precautions are being taken. Equipment and materials should be properly stored; hazardous materials should not be left exposed in the classroom.
2. Be extra cautious when dealing with fire and instruct your students to take appropriate precautions.
3. At the start of each science Activity, instruct students regarding potential hazards and the precautions to be taken.
4. The group size of students working on an experiment should be limited to a number that can safely perform the experiment without causing confusion and accidents.
5. Students should be instructed never to taste or touch substances in the science classroom without first obtaining specific instructions from the teacher.
6. All accidents or injuries—no matter how small—should be reported to you immediately.
7. Students should be instructed that it is unsafe to touch the face, mouth, eyes, and other parts of the body while they are working with plants, animals, or chemical substances until they have washed their hands and cleaned their nails.

HANDLING OF ANIMALS AND PLANTS

1. Do not allow students to bring live or diseased wild animals, such as snapping turtles, snakes, insects, or arachnids (spiders, ticks, mites), into the classroom.
2. Provide proper living quarters for animals. They must be kept clean and free from contamination in a securely closed cage. Provisions for their care during weekends and holidays must be made.
3. Discourage students from bringing personal pets to school. If they are brought into the room, they should be handled only by their owners and provisions should be made for their care during the day by providing fresh water and a place to rest.
4. Caution students never to tease animals, or to insert their fingers or objects through wire mesh cages. Report animal bites and scratches immediately to the school's medical authority. Provide basic first aid.

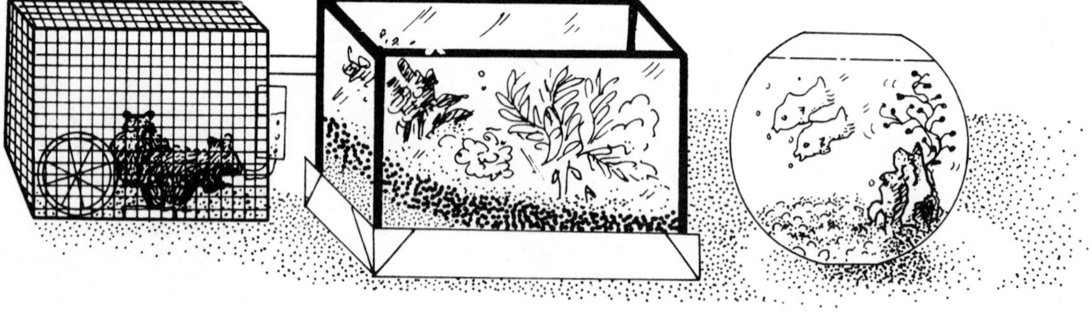

5. Rats, rabbits, hamsters, and mice are best picked up by the scruff of the neck, with a hand placed under the body for support. If the young are to be handled, the mother should be removed to another cage. By nature she will be fiercely protective.
6. Use heavy gloves for handling animals and have students wash their hands before and after they handle animals.
7. Prior to allowing animals to be brought into the classroom, check school district procedures to determine if there are any local regulations to be observed. Personnel at the local humane society or zoo are often very cooperative in assisting teachers to create a wholesome animal environment in the classroom.
8. Students should be instructed never to place any part of a plant in their mouth. (Note: Teachers may want to emphasize the distinction between edible plants, fruits and vegetables, and nonedible plants.)
9. Students should never allow any sap or fruit to set into their skin.
10. Students should never inhale or expose their skin or eyes to the smoke of any burning plant.
11. Do not allow students to pick any unknown wildflowers, seeds, berries, or cultivated plants.

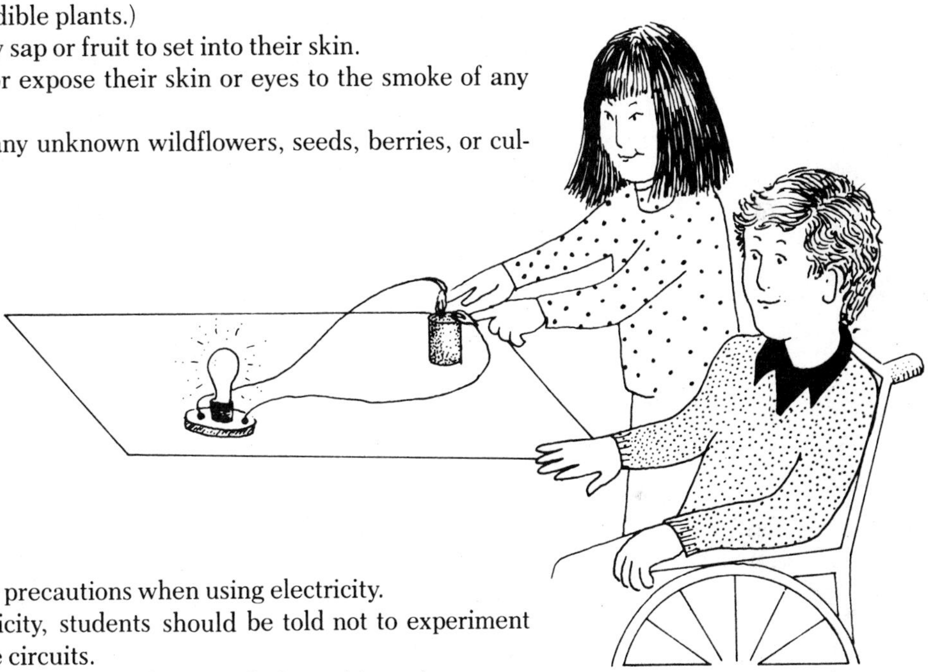

ELECTRICITY

1. Students should be taught safety precautions when using electricity.
2. At the start of any unit on electricity, students should be told not to experiment with the electric current of home circuits.
3. Connecting cords should be short, in good condition, and plugged in at the nearest outlet; electrical extensions should not be used.
4. Tap water is a conductor of electricity. Students' hands should be dry when touching electrical cords, switches, or appliances.
5. Instruct students never to grasp any electrical device which has just been used. Most electrical devices remain hot after use and serious burns may result.
6. Students should never short circuit (connect the terminals) dry cells or storage batteries. High temperature will develop in the connecting wire and can cause serious burns.
7. In removing an electrical plug from its socket, pull the plug, not the electric cord.
8. The following items should be used with caution: heating element for a fish tank, small motors, soldering irons, hot plates, and electrical fans.

[1]The information above is taken from *Safety in the Elementary Science Classroom* prepared by the National Science Teachers' Association Subcommittee on Safety. The complete publication may be ordered from NSTA, 1742 Connecticut Ave. NW, Washington, DC 20009.

KEEPING PLANTS

PLANTS

Children like to care for plants and watch them grow and change. Hardy plants, such as snake plants, coleus, philodendron, English ivy, geranium, Swedish ivy, cacti, spider plants, and grape ivy are the most likely to thrive in the classroom. Although there are many good books about plant care available, following these general rules will keep your plants healthy:

Pots and Potting: Most plants grow well in plastic or clay pots. Whichever you choose, it is important that the pot has drainage holes in the bottom. Some pots come with their own catch saucer, which collects the drained water. If yours does not, place a small saucer or aluminum pie plate under the pot. As the plant grows, check it periodically to see if it needs repotting. Remove the plant by tapping the inverted pot while holding your fingers on either side of the plant stem. If the roots have grown to the edges of the pot and form a thick mass, then the plant should be repotted. A good general rule is to repot the plant in a container with a diameter about 2½ centimeters (1 inch) larger than the container the plant was in. Thoroughly wash the new pot with soap and water before repotting and always use fresh potting soil. Take care not to damage the roots when repotting. Do not leave the roots exposed to the air for too long, since they will dry out. After repotting, water the plant thoroughly.

Watering: Do not overwater! This is a common mistake that often kills plants. Water the plant only when the soil feels dry (usually once or twice a week), and water thoroughly (until water comes out the drainage hole). Plants need different amounts of water, depending on the season, light conditions, temperature, and humidity. As a general rule, the higher the temperature and light intensity, and the lower the humidity, the more water the plant will need. In winter, the light intensity is lower, and plants do not grow as much or need as much water.

Temperature: Plants should be placed in an area where the temperature remains constant, with neither excessive heat nor drafts. Plants should not be placed near heating or cooling units, or too close to windows in winter.

Lighting: Green plants will not survive without light. Some plants (e.g., philodendra, snake plants, grape ivy) will survive in low light conditions. Others (coleus, geranium, Swedish ivy, spider plants) need direct sunlight. We suggest you check a reference source to find out the light requirements for specific plants.

Soil: Different plants have different soil requirements. Usually, however, any good potting soil (easily obtainable at a five-and-dime or garden supply store) is appropriate. Do not use soil dug up from outside. It is much too heavy for a potted plant and may contain weed seeds and disease organisms.

Cleansing and Checking: Gently wash the leaves of smooth-leaved plants once a week to remove the dust and dirt that clog the plant's pores. Check the leaves for insects and diseases. Isolate any infected plants from other plants. During times of rapid growth, plants may need fertilizer. Obtain some plant fertilizer and carefully follow the instructions on the package. Some plants, like Swedish ivy and avocado, need to be pruned so that the stems do not get long and stringy. Start new plants with the cuttings.

Terrariums can be made and can serve as a temporary home for small salamanders, frogs, and toads. Put a thin layer of charcoal fragments at the bottom. Then add one-half inch of sand and two inches of rich forest soil. Dig up small, compact woodland

AND ANIMALS

plants such as moss, ferns, and wintergreen. Dig up a lot of soil with the roots so that they will be disturbed as little as possible when transplanted into the terrarium. Imbed a water dish so that the edge is level with the soil surface. Water the plants and cover the terrarium.

ANIMALS

Animals in the classroom require more care than plants. However, they provide a continual source of motivation for all kinds of learning. Keeping animals in the classroom helps youngsters develop enthusiasm, respect, and love for all forms of life. Before bringing an animal into the classroom, be sure that you are fully prepared. Obtain a handbook on the care and feeding of the animal and determine the animal's needs. Have food, water, and other supplies ready beforehand.

The students should share the responsibility for the care of the animals. Teach them how to properly handle them. They will be enthusiastic and should be cautioned not to handle them too much or too harshly. Animals should be handled gently, and never hurriedly or nervously. Here are some general rules for animal care:

1. The animal should have enough space to move around and be comfortable.
2. Create a habitat as nearly like the animal's natural habitat as possible.
3. Provide a place to hide from sight.
4. The animal should have proper food, clean water, and fresh air.
5. The cage should be clean and free from odor at all times.
6. The animal should be provided with adequate food, water, and heat over the weekends and during vacations.
7. Unless accustomed to captive life, the animal should not be kept for a long time.

Mammals: Hamsters, white rats, white mice, and guinea pigs can be kept in 2-foot cages. Gerbils should be kept in 10-gallon aquariums with a generous layer of sand for burrowing. Metal cages should be washed with soap and rinsed in laundry bleach solution once per week. There should be a debris-catching metal tray with sawdust in it at the bottom of the cage. Remove water, food, and soiled bedding daily. Heavy glass ashtrays work well for food, and water bottles work best for water. Keep a nest box in the cage where the animal can retreat for rest and escape drafts. Rats and mice need an exercise wheel.

Amphibians and Reptiles: Tadpole eggs can be collected in the spring. Keep them in covered glass containers to reduce evaporation. They should be kept relatively cool, and should be exposed to some sunlight. After hatching, make sure there is scum in the water for the tadpoles to feed on. Most frog eggs hatch in three months. Small amphibians can be kept in moist woodland terrariums. Keep a shallow dish of water in the terrarium so that they can soak their skins. This should be cleaned and refilled daily. They can be induced to eat by dangling insects, worms, or hamburger before them. Some reptiles, such as small snakes and chameleons, can be kept in the classroom if the right conditions are provided. A cage can be constructed from an aquarium. The optimum temperature for most reptiles is 80°F. They should not be exposed to temperatures below 65°F. Provide a shady place, such as a broken pot, as well as bark, branches, rocks, and a heavy, shallow dish of water.

Fish: As a rule of thumb, provide one gallon of water per fish. Goldfish and guppies are hardy and easy to care for. You will need fish food, aquarium plants (to provide oxygen), snails (to clean debris), and washed sand. Tropical fish need a heater and thermostat. Pond, stream, or rain water is best. If you use tap water, let it stand for three days so that chlorine can evaporate from it. Do not put the tank near radiators.

MATERIALS LIST

MATERIAL	AMOUNT	PAGE
aluminum foil		T-80, T-98
apple	1	T-13
aquarium (or plastic shoe box)	1	T-146
bags, paper (large)	2	T-131
ball, golf	1	T-38
blocks of wood	4	T-38, T-186, T-200
board	1	T-181
books	12	T-177, T-181, T-217
bowls	4	T-134, T-139
box (small)	1	T-190
broomstick	1	T-131
can, metal	1	T-144
cardboard or plastic	1 piece	T-146
cards, file (index)	5	T-68, T-88, T-177
cards, weather	1 set	T-125
chair	1	T-131
chalk	1 box	T-177
chalkboard erasers (used)	3	T-65, T-94
clay		T-38, T-68, T-83, T-88, T-131
coat hangers	3	T-118, T-139
coloring, food, red		T-146
container, plastic (2-liter)	1	T-52
crane, toy	1	T-208
crayons	all colors	T-103, T-186, T-204
cups, paper (small)	2	T-190
cups, plastic	2	T-139
drill, hand	1	T-208
egg, hard-boiled	1	T-33
egg beater	1	T-204
fabrics		T-76
flashlight	1	T-65, T-72, T-76, T-80, T-98, T-103, T-107
glass		T-76
glass, drinking	1	T-24
glue		T-56, T-152
gravel	handful	T-52
hole punch	1	T-68
ice		T-139
ice cubes		T-144
jars	5	T-44, T-48, T-98
knife, plastic	1	T-38
knives, dinner	1	T-13, T-33
lamp, 150-w	1	T-131
lens, hand	1	T-166
light box or flashlight	1	T-83, T-88, T-94
light source	1	T-68
magazines, old	several	T-56
map, outline of U.S.	1	T-152
maps, newspaper weather	3	T-152
marbles	4	T-221
metal		T-76
meter stick	1	T-72, T-131, T-196
metric ruler	1	T-177

MATERIAL	AMOUNT	PAGE
milk	4–5 drops	T-94
mirrors	7	T-80, T-83, T-88, T-103
pail	1	T-196
paper		T-76
paper, black	1 sheet	T-94
paper, blue	1 sheet	T-107
paper, construction	2 sheets	T-28, T-152
paper, graph (cm)	1 sheet	T-72
paper, green	1 sheet	T-107
paper, poster	1 sheet	T-56
paper, red	1 sheet	T-107
paper, tracing	1 sheet	T-28
paper, wax	1 piece	T-214
paper, white	5 sheets	T-80, T-83, T-88, T-98, T-107
paper clips		T-131, T-177, T-190
paste		T-28
pebbles, small	handful	T-48
pencil (flat-sided)	1	T-190
pencil sharpener	1	T-208
pencils	2	T-186
pencils (round) or dowels	3	T-217
petroleum jelly		T-166
plastic		T-76
pulley, small	1	T-196
rocks, limestone/marble chips		T-44
rocks, volcanic, sample of	1 set	T-24
rubber band (medium-sized)	1	T-177
ruler	1	T-98
ruler, metric	1	T-190, T-200
salt		T-146
sand		T-196, T-214
sandpaper	1 piece	T-214
scales, spring	1	T-181, T-196, T-214, T-217
scissors	1	T-28, T-56, T-152, T-177, T-208
screwdriver	1	T-186
screwdrivers with different diameter handles	2	T-200
screws (same size)		T-200
shoe boxes	2	T-214, T-217
shoe box, clear plastic	1	T-46, T-94
slides, plastic microscope	4	T-166
soap, liquid		T-221
soil, potting		T-134
string		T-131, T-177, T-196, T-217
Styrofoam cups	2	T-118
tape		T-76, T-186, T-190
thermometers	2	T-118, T-122, T-125, T-134, T-139, T-144
towels, paper		T-33, T-166, T-221
toy car or truck	1	T-181
tray of water	1	T-103
triangles, paper	2	T-186
vinegar, white		T-44
wall clock or watch	1	T-134
wood		T-76

A/V EQUIPMENT AND SUPPLIERS

FILM/FILMSTRIP SUPPLIERS

ABC Wide World of Learning
1330 Avenue of the Americas
New York, NY 10019

Aevac
1500 Park Avenue
South Plainfield, NJ 07080

Agency for Instructional Television
Box A
Bloomington, IN 47042

Alfred Higgins Productions, Inc.
9100 Sunset Boulevard
Los Angeles, CA 90069

Audio Visual Narrative Arts, Inc.
Box 9
Pleasantville, NY 10570

Barr Films
P.O. Box 5667
3490 East Foothill Boulevard
Pasadena, CA 91107

Bullfrog Films
Oley, PA 19547

Captioned Films for the Deaf
814 Thayer Avenue
Silver Spring, MD 20900

Centron Educational Films
1621 West 9th Street
Lawrence, KS 66044

Churchill Films
662 North Robertson Boulevard
Los Angeles, CA 90060

Coronet Films
65 East South Water Street
Chicago, IL 60601

CRM/McGraw-Hill
110 15th Street
Del Mar, CA 92104

Educational Activity
Box 392
Freeport, NY 11520

Educational Dimensions Group
Box 126
Stamford, CT 06904

Educational Images
P.O. Box 367
Lyon Falls, NY 13368

Encyclopaedia Britannica
Educational Corp.
425 North Michigan Avenue
Chicago, IL 60611

Focus Media, Inc.
16 South Oaks Boulevard
Plainview, NY 11803

Green Mountain Post Films
P.O. Box 229
Turner Falls, MA 01376

Guidance Associates
Communications Park, P.O. Box 3000
Mt. Kisco, NY 10549

Human Relations Media
175 Tompkins Avenue
Pleasantville, NY 10570

Indiana University Films
Audio-Visual Center
Bloomington, IN 47401

International Film Bureau, Inc.
332 South Michigan Avenue
Chicago, IL 60604

National Geographic Society,
Educational Services
17th and M Streets, NW
Washington, DC 20036

Phoenix/BFA Films
468 Park Avenue South
New York, NY 10016

Random House
201 East 50th Street
New York, NY 10022

Shell Film Library
1433 Sadlier
Circle West Drive
Indianapolis, IN

Society for Visual Education, Inc.
1345 West Diversey Parkway
Chicago, IL 60614

Sterling Educational Films
241 East 34th Street
New York, NY 10016

Stuart Finley, Inc.
3428 Mansfield Road
Falls Church, VA 20041

Time-Life Films
100 Eisenhower Drive
Paramus, NJ 07652

United Learning
6633 West Howard
Nibo, IL 60648

Universal Education and Visual Arts
100 Universal City Plaza
Universal City, CA 91608

Walt Disney Educational Media Co.
500 South Buena Vista Street
Burbank, CA 91521

Wombat Productions, Inc.
Little Lake, Glendale Road
P.O. Box 70
Ossining, NY 10562

SOFTWARE PRODUCERS

Atari Program Exchange
155 Moffett Park
Box 427
Sunnyvale, CA 94086

Creative Computing Software
Dept. T52
One Park Avenue
Room 458
New York, NY 10016

Educational Activities Inc.
P.O. Box 392
Freeport, NY 11520

Med System Software
66 Church Street
Ellenville, NY 12428

Micro Power and Light
12820 Hillcrest Road #224
Dallas, TX 75230

National Coordinating Center for
Curriculum Development
SUNY of Stonybrook
Stonybrook, NY 11794
Attn: Professor Braun

Project Sereal Software
c/o Dresdan Associates
P.O. Box 426
Dresden, ME 04342

Right On Programs
P.O. Box 977
Huntington, NY 11743

T.I.E.S.
1925 West Country Road B2
St. Paul, MN 55113

SOURCES OF EQUIPMENT AND SUPPLIES

American Science and Engineering,
Inc.
20 Oberland Street
Boston, MA 02215

Carolina Biological Supply Co.
2700 York Road
Burlington, NC 27215

Central Scientific Co.
2600 South Kostner Avenue
Chicago, IL 60623

Edmund Scientific Co.
101 East Gloucester Pike
Barrington, NJ 08007

Fisher Scientific
Educational Materials Division
1259 North Wood Street
Chicago, IL 60622

Sargent-Welch Scientific Co.
1300 Lindere Avenue
Skokie, IL 60076

Science Kit, Inc.
777 East Park Drive
Tonawanda, NY 14150

Selective Educational Equipment
(SEE), Inc.
3 Bridge Street
Newton, MA 02195

Ward's Natural Science
Establishment, Inc.
300 Ridge Road East
Rochester, NY 14683

HELPING THE EXCEPTIONAL STUDENT

P.L. 94-142: Education For All Handicapped Children Act: Federal Law P.L. 94-142 states that all handicapped children are entitled to a free appropriate public education with services designed to meet each child's individual needs. The law requires all students with handicapping conditions to be identified, tested, and evaluated by the appropriate agencies or school services. The school service, in agreement with the student and his or her parents, selects the most appropriate least restrictive educational environment.

Mainstreaming: The least restrictive environment for many exceptional students may be total or partial integration into the mainstream classes. Some children, however, need to be in self-contained special education classes during the entire day. The goal is to mainstream each child into as many regular classes as possible.

Individualized Education Planning (IEP): Any child who has been classified by state or local agencies as handicapped must have an Individualized Educational Plan. An IEP is an individualized written statement which projects the student's achievements of particular goals within a specific time frame. Contributors to the IEP include the parents, the teacher, and a representative of the local educational agency. The IEP is updated when appropriate.

Using the Exceptional Student Suggestions and IEP goals: Suggestions for the Exceptional Student are included in the Teacher's Edition to aid the classroom teacher who has a handicapped child in the class. A teacher of the special education class can utilize the suggestions when adapting the curriculum for the specific population of that class. All suggestions are not appropriate for all children. An activity will often need to be varied depending on the degree of impairment.

The IEP goals are to aid the teacher in focusing in on specific objectives of each chapter and/or unit. These goals may be used on the IEP.

STRATEGIES	ORTHOPEDIC AND OTHER HEALTH IMPAIRMENTS	VISUAL IMPAIRMENT	HEARING IMPAIRMENT	SPEECH IMPAIRMENT	SPECIFIC LEARNING DISABILITY	MILD MENTAL RETARDATION	EMOTIONAL DISTURBANCE
CLASSROOM MANAGEMENT	Restricted movement Special furniture	Front-row seating Assign "buddy" for assignments	Front- or second-row seating Face child when speaking	No adjustment necessary	Structured daily procedures Concepts presented by varied methods (Visual, tactile, auditory) Environment with minimal distraction	Structured daily procedures	Structured daily procedures Calm atmosphere, low in tension Positive verbal reinforcement
TEXT BOOK MANAGEMENT	No adjustment necessary	Text read orally to student Use of magnifying glass †Use of Braille reader °°Taped texts	No adjustment necessary	No adjustment necessary	°°Taped text Text read to student Modify content as needed	Modify content as needed	No adjustment necessary
ADDITIONAL INSTRUCTIONAL MATERIAL	No adjustment necessary	Use concrete materials	°Captioned films for the deaf	No adjustment necessary	Use of concrete materials	Use of concrete materials	Motivating materials
ACHIEVEMENT MONITORING/ TESTING MODIFICATIONS	Answers to exams recorded on tape Exam administered orally	Exam administered orally or on tape Exam sheet enlarged †Exam transcribed into Braille	Committee assignments or oral reports	Committee assignments for reports	Committee assignments for oral reports Written exams rephrased when necessary Oral exam administered when necessary Answers recorded in any manner appropriate Time limit extended	Time limit extended Written exam rephrased when necessary	Time limit extended

†Local Braillists will transcribe books. Check with your local church or synagogue.

°Films can be borrowed from the distribution center nearest your school and shown in any classroom where there is one hearing-impaired student. Write: Department of Education.

°°Cassettes available at the Library of Congress, Washington, D.C.